CONTROL SYSTEMS THEORY

CONTROL SYSTEMS THEORY

OLLE I. ELGERD

Professor of Electrical Engineering
University of Florida

McGRAW-HILL BOOK COMPANY

New York   St. Louis
San Francisco
Toronto   London
Sydney

CONTROL SYSTEMS THEORY

ISBN 07-019174-3
567890 HDBP 76543

Till
min Mor
och
till minne
av
min Far

PREFACE

As of this writing (1966), there are over one hundred books and monographs on the general topic of control and servomechanisms in the English language alone. Any new author venturing into this field should therefore be prepared to motivate the need for his particular product and to define its specific *raison d'être*. I believe the time is ripe for a "new look" in control textbooks and offer the following reasons for this assumption:

It is current praxis to distinguish between "classical" and "modern" control, a distinction that not only is arbitrary but also has resulted in an unfortunate and often artificial division between topic areas usually covered in the graduate and undergraduate control programs at our universities.

The vast majority of present texts take the classical view of control. With few exceptions, these texts are direct descendants—first, second, or later generation—of the classic treatises by James, Nichols, and Phillips and Truxal. The outstanding features of the classical approach are:

1. A linear model of the control system is assumed, and the designer then proceeds to describe the system in terms of transfer functions of either the frequency or the Laplace variety, depending upon the type of information he has available.
2. An almost exclusive emphasis is placed upon those specific control systems classified as servomechanisms. In addition, attention is directed in most cases to systems of the single-input–single-output variety.
3. The performance criteria usually specified make it necessary to utilize *indirect* design techniques of the trial-and-error type.

The classical approach, typically relegated to the undergraduate control programs at our universities, has many outstanding and time-tested advantages. No sophisticated mathematics is required beyond the elements of linear differential equations and complex algebra. The present generation of control engineers is thoroughly indoctrinated with classical design techniques, and the majority of the control systems now being manufactured are designed by classical methods.

However, classical design methods have numerous shortcomings. Empiricism, trial-and-error design, and a lack of a *fundamental* theory combine to make conventional control more an art than a science. For the exacting requirements of the more complex automatic-control problems in modern technology, classical methods are, in effect, entirely inadequate. This is where "modern control" enters the picture.

The modern theory approaches the control problem in a more fundamental fashion. For example, it defines the concept of control and establishes test procedures for determining when and under what conditions a system is *controllable*. *Direct* synthesis methods are proposed which lead to *unique* system designs that are *optimal* in some defined sense. Extensive use is made of the modern computer. Theories are developed for systems with learning and adaptive capabilities.

Modern control theory leans heavily on mathematics that typically are not included on the undergraduate menu, e.g., calculus of variation and matrix algebra. It prefers time-domain system description (state variables) to transfer-function methods since it does not limit itself to linear models. The methods of modern control have been developed in many instances by applied and pure mathematicians, with the result that much of the written presentation is very formal and quite inaccessible to most control engineers. At our universities, modern control theory is reserved for the graduate programs and is presented in courses which are usually completely unintegrated with classical viewpoints. Formalism, isolation from the undergraduate program, and unwillingness to merge the modern concepts with existing conventional methods have prevented a wide dissemination of the modern ideas.

This book undertakes the task of bridging the existing gap between the conventional techniques and modern theory. Its objectives are, specifically:

1. To give a basic presentation of the fundamental control problem
2. To integrate modern concepts with conventional design techniques
3. To strip some of the new theories of some of the mathematical clothing in which they are obscured in order to make them understandable to the senior undergraduate engineering student
4. To bring into focus the importance of the modern computer—analog, digital, and hybrid—in design and on-line operation of control systems

The book aims at an audience consisting of the senior undergraduate and the first-year graduate student and the practicing control engineer. Its contents correspond approximately to six semester credit hours, which could be covered entirely in an undergraduate course sequence, or its first half (through Chap. 7) could be offered on the undergraduate level and the second half on the first-year graduate level.

In order to meet the stated objectives, I have chosen an approach which is very different from the usual one. Examples are used prolifically, but instead of starting with a mathematical model divorced from reality, the origin of the model is discussed and every step of the analysis is clearly motivated from there on. The elements of matrix algebra and variational calculus have been included, but it has been assumed that the student has had at least an elementary background in linear differential equations and transform calculus. However, a summary of Laplace and Fourier transform theorems has been included as Appendix B.

On occasion, mathematical shortcuts have been taken to preserve simplicity and continuity in the presentation, and for the same purpose, formalism has been avoided.

It has not been possible to cover componentry to any great extent. It is hoped that the examples chosen are sufficiently practical to give the reader a feeling that he always has "one foot on the ground." I have found that the presentation of the material is greatly enhanced by a parallel laboratory course taking the form of a series of simulation experiments. The examples in the text and also the end-of-chapter exercises are put on the analog computer, and the student is given a comparison between analytical results and computer recordings.

It is, of course, impossible to cover in one volume the entire spectrum of topic areas in a field as wide as control. It has been very difficult to decide where to draw the line, but I finally decided that the most natural grouping is the following one:

1. Deterministic control
2. Stochastic control

Stochastic control encompasses topics such as estimation, filtering, adaptive and learning systems, and also biocontrol and has therefore not been included in the present volume.

The methods and philosophy of teaching control courses as reflected in this book were developed in the graduate and undergraduate programs of the Department of Electrical Engineering, University of Florida. I was given the opportunity to write this text during a year as Visiting Professor at the University of Colorado, and I am particularly indebted to Dr. Max Peters, Dean of the College of Engineering, and Dr. Frank Barnes, Chairman of the Department of Electrical Engineering. Dr. John G. Truxal, Dean of the Polytechnic Institute of Brooklyn, reviewed the entire manuscript, and his comments and suggestions have been of considerable assistance in the preparation of the final manuscript. I also wish to express my special gratitude to Mrs. Barbara Salaman, Mrs. Thyra S. Johnston, and my wife, Margaret, for typing the manuscript.

My former and present students at the Universities of Florida and Colorado supplied the incentive for this project. Their enthusiasm has been truly inspirational, and their questioning minds have provided the necessary feedback. In a real sense, this book represents a joint effort in which the collective contributions of all these students constitute an essential ingredient.

Olle I. Elgerd

CONTENTS

APPENDIXES

A ELEMENTS OF VECTOR AND MATRIX ALGEBRA   533

B FOURIER AND LAPLACE TRANSFORMS—A SUMMARY   545

INDEX   555

chapter 1

INTRODUCTION

1-1 DEFINITION OF A CONTROL SYSTEM

One of the most attractive aspects of control-systems theory is its general applicability to control problems of the most varying engineering types. In the following, maximum advantage will be taken of this fact in order that the presentation will be fully acceptable to any senior engineering student. Indeed, the book should not prove impenetrable to students of biology, medicine, and business, who quite often are concerned with control problems of great complexity.

At the outset, it should be pointed out that, as the title of the book implies, we shall be concerned with *systems*. Webster defines a "system" as a "collection of objects united by some form of interaction or interdependence." This broad definition will suffice for the present; however, it will be necessary later to somewhat narrow the meaning.

The control engineer invariably will be interested in the *dynamic*, or *live*, characteristics of a system. As a rule, the "objects" making up the system will not be in a state of equilibrium relative to each other and the surrounding world. Under the influence of external stimuli, the *state* of the system will be changing with time in a manner entirely attributable to the character of the stimuli and the bonds of interaction. The reader must be satisfied at this time with his own intuitional concept of system "state." It may perhaps be helpful to make comparisons with expressions like "state of health" and "state of mind." A complete definition will be given in Chap. 3.

In principle, it is possible to change the state of a system in any prescribed fashion by properly choosing the inputs, *at least within reasonable limits*. In other words, one may exert influence on the system state by means of intelligent manipulation of its inputs. This then, in a general sense, constitutes a *controlled system*. The theory of control is concerned with the mathematical formulation of laws for control actions. The control engineer develops the techniques and hardware necessary for the implementation of the control laws to the specific systems in question.

Figure 1-1 depicts the general structure of a control system. The output of the system, or *plant*,† is measured by the p variables $c_1, c_2, \ldots, c_p$, which in some

† This term is borrowed from the area of process control and has become thoroughly incorporated in the vocabulary of control engineers.

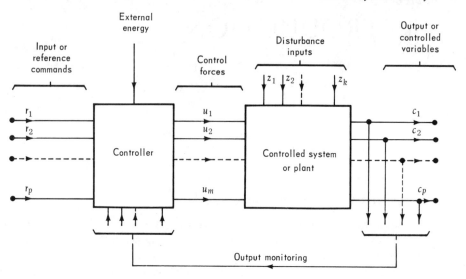

Fig. 1-1   General control-system structure.

way are related to the state of the system.   It should be pointed out that these output variables do not necessarily need to tell the whole story about the state of the controlled system.   It may be desired to control only part of the system, or it may not be physically possible to measure all the so-called "state variables." In the following, the c variables will be referred to alternately as *outputs* and *controlled variables.*

Direct control of the system is exerted by means of the m *control forces* u_1, $u_2, \ldots, u_m$.   These forces are applied by the *controller*, which always constitutes both the brain and the brute-force portion of the overall system.†   The controller determines proper control action based upon the *input* or *reference commands* r_1, $r_2, \ldots, r_p$ and information obtained, via output sensors, concerning the actual output.   This *constant output monitoring*, made possible through the presence of *feedback channels*, is the distinguishing mark of all high-precision control systems. The feedback results in a *closed-loop* signal flow, and the term *closed-loop control* is often used.   *Open-loop* control systems are used in certain applications, e.g., preset-type traffic-control systems.   Optimal control systems, to be discussed in the later chapters of this book, are often of the open-loop type.

The general block diagram in Fig. 1-1 would not be complete without the inclusion of the k *disturbance inputs* $z_1, z_2, \ldots, z_k$.   In most practical situations, it is necessary to control the plant in spite of the corruptive influence of various effects that we may classify collectively as disturbances.   These inputs may be of external origin, or they may emanate from within the system itself.   For example, in controlling an aircraft, we must anticipate either external disturbance forces caused by atmospheric turbulence or the corruptive influence due to component failures, which we, of course, must classify as internal disturbances.

† It should be noted that the physical dimension of a control "force" may not necessarily be that of mechanical force (ML/T^2).

The disturbance forces may be totally *random* in nature, or they may be predictable to various degrees of accuracy. For example, in designing a fin stabilizer for a ship, we must assume complete unpredictability of the wave motions. Consider, on the other hand, the control system for a space booster. Such a booster must penetrate the layer of jetwinds without ill effects. We know a considerable amount about this layer, and it is possible to assume a wind profile that with considerable accuracy represents the true conditions.

The controller in Fig. 1-1 may be a human operator; the system is then *manually* controlled. In an *automatic* control system, a machine has replaced the man. As a general rule, high-speed, high-precision control systems are automatic. The control engineer's job usually is centered around the problem of properly designing a controller that will fit the specific job. He usually is stuck with a plant the physical characteristics of which lie beyond his control. The complexity of the controller that finally will be chosen is a function of the complexity of the plant and the stringency of the control requirements. It may range from a device that simply compares the input command with the actual output, as is often the case in a simple *servomechanism,* to a large digital *control computer* in a complex multidimensional industrial process.

It may be of interest to mention a few examples of control systems which fit the above general description. Consider first an automobile. The vehicle operator continuously and in a closed-loop fashion exerts control over various outputs of this system, e.g., velocity, inside temperature, and (most important) vehicle position in the traffic lane. This is certainly a manually controlled system.

A jet fighter in pursuit of an evasive target is a good example of a semiautomatically controlled system. Certain control functions are in the hands of the pilot, but others, like weapons aiming, are executed automatically.

The temperature-control system of the human body is an example of a high-precision, fully automatic control system. The human body contains a large number of perfectly operating, fully automatic control systems which, in view of the low-level signals they utilize, are marvels of "engineering." Consider, for example, the positioning mechanisms of the eyes. Compare the precision of this system when the person is walking or running with that of a gun-turret positioning servo on a ship heaving in the seas.

Modern control theory is finding increased use in such areas as economics and business administration. An economic system the state of which may be represented by measures such as gross national product and stockmarket indexes may be controlled by manipulation of interest rates and other economic "control forces."

1-2 EVOLUTION OF THE SCIENCE OF CONTROL

Proper functioning of biological systems clearly requires controls of a more or less complicated nature. Control systems have thus been with us for as long as life itself.

Early man probably found use for crude control mechanisms long before he decided to record his own history. Indeed, the earliest known civilization—in the river valleys of Mesopotamia—was sustained by a properly regulated water supply, since this was necessary for agriculture.

Truly automatic control systems did not appear until the middle of the eighteenth century. By that time, man had learned to harness nature's forces in excess of his own, and he realized he had to be able to control these forces. Windmill turners were designed that automatically pointed the main sails up against the wind.[1] At about this time, James Watt developed his flyball regulator for speed control of the steam engine. During the second half of the nineteenth century, steam-operated control mechanisms were introduced as power amplifiers on ship rudders. Ships had reached such sizes that manual control of the steering mechanism had become very difficult. Maxwell, more famous for his work in field theory, presented in 1868 the first mathematical treatment of a control mechanism.[2] The next half-century produced, remarkably enough, few important contributions to the control literature.[3,22]

During the two decades preceding World War II, important developments occurred in the fields of aviation and electronics and great advances were made in electric-circuit theory. Nyquist's classic work on stability of linear feedback systems was prompted not by stability problems in control systems but by a desire to understand better the characteristics of certain communication networks.[4] It was during World War II that his ideas were first rediscovered by control people, and they came to play a tremendous role in the control field from then on. Hazen's work in the middle thirties may possibly be considered as the first struggling attempt to develop some general theory for servomechanisms.[5] The word "servo" was at this time used for the first time. Derived from the Latin word *servus*, meaning "slave," it conveys the rather special function of those control mechanisms that were being designed for ship and aircraft steering systems at the time.

During the decade preceding World War II and in parallel with, but independent of, the progress in the servo area, important advances were made in control of chemical processes. Even today, the term "process control" is associated with the specific problem areas of chemical engineering, and in view of the physical disparity between processing and electromechanical systems, it is only natural that differences in terminology and design techniques should exist.

Process control received attention during the thirties both in this country and in Europe. As early as 1926, in Germany, Stein,[6] writing on steam generation, described automatic feedback as applied to steam-generating processes. Later, Wünsch and Oldenbourg[7] dealt with control of single-capacitance systems, particularly with pressure and flow control in pipelines and boilers.

In this country at this time, Behar[8] and Grebe, Boundy, and Cermak[9] investigated the effects of dead time and process lags on controller action. Smith[10] in 1936 studied the characteristics of regulators in regard to sensitivity, stability, and speed of action.

The pioneering work in process control by Mason should be mentioned.[11-13]

His work on establishing mathematical models and analogies of processes must be considered as fundamental in process control as Hazen's work in servomechanisms.

It took World War II to establish control as a science in its own right. New high-performance weapons systems required the development of a whole series of new control components, and furthermore, in order to predict the dynamic characteristics of the new complex systems that were proposed, it became necessary to invent an entirely new theory, the outlines of which first became clear when the veils of secrecy parted in 1945. In retrospect, it is not easy to give the credit to those who most deserve it. Under the pressure of the war effort and due to secrecy considerations, publications were limited. It is safe to say, however, that the contribution made by MIT Radiation Laboratory personnel was highly significant. It is also of interest to observe that researchers representing many engineering disciplines were responsible for the advances.

In summary, it can be stated that by 1945 the theory of linear servomechanisms was well developed. Before the war, Taplin and Harris[14] had introduced the concept of steady-state (frequency) transfer function. This concept was now improved upon, and the earlier work by Nyquist was now, for the first time, made use of by control people.[15] Most important, however, was the introduction of transform calculus into the picture. This particular mathematical tool was popularized by Gardner and Barnes in their classic book, published in 1942.[16] In fairness, it should be pointed out also that many ideas were borrowed from Bode and other communication engineers.[17]

The war effort also brought forth the analog computer, which probably has meant as much to the later progress of control as transform calculus has. Measured with today's standard, the analog computers of the forties were quite crude. (The stabilized d-c amplifier was not invented until 1950—by Goldberg.)

During the postwar years, the first books on servomechanisms were published.[18,19] All these early works incorporated the results of wartime research and development efforts. We may say that the years between 1945 and 1950 were characterized by an effort to consolidate the advances made during the early part of the decade. Also, a few universities started to offer servomechanism courses.

The theory as developed by the end of the forties was concerned with linear continuous-signal systems. It was basically limited to analysis or synthesis by trial and error. Around 1950, W. R. Evans introduced his so-called root-locus methods, which for the first time gave the control engineer a means for direct synthesis.[20] These techniques, which have since been further developed, permit the designer to obtain a simple correlation between parameter variations and system response. Indeed, root-locus methods combined with modern computational techniques still (in 1966) represent one of the most powerful synthesis approaches available for linear systems.

At about this same time (around 1950), great progress was made in design of digital computers, and now emphasis shifted from continuous to discrete-data systems. Much effort was expended during the fifties to develop the theory of sampled-data systems.

Control engineering has enjoyed an unprecedented growth during the years since 1955. Truxal's timely treatise on control-system synthesis appeared in 1956.[21] New application areas have opened up, of which, of course, the aerospace field has been the most important. Computers, both analog and digital, have reached high levels of perfection and, more important, become universally available. Hybrid computing devices have entered the scene. Today, it is probably hard to find a university or industry which does not have adequate computer facilities available, often on an open-shop basis. Most universities have developed excellent programs in control, and the general control field has become one of the most popular research areas in engineering.

Inspired by the work of research teams (usually Russian or American), the field of control has entered an era that sometimes is referred to as "modern control," encompassing the general areas of optimum and adaptive control and learning systems. The research initiative has often been taken by applied mathematicians rather than engineers, with the result that the new theories are highly mathematical. Indeed, as of this writing, comparatively few engineering applications have been reported. *However, modern control theory should not be judged on the basis of its explicit usefulness in system design.* Its greatest qualities, although immeasurable, are of a more subtle nature. It may be said that the new theories have elevated an empiric art of control-system design to the status of an exact science. In the process, the need for the old art has *not* been eliminated.

References

1. A. Wolf, "A History of Science, Technology and Philosophy in the 18th Century," The Macmillan Company, New York, 1939.

2. J. C. Maxwell, On Governors, *Proc. Roy. Soc. (London)*, **16** (1868).

3. N. Minorsky, Directional Stability of Automatically Steered Bodies, *J. Am. Soc. Naval Engrs.*, **34** (1922).

4. H. Nyquist, Regeneration Theory, *Bell System Tech. J.*, **11** (1932).

5. H. L. Hazen, Theory of Servomechanism, *J. Franklin Inst.*, **218** (1934).

6. T. Stein, "Regelung und Ausgleich in Dampfanlagen," Springer-Verlag OHG, Berlin, 1926.

7. G. Wünsch and R. Oldenbourg, "Regler für Druck und Menge," R. Oldenbourg KG, Munich, 1930.

8. M. F. Behar, "Fundamentals of Instrumentation," Instruments Publishing Company, Pittsburgh, 1932.

9. J. J. Grebe, R. H. Boundy, and R. W. Cermak, The Control of Chemical Processes, *Trans. AIChE*, **29** (June, 1933).

10. E. S. Smith, Jr., Automatic Regulators, Their Theory and Application, *Trans. ASME*, **9**(4) (May, 1936).

11. C. E. Mason, Quantitative Analysis of Process Lags, *ibid.*, **40**(4) (May, 1938).

12. C. E. Mason and G. A. Philbrick, Automatic Control in the Presence of Process Lags, *ibid.*, **62**(4) (May, 1940).

13. C. E. Mason, Mathematics of Surge Vessels and Automatic Averaging Control, *ibid.*, **63** (October, 1941).

14. H. Harris, The Analysis and Design of Servomechanisms, *OSRD Rept.* 454 (January, 1942).

15. G. S. Brown and A. C. Hall, Dynamic Behavior and Design of Servomechanisms, *Trans. ASME*, **68** (1946).

16. M. F. Gardner and J. L. Barnes, "Transients in Linear Systems," John Wiley & Sons, Inc., New York, 1942.

17. H. W. Bode, Feedback Amplifier Design, *Bell System Tech. J.*, **19** (1940).

18. L. A. MacColl, "Fundamental Theory of Servomechanisms," D. Van Nostrand Company, Inc., Princeton, N.J., 1945.

19. H. M. James, N. B. Nichols, and R. S. Phillips, "Theory of Servomechanisms," McGraw-Hill Book Company, New York, 1947.

20. W. R. Evans, Graphical Analysis of Control Systems, *Trans. AIEE*, **67** (1948).

21. John G. Truxal, "Automatic Feedback Control System Synthesis," McGraw-Hill Book Company, New York, 1955.

22. A. Stodola, Über die Regulierung von Turbinen, *Schweiz. Bauzeitung*, **22** (1893); **23** (1894).

chapter 2

INTRODUCTORY EXAMPLE

2-1 DESCRIPTION OF SYSTEM

In this chapter, a control system will be discussed which is uncomplicated enough to permit simple mathematical description but which nevertheless demonstrates many of the fundamental and general aspects of control. The system is depicted in Fig. 2-1 and consists of a mixed mechanical and electrical arrangement. A "broom" *B*, restricted to move only in the paper plane, is balanced on top of a carriage *C*. A primary requirement, or control objective, is to keep the broom in a vertical position or as nearly vertical as possible. Other secondary objectives also may have to be met, but for the time being, they will not be considered.

In the chosen example, the broom-carriage assembly represents the "plant" of Fig. 1-1. This plant is *unstable* as it cannot remain in the desired position, or state, without the assistance of the control force *u*.† This, of course, is *not* a general feature of controlled systems; the reason for our choice is to emphasize that even unstable systems can be properly controlled.

As we do not wish in this introductory example to complicate our analysis unnecessarily, we shall study the chosen system in the total absence of *predictable* disturbance forces. (It is quite obvious that a control-system design based upon this simplifying assumption could be quite useless from a practical point of view. The chances are that the first wind gust would topple the broom.)

To meet our stated control objective, it is obviously necessary to exert some control over the system. The straightforward solution certainly would be to fasten a string to the top of the broom and hang the entire contraption from the ceiling. However, a more sophisticated approach will be chosen. An electric motor will be installed on the carriage, and this motor will be made to exert a force *u*, via gears, on the wheels of the carriage. Although this is not the simplest solution, from an engineering viewpoint, it is an interesting one. It turns out that this somewhat artificial method of balancing a broom represents a very accurate dynamic model of a space booster on takeoff, as depicted in Fig. 2-2. The booster

---

† In the strictest sense the broom could *theoretically* be kept vertical for an indefinite period of time assuming no disturbance forces. We know, however, that in a *practical* situation even the most minute offset or disturbance will cause the broom to fall. Whenever we have reason to consider *unstable* systems in the following chapters, we will always tacitly assume the presence of such *unpredictable* disturbances, which invariably cause the system to "take off."

is balanced on top of the rocket-engine thrust vector **T**.   By gimbaling the entire engine assembly (or by "secondary-injection" techniques), the thrust vector can be given small horizontal components which have the same effect on the rocket as the force u has on the broom system.   Therefore, if it is possible to develop a system which will be capable of balancing the broom, analogous approaches can be taken to the booster control problem.   It should be noted that a basic difference exists between the systems in Figs. 2-1 and 2-2.   The broom was restricted to perform dynamics in only one vertical plane, whereas the rocket may fall (and often does) in any direction.   It can be shown, however, that if attention is limited to small angular deviations, the dynamics in the paper plane or the "pitch plane" is *decoupled* from the dynamics in the "yaw plane," i.e., the vertical plane perpendicular to the pitch plane.   This means, in effect, that we can treat the pitch and yaw dynamics *separately*.

It should be noted that the engineering solution proposed above is based on pure intuition.   The only thing that we can say at this point is that the system

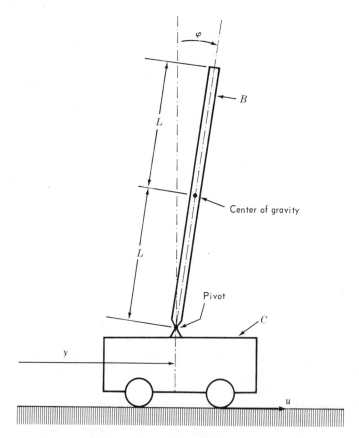

Fig. 2-1   Broom balancer (inverted pendulum).

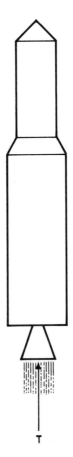

Fig. 2-2   Booster vehicle balanced on top of thruster engine.

should work, and the control engineer probably makes this assumption on the basis of his past experience, which tells him that it is possible to keep a broom balanced on top of a finger by moving the finger rapidly in a horizontal plane, thus applying horizontal forces on the lower support.

Thus, experience and intuition combined often can inform us about the feasibility of a workable system. However, as we increase the complexity of the system, it becomes more and more difficult to prophesy about the success of a proposed solution and to rely upon intuition alone. Consider, for example, the two double-broom systems depicted in Fig. 2-3. The reader who "feels" that system *b* can be kept balanced but who has his doubts concerning system *a* is right, and his intuition serves him well. But is he equally capable of explaining why? Modern control theory has produced the very useful concept of *controllability*, and it is fairly simple to prove that system *b* is *controllable* whereas system *a* is not. These ideas will be further explained in Chap. 5. Until then, let us rely upon intuition.

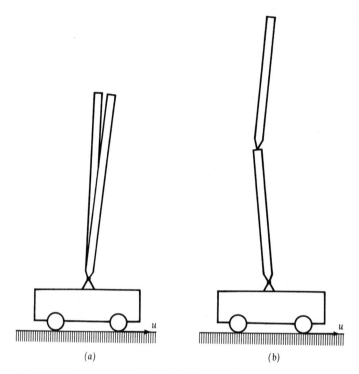

(a)   (b)

Fig. 2-3   The arrangement *b* can be balanced, but not *a*.

2-2 CONSTRUCTION OF MATHEMATICAL MODEL

We return to our single-broom problem and confirm first that a further analysis of the system necessitates the establishment of a mathematical model for it. In particular, the model should reveal how the system output represented by the angular deviation φ is affected by the control force u. Note that φ is only *partially* describing the dynamic state of the broom-carriage assembly. Indeed, a full description of this particular system would require knowledge of *four* variables. In addition to the angular position φ, it is necessary also to know the carriage position y and the two velocities $\dot{\varphi}$ and $\dot{y}$. The reader is asked to take this important statement at face value for the time being. We shall explain it in detail in Chap. 3 in connection with our introduction of *state variables*.

The mathematical model to be constructed will have to reveal the dynamic features of the mechanical system and will therefore by necessity turn out to be a system of *differential equations*. These equations can only be obtained from a knowledge of the fundamental physics of the system; in this case, it is obviously necessary to resort to the basic relationships of classical mechanics.

The control engineer is always faced with this problem of establishing initially a model of the system he wishes to control. This may be a relatively simple job (as exemplified by the present problem), or it may be a problem of great complexity. In general, a control engineer will benefit from a broad educational background in engineering. Whereas the majority of today's engineers face the necessity of narrow specialization, a good control engineer may apply his talents with equal success to widely different problem areas.

Returning to our broom problem, we proceed by writing the newtonian differential equations for the two rigid bodies of which the system is composed. First we note (Fig. 2-4) that the centers of gravity (CG) of each body have the following space coordinates in relation to an arbitrarily chosen fixed origin:

Carriage: Horizontal position $= y$

Broom: Horizontal position $= y + L \sin \varphi$

                  Vertical position $= L \cos \varphi$

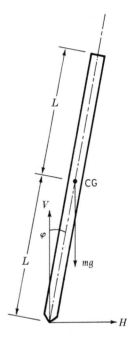

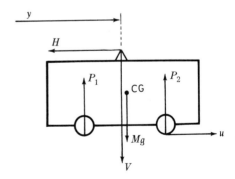

Fig. 2-4   Forces acting on the broom and carriage portions of system in Fig. 2-1.

By taking moments around the center of gravity of the broom and by summing up all forces acting on the carriage and broom in vertical and horizontal directions, we now obtain the following system of equations:

$$I\frac{d^2\varphi}{dt^2} = VL \sin \varphi - HL \cos \varphi$$

$$V - mg = m\frac{d^2}{dt^2}(L \cos \varphi)$$

$$H = m\frac{d^2}{dt^2}(y + L \sin \varphi)$$

$$u - H = M\frac{d^2y}{dt^2}$$

(2-1)

The symbols used in these equations are defined in Fig. 2-4.   Note that the *moment of inertia I* is computed with respect to the center of gravity and equals

$$I = \tfrac{1}{3}mL^2$$

(2-2)

By performing the required differentiation and by using the shorter notation (·) for the time derivative, the equations obtain the final form

$$I\ddot{\varphi} = VL \sin \varphi - HL \cos \varphi$$
$$V - mg = -mL(\ddot{\varphi} \sin \varphi + \dot{\varphi}^2 \cos \varphi)$$
$$H = m\ddot{y} + mL(\ddot{\varphi} \cos \varphi - \dot{\varphi}^2 \sin \varphi)$$
$$u - H = M\ddot{y}$$

(2-3)

Before we proceed, we make the following important observations regarding this system of equations:

1. The four equations are enough to solve for the four unknowns V, H, φ, and y.
2. As the reaction forces V and H are of no further interest, they may be eliminated, leaving us with two equations for the two unknowns φ and y.
3. The two equations thus obtained for φ and y (the student is advised to actually perform the required elimination of H and V) are both second-order, ordinary nonlinear differential equations.   From the theory of differential equations, we know that four *independent initial conditions* can be specified: initial positions $\varphi(0)$ and $y(0)$ and initial velocities $\dot{\varphi}(0)$ and $\dot{y}(0)$.
4. In spite of the fact that the number of independent equations matches the number of unknowns, the system of equations is, in principle, *unsolvable because the control force u is as yet unspecified.*

The last observation is indeed of fundamental importance as it typifies the situation that the control engineer always faces.

In this case, he is presented with a problem of *synthesis* rather than *analysis*. The student who has taken a course in differential equations should be quite familiar with problems of analysis.   With rare exceptions, he has been presented in such a course with examples where he has had to solve equations with the inputs or forcing terms a priori known.

The basic problem facing the control engineer at this juncture is one of selecting proper *control strategy* or, in other words, specifying a suitable form for the control force *u*. This is by no means a simple problem, neither does it have a unique solution. The choice will have to be guided by intuition, experience, and quite often, luck. More will be said about this in a later section. It will suffice at this time to conclude that this problem is a basic one and can be said to be the *raison d'être* for control engineering.

We shall turn our attention now to a different problem. It has already been pointed out that the differential equations (2-1) and (2-3) are *nonlinear*. This fact is disturbing since the solutions of nonlinear differential equations cannot in general be found even when the forcing terms are specified. Indeed, only very restricted classes of such equations have known solutions. It should be understood, of course, that with *u* assumed known, it is always possible to obtain a *numerical* solution or an analytic solution in the form of an infinite power series. Such solutions usually are difficult to obtain and are of little value for synthesis work as they do not show the correlation between parameter changes and the resulting effects on time responses.

More will be said later about solution methods of differential equations. The reader is reminded that differential equations are classified in two basic groups:

1. Nonlinear
2. Linear

As pointed out above, the first class of equations generally does not possess elementary solutions. Equations belonging to the second class, particularly if they also have *time-independent* parameters, have simple analytic solutions. Unfortunately, in constructing models for physical systems, one arrives more often than not at nonlinear systems of equations. Somebody has said that nature is inherently nonlinear. Great research efforts are under way which have the objective of increasing our knowledge of nonlinear differential equations. Our present mathematical toolbox is, however, woefully inadequate to handle any but the very simplest (and from an engineering viewpoint, quite uninteresting) types of differential equations. A few very limited techniques will be discussed in Chap. 8 for the sake of completeness.

The seemingly hopeless problem posed by the model nonlinearity fortunately can be resolved. Actually, two different approaches can be chosen, both with general applicability and both very powerful, from a synthesis point of view. Both approaches are characterized by a certain degree of approximation, but this is often acceptable. They are, in order of importance:

1. Solution by simulation
2. Solution by linearization

Both approaches will be discussed in great detail in later chapters. The latter method will be applied now to our unfinished broom-balancing system.

2-3 LINEARIZATION OF MATHEMATICAL MODEL

It will be proved in a subsequent chapter that any nonlinear system of differential equations can be linearized if attention is limited to small excursions of the dependent system variables. Usually this is not too restrictive a limitation, and the method has in reality a very wide applicability. We proceed now to demonstrate the salient features of this linearization technique as applied to our problem at hand. Inspection of Eq. (2-3) reveals immediately that the nonlinearities appear in the variable φ, but not in y. We decide now to restrict our attention to relatively small angular deviations, so small in fact that

$$\varphi \ll 1 \tag{2-4}$$

In passing, it is interesting to observe that in properly attitude-controlled large space boosters, the attitude deviations are not permitted to exceed angles in excess of a few degrees of arc. Larger excursions would cause excessive structural bending moments. Our limitation on φ (which in our formulas is measured in radians) is thus very realistic from an engineering viewpoint.

In view of the inequality (2-4), we can set with sufficient accuracy

$$\sin \varphi = \varphi - \frac{\varphi^3}{6} + \cdots \approx \varphi$$

$$\cos \varphi = 1 - \frac{\varphi^2}{2} + \cdots \approx 1$$

and Eq. (2-3) thus can be written

$$\begin{aligned} I\ddot{\varphi} &\approx VL\varphi - HL \\ V - mg &\approx -mL(\varphi\ddot{\varphi} + \dot{\varphi}^2) \\ H &\approx m\ddot{y} + mL(\ddot{\varphi} - \varphi\dot{\varphi}^2) \\ u - H &= M\ddot{y} \end{aligned} \tag{2-5}$$

Product terms of "second order," that is, $\varphi\dot{\varphi}$, $\dot{\varphi}^2$, $\varphi\ddot{\varphi}$, are now neglected in favor of "first-order" terms, and as a result we end up with the following set of *linear* equations:

$$\begin{aligned} I\ddot{\varphi} &\approx VL\varphi - HL \\ V - mg &\approx 0 \\ H &\approx m\ddot{y} + mL\ddot{\varphi} \\ u - H &= M\ddot{y} \end{aligned} \tag{2-6}$$

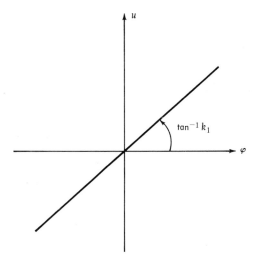

$$\tan^{-1} k_1$$

Fig. 2-6   Proportional-control strategy.

The constant k_1 has in MKS units the dimension newtons/radian and expresses the vigor with which the controller reacts. Note that, in making this assumption, we have neglected all time lags of the sensor plus motor; i.e., we have assumed an *inertia-less* transducer. It is possible, of course, to make the transducer fast compared with the rest of the system, *but it is not physically possible to make it instantaneous.* Therefore, in the strictest sense, our mathematical model is not physically justifiable, but the approximation is of a realistic nature. Also, it fits nicely into our analytical picture inasmuch as substitution of (2-8) into Eq. (2-7) results in the linear system of differential equations

$$(I + mL^2)\ddot{\varphi} + mL\ddot{y} - mgL\varphi = 0$$
$$mL\ddot{\varphi} + (m + M)\ddot{y} - k_1\varphi = 0 \tag{2-9}$$

Elimination of $\ddot{y}$ results in the following linear second-order equation for φ:

$$\ddot{\varphi} + \frac{k_1 - g(m + M)}{I(m + M) + mML^2} mL\varphi = 0 \tag{2-10}$$

For shorter notation, we define

$$\omega^2 \triangleq \frac{k_1 - g(m + M)}{I(m + M) + mML^2} mL \tag{2-11}$$

$$a \triangleq \frac{k_1}{m + M} \tag{2-12}$$

$$b \triangleq \frac{mL}{m + M} \tag{2-13}$$

We thus have

$$\ddot{\varphi} + \omega^2\varphi = 0 \tag{2-14}$$

$$\ddot{y} = a\varphi - b\ddot{\varphi} \tag{2-15}$$

Note that the first equation which governs the variation of φ does not contain y explicitly. This means, in effect, that φ is *independent of y;* that is, the angular dynamics is independent of the translational dynamics in y. The opposite is *not* true. As indicated by Eq. (2-15), the solution of y is actually obtained by a double integration of $a\varphi - b\ddot{\varphi}$. Another way of expressing this is to say that the φ solution will be independent of any arbitrary initial conditions assigned to $y(0)$ and $\dot{y}(0)$ but the y solution will depend upon $\varphi(0)$ and $\dot{\varphi}(0)$ [and also, of course, upon $y(0)$ and $\dot{y}(0)$].

Equations (2-14) and (2-15) are easily integrated. Solutions could be given for a general set of initial conditions, but in order to preserve simplicity without losing any essential information, we have assigned

$$y(0) = \dot{y}(0) = \dot{\varphi}(0) = 0$$

$$\varphi(0) = \varphi_0$$

For these initial conditions, the solutions are†

$$\varphi = \varphi_0 \cos \omega t$$

$$y = \varphi_0 \frac{a + b\omega^2}{\omega^2} (1 - \cos \omega t) \tag{2-16}$$

It is important to note from Eq. (2-11) that the parameter ω in these expressions may become imaginary if k_1 is less than $g(m + M)$. We shall define this limit value of k_1 as the "critical" gain k_{cr}; that is,

$$k_{cr} \overset{\Delta}{=} g(m + M) \tag{2-17}$$

An exhaustive response study thus necessitates our investigation of the following three cases:

case 1 $k_1 > k_{cr}$ *Supercritical* gain setting

case 2 $k_1 = k_{cr}$ *Critical* gain setting

case 3 $k_1 < k_c.$ *Subcritical* gain setting

Equations (2-16) pertain to case 1. We may readily obtain the solutions for cases 2 and 3 from (2-16). For example, the response equations in case 2 are derived by letting $\omega \to 0$, i.e.,

$$\varphi = \lim_{\omega \to 0} (\varphi_0 \cos \omega t) = \varphi_0$$

---

† We must assume that the reader possesses an *elementary* knowledge of solution methods for linear differential equations with constant coefficients. Solution by means of Laplace transforms is by far the most practical method. A short review of this method is given in Appendix B. In Chap. 4, we shall review linear analysis for the multidimensional (vector) case.

and

$$y = \lim_{\omega \to 0}\left[\varphi_0 \frac{a + b\omega^2}{\omega^2}(1 - \cos \omega t)\right] = a\varphi_0 \lim_{\omega \to 0}\left(\frac{1 - \cos \omega t}{\omega^2}\right)$$

$$= a\varphi_0 \lim_{\omega \to 0}\left[\frac{1 - \left(1 - \dfrac{\omega^2 t^2}{2} + \cdots\right)}{\omega^2}\right] = a\varphi_0 \frac{t^2}{2}$$

Case 3 can be obtained from (2-16) by making use of the formula

$$\cos jx = \cosh x$$

The reader should work out the details of these derivations.
We summarize the results:
For $k_1 > k_{cr}$

$$\varphi = \varphi_0 \cos \omega t$$

$$y = \varphi_0 \frac{a + b\omega^2}{\omega^2}(1 - \cos \omega t) \tag{2-18}$$

For $k_1 < k_{cr}$

$$\varphi = \varphi_0 \cosh |\omega| t$$

$$y = \varphi_0 \frac{a - b|\omega|^2}{|\omega|^2}\left(\cosh |\omega| t - 1\right) \tag{2-19}$$

For $k_1 = k_{cr}$

$$\varphi = \varphi_0$$

$$y = \varphi_0 \frac{a}{2} t^2 \tag{2-20}$$

The graphs in Fig. 2-7 depict the behavior of the broom should it be released from an initial angular offset φ_0. All three possible gain cases are shown. Clearly, this proportional-control system has a completely unacceptable response for too low k_1 values. The motor simply is too weak to correct the angular deviations, and the deviation will grow indefinitely; i.e., the broom will fall. The system is said to be *unstable*.

For k_1 values in excess of the critical value, both the broom and the carriage will perform harmonic oscillations. The system dynamics is similar to that of an undamped pendulum. The system tries to correct the initial offset, but it overshoots, and it never settles down. However, the broom does not fall, and it can be argued that the weakly stated control objective is actually met. Note that the harmonic oscillations of the carriage will have very high amplitudes for k_1 values close to the critical value. Explain why.

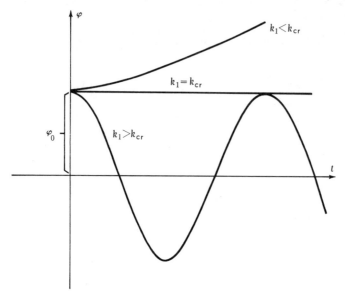

Fig. 2-7 Response of the proportional-control loop for different gain settings.

2-4.2 PROPORTIONAL-PLUS-DERIVATIVE CONTROL (PPD CONTROL)

The oscillations resulting from the simple proportional-control action just described can be damped out by means of so-called *derivative* control. The presence of the undamped oscillations is clearly due to the fact that the motor takes action only after the angular deviations already have occurred. It makes sense, therefore, to arrange for the motor to take action when the deviations *are about to occur;* i.e., we arrange for the corrective force to be on the job *before* a deviation has actually occurred. A possible solution is to make the control force a linear combination of φ and $\dot{\varphi}$ as follows:

$$u = k_1\varphi + k_2\dot{\varphi} \tag{2-21}$$

Clearly, this solution requires either a more sophisticated sensor or a means of actually differentiating the φ signal. For example, in booster controllers, one must add to the position gyro (which provides φ) a *rate gyro* supplying the $\dot{\varphi}$ part.†

The second of Eqs. (2-7) will now change to

$$mL\ddot{\varphi} + (m + M)\ddot{y} - k_1\varphi - k_2\dot{\varphi} = 0 \tag{2-22}$$

† The inclusion of a derivative signal means physically that we now are able to perform a certain degree of *prediction* of the future values of φ, because $\dot{\varphi}$ is a measure of the rate of change of φ and thus gives us an indication of where φ "is going." We shall find reasons later (Chap. 7) to include *integral* control, which, on the contrary, "looks backward" in time, i.e., introduces *memory* into our system.

By eliminating $\ddot{y}$ between this new equation and the first of Eqs. (2-7), we obtain

$$\ddot{\varphi} + \frac{mLk_2}{I(m+M)+mML^2}\dot{\varphi} + \frac{k_1 - g(m+M)}{I(m+M)+mML^2}mL\varphi = 0 \qquad (2\text{-}23)$$

or, more compactly,

$$\ddot{\varphi} + 2\alpha\dot{\varphi} + \omega^2\varphi = 0 \qquad (2\text{-}24)$$

where the damping coefficient α is defined by

$$\alpha \stackrel{\Delta}{=} \frac{1}{2}\frac{mLk_2}{I(m+M)+mML^2} \qquad (2\text{-}25)$$

Assuming the same initial conditions as before, the solution of (2-24) is easily found:

$$\varphi = \varphi_0 \frac{\omega}{\sqrt{\omega^2 - \alpha^2}} e^{-\alpha t} \sin\left(\sqrt{\omega^2 - \alpha^2}\,t + \tan^{-1}\frac{\sqrt{\omega^2 - \alpha^2}}{\alpha}\right) \qquad (2\text{-}26)$$

This solution is depicted in the graph of Fig. 2-8. The graph is, of course, correct for only those α and ω values that render the radical of Eq. (2-26) real. If the derivative term in (2-21) is large in comparison with the proportional one, then the radical will be imaginary and the system response will be *overdamped:*

$$\varphi = \tfrac{1}{2}\varphi_0\frac{1}{\sqrt{\alpha^2 - \omega^2}}\left[(\alpha + \sqrt{\alpha^2 - \omega^2})e^{-(\alpha - \sqrt{\alpha^2 - \omega^2})t} - (\alpha - \sqrt{\alpha^2 - \omega^2})e^{-(\alpha + \sqrt{\alpha^2 - \omega^2})t}\right] \qquad (2\text{-}27)$$

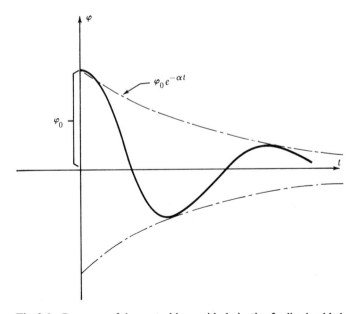

Fig. 2-8   Response of the control loop with derivative feedback added.

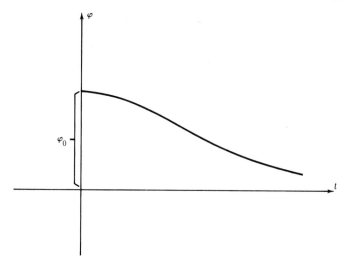

Fig. 2-9   PPD response with strong rate feedback.

This solution, depicted in Fig. 2-9, applies when

$$\alpha > |\omega|$$

where α and ω are defined by Eqs. (2-25) and (2-11), respectively. Comparing the responses of Figs. 2-8 and 2-7, there should be no doubt about the superiority of derivative control over proportional control. Indeed, this type of control is the present standard of large space boosters.

The reader may note that no decision has been reached as to *how much* damping we should build into our systems; i.e., what specific k_2 value should be chosen. We shall postpone this decision until Chap. 7, when we have more carefully studied the problem of choosing proper figure of merit for quantitative judgment of our system response.

Two different control strategies were discussed above. Both were chosen on an intuitive basis, and subsequent analysis confirmed that both strategies resulted in acceptable system responses. The analysis was very much simplified by the fact that the specific strategies resulted in overall *linear* systems. It is appropriate at this time to point out that there exists an infinite number of other workable control strategies, linear and nonlinear. A very important nonlinear candidate, which also should work on an intuitive basis, is the *maximum-effort* control strategy, often referred to as *on-off* control or *bang-bang* control, defined by

$$u = \frac{\varphi}{|\varphi|} u_{\max} \qquad (2\text{-}28)$$

and shown in Fig. 2-10.

The actual analysis of the system response for a control action of this type is laborious. Exact and approximate techniques will be discussed in Chap. 8.

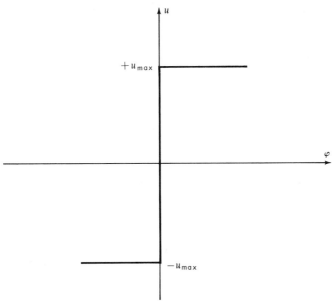

Fig. 2-10 Maximum-effort control strategy.

2-5 SUMMARY

We attempted in this chapter to introduce the reader to the fundamental control problem via a reasonably simple demonstration example. Initially, we were faced with the problem of establishing a mathematical model for the plant to be controlled. Then we had to settle on a control criterion, and finally, we had to decide on a proper control strategy. The overall control-system design consisted of a mixed analysis-synthesis procedure. In order to make the problem amenable to simple mathematical analysis, it might be necessary to simplify the mathematical model by linearization. We were led in a natural way to a system structure of the closed-loop type, and we concluded that feedback is an essential feature of control. However, we did not elaborate on the particular advantages (and possible disadvantages) of feedback.

We also surmised that a particular control system does not have a *unique* solution, but instead we found reason to believe that a system can be controlled in an infinite number of different ways.

We also found reasons to suspect that certain systems are "noncontrollable," but we made no attempt to define what controllability really implies. Neither did we make any attempt to account for the effects of disturbance inputs.

It is appropriate to conclude the chapter with a word of caution:

We really have no guarantee that the proposed controller in the above example will work for any conditions other than those assumed in the analysis, i.e., for small (in a strict sense, infinitesimal) perturbations. If the specifications call for operation over large angular excursions, then we have no choice but to analyze our system for the largest possible excursions that we may encounter. Such an analysis involves solution of nonlinear differential equations, and we now have on our hands a mathematical problem of great complexity. Fortunately, we are equipped to handle such cases. Our most powerful tool is the analog computer, which will be discussed in detail in Chap. 12.

Exercises†

▲ **2-1** Equation (2-8) neglects unavoidable time lags in the proportional-control system discussed. A more realistic mathematical model of the sensor transducer provides for a time lag of T sec between the appearance of φ and the application of the force u. Therefore, instead of Eq. (2-8), we should use

$$u + T\dot{u} = k_1\varphi \qquad (2\text{-}29)$$

This assumption means that a step change in φ results, not in an instantaneous force u, but in a force that reaches full magnitude *exponentially*; that is,

$$u = k_1\varphi(1 - e^{-t/T}) \qquad (2\text{-}30)$$

as shown in Fig. 2-11.‡

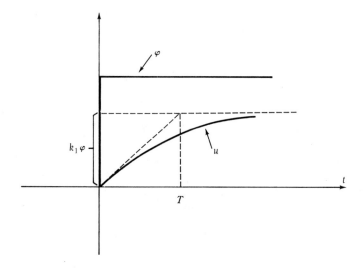

Fig. 2-11   Response of transducer containing lag.   (The graph shows the u response assuming a step in φ.)

    Take this time lag into account and analyze the overall system.   Prove in particular that:
    a Proportional control results in unstable response.

† The end-of-chapter problems here and throughout the book which are marked by a triangle (▲) are considered relatively difficult and/or time-consuming and perhaps should not be used as regular class assignments.   They are intended for those students who are willing to devote the additional time needed to penetrate the chapter topics to greater depth.

‡ Note that (2-29) reduces to (2-8) for vanishing T.

    b Proportional-plus-derivative control gives acceptable control action, assuming a certain minimum value of k_2.   Show that the necessary and sufficient conditions for stability are

$$k_1 > (M + m)g$$
$$k_2 > Tk_1$$

Hint: Make use of Routh criterion (see Appendix B).

▲ *2-2* In the introductory example, no particular attention was paid to the excursions of the carriage.   It was mentioned in connection with Eq. (2-18) that these excursions can be of considerable magnitude for small ω values.   Worse yet, had we assumed a different set of initial values with nonzero initial velocity $\dot{y}(0)$, we would have found that its horizontal position $y(t)$ would grow beyond all limits.   Prove this statement.   Assume then that we wish to control not only the angular but also the horizontal position.   In accordance with Fig. 2-12, we attempt a

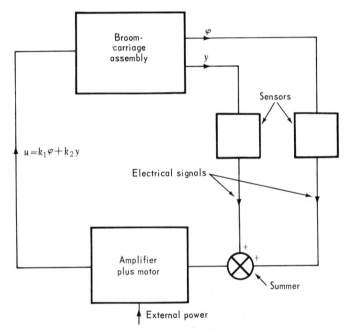

Fig. 2-12   Proposed system for controlling the positions of both the broom and the carriage.

control strategy where the control force is made proportional to *both* φ and y; that is,

$$u = k_1\varphi + k_2 y \tag{2-31}$$

(Note that k_2 has a different meaning than in the text.)   Write the differential equations for this control system, assuming an inertia-less transducer.   As the equations for φ and y will be of fourth order, it is recommended that an analog computer be employed for their solution.

2-3 In the analysis of the broom-balancing system in the text, no external forces or moments were taken into account.   A well-designed control system should perform its job with as few side effects as possible from external disturbances.   Investigate how the PPD system described in the text would react if subjected to a side force z caused by winds, for instance.   Assume for simplicity that the wind force is constant and attacks in the CG of the broom.‡   Study both the *y* and the *φ* dynamics.

2-4 A vehicle is kept hovering above the surface of the moon on top of its thrust vector **T** (Fig. 2-13), controllable in both magnitude and direction.   (The magnitude must be kept constant =

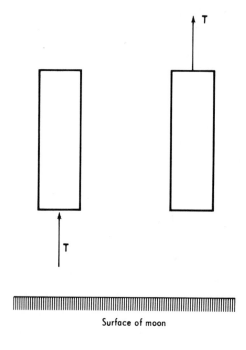

T

T

Surface of moon

Fig. 2-13   Moon-landing vehicle controlled by either bottom- or top-mounted engine.

mg_m, where g_m is the gravity of the moon, if a hovering position is to be maintained.)†   Theoretically, we may assume that the rocket engine is arranged either at the bottom of the vehicle (pushing thrust) or at the top (pulling thrust).   The latter design is hard to engineer.   Remembering that the job of the pilot in this position of the craft probably will be to scout for a suitable landing spot, make a study of these two possible types of craft and determine which one would be preferable from a control point of view.   *Hint:* Assume proportional control and study the horizontal excursions of the vehicle in each case.

2-5 Would the broom-balancing system described in the text work if k_1 in Eq. (2-21) were made equal to zero; i.e., if instead of PPD control, we were using pure D control?

2-6 Find solutions to the differential equations describing the broom and carriage dynamics for other combinations of the initial conditions than those used in the text.   In particular, study the case when the carriage has a non-zero initial velocity.

2-7 Develop the mathematical model for some simple control mechanism with which you are familiar.

† Strictly speaking, the mass *m* will change as the fuel is being consumed; however, for simplicity, assume constant mass and also constant moment of inertia.

‡ Under the influence of this force the broom-carriage assembly will accelerate in the wind direction and eventually "catch up" with the wind.   The force *z* will therefore decrease and eventually disappear.   Your analysis results will therefore apply only as long as the carriage velocity is relatively small.

chapter 3

CONCEPTS OF STATE
AND STATE VARIABLES

3-1 INTRODUCTION

Studying the introductory control system in the previous chapter should have made it perfectly clear that the initial problem facing the control engineer in each particular case is that of establishing a dynamic model of the system. The present chapter is devoted to the problem of mathematical model building in general, with particular emphasis on the so-called *state-space* techniques. In the next chapter, attention will be directed toward linear systems and *transfer function* models.

We shall concern ourselves now with *deterministic* systems only. A deterministic system is characterized by the fact that its future behavior is fully predictable. In a true sense, physical systems are never completely deterministic because our observations and measurements and thus our mathematical models are clouded by uncertainty. The engineer is always aware of this, and when he feels too uncertain about the validity of his model, he resigns himself to the fact that the best he can expect to predict is that his system behavior will lie within certain probabilistic bounds.

In this chapter, we shall assume that all signals throughout the systems under study are appearing at all instants of time. Many important control systems are characterized by the fact that certain or possibly all signals appear only at discrete instants. Such systems, referred to as *sampled-data systems*, will be considered in Chap. 9.

The dynamic models of most physical systems of interest will, under the above assumptions, consist of sets of either *partial* or *ordinary* differential equations. The differential equations are referred to as "ordinary" when time t is the only independent variable and "partial" when, in addition, derivatives with respect to *space* coordinates appear in the equations. If we thus in a particular case construct a model consisting only of ordinary equations, *we have tacitly assumed that none of the dependent variables is space-dependent*. In the strictest sense, this is always an approximation.

Consider as an example the ordinary differential equations we arrived at for the broom-carriage system in the previous chapter. Why did they turn out to be of the ordinary variety? Obviously, because we could assume on a rather solid basis that the position of the system could be expressed adequately in terms of two space coordinates, y and φ, only. However, a more critical examination will reveal that this assumption is erroneous. When the broom performs dynamics, it is obviously subject to time-variant bending moments. These moments certainly will cause deflections of the broom, and we conclude therefore that *the pitch angle φ will vary along the broom.* Our "mistake" has thus been to consider a broom with an infinite modulus of elasticity—i.e., a "perfectly stiff" broom. How permissible this assumption is in reality can only be judged from case to case. It is worth mentioning, for instance, that we *cannot* make this assumption in the study of the dynamics of huge liquid-fueled space boosters. Due to the structurally weak body, the effect of bending is here very pronounced and *must* be incorporated in the mathematical model.

What we really should have done in Chap. 2 was introduce a *space* coordinate x along the broom and then introduce a pitch angle φ which was a function of both t and x, that is, $\varphi = \varphi(x,t)$. We then should have studied the dynamics of an *element dx* of the broom. This would have led to a partial differential equation in two independent variables, x and t. This approach does not involve any principal difficulties *except an exorbitant amount of work.* The mathematical model finally arrived at would be extremely complicated, and what we would gain in accuracy we would lose many times over in simplicity. We could make a compromise, of course, and consider the broom as consisting of two or possibly more stiff segments spring-coupled to each other. (This is actually the approach usually taken in the above-mentioned example with space boosters.) This, then, would mean that instead of doing the rough "lumping" of all pitch angles $\varphi(x)$ into one, φ, as we did in Chap. 2, we introduce two, φ_1 and φ_2, or several.

We note from this example that, in our attempt to refine the model, we need to introduce more and more variables φ_1, φ_2, etc., until, in the limit case, when we consider the *continuous* character of the broom, we need an infinite number of variables, i.e., the *continuous* pitch-angle *function* $\varphi(x)$.

We have discussed the above example in considerable detail in order to accentuate the following very important point: *In establishing the mathematical model for a system, we are faced with a compromise between accuracy and complexity on one hand and approximation and simplicity on the other.* Each case must be judged on its own merits, and it would be impossible to give any general rules. Experience teaches us, however, that in the majority of cases, we can reduce the model to a set of ordinary differential equations, and our following discussion will be based upon the existence of such a set.

It is possible under very general assumptions to reduce such a set of equations to what is known as a *normal* form.[1] By putting the equations in this form, many advantages can be gained, of which we enumerate a few:

1. The equations lend themselves conveniently to general discussions.
2. When the equations represent a system of high order, i.e., when many dependent variables are involved, the normal form combined with the compact notation

features of matrix and vector algebra makes it possible to utilize a very convenient and elegant mathematical language.

3. The system equations expressed in this form are well suited to direct programming on both analog and digital computers.

4. The equations serve as an excellent starting point in defining the *state* of a system.

3-2 REDUCTION OF DIFFERENTIAL EQUATIONS TO THEIR NORMAL FORM

The concepts introduced in the following presentation can be fully appreciated only if the reader possesses a knowledge of the elementary rules of vector and matrix algebra. As it cannot be assumed that all students will have had a background in linear algebra at this level, the basic features of this algebra have been included in Appendix A. It should be stressed that only a most elementary knowledge will prove sufficient for our specific needs.

We shall present the topic of normalization of differential equations by working with the specific equations derived for the control system in the previous chapter. For easy reference, we restate them here:

$$(I + mL^2)\ddot{\varphi} + mL\ddot{y} - mgL\varphi = 0$$
$$mL\ddot{\varphi} + (m + M)\ddot{y} = u$$

(3-1)

[The fact that we have chosen the linearized set of equations should not be construed to mean that the methods to be discussed have applicability to linear systems only. The only reason for the choice is that it will result in simpler expressions than would have resulted from the nonlinear set (2-3).]

We then rewrite the equations by *solving for the highest derivatives*. This can always be done for a reducible set of equations and indeed can be considered a characteristic feature of such a set. We obtain, in this case,

$$\ddot{\varphi} = \frac{g(m + M)mL}{I(m + M) + mML^2}\varphi - \frac{mL}{I(m + M) + mML^2}u$$
$$\ddot{y} = \frac{I + mL^2}{I(m + M) + mML^2}u - \frac{gm^2L^2}{I(m + M) + mML^2}\varphi$$

(3-2)

These two second-order equations define together a fourth-order system. The set can be further reduced by introducing four new variables x_1, x_2, x_3, and x_4, defined by

$$x_1 \overset{\Delta}{=} \varphi$$
$$x_2 \overset{\Delta}{=} \dot{\varphi}$$
$$x_3 \overset{\Delta}{=} y$$
$$x_4 \overset{\Delta}{=} \dot{y}$$

(3-3)

In terms of these new variables, we may rewrite Eqs. (3-2) as a set of four first-order differential equations

$$\dot{x}_1 = x_2$$

$$\dot{x}_2 = \frac{g(m + M)mL}{I(m + M) + mML^2} x_1 - \frac{mL}{I(m + M) + mML^2} u$$

$$\dot{x}_3 = x_4 \qquad\qquad (3\text{-}4)$$

$$\dot{x}_4 = \frac{I + mL^2}{I(m + M) + mML^2} u - \frac{gm^2L^2}{I(m + M) + mML^2} x_1$$

In a more compact fashion, these equations obviously can be written in the form

$$\dot{x}_i = f_i(x_1, x_2, x_3, x_4; u) \qquad i = 1, \ldots, 4 \qquad\qquad (3\text{-}5)$$

A system of differential equations transformed in this manner is said to be reduced to its *normal* form. It should be pointed out that the form is not unique, as it is possible to find different sets of x variables which result in a form of type (3-5) (with different f functions, of course).

In the chosen example, which was of the fourth order, it was necessary to introduce four new x variables. Generally, for an nth-order system, reduction to its normal form will necessitate the involvement of n x variables $x_1, x_2, \ldots, x_n$. Also, whereas in the example we only had one control force u, in a more general case (as shown in Fig. 1-1), m separate forces $u_1, u_2, \ldots, u_m$ will be present. In this more general case, the normal set of differential equations will thus read

$$\dot{x}_1 = f_1(x_1, x_2, \ldots, x_n; u_1, u_2, \ldots, u_m)$$

$$\dot{x}_2 = f_2(x_1, x_2, \ldots, x_n; u_1, u_2, \ldots, u_m)$$

$$\cdots\cdots\cdots\cdots\cdots\cdots\cdots\cdots \qquad\qquad (3\text{-}6)$$

$$\dot{x}_n = f_n(x_1, x_2, \ldots, x_n; u_1, u_2, \ldots, u_m)$$

It is worth noting that the more complicated it is necessary to make our model, i.e., the more dependent variables we have to put into play, the more x variables we shall be forced to define.

In encountering a set of differential equations like (3-6), a mathematician would always ask two pertinent questions:

1. Does a solution exist?
2. If a solution exists, is it unique?

It is perfectly possible to construct differential equations which do not possess a solution—certainly not a unique one. The functions $f_1, f_2, \ldots, f_n$ determine the existence and uniqueness of solution. We shall not attempt to go into the specific details of these interesting but rather academic questions. It can be proved[1] that both uniqueness and existence of solution are guaranteed if the functions f_i themselves and their partial derivatives $\partial f_i/\partial x_j$ are *defined* and *continuous* for $i, j = 1, 2, \ldots, n$.

Assuming that we have a system satisfying these conditions, we wish now to point out some important characteristics of the dynamics of this system. In order to do so, we study the system throughout a time interval 0 to t. By integrating (3-6), we obtain

$$x_i(t) - x_i(0) = \int_0^t f_i(x_1, \ldots, u_m) \, d\tau \qquad i = 1, 2, \ldots, n \tag{3-7}$$

or

$$x_i(t) = x_i(0) + \int_0^t f_i(x_1, \ldots, u_m) \, d\tau \qquad i = 1, 2, \ldots, n \tag{3-8}$$

From Eq. (3-8), we draw immediately the following important conclusion:

Each of the n x variables can be determined uniquely at any moment of time t if and only if:

1. Each variable is initially known (that is, if n "initial conditions" $x_i(0)$ are specified).
2. All m control forces are specified throughout the interval 0 to t.

3-3 CONCEPTS OF STATE AND STATE VARIABLES

In view of these results, we may interpret the n independent x variables as carriers of the full information about the dynamic *state* of the system. Initially, at $t = 0$, the total system state can be expressed by the n numbers $x_1(0), x_2(0), \ldots, x_n(0)$. Under the influence of the m control forces and the bonds of interaction, the state of the system will change. The *updated* state expressed by the n numbers $x_1(t), x_2(t), \ldots, x_n(t)$ can be continuously obtained from Eq. (3-8). In consequence of this interpretation, we define the *state* of the system as the n-dimensional vector $\mathbf{x}(t)$, which has as its components the n numbers or *state variables* $x_1(t), x_2(t), \ldots, x_n(t)$, that is,

$$\mathbf{x}(t) \triangleq \begin{bmatrix} x_1(t) \\ x_2(t) \\ \vdots \\ x_n(t) \end{bmatrix} \tag{3-9}$$

or, more concisely,

$$\mathbf{x} \triangleq \begin{bmatrix} x_1 \\ x_2 \\ \vdots \\ x_n \end{bmatrix} \tag{3-10}$$

Although the noncommittal symbol x does not reveal it directly, each state variable as a rule has a very obvious physical meaning.   This was illustrated by the example of the broom balancer.   In this example, the four state variables were represented by the two position coordinates φ and y and the corresponding velocities $\dot{\varphi}$ and $\dot{y}$ [see Eq. (3-3)].   The state of this system thus was specified completely by the four quantities.   This, by the way, is a good example of a system the state of which is fairly simple to define.   For many classes of engineering systems, this is not the case.   This is particularly true in the process-control area, where establishing a realistic mathematical model often constitutes a major problem simply because not all the factors that affect the system dynamics are known.   In other words, we have not been able to identify all state variables that characterize the system.

Sometimes we also run the opposite risk of overspecifying a system by defining too many state variables, i.e., the chosen state variables are not all *independent*.

It is appropriate in this connection to give the following strictly general definition of system state:

The state of a system is the minimum set of numbers or variables, the state variables, which contain sufficient information about the past history of the system to permit us to compute all future states of the system—assuming, of course, that all future inputs (control forces) are known and also the equations (bonds of interactions) describing the system.

The number n of state variables defines the *order* or the *dimensionality* of the system.

Sometimes the term *state-space* is used to designate the *n*-dimensional coordinate space in which **x** ranges.   Figure 3-1 depicts the situation in a three-dimensional case.   (For higher dimensions, it is difficult to visualize the situation

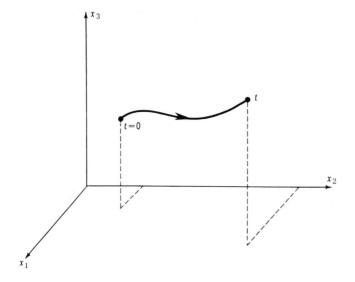

Fig. 3-1   State trajectory in three-dimensional state space.

geometrically.) The state vector

$$\mathbf{x}(t) = \begin{bmatrix} x_1(t) \\ x_2(t) \\ x_3(t) \end{bmatrix}$$

will trace a *state* or *phase trajectory* in the 3-space with passing time. The instantaneous values of the individual state variables form the components of the state vector. In a trajectory of this type, the role of t has been reduced to that of a parameter. In the two-dimensional case, the state space reduces to a *state plane*, sometimes called a *phase plane*.

Equations (3-6) may be written in very compact form utilizing vector notation. In order to do so, it is necessary for us to define two additional vectors [in addition to the state vector **x**, which was defined by Eq. (3-10)], the m-dimensional *control-force vector* **u** and the n-dimensional *function vector* **f**:

$$\mathbf{u} \triangleq \begin{bmatrix} u_1 \\ u_2 \\ \cdot \\ \cdot \\ \cdot \\ u_m \end{bmatrix} \tag{3-11}$$

$$\mathbf{f} \triangleq \begin{bmatrix} f_1 \\ f_2 \\ \cdot \\ \cdot \\ \cdot \\ f_n \end{bmatrix} \tag{3-12}$$

In terms of the three vectors **x**, **u**, and **f**, the entire system of Eqs. (3-6) reduces to the vector equation

$$\dot{\mathbf{x}} = \mathbf{f}(\mathbf{x},\mathbf{u}) \tag{3-13}$$

The symbol $\dot{\mathbf{x}}$ is of course understood to mean the column vector

$$\dot{\mathbf{x}} \triangleq \begin{bmatrix} \dot{x}_1 \\ \dot{x}_2 \\ \cdot \\ \cdot \\ \cdot \\ \dot{x}_n \end{bmatrix}$$

The broom balancer was an example of a system characterized by *time-invariant* parameters; i.e., the parameters g, L, etc., which characterize the function vector **f** are all independent of time. Many important control systems are of the *time-variant* variety; e.g., masses may change due to fuel consumption, gravity forces are changing as a vehicle moves away from earth, air pressure changes as an aircraft flies at different altitudes. In systems of this type, the function vector **f** will be an *explicit* function of time *t*, and Eq. (3-13) will be of the form

$$\dot{\mathbf{x}} = \mathbf{f}(\mathbf{x},\mathbf{u},t) \tag{3-14}$$

It is appropriate to warn the student not to confuse the state variables of a system with the system *outputs* $c_1, c_2, \ldots, c_p$ shown in Fig. 1-1. It is true that in certain cases they are identical, but more often than not the *output vector* is not equal to the state vector. We define the output vector **c** as the *p*-dimensional column vector

$$\mathbf{c} \triangleq \begin{bmatrix} c_1 \\ c_2 \\ \cdot \\ \cdot \\ \cdot \\ c_p \end{bmatrix} \qquad p \leqslant n \tag{3-15}$$

Ordinarily, the output vector is related to the state vector in the linear fashion

$$\mathbf{c} = \mathbf{C}\mathbf{x} \tag{3-16}$$

where **C** is a $p \times n$ matrix referred to as the *output* or *measurement matrix*. For example, in the broom-balancing system, we had

$$\mathbf{x} = \begin{bmatrix} x_1 \\ x_2 \\ x_3 \\ x_4 \end{bmatrix} \triangleq \begin{bmatrix} \varphi \\ \dot{\varphi} \\ y \\ \dot{y} \end{bmatrix}$$

If we choose (as in Exercise 2-2)

$$\mathbf{c} \triangleq \begin{bmatrix} \varphi \\ y \end{bmatrix} = \begin{bmatrix} x_1 \\ x_3 \end{bmatrix}$$

then we have

$$\mathbf{c} = \begin{bmatrix} c_1 \\ c_2 \end{bmatrix} \triangleq \begin{bmatrix} x_1 \\ x_3 \end{bmatrix} = \begin{bmatrix} 1 & 0 & 0 & 0 \\ 0 & 0 & 1 & 0 \end{bmatrix} \begin{bmatrix} x_1 \\ x_2 \\ x_3 \\ x_4 \end{bmatrix}$$

Therefore,

$$\mathbf{C} = \begin{bmatrix} 1 & 0 & 0 & 0 \\ 0 & 0 & 1 & 0 \end{bmatrix}$$

Sometimes the output is a function not only of the state, as in Eq. (3-16), but also of the control vector **u**, in accordance with

$$\mathbf{c} = \mathbf{Cx} + \mathbf{Du} \tag{3-17}$$

where **D** is a $p \times m$ matrix.† (An example is given in Sec. 3-4.)

The very compact equation (3-13) will serve as a starting point for many of our discussions in later chapters.

Having defined the concepts of state and state variables, we should say a few words about how to find the state variables in a specific case. We already have seen how, in the example of the broom-balancing control system, starting with the newtonian equations, we quite naturally arrived at a state vector. We also concluded that the dimensionality or the order of this vector is a measure of the complexity of a dynamic system. What then, in general, determines this order?

To find an answer to this question, it is necessary to look deeper into the fundamental physical nature of system dynamics. In so doing, it is not possible to treat all systems as equals. Quite obviously, we cannot hope to find many similarities between, say, an electromechanical system like the one we discussed in Chap. 2 and an economic or biological system. For a very large and, from an engineering viewpoint, important group of systems—composed mainly of electro-mechanical, electrical, and certain (but not all) chemical systems—it is possible to relate the system dynamics *directly* to the energy concept. Any transients or dynamic changes of a system selected from this group are caused basically by the redistribution of energy within the system. Energy appears in many different physical forms and can be transformed from one form to another with or without accompanying losses. Actually, we may view any control system as an energy-redistribution process where energy is transferred from one stored form to another in a *planned* fashion. The fact is that no energy transfer can take place instantaneously. This obviously would require infinite energy rates and therefore is physically impossible. Instead, all energy changes within the system take place with finite flow rates, and time is thus required for the redistribution process.

The number of independent energy-storage possibilities within a system equals the number of dependent state variables, and the complexity or dimensionality is therefore directly related to this number. An example will demonstrate this point. Consider the two mechanical spring-mass systems depicted in Fig. 3-2. In the first, energy can be stored in *two* independent and different forms:

1. Potential energy in the springs = $\frac{1}{2}ky^2$, where k is the total spring constant of both springs.
2. Kinetic energy in the mass = $\frac{1}{2}m\dot{y}^2$.

---

† The output relationships (3-16) and (3-17) are but special linear cases of the more general relationship

$$\mathbf{c} = \mathbf{c(x,u)}$$

We shall in this book limit ourselves to the practically important linear case (3-16).

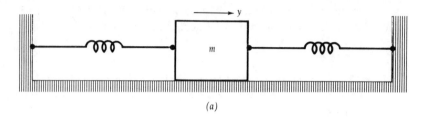

(a)

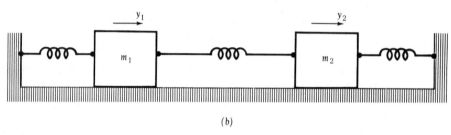

(b)

Fig. 3-2   Mechanical systems used to demonstrate relationship between energy storages and system dimensionality.

Note that we may specify y and $\dot{y}$ completely independently, and note also that although we have *two* springs, only *one* independent potential energy amount is present in this system.   Why?

This is therefore a second-order system, and two state variables suffice to specify its dynamics.   For instance, we may choose

$$\mathbf{x} \triangleq \begin{bmatrix} y \\ \dot{y} \end{bmatrix}$$

If we now turn our attention to the second system in Fig. 3-2, we realize that we can independently specify four energy amounts, two kinetic and two potential.   We thus have a fourth-order system, specifiable with four state variables.

The dynamics of biological processes, for example, is not related in this simple fashion to the energy stored within the system.   Consider the interactions between two bacteria populations.   If we let x_1 and x_2 represent the number of bacteria in each population, then we can find empirically that the growth rates are of the form

$$\dot{x}_1 = a_{11}x_1 + a_{12}x_1x_2$$
$$\dot{x}_2 = a_{21}x_2 + a_{22}x_1x_2$$

It is interesting to note that these empirically found equations are of the form (3-13) (with $u = 0$) and that the example emphasizes the general nature of the state concept. In Chap. 8, we shall show how we can also generalize the energy concept by means of the so-called Liapunov functions. It is thus possible to extend the concepts of *state* and *energy* beyond our immediate engineering-application areas.

It is beyond the scope of this presentation to try to cover in a comprehensive fashion mathematical model building as it would apply to all phases of engineering. Indeed, in most undergraduate curricula, considerable time is spent describing various engineering processes. However, as the state-space techniques may be unfamiliar to most readers, it may be of interest to discuss a few additional examples drawn from various engineering disciplines.

3-4 STATE-MODEL DESCRIPTION OF SOME TYPICAL ENGINEERING SYSTEMS

Example 3-1

In the preceding section, we applied the theory to a mechanical system. Let us consider now the dynamics of the electrical network shown in Fig. 3-3. The average electrical student would hardly refer to this network as a "control system." Nevertheless, if we assume that the two voltage sources e_1 and e_2 may be arbitrarily adjustable, we can designate them as our control forces

$$\mathbf{u} = \begin{bmatrix} u_1 \\ u_2 \end{bmatrix} \triangleq \begin{bmatrix} e_1 \\ e_2 \end{bmatrix} \tag{3-18}$$

and then we have a system the state of which can be "controlled" by this control-force vector.

Our immediate concern is to determine the order of this system and designate a suitable state vector. We note first that energy can be stored in this network both in the two coils as magnetic energy $\frac{1}{2}Li^2$ and in the capacitor as electrostatic energy $\frac{1}{2}Cv^2$. We note also that we can assign *independently* arbitrary values to

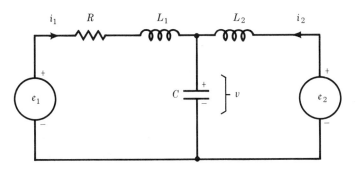

Fig. 3-3 Electric circuit viewed as a controlled plant.

the currents through the two coils i_1 and i_2 and to the voltage v across the capacitor. We therefore conclude that this is a third-order system, and we prefer to choose the following three-dimensional state vector for the simple reason that all three state variables are easily measurable and represent physically meaningful quantities:†

$$
\mathbf{x} = \begin{bmatrix} x_1 \\ x_2 \\ x_3 \end{bmatrix} \triangleq \begin{bmatrix} i_1 \\ i_2 \\ v \end{bmatrix}
\tag{3-19}
$$

(Because this is a two-loop network, one might be tempted to assume that a two-dimensional state vector would suffice to describe the system. What is the fallacy in this thinking?)

Two of the system differential equations are obtained by requiring voltage equilibrium in the two loops; that is,

$$
\begin{aligned}
e_1 &= Ri_1 + L_1 \dot{i}_1 + v \\
e_2 &= L_2 \dot{i}_2 + v
\end{aligned}
\tag{3-20}
$$

We need an additional equation, and we obtain it from the knowledge that the rate of change of the capacitor voltage is proportional to the current entering the terminals; that is,

$$
\dot{v} = \frac{1}{C}(i_1 + i_2)
\tag{3-21}
$$

By rearrangement of the terms in these equations and by substitution of the state variables and control forces already defined, we obtain the following normalized set of equations:

$$
\begin{aligned}
\dot{x}_1 &= -\frac{R}{L_1} x_1 - \frac{1}{L_1} x_3 + \frac{1}{L_1} u_1 \\
\dot{x}_2 &= -\frac{1}{L_2} x_3 + \frac{1}{L_2} u_2 \\
\dot{x}_3 &= \frac{1}{C} x_1 + \frac{1}{C} x_2
\end{aligned}
\tag{3-22}
$$

† This is really a deceptively simple electrical system. We do not wish to hide the fact that construction of state models for electric circuits is not always so straightforward as this example would lead us to believe. A more detailed discussion, with more difficult examples, is given in Ref. 10.

We define the two matrices

$$\mathbf{A} \triangleq \begin{bmatrix} -\dfrac{R}{L_1} & 0 & -\dfrac{1}{L_1} \\[2ex] 0 & 0 & -\dfrac{1}{L_2} \\[2ex] \dfrac{1}{C} & \dfrac{1}{C} & 0 \end{bmatrix} \tag{3-23}$$

$$\mathbf{B} \triangleq \begin{bmatrix} \dfrac{1}{L_1} & 0 \\[2ex] 0 & \dfrac{1}{L_2} \\[2ex] 0 & 0 \end{bmatrix} \tag{3-24}$$

In terms of the *system matrix* **A**, the *distribution matrix* **B**, and the earlier-defined **x** and **u** vectors, Eq. (3-22) can be written in compact vector form

$$\dot{\mathbf{x}} = \mathbf{A}\mathbf{x} + \mathbf{B}\mathbf{u} \tag{3-25}$$

In passing, we observe that when we are able to reduce the system equation to this very special normal form, then our system is *linear*. More will be said about such systems in the next section.

Before we leave this example, let us show how sometimes we must define an output equation of the type (3-17).

Assume, for instance, that we define the voltage across the coil L_1 as our only output; that is,

$$c \triangleq L_1 \dot{i}_1$$

By using the first of Eqs. (3-22), we obtain

$$c = -Rx_1 - x_3 + u_1$$

Therefore,

$$c = [-R \quad 0 \quad -1] \begin{bmatrix} x_1 \\ x_2 \\ x_3 \end{bmatrix} + [1 \quad 0] \begin{bmatrix} u_1 \\ u_2 \end{bmatrix}$$

which is the form (3-17) with

$$\mathbf{C} = [-R \quad 0 \quad -1]$$
$$\mathbf{D} = [1 \quad 0]$$

Example 3-2

As another example, we shall find the mathematical model for a double-capacitance heat system. The electrically heated oven depicted in Fig. 3-4 will be temperature-controlled by manipulation of the heat input u to the jacket.

The outside, jacket, and inside temperatures are T_o, T_j, and T_i, respectively. For simplicity, we shall assume that the temperatures are uniformly and instantaneously distributed throughout both the jacket and the inside of the oven.

We introduce the following pertinent system parameters:

A_i, A_o = inside and outside jacket surfaces

C_i, C_j = heat capacities of inside space and jacket, respectively

h_i, h_o = film coefficients for the inside and outside surfaces, respectively

We establish then the condition for heat balance in the jacket and for the inside space.

For jacket:

$$C_j \dot{T}_j = A_o h_o (T_o - T_j) + A_i h_i (T_i - T_j) + u \tag{3-26}$$

For inside space:

$$C_i \dot{T}_i = A_i h_i (T_j - T_i) \tag{3-27}$$

The temperature differences $T_j - T_o$ and $T_i - T_o$ are probably of more interest than the actual temperatures themselves, and we therefore define our state variables accordingly—

$$\mathbf{x} = \begin{bmatrix} x_1 \\ x_2 \end{bmatrix} \triangleq \begin{bmatrix} T_j - T_o \\ T_i - T_o \end{bmatrix}$$

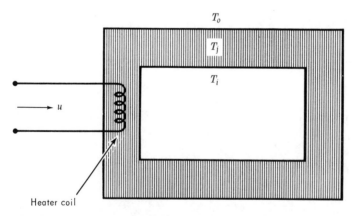

Fig. 3-4 Temperature-controlled oven.

Assuming the outside temperature constant, we thus get

$$C_j \dot{x}_1 = -A_o h_o x_1 + A_i h_i (x_2 - x_1) + u$$
$$C_i \dot{x}_2 = A_i h_i (x_1 - x_2) \tag{3-28}$$

Again we have obtained a linear system, and therefore we define the system and distribution matrices as

$$\mathbf{A} \triangleq \begin{bmatrix} -\dfrac{1}{C_j}(A_o h_o + A_i h_i) & \dfrac{A_i h_i}{C_j} \\[2ex] \dfrac{A_i h_i}{C_i} & -\dfrac{A_i h_i}{C_i} \end{bmatrix}$$

$$\mathbf{b} \triangleq \begin{bmatrix} \dfrac{1}{C_j} \\[1ex] 0 \end{bmatrix}$$

In terms of these matrices, we may write Eqs. (3-28) in vector form

$$\dot{\mathbf{x}} = \mathbf{A}\mathbf{x} + \mathbf{b}u \tag{3-29}$$

(Note that the distribution matrix in this case reduces to a column matrix, and therefore we prefer to use the symbol **b** rather than **B**.)

Example 3-3

As a final example, we shall consider an electromechanical system, specifically a d-c motor-driven *reaction-wheel* attitude-control system for spacecrafts. Vehicles in orbit may be attitude-controlled by several different methods, of which the most important are:

1. By means of thrusting (usually gas jets)
2. By using reaction wheels

The latter method (Fig. 3-5) utilizes the principle of conservation of angular momentum. For controlling the attitude in three dimensions, three reaction wheels are needed. In this example, we shall limit our attention to attitude control in one plane (the paper plane) only. Conservation of the angular momentum means that if the reaction wheel is being driven, say, in clockwise direction, the vehicle turns in counterclockwise direction. The reaction wheel may simply be the rotor of the drive motor. For the analysis, we introduce the following pertinent parameters:
For the vehicle:

Moment of inertia $= I_v$ kg-m^2
Angular reference position $= \varphi$ rad

For the reaction wheel:

Moment of inertia $= I_w$ kg-m²

Angular velocity (as measured relative to the vehicle and considered positive in counterclockwise direction) $= \omega$ rad/sec

Conservation of angular momentum requires that

$$I_v\dot{\varphi} + I_w(\dot{\varphi} - \omega) = 0 \tag{3-30}$$

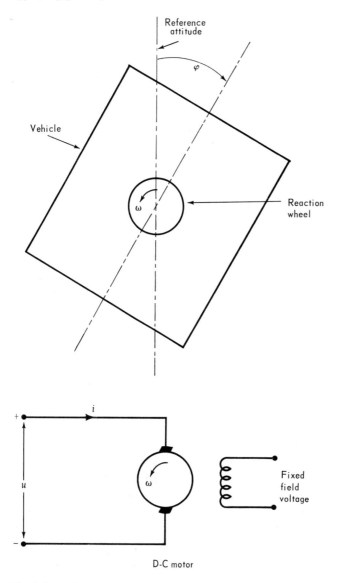

Fig. 3-5 Attitude-control system utilizing reaction wheel.

(This equation is based upon the assumption that both angular rates $\dot{\varphi}$ and ω initially are zero.)

The angular rate ω of the motor is controlled by the d-c motor, which is armature-controlled with constant field excitation. Such a motor delivers a torque proportional to the armature current i. If we call this proportionality constant k_T, we have the following relationship for the angular acceleration of the motor:

$$I_w \dot{\omega} = k_T i \tag{3-31}$$

Finally, voltage equilibrium in the armature circuit gives

$$u = Ri + Li + k_E \omega \tag{3-32}$$

The last term in Eq. (3-32) represents the motor back emf, which is proportional to the speed.

We now define a state vector

$$\mathbf{x} = \begin{bmatrix} x_1 \\ x_2 \\ x_3 \end{bmatrix} \triangleq \begin{bmatrix} \varphi \\ \omega \\ i \end{bmatrix} \tag{3-33}$$

Another convenient choice would have been

$$\mathbf{x} \triangleq \begin{bmatrix} \varphi \\ \dot{\varphi} \\ i \end{bmatrix}$$

In terms of these state variables, the following normal system of differential equations can be obtained:

$$
\begin{aligned}
\dot{x}_1 &= \frac{I_w}{I_w + I_v} x_2 \\
\dot{x}_2 &= \frac{k_T}{I_w} x_3 \\
\dot{x}_3 &= -\frac{R}{L} x_3 - \frac{k_E}{L} x_2 + \frac{1}{L} u
\end{aligned}
\tag{3-34}
$$

This system is obviously also linear, and if we wish, we therefore may define a system matrix $\mathbf{A}$ and a (column) distribution matrix $\mathbf{b}$ and write Eq. (3-34) in the form

$$\dot{\mathbf{x}} = \mathbf{A}\mathbf{x} + \mathbf{b}u \tag{3-35}$$

3-5 DEFINITION OF LINEAR SYSTEMS; METHODS FOR LINEARIZATION

On several occasions in the previous chapters, systems were encountered which we referred to as *linear*. We have so far found no reason to dwell to any extent on the concept of linearity.   We noted that linearity results in simplicity in analysis, but we did not elaborate.

In view of the great emphasis we shall place on linear systems throughout this book, we shall find it useful not only to give a general definition of linearity but also to discuss in more detail how nonlinear systems can be linearized.

definition   *A system is said to be linear if it obeys the principle of superposition.*

This definition is not one a mathematician would use, but inasmuch as we shall be concerned with physical systems only, we prefer it because it is simple and concise.   It must be added that it does not, of course, conflict with the mathematical definition of linearity.   It should be added also that the superposition principle serves as a natural basis in those instances when we may wish to test for linearity *experimentally.*

The principle of superposition specifically states: Apply the arbitrary input vector $\mathbf{u}_I$ to the system under test.   Record the response $\mathbf{x}_I$.   Then (with $\mathbf{u}_I$ removed) apply the arbitrary input $\mathbf{u}_{II}$ and record the corresponding response $\mathbf{x}_{II}$.   If now the sum of the inputs $\mathbf{u}_I$ and $\mathbf{u}_{II}$ are applied *simultaneously* and if the corresponding response turns out to be the sum $\mathbf{x}_I + \mathbf{x}_{II}$, then the principle of superposition applies and the system is linear.

It is assumed that the initial state $\mathbf{x}(0)$ in all three cases is zero.   (We also could have assumed the initial states to be nonzero.   By "response," we then would have to understand only that portion of the total $\mathbf{x}(t)$ which is caused by the control force.)

As can be expected, the principle of superposition is highly restrictive. Only those systems the normal form of which can be written

$$\dot{\mathbf{x}} = \mathbf{A}\mathbf{x} + \mathbf{B}\mathbf{u} \tag{3-36}$$

are included in the category.

It is simple to prove that this type of system is linear.   In accordance with the assumptions, we must have

$$\dot{\mathbf{x}}_I = \mathbf{A}\mathbf{x}_I + \mathbf{B}\mathbf{u}_I \tag{3-37}$$

and

$$\dot{\mathbf{x}}_{II} = \mathbf{A}\mathbf{x}_{II} + \mathbf{B}\mathbf{u}_{II} \tag{3-38}$$

Adding these two equations, we obtain

$$\dot{\mathbf{x}}_I + \dot{\mathbf{x}}_{II} = \mathbf{A}\mathbf{x}_I + \mathbf{A}\mathbf{x}_{II} + \mathbf{B}\mathbf{u}_I + \mathbf{B}\mathbf{u}_{II}{}' \tag{3-39}$$

The last vector equation can be written

$$\frac{d}{dt}(\mathbf{x}_I + \mathbf{x}_{II}) = \mathbf{A}(\mathbf{x}_I + \mathbf{x}_{II}) + \mathbf{B}(\mathbf{u}_I + \mathbf{u}_{II}) \tag{3-40}$$

and as this equation tells us that the *sum* $\mathbf{x}_I + \mathbf{x}_{II}$ indeed satisfies the given equation (3-36), we conclude that the superposition principle applies.

It should be pointed out that the above proof holds true even in the case where the elements of the **A** and **B** matrices are *time-variant*.† In all the linear systems encountered so far, these matrices have been constants, but this is not a necessary constraint for linearity.

Linearity obviously implies an extremely severe restriction on the function vector **f** in the general normalized vector differential equation (3-13).

The reason why linear theory nevertheless has had and still has such an enormous impact on control-system theory is primarily that only in linear cases do we possess analytical techniques of sufficiently general applicability. This in itself is, quite naturally, not a sufficiently good reason. Were it not for the fact that a very large number of very important engineering systems actually are linear, as exemplified in the preceding sections, then clearly linear theory would be quite useless.

The case for linear theory is further strengthened by the fact that in numerous nonlinear situations, the nonlinear equations can be linearized by limiting attention to small *perturbations around a reference state*. This was amply demonstrated in the case of the broom-balancing system in Chap. 2. The technique of linearizing nonlinear systems is extremely important and provides in many instances the standard approach of analysis. For example, the method is commonly employed in process control where a process is being regulated around certain set points. These linearization techniques are also used in designing space navigation and control systems the purpose of which is to keep a vehicle along a specified reference trajectory. The corrective control forces needed to keep the vehicle on the desired flight path can be obtained from a system of *linear* differential equations, although the differential equations describing the reference flight trajectory are highly *nonlinear*.

We shall now present a general method for obtaining the system and distribution matrices in the linearized version of a nonlinear system of differential equations. It is assumed that the differential equations for the system under study have been written in the form

$$\dot{\mathbf{x}} = \mathbf{f}(\mathbf{x},\mathbf{u})$$

and it is further assumed that the function vector **f** is nonlinear. The reference (or nominal) state vector will be called $\mathbf{x}^0$, and the corresponding control-force vector $\mathbf{u}^0$. The meaning of these vectors is depicted in Fig. 3-6, showing a three-dimensional situation. If the system input is chosen *exactly* equal to $\mathbf{u}^0$, then the system response will be *exactly* $\mathbf{x}^0$. In other words, $\mathbf{x}^0$ satisfies the vector equation

$$\dot{\mathbf{x}}^0 = \mathbf{f}(\mathbf{x}^0,\mathbf{u}^0) \tag{3-41}$$

† Note that the test for linearity described earlier cannot be applied *experimentally* in this case, as it is physically impossible to apply three different test inputs *simultaneously* and measure the separate responses. In the time-invariant case, the test inputs could be applied *sequentially* as the system behavior did not change with time.

It is important to realize that both $\mathbf{x}^0$ and $\mathbf{u}^0$ may be *functions of time*. It therefore would have been more proper to use the symbols $\mathbf{x}^0(t)$ and $\mathbf{u}^0(t)$, but we shall prefer the abbreviated symbols.

We shall now assume that we are slightly off the reference trajectory due to the fact that the input is not exactly $\mathbf{u}^0$.

We define the actual state and control vectors $\mathbf{x}$ and $\mathbf{u}$, respectively, by the equations

$$\mathbf{x} = \mathbf{x}^0 + \boldsymbol{\delta}\mathbf{x}$$
$$\mathbf{u} = \mathbf{u}^0 + \boldsymbol{\delta}\mathbf{u} \tag{3-42}$$

The vectors $\boldsymbol{\delta}\mathbf{x}$ and $\boldsymbol{\delta}\mathbf{u}$ represent the *deviations* from the reference vectors.

Clearly, $\mathbf{x}$ and $\mathbf{u}$ must also satisfy our given nonlinear system equation; that is,

$$\frac{d}{dt}(\mathbf{x}^0 + \boldsymbol{\delta}\mathbf{x}) = \dot{\mathbf{x}}^0 + \boldsymbol{\delta}\dot{\mathbf{x}} = \mathbf{f}(\mathbf{x}^0 + \boldsymbol{\delta}\mathbf{x}, \mathbf{u}^0 + \boldsymbol{\delta}\mathbf{u}) \tag{3-43}$$

Consider now the *i*th component of this vector equation. As the actual deviations are assumed to be *small*, we can expand f_i in a Taylor series around the reference

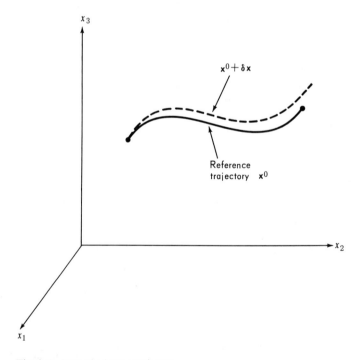

Fig. 3-6   Perturbed-state trajectory.

trajectory

$$\dot{x}_i^0 + \delta\dot{x}_i \approx f_i(\mathbf{x}^0,\mathbf{u}^0) + \frac{\partial f_i}{\partial x_1}\,\delta x_1 + \cdots + \frac{\partial f_i}{\partial x_n}\,\delta x_n$$

$$+ \frac{\partial f_i}{\partial u_1}\,\delta u_1 + \cdots + \frac{\partial f_i}{\partial u_m}\,\delta u_m \quad (3\text{-}44)$$

The existence of the partial derivatives is assumed.   *Note that all these derivatives will be computed along the reference trajectory.*

In view of Eq. (3-41), we thus obtain the following *linear* differential equations for the deviations:

$$\delta\dot{x}_i \approx \left(\frac{\partial f_i}{\partial x_1}\right)^0\delta x_1 + \cdots + \left(\frac{\partial f_i}{\partial x_n}\right)^0\delta x_n + \left(\frac{\partial f_i}{\partial u_1}\right)^0\delta u_1 + \cdots$$

$$+ \left(\frac{\partial f_i}{\partial u_m}\right)^0\delta u_m \quad i = 1, 2, \ldots, n \quad (3\text{-}45)$$

The symbol $(\cdot)^0$ implies computation of the partials along the reference trajectory.

We introduce now the *Jacobian matrices*

$$\mathbf{A} \triangleq \begin{bmatrix} \dfrac{\partial f_1}{\partial x_1} & \cdots & \dfrac{\partial f_1}{\partial x_n} \\ \cdots\cdots\cdots\cdots \\ \dfrac{\partial f_n}{\partial x_1} & \cdots & \dfrac{\partial f_n}{\partial x_n} \end{bmatrix} \quad (3\text{-}46)$$

$$\mathbf{B} \triangleq \begin{bmatrix} \dfrac{\partial f_1}{\partial u_1} & \cdots & \dfrac{\partial f_1}{\partial u_m} \\ \cdots\cdots\cdots\cdots \\ \dfrac{\partial f_n}{\partial u_1} & \cdots & \dfrac{\partial f_n}{\partial u_m} \end{bmatrix} \quad (3\text{-}47)$$

To avoid the possibility that these reduce to *null matrices* we shall assume that at least one partial derivative in each is nonzero.

Equations (3-45) may thus be written in vector form

$$\boldsymbol{\delta\dot{x}} \approx \mathbf{A}\,\boldsymbol{\delta x} + \mathbf{B}\,\boldsymbol{\delta u} \quad (3\text{-}48)$$

In words: Although the system differential equations themselves are non-linear, the differential equations describing the perturbations around the nominal trajectory are linear, at least with first-order accuracy.

Example 3-4

Let us demonstrate the techniques proposed in this section by studying the control system for the pilot centrifuge depicted in Fig. 3-7.   The specifications call for a drive system capable of providing a speed-versus-time test-run envelope of the type shown in the figure.   The control system must be capable of providing a centrifuge speed that follows this envelope, or nominal trajectory, within specified close tolerances.

A study of the torque requirements reveals that the motor must overcome both the inertia of the centrifuge and a windage torque proportional to the square of the velocity. We therefore obtain the differential equation

$$u = I\ddot{\varphi} + k_w\dot{\varphi}^2 \qquad (3\text{-}49)$$

where u = drive torque

φ = angular centrifuge coordinate

k_w = windage torque constant

(It is assumed that all quantities are referred to the same side of the gear train.)

We define a state vector

$$\mathbf{x} = \begin{bmatrix} x_1 \\ x_2 \end{bmatrix} \triangleq \begin{bmatrix} \varphi \\ \dot{\varphi} \end{bmatrix}$$

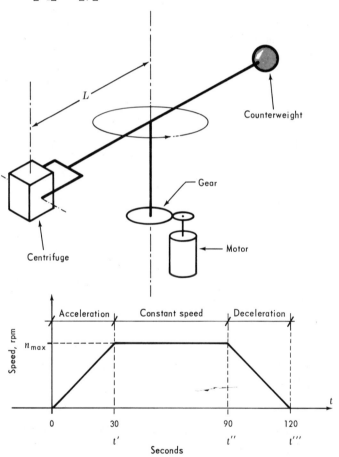

Fig. 3-7 Pilot centrifuge. The graph depicts nominal-speed trajectory.

and then transform (3-49) to a normal form

$$\dot{x}_1 = x_2$$

$$\dot{x}_2 = \frac{1}{I} u - \frac{k_w}{I} x_2^2 \tag{3-50}$$

The state differential equations are obviously nonlinear. As our control system will be required to keep the speed close to the nominal trajectory, we shall develop a perturbation model which will reveal the relationship between the deviations in $\mathbf{x}$ and u. (Note that u is a scalar in this case.) First, we must determine the reference values $\mathbf{x}^0$ and u^0. As the acceleration $\ddot{\varphi}$ $(= \dot{x}_2)$ is discontinuous at $t = t'$ and $t = t''$ (Fig. 3-7), we divide the total trajectory into three parts:

1. The acceleration period, $0 < t < t'$
2. The constant-velocity period, $t' < t < t''$
3. The deceleration period, $t'' < t < t'''$

The acceleration period is characterized by constant acceleration:

$$\ddot{\varphi} = \dot{x}_2 = a = \text{const}$$

Therefore

$$\dot{\varphi} = x_2 = \dot{x}_1 = at$$

and

$$\varphi = x_1 = \frac{a}{2} t^2$$

The second of Eqs. (3-50) thus yields

$$u^0 = Ia + k_w a^2 t^2 \tag{3-51}$$

This reference torque u^0 represents the torque needed to keep the centrifuge accelerating with the constant acceleration a. In Fig. 3-8, we have plotted u^0 and also x_1^0 and x_2^0. The reference values in the constant-speed and deceleration periods can be obtained in an analogous fashion and are also plotted in Fig. 3-8. The details are left as an exercise for the reader.

We next turn our attention to the perturbation equations (3-48). We first must compute the Jacobian matrices. By again limiting our attention to the acceleration period, we get directly from Eqs. (3-46) and (3-47)

$$\mathbf{A} = \begin{bmatrix} 0 & 1 \\ 0 & -\dfrac{2k_w}{I} x_2 \end{bmatrix} = \begin{bmatrix} 0 & 1 \\ 0 & -\dfrac{2k_w}{I} at \end{bmatrix}$$

$$\mathbf{B} = \begin{bmatrix} 0 \\ \dfrac{1}{I} \end{bmatrix}$$

During the acceleration period, the perturbation equations thus read

$$\begin{bmatrix} \delta\dot{x}_1 \\ \delta\dot{x}_2 \end{bmatrix} = \begin{bmatrix} 0 & 1 \\ 0 & -\dfrac{2k_w}{I}\,at \end{bmatrix} \begin{bmatrix} \delta x_1 \\ \delta x_2 \end{bmatrix} + \begin{bmatrix} 0 \\ \dfrac{1}{I} \end{bmatrix} \delta u \tag{3-52}$$

or, in component form,

$$\delta\dot{x}_1 = \delta x_2$$
$$\delta\dot{x}_2 = -2\frac{k_w}{I}\,at\,\delta x_2 + \frac{1}{I}\,\delta u \tag{3-53}$$

We make the important observation that the a_{22} element of the **A** matrix is *time-variant; i.e., the perturbation dynamics changes character throughout the acceleration interval.*

If the final control system is to be of any value whatsoever, we must require that any speed deviations δx_2 that may occur will be reduced to zero rapidly. By "rapidly," we mean in comparison with the speed changes in the nominal speed. *Another way of expressing this is to say that the perturbation dynamics must be rapid compared with the changes in the **A** matrix.* It is customary, in view of this situation, to treat **A** as a *constant* in solving Eqs. (3-53). Representative

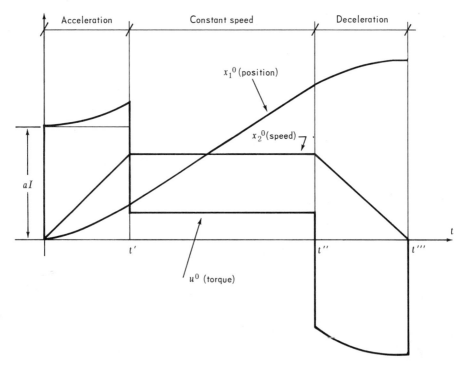

Fig. 3-8   Nominal-speed, position, and torque trajectories for pilot centrifuge in Fig. 3-7.

points are chosen along the reference trajectory (every 5 sec, for instance), and for each point, the a_{22} element is computed. The advantage of such a procedure is obvious: The *exact* equations (3-53), characterized by *time-variant* parameters, are reduced to a set of differential equations with *time-invariant* parameters, and for this latter type of equation, we possess an arsenal of very powerful analysis tools—Laplace transforms *par préférence*.

Under these assumptions, the actual solution of Eqs. (3-53) represents little difficulty. As we are concerned basically with model building in this chapter, we shall not discuss this system any further here. The reader is given an opportunity to suggest a total control-system design for this centrifuge in Chap. 7 (Exercise 7-9) when he has acquired more knowledge of synthesis techniques.

3-6 EFFECTS OF DISTURBANCES ON THE STATE DIFFERENTIAL EQUATION

The mathematical models constructed so far have taken no account of the disturbance inputs $z_1, z_2, \ldots, z_k$. If such inputs are present, the state equations (3-6) will be modified as follows:

$$\dot{x}_i = f_i(x_1, x_2, \ldots, x_n; u_1, u_2, \ldots, u_m; z_1, z_2, \ldots, z_k) \qquad i = 1, 2, \ldots, n \quad (3\text{-}54)$$

If we define a *disturbance-force vector*

$$\mathbf{z} = \begin{bmatrix} z_1 \\ \cdot \\ \cdot \\ \cdot \\ z_k \end{bmatrix} \qquad (3\text{-}55)$$

we can write the system (3-54) in the compact form

$$\dot{\mathbf{x}} = \mathbf{f}(\mathbf{x}, \mathbf{u}, \mathbf{z}) \qquad (3\text{-}56)$$

which is therefore a more general version of Eq. (3-13).

If, in particular, the system is linear in all these variables, then the state differential equation will attain the form

$$\dot{\mathbf{x}} = \mathbf{Ax} + \mathbf{Bu} + \mathbf{Fz} \qquad (3\text{-}57)$$

where the $n \times k$ matrix $\mathbf{F}$ is referred to as the *disturbance matrix*.

3-7 SUMMARY

In this chapter, we considered the problem of establishing mathematical models for deterministic dynamic systems, with particular emphasis on controlled plants. We concluded that such models invariably consist of sets of differential equations. If "lumping" techniques are permitted (and it is always possible[7] to achieve any accuracy desired by choosing sufficiently fine "lumps"), the differential equations are of the ordinary type, with time as the only independent variable. The order or dimensionality of a system depends upon the minimum number of independently chosen dependent variables needed to fully characterize the system.

We found it convenient to reduce the model to a normal form, consisting of a set of first-order differential equations. This form, which is not unique, was chosen as a basis for defining the state of a system. At least for certain classes of physical systems, we were able to relate the state variables to the energy storages within the system. It was hinted that this relationship can be generalized.

By severely restricting the functional appearance of the state model, we defined a system to be linear, and we demonstrated that if attention is limited to perturbed (small-scale) dynamics, nonlinear models can be linearized to first-order accuracy.

The following observations are pertinent:

1. Finding *one* particular state vector does not mean that we have found *the* vector. Generally, it is possible to find an *infinite* number of vectors which would qualify under the chosen definition. Consider, for example, a two-dimensional mechanical linear system where the components of the chosen state vector $\mathbf{x}$, as in some of the examples we have treated, represent position and velocity, respectively. Define then an alternate state vector $\mathbf{x}^1$ in accordance with

$$x_1^1 \overset{\Delta}{=} q_{11}x_1 + q_{12}x_2$$
$$x_2^1 \overset{\Delta}{=} q_{21}x_1 + q_{22}x_2$$

Or, in compact form,

$$\mathbf{x}^1 \overset{\Delta}{=} \mathbf{Qx}$$

By substitution into the original equation

$$\dot{\mathbf{x}} = \mathbf{Ax} + \mathbf{Bu}$$

we obtain a new normal form

$$\dot{\mathbf{x}}^1 = \mathbf{QAQ}^{-1}\mathbf{x}^1 + \mathbf{QBu} \tag{3-58}$$

The new state vector is certainly *mathematically* a perfect choice if $\mathbf{Q}$ is a nonsingular matrix. *Physically*, however, one particular choice may be preferable. In the given example, the first choice defines state variables with *clear physical meaning*—something that certainly does not apply to the set $\mathbf{x}^1$.

2. It should be noted that Eq. (3-13) represents those systems where the rates of change of the state variables are functions of the *present* values of those variables. In some types of processes where time lags are involved, the rates are proportional to *previous* values of the state variables; that is,

$$\dot{\mathbf{x}} = \mathbf{f}[\mathbf{x}(t - t_0), \mathbf{u}]$$

In such cases, the behavior for $t > 0$ requires a knowledge of $\mathbf{x}$ over the entire time interval $(-t_0 \cdots 0)$.[8]

3. In our discussion throughout this chapter, we have assumed *continuous* signals. When the signals are *discretized*, i.e., when data appear only at certain discrete instants of time in the form of *data sequences*, then the models will appear as *difference* rather than differential equations (Chap. 9).

4. We developed the state models in this chapter directly from the physical properties of the systems. In many situations involving linear time-invariant systems, we know the dynamic properties only in terms of *transfer functions*. It is possible to derive state models directly from the transfer functions, or vice versa. These matters will be discussed in next chapter, which is devoted in its entirety to linear systems.

5. The subject of linearization around a reference trajectory as presented in this chapter has, for the sake of simplicity, been somewhat oversimplified. Whereas an engineer would unhesitatingly make use of the perturbation Eq. (3-48), a mathematician would require additional proof of its validity. The truth is that the linearized set (3-48) under certain (rare) conditions can give results that in a true mathematical sense are misleading. These situations are always encountered when the **A** matrix vanishes. We demonstrate by a simple example.

Example 3-5

Consider the nonlinear uncontrolled equation

$$\dot{x} = -x^2 \tag{3-59}$$

We wish to study small perturbations around the reference point $x^0 = 0$. The Jacobian matrix **A** degenerates in this case to the scalar coefficient a computed as follows:

$$a = \left(\frac{\partial f}{\partial x}\right)^0 = -2x\Big]_{x=0} = 0 \tag{3-60}$$

The perturbation equation therefore reads

$$\dot{x} = 0 \tag{3-61}$$

(Note that we have dropped the prefix δ which is superfluous when the reference point is $x^0 = 0$.) Equation (3-61) clearly has the solution:

$$x(t) = \text{const} = x(0) \tag{3-62}$$

This solution implies that if we were to give the system a slight initial perturbation $x(0)$ it would remain in this offset position indefinitely.

Let us now look at the *true* situation. We are able in this case to solve the original equation (3-59) *exactly* by the method of variable separation. The *exact* solution is as the reader may easily verify:

$$x(t) = \frac{x(0)}{1 + tx(0)} \tag{3-63}$$

This solution, in contradiction to the previous one, informs us that the system state will return to zero from a nonzero *positive* initial offset. If the initial offset is *negative* the system state obviously will become unbounded after a finite time.

Exercises

3-1 Model both systems depicted in Fig. 2-3. In order not to get involved in expressions that are too formidable, make the following simplifying assumptions:

1. Neglect the mass of the carriage.

2. Assume identical brooms.

   a First write the exact differential equations, assuming *large* angular deviations from the vertical reference.

   b Then linearize the equations.

   c Define an appropriate state vector and write the equations in *b* in the form

$$\dot{\mathbf{x}} = \mathbf{A}\mathbf{x} + \mathbf{b}u$$

You are *not* asked to solve the equations.

▲ **3-2** Consider the broom balancer described in Chap. 2. Study the requirements for a control system that will balance the broom not vertically but leaning at a *constant* angle φ^0.

   In order not to obtain expressions that are too formidable, use the following simple numerical values, given in MKS units:

$$M = m = L = 1.00$$
$$g = 10.0$$

Choose $\varphi^0 = 45^0$

   a You must first determine from the exact equations whether the problem as stated is feasible from a physical point of view. When you have confirmed that it is, you should determine the nominal control force u^0 that will do the job. Also find the corresponding nominal state vector $\mathbf{x}^0$.

   b Having thus found the "reference trajectory," linearize the dynamics around this trajectory.

   c Settle upon a simple linear control strategy, sketch the corresponding control system in block-diagram form, and solve the resulting *closed-loop* equations. You should arrive at a stable system.

3-3 Consider the system depicted in Fig. 3-5, consisting of a reaction wheel plus a d-c motor.

   a Give in block-diagram fashion a closed-loop control system that will keep the attitude angle φ at any desired adjustable value. Choose the simplest control strategy you can think of and then write the resulting closed-loop differential equations. If you can, please solve them and confirm whether your system works. At least you should be able to check whether the loop is stable by using Routh's criterion.

   b The same as problem *a*, but now you are required to design a system that will keep the attitude *rate* $\dot{\varphi}$ at a fixed, adjustable value.

3-4 Consider the hydraulic system depicted in Fig. 3-9, consisting of two communicating vessels of equal sectional areas. *u* represents the "control force," having the physical dimension cubic meters per second. It is assumed that the flow rate q through the value V is proportional to the difference head; that is,

$$q = \frac{1}{R}(x_1 - x_2) \qquad R = \text{valve "resistance," (units} = \text{sec/met}^2)$$

Construct the state model for this system.

3-5 Let us return to the nonlinear system discussed in Example 3-5. We add a control term u and have then

$$\dot{x} = -x^2 + u$$

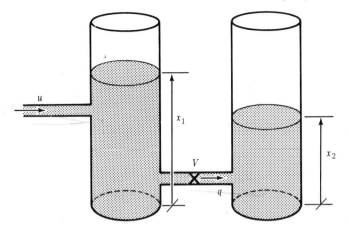

Fig. 3-9 Communicating vessels.

Study the perturbation dynamics of the system around the reference state $x^0 = 1$. Compare the results obtained by using the approximate equation (3-48) with those you are able to arrive at by exact analysis. Explain why you now get better agreement than we did in Example 3-5.
3-6 Consider the electric circuit shown in Figure 3-3. Let us make the assumption that the capacitor has a capacitance that depends upon the voltage v in the quadratic manner:

$$C = C_0 \left(\frac{v}{v_0}\right)^2$$

C_0 and v_0 are constants.

Develop a perturbation model for the circuit useful for analysis of small amplitude dynamics around $v = v_0$.
3-7 In Figure 3-10 is shown a mechanical system which often is used as an analog for demonstrating the nature of electromechanical oscillations of synchronous machines in interconnected power systems. A pendulum the mass m_1 of which is assumed concentrated at a distance L from the center is fixed to a pulley over which an endless non-elastic string is attached. The mass m_2 can perform vertical dynamics and the pendulum performs swings in the φ-direction.

    a Write the nonlinear state model for the system (note that no control force is shown). Consider the pulley and pendulum arm weightless. Use the state vector

$$\begin{bmatrix} x_1 \\ x_2 \end{bmatrix} \overset{\Delta}{=} \begin{bmatrix} \varphi \\ \dot{\varphi} \end{bmatrix}$$

Hint: the string tension is *not* equal to $m_2 g$.

    b Prove that the system is in *balanced position* (see also *equilibrium state* in Chapter 8) for φ values satisfying the equation

$$\sin \varphi = \frac{m_2 R}{m_1 L}$$

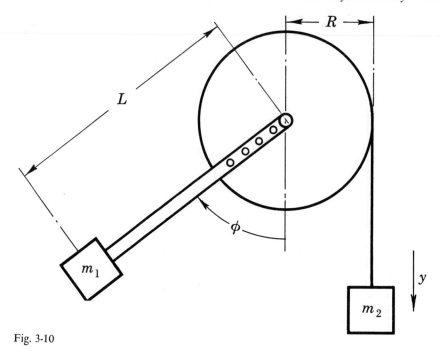

Fig. 3-10

Note: This condition can be satisfied for *two* different pendulum positions if and only if

$m_1L > m_2R$

    c Develop a perturbation model around each of the two balanced positions in *b*. You are not asked to solve the differential equations.

    d You can make a more complex system by assuming the string elastic. Explain why we now must introduce additional state variables into the picture.

References

1. L. S. Pontryagin, "Ordinary Differential Equations," Addison-Wesley Publishing Company, Inc., Reading, Mass., 1962.

2–6. Five tutorial papers by Bertram, Kazda, Zadeh, Desoer, and Schmidt were presented at the June, 1962, JACC meeting in New York (NYU). They are published in the *Proceedings* from that conference. (Also, these proceedings contain a bibliography compiled by Dr. T. Higgins on the topic of state variables.)

7. O. I. Elgerd, Transient Suspension Forces Caused by Broken Transmission Line Conductors, *J. Franklin Inst.*, **275**(3) (March, 1963).

8. R. E. Bellman and J. M. Danskin, Jr., Survey of the Mathematical Theory of Time-lag, Retarded Control, and Hereditary Processes, *Rand Rept.* R-256 (March 1, 1954).

9. R. E. Roberson (ed.), Methods for the Control of Satellites and Space Vehicles; vol. II—Control System Mechanization and Analysis, *WADD Tech. Rept.* 60-643 (July, 1960).

10. J. G. Truxal, "State Models, Transfer Functions and Simulation," monograph, Polytechnic Institute of Brooklyn, Brooklyn, N.Y.

11. L. A. Zadeh and C. A. Desoer, "Linear System Theory," McGraw-Hill Book Company, New York, 1963.

chapter 4

LINEAR ANALYSIS

The entire previous chapter was devoted to mathematical model building. The models we came up with appeared in the form of normalized sets of differential equations. No attempt was made to solve these equations. In this chapter, we shall attempt to give an exposé of the most useful analytical solution methods available. General methods are known only for linear systems and specifically for those which are characterized by time-invariant parameters. We shall therefore be concerned with the solution of vector differential equations of the type

$$\dot{\mathbf{x}} = \mathbf{A}\mathbf{x} + \mathbf{B}\mathbf{u} \qquad \text{with } \mathbf{x}(0) = \mathbf{x}_0 \tag{4-1}$$

where $\mathbf{A}$ and $\mathbf{B}$ are *constant* matrices and $\mathbf{x}_0$ is the initial-state vector.

The importance of such systems was stressed in the previous chapter.

Note that, *without loss of generality*, we have assumed that the initial time equals zero. We can do this because we have assumed a *stationary* process, i.e., a process the parameters (that is, the elements of $\mathbf{A}$ and $\mathbf{B}$) of which are constants. For a stationary process, the change of state does *not* depend upon the initial time but only upon the control interval, i.e., the length of time during which the control force is applied.

Note also that although we have restricted our studies to the vector equation of the form (4-1), our results will be *fully applicable* to the more general linear form

$$\dot{\mathbf{x}} = \mathbf{A}\mathbf{x} + \mathbf{B}\mathbf{u} + \mathbf{F}\mathbf{z}$$

The reader immediately will agree with this if he realizes that the last equation actually can be written

$$\dot{\mathbf{x}} = \mathbf{A}\mathbf{x} + \mathbf{B}'\mathbf{u}'$$

where $\mathbf{B}'$ is the new $n \times (m + k)$ distribution matrix defined by

$$\mathbf{B}' \triangleq [\mathbf{B}, \mathbf{F}]$$

and $\mathbf{u}'$ the new $(m + k)$-dimensional control-force vector defined by

$$\mathbf{u}' \triangleq \begin{bmatrix} \mathbf{u} \\ \mathbf{z} \end{bmatrix}$$

4-1   SOLUTION IN TERMS OF THE
MATRIX EXPONENTIAL

The solution method that will be discussed now is basically a numerical technique which, for reasons that will be clear, lends itself well to digital-computer solution. Also, it is closely related to the "classical solution methods" of linear differential equations, so we find it appropriate to use it as a starting point in our story.

Before we attack the *vector* equation (4-1), let us review the nature of the solution of the *scalar* equation

$$\dot{x} = ax + bu \qquad \text{with } x(0) = x_0 \tag{4-2}$$

The student is reminded that the total solution of this equation can be written†

$$x = x_h + x_p$$

where x_h is the solution of the *homogeneous* (*undriven, unforced,* or *uncontrolled*) equation

$$\dot{x} = ax \qquad \text{with } x(0) = x_0 \tag{4-3}$$

and x_p is a *particular* solution to the entire (*driven, forced,* or *controlled*) equation (4-2).

We *assume* a solution x_h in the form of an infinite power series in t

$$x_h = a_0 + a_1 t + a_2 t^2 + \cdots + a_\nu t^\nu + \cdots \tag{4-4}$$

If this series indeed represents a solution, it must satisfy the homogeneous equation; i.e., we must require the identity

$$a_1 + 2a_2 t + 3a_3 t^2 + \cdots = a(a_0 + a_1 t + a_2 t^2 + \cdots)$$

for all values of t, and by thus forcing all coefficients for equal powers to be identical, we get

$$a_1 = a a_0$$
$$a_2 = \tfrac{1}{2} a a_1 = \tfrac{1}{2} a^2 a_0$$
$$a_3 = \tfrac{1}{3} a a_2 = \frac{1}{3 \times 2} a^3 a_0$$
$$\cdots \cdots \cdots \cdots \cdots \cdots$$
$$a_\nu = \frac{1}{\nu!} a^\nu a_0$$

---

† It should be understood that solution of differential equations in general (and this includes linear equations) is nothing but a sophisticated guessing game. A "reasonable" guess is made about how the solution should look. By differentiation and substitution into the given equation, we then determine whether the guess was any good.

The as yet undetermined coefficient a_0 must be given the value x_0 since we must require (4-4) to approach this value for vanishing t. We have thus found the solution

$$x_h = \left(1 + at + \tfrac{1}{2}a^2t^2 + \cdots + \frac{1}{\nu!}a^\nu t^\nu + \cdots\right)x_0 \tag{4-5}$$

The infinite power series within $(\cdot)$ is *defined* as the scalar exponential e^{at}, and we thus obtain

$$x_h = e^{at}x_0 \tag{4-6}$$

By using one of several "classical" approaches, we can also find the particular solution†

$$x_p = e^{at}\int_0^t e^{-a\tau}bu(\tau)\,d\tau \tag{4-7}$$

and the total solution of (4-2) is therefore

$$x = e^{at}x_0 + e^{at}\int_0^t e^{-a\tau}bu(\tau)\,d\tau \tag{4-8}$$

The homogeneous solution part is *independent* of the control input u and depends only upon the initial state x_0. We sometimes refer to it as the *transient* part. The particular solution part is independent of the initial state but depends upon the control input u *throughout the whole control interval* $0 \cdots t$. We refer to this part as the *forced* solution.

We are now adequately prepared to attack the *vector* case, i.e., Eq. (4-1).

In analogy with the scalar case, we try first to obtain a solution for the undriven, or homogeneous, system

$$\dot{\mathbf{x}} = \mathbf{A}\mathbf{x} \qquad \text{with } \mathbf{x}(0) = \mathbf{x}_0 \tag{4-9}$$

We assume a solution in the form of a *vector power series* in t; that is,

$$\mathbf{x} = \mathbf{a}_0 + \mathbf{a}_1 t + \mathbf{a}_2 t^2 + \cdots + \mathbf{a}_\nu t^\nu + \cdots \tag{4-10}$$

The vector coefficients $\mathbf{a}_\nu$ can be determined if we substitute our assumed solution back into (4-9); that is,

$$\mathbf{a}_1 + 2\mathbf{a}_2 t + 3\mathbf{a}_3 t^2 + \cdots = \mathbf{A}(\mathbf{a}_0 + \mathbf{a}_1 t + \mathbf{a}_2 t^2 + \cdots)$$

Since we require that this be an identity for all t, it is necessary that the vector coefficients for equal powers of t be identical; that is,

$$\mathbf{a}_1 = \mathbf{A}\mathbf{a}_0$$
$$2\mathbf{a}_2 = \mathbf{A}\mathbf{a}_1$$
$$\cdots\cdots\cdots$$

---

† It is simple to prove by direct substitution that (4-7) is indeed a solution to (4-2).

From these equations, we obtain

$$\mathbf{a}_1 = \mathbf{A}\mathbf{a}_0$$

$$\mathbf{a}_2 = \tfrac{1}{2}\mathbf{A}\mathbf{a}_1 = \tfrac{1}{2}\mathbf{A}\mathbf{A}\mathbf{a}_0 = \tfrac{1}{2}\mathbf{A}^2\mathbf{a}_0$$

$$\cdots\cdots\cdots\cdots\cdots\cdots$$

$$\mathbf{a}_\nu = \frac{1}{\nu!}\mathbf{A}^\nu\mathbf{a}_0$$

The as yet undetermined vector coefficient $\mathbf{a}_0$ must equal $\mathbf{x}_0$ in order for the solution (4-10) to approach the proper initial state for vanishing t. All coefficients are thus known, and the solution of the homogeneous equation reads

$$\mathbf{x} = \mathbf{x}_0 + \mathbf{A}\mathbf{x}_0 t + \tfrac{1}{2}\mathbf{A}^2\mathbf{x}_0 t^2 + \cdots + \frac{1}{\nu!}\mathbf{A}^\nu\mathbf{x}_0 t^\nu + \cdots$$

$$= (\mathbf{I} + \mathbf{A}t + \tfrac{1}{2}\mathbf{A}^2 t^2 + \cdots + \frac{1}{\nu!}\mathbf{A}^\nu t^\nu + \cdots)\mathbf{x}_0 \tag{4-11}$$

The expression within parentheses is quite obviously an $n \times n$ matrix, and because of its *formal* similarity with the infinite power series for a scalar exponential, we find reason to name it the *matrix exponential* and denote it with the symbol $e^{\mathbf{A}t}$, that is,

$$e^{\mathbf{A}t} \triangleq \mathbf{I} + \mathbf{A}t + \tfrac{1}{2}\mathbf{A}^2 t^2 + \cdots + \frac{1}{\nu!}\mathbf{A}^\nu t^\nu + \cdots \tag{4-12}$$

It can be shown that this matrix series (in analogy with the scalar one) converges absolutely and uniformly for all finite t.

We therefore can write in compact form the homogeneous solution of (4-9)

$$\mathbf{x}(t) = e^{\mathbf{A}t}\mathbf{x}_0 \tag{4-13}$$

The matrix exponential is also known in the literature under the names of *transition matrix* and *fundamental matrix* and is often symbolized by $\boldsymbol{\Phi}(t)$ or, simply, $\boldsymbol{\Phi}$. It will be convenient from time to time to use this symbol alternatively with $e^{\mathbf{A}t}$.

Realizing that $e^{\mathbf{A}t}$ is an $n \times n$ matrix, we may view the expression (4-13) as a *linear transformation* through which the initial state $\mathbf{x}_0$ is being transformed into the updated state $\mathbf{x}(t)$.

It is of great interest to note that several of the characteristics of the scalar exponential also apply to the matrix exponential. For instance, we find directly from (4-12) that

$$\frac{d}{dt}(e^{\mathbf{A}t}) = \mathbf{A}e^{\mathbf{A}t} = e^{\mathbf{A}t}\mathbf{A} \tag{4-14}$$

We should point out at this juncture that the derivative of a matrix $\mathbf{X}$ is defined as

$$\frac{d\mathbf{X}}{dt} \triangleq \dot{\mathbf{X}} \triangleq \begin{bmatrix} \dot{x}_{11} & \cdots & \dot{x}_{1n} \\ \cdots\cdots\cdots\cdots \\ \dot{x}_{n1} & \cdots & \dot{x}_{nn} \end{bmatrix}$$

Also, we may prove that

$$e^{A(t_1+t_2)} = e^{At_1}e^{At_2} = e^{At_2}e^{At_1} \tag{4-15}$$

The proof goes as follows:

$$e^{At_1}e^{At_2} = (I + At_1 + \tfrac{1}{2}A^2t_1{}^2 + \cdots)(I + At_2 + \tfrac{1}{2}A^2t_2{}^2 + \cdots)$$
$$= I + A(t_1 + t_2) + \tfrac{1}{2}A^2(t_1 + t_2)^2 + \cdots$$
$$= e^{A(t_1+t_2)}$$

We also realize immediately that the two matrices e^{At_1} and e^{At_2} commute. From this very important formula, we note by setting

$$t_1 = -t_2 = t$$

that

$$e^{At}e^{-At} = I \tag{4-16}$$

In words: The inverse of the matrix e^{At} is computed simply by replacing t with $-t$ in the defining equation (4-12).

   Note: Equation (4-15) does *not* mean that $e^{At}e^{Bt}$ should equal $e^{(A+B)t}$. Actually, the formula

$$e^{At}e^{Bt} = e^{(A+B)t}$$

holds true *only* if **A** and **B** *commute*.[1]

   Formula (4-15) may be used to expose an interesting feature of the homogeneous solution (4-13). Consider a linear process unfolding in the following manner: Initially, at $t = 0$, the state is x_0; at a later time $t = t_1$, the state is x_1; and at a still later time $t = t_2$, the state is x_2.

   From (4-13), we have

$$x_1 = e^{At_1}x_0$$
$$x_2 = e^{At_2}x_0$$

By use of formula (4-15), the latter equation can be written

$$x_2 = e^{A(t_2-t_1)}e^{At_1}x_0 = e^{A(t_2-t_1)}x_1$$

In words: The state of the system at *any* time t_2 can be obtained by a transformation of the state at *any* other time t_1 using the matrix exponential as transformation matrix. It is *not* necessary, of course, that t_2 be larger than t_1; in other words, the transformation also works backward in time.

Example 4-1

We shall demonstrate at this time the usage of the matrix exponential and point out some of its computational aspects.

   Consider the system

$$\begin{bmatrix} \dot{x}_1 \\ \dot{x}_2 \end{bmatrix} = \begin{bmatrix} 1 & 0 \\ 1 & 1 \end{bmatrix}\begin{bmatrix} x_1 \\ x_2 \end{bmatrix} \qquad \text{with } x(0) = \begin{bmatrix} 1 \\ 1 \end{bmatrix}$$

We have, in this case,

$$\mathbf{A} = \begin{bmatrix} 1 & 0 \\ 1 & 1 \end{bmatrix} \qquad \mathbf{A}^2 = \begin{bmatrix} 1 & 0 \\ 2 & 1 \end{bmatrix} \qquad \mathbf{A}^3 = \text{etc.}$$

The matrix exponential is then computed. We obtain, by including only the three first terms,

$$e^{\mathbf{A}t} = \begin{bmatrix} 1 + t + 0.5t^2 + \cdots & 0 \\ t + t^2 + \cdots & 1 + t + 0.5t^2 + \cdots \end{bmatrix}$$

Thus,

$$\begin{bmatrix} x_1 \\ x_2 \end{bmatrix} = \begin{bmatrix} 1 + t + 0.5t^2 + \cdots \\ 1 + 2t + 1.5t^2 + \cdots \end{bmatrix}$$

The solution for each $\mathbf{x}$ component is obtained in the form of a truncated power series in t. The computational method using $e^{\mathbf{A}t}$ results obviously in the *asymptotic* solution of $\mathbf{x}$ for small t. The solution is characterized by an increasing accuracy for decreasing t. (Note that it will be exact in the limit $t \to 0$.) If we require a solution exact within prescribed accuracy limits in the entire range $0 < t < t_f$, then we need to include a larger number of terms; the longer the interval t_f we choose, the larger the numbers of terms we need.

A digital computer is singularly well suited to the performing of a computation of this type. It is noted that the only numerical operations involved in computing $e^{\mathbf{A}t}$ are scalar multiplications and additions. Programming a digital computer for computing $e^{\mathbf{A}t}$ is therefore a relatively simple procedure. However, how will the computer be made to know when to truncate the series? To find the answer to this question, let us again study the simpler scalar case. In computing e^{at}, a digital computer is programmed to compute and then add term after term in the series

$$e^{at} = 1 + at + \tfrac{1}{2}(at)^2 + \cdots + \frac{1}{m!}(at)^m + R(m,t)$$

until finally so many terms m have been included that the *remainder* term $R(m,t)$ is less than a prescribed limit value. The situation is quite similar in the *matrix* case. A *remainder* term $\mathbf{R}(m,t)$ can be found; this term, however, is an $n \times n$ matrix. The computation of the matrix series will proceed until this matrix is less than a prescribed limit value. However, what will be meant by the term "less than" in this case, where we actually have n^2 elements to keep track of and *all* must be within bounds?

For computational purposes, it is customary to define the *norm* of a matrix. The norm is a scalar the value of which is a measure of the absolute magnitude of all n^2 elements in the matrix. Consider the matrix

$$\mathbf{X} = \begin{bmatrix} x_{11} & \cdots & x_{1n} \\ \cdots\cdots\cdots\cdots \\ x_{n1} & \cdots & x_{nn} \end{bmatrix}$$

We define now a norm as

$$\|\mathbf{X}\| \triangleq \sum_{i,j=1}^{n} |x_{ij}| \tag{4-17}$$

It is worth mentioning that other definitions exist. For example, a definition that often is more suitable for analytical purposes is

$$\|\mathbf{X}\| \triangleq \sum_{i,j=1}^{n} x_{ij}^{2} \tag{4-18}$$

We now apply this concept to the matrix remainder term $\mathbf{R}(m,t)$. In addition to computing and adding the terms in the series of $e^{\mathbf{A}t}$, the computer keeps a continuous check on the norm $\|\mathbf{R}(m,t)\|$ and stops the computation when a prescribed minimum has been reached.†

We have obtained a solution for the homogeneous equation. We proceed now to seek a solution to the complete, or inhomogeneous, vector equation (4-1).

The solution of the homogeneous vector equation had a great formal likeness to the solution of the scalar case. This encourages us to seek for the inhomogeneous vector equation a solution which has a formal likeness to the scalar solution (4-8).

We thus attempt a solution

$$\mathbf{x}(t) = e^{\mathbf{A}t}\mathbf{x}_0 + e^{\mathbf{A}t}\int_0^t e^{-\mathbf{A}\tau}\mathbf{Bu}(\tau)\,d\tau \tag{4-19}$$

Before we prove the correctness of our assumption, let us define the meaning of the second term in the above equation. The integrand is obviously an n-dimensional vector, which we may denote $\mathbf{v}$. By definition, we shall understand a vector integral to be a new vector having as its components the integrals of the components of $\mathbf{v}$, that is,

$$\int \mathbf{v}\,dt \triangleq \begin{bmatrix} \int v_1\,dt \\ \cdot \\ \cdot \\ \cdot \\ \int v_n\,dt \end{bmatrix} \tag{4-20}$$

It remains to be proved that (4-19) indeed represents a solution to Eq. (4-1). If this is the case, then (4-19) will:

1. Satisfy the differential equation (4-1)
2. Reduce to $\mathbf{x}_0$ for vanishing t

† Compare discussion in Sec. 12-3.

The latter condition is certainly satisfied. By letting $t \to 0$, we note immediately that

$$\lim_{t \to 0} \mathbf{x}(t) = \mathbf{I}\mathbf{x}_0 + \mathbf{I}\mathbf{0} = \mathbf{x}_0$$

In order to prove the first condition, we differentiate (4-19) with respect to t

$$\dot{\mathbf{x}}(t) = \mathbf{A}e^{\mathbf{A}t}\mathbf{x}_0 + e^{\mathbf{A}t}e^{-\mathbf{A}t}\mathbf{B}u(t) + \mathbf{A}e^{\mathbf{A}t}\int_0^t e^{-\mathbf{A}\tau}\mathbf{B}u(\tau)\,d\tau$$

We have here made use of the following easily verifiable rules:

$$\frac{d}{dt}(\mathbf{X}\mathbf{x}) = \mathbf{X}\dot{\mathbf{x}} + \dot{\mathbf{X}}\mathbf{x}$$

$$\frac{d}{dt}\int_0^t \mathbf{v}(\tau)\,d\tau = \mathbf{v}(t)$$

(4-21)

The above expression for $\dot{\mathbf{x}}$ can now be written

$$\dot{\mathbf{x}}(t) = \mathbf{A}e^{\mathbf{A}t}\mathbf{x}_0 + \mathbf{I}\mathbf{B}u(t) + \mathbf{A}e^{\mathbf{A}t}\int_0^t e^{-\mathbf{A}\tau}\mathbf{B}u(\tau)\,d\tau$$

$$= \mathbf{A}\left[e^{\mathbf{A}t}\mathbf{x}_0 + e^{\mathbf{A}t}\int_0^t e^{-\mathbf{A}\tau}\mathbf{B}u(\tau)\,d\tau\right] + \mathbf{B}u(t)$$

$$= \mathbf{A}\mathbf{x}(t) + \mathbf{B}u(t)$$

This completes the proof.

From a computational viewpoint, Eq. (4-19) does not introduce any difficulties other than those discussed above in connection with the solution of the homogeneous equation. The integrand is obtained by matrix-vector multiplication and will be in the form of a vector the components of which consist of truncated power series in t, which can easily be integrated. We demonstrate with an example.

Example 4-2

Consider the system

$$\begin{bmatrix} \dot{x}_1 \\ \dot{x}_2 \end{bmatrix} = \begin{bmatrix} 1 & 0 \\ 1 & 1 \end{bmatrix}\begin{bmatrix} x_1 \\ x_2 \end{bmatrix} + \begin{bmatrix} 1 \\ 1 \end{bmatrix}u(t) \qquad \text{with } \mathbf{x}_0 = \begin{bmatrix} 1 \\ 1 \end{bmatrix}$$

where we choose for $u(t)$ a unit-step function defined by

$$u(t) = \begin{cases} 0 & \text{for } t < 0 \\ 1 & \text{for } t > 0 \end{cases}$$

From Example 4-1 we have

$$e^{\pm \mathbf{A}t} = \begin{bmatrix} 1 \pm t + 0.5t^2 \pm \cdots & 0 \\ \pm t + t^2 \pm \cdots & 1 \pm t + 0.5t^2 \pm \cdots \end{bmatrix}$$

Hence,

$$e^{-A^\tau}Bu(\tau) = \begin{bmatrix} 1 - \tau + 0.5\tau^2 - \cdots \\ 1 - 2\tau + 1.5\tau^2 - \cdots \end{bmatrix}$$

Therefore,

$$\int_0^t e^{-A^\tau}Bu(\tau)\,d\tau = \begin{bmatrix} t - \frac{1}{2}t^2 + \frac{1}{6}t^3 - \cdots \\ t - t^2 + \frac{1}{2}t^3 - \cdots \end{bmatrix}$$

From (4-19), we have

$$\mathbf{x}(t) = e^{At}\left[\mathbf{x}_0 + \int_0^t e^{-A^\tau}\mathbf{B}u(\tau)\,d\tau\right]$$

Therefore,

$$\mathbf{x}(t) = e^{At}\begin{bmatrix} 1 + t - \frac{1}{2}t^2 + \cdots \\ 1 + t - t^2 + \cdots \end{bmatrix} = \begin{bmatrix} 1 + 2t + t^2 + \cdots \\ 1 + 3t + 2.5t^2 + \cdots \end{bmatrix}$$

4-2 SOLUTION OF TIME-VARIANT LINEAR SYSTEMS

It was pointed out in the beginning of the chapter that the above theory applies only to *time-invariant*, or *stationary*, linear systems. If the **A** matrix in (4-1) has elements which are *time-dependent*, then it will not be possible to express the solution in terms of a matrix exponential. We encountered such an equation in the previous chapter [Eq. (3-53)], and we suggested at the time an *approximate* solution method, which is applicable in those cases where the parameters are changing *slowly*. Time-variant systems are of great importance in the theory of adaptive systems, and we shall therefore briefly point out some of the solution features of such systems.

We note first that we cannot arbitrarily set the initial time equal to zero. We therefore restate our problem as follows:

Solve the vector equation

$$\dot{\mathbf{x}}(t) = \mathbf{A}(t)\mathbf{x}(t) + \mathbf{B}(t)\mathbf{u}(t)$$

subject to the initial conditions $\mathbf{x}(t_0) = \mathbf{x}_0$.

We first easily verify that the *homogeneous* equation has the solution

$$\mathbf{x}(t) = \mathbf{\Phi}(t,t_0)\mathbf{x}_0$$

where the transition matrix $\mathbf{\Phi}(t,t_0)$ is to meet the following two conditions:

1. It shall satisfy the differential equation

$$\dot{\mathbf{\Phi}}(t,t_0) = \mathbf{A}(t)\mathbf{\Phi}(t,t_0) \tag{4-22}$$

2. $\mathbf{\Phi}(t_0,t_0)$ must equal **I** $\tag{4-23}$

[Note that Eq. (4-22) corresponds to Eq. (4-14) in the time-invariant case.]

If a $\boldsymbol{\Phi}$ matrix can be found that satisfies both of these requirements, we can write the solution to the complete equation as

$$\mathbf{x}(t) = \boldsymbol{\Phi}(t,t_0)\mathbf{x}_0 + \int_{t_0}^{t} \boldsymbol{\Phi}(t,\tau)\mathbf{B}(\tau)\mathbf{u}(\tau)\,d\tau \tag{4-24}$$

This follows from the principle of superposition, and the student is urged to complete the details of the proof.

As can be guessed, the crux of the matter is to find the $\boldsymbol{\Phi}$ matrix. In the time-invariant case, the transition matrix could be computed from a relatively simple power series (4-12). This is not the case here. For numerical computation, the following series expansion (due to Neumann) can be used:

$$\boldsymbol{\Phi}(t,t_0) = \mathbf{I} + \int_{t_0}^{t} \mathbf{A}(\tau)\,d\tau + \int_{t_0}^{t} \mathbf{A}(\tau_1)\left[\int_{t_0}^{\tau_1} \mathbf{A}(\tau_2)\,d\tau_2\right]d\tau_1 + \cdots \tag{4-25}$$

[It is fairly simple to show that the Neumann series satisfies (4-22) and (4-23).]

Example 4-3

Find the solution of

$$\begin{bmatrix} \dot{x}_1 \\ \dot{x}_2 \end{bmatrix} = \begin{bmatrix} 1 & 0 \\ 1 & t \end{bmatrix}\begin{bmatrix} x_1 \\ x_2 \end{bmatrix} \qquad \text{with } \mathbf{x}(0) = \begin{bmatrix} 1 \\ 0 \end{bmatrix}$$

Here we have $t_0 = 0$.

We compute term by term in Neumann's series:

$$\int_0^t \begin{bmatrix} 1 & 0 \\ 1 & \tau \end{bmatrix} d\tau = \begin{bmatrix} t & 0 \\ t & \dfrac{t^2}{2} \end{bmatrix}$$

$$\int_0^t \begin{bmatrix} 1 & 0 \\ 1 & \tau_1 \end{bmatrix}\left(\int_0^{\tau_1}\begin{bmatrix} 1 & 0 \\ 1 & \tau_2 \end{bmatrix} d\tau_2\right) d\tau_1 = \int_0^t \begin{bmatrix} 1 & 0 \\ 1 & \tau_1 \end{bmatrix}\begin{bmatrix} \tau_1 & 0 \\ \tau_1 & \dfrac{\tau_1^2}{2} \end{bmatrix} d\tau_1$$

$$= \int_0^t \begin{bmatrix} \tau_1 & 0 \\ \tau_1 + \tau_1^2 & \dfrac{\tau_1^3}{2} \end{bmatrix} d\tau_1 = \begin{bmatrix} \dfrac{t^2}{2} & 0 \\ \dfrac{t^2}{2} + \dfrac{t^3}{3} & \dfrac{t^4}{8} \end{bmatrix}$$

Therefore,

$$\mathbf{x}(t) = \left\{\begin{bmatrix} 1 & 0 \\ 0 & 1 \end{bmatrix} + \begin{bmatrix} t & 0 \\ t & \dfrac{t^2}{2} \end{bmatrix} + \begin{bmatrix} \dfrac{t^2}{2} & 0 \\ \dfrac{t^2}{2} + \dfrac{t^3}{3} & \dfrac{t^4}{8} \end{bmatrix} + \cdots\right\}\begin{bmatrix} 1 \\ 0 \end{bmatrix}$$

Hence,

$$\mathbf{x}(t) = \begin{bmatrix} 1 + t + \tfrac{1}{2}t^2 + \cdots \\ t + \tfrac{1}{2}t^2 + \tfrac{1}{3}t^3 + \cdots \end{bmatrix}$$

4-3 SOLUTION BY MEANS OF LAPLACE TRANSFORMS

The solution method discussed in Sec. 4-1 was particularly well suited to the digital computer. We shall now attack the problem from a different angle, making use of the Laplace-transform techniques. The basic features of this technique should be well known to the student; however, a review of Laplace and Fourier transform methods is presented in Appendix B for those wishing to refresh their knowledge.

Explicit solutions can be found only for time-invariant equations, and therefore in the following we shall limit our study to the vector differential equation (4-1), where **A** and **B** are *constant* matrices.

The great popularity of the Laplace transform depends partly on its ability to transform a certain class of differential equations into algebraic equations and partly on the ease with which the "bookkeeping" of the initial conditions can be handled.

Laplace transforms, to be sure, cannot perform any job that could not be handled by the "classical" methods. In the classical method (due to Euler), we attempt solutions of the exponential form, and by substitution into the original differential equations, we can determine the exact nature of the exponentials. Great care must be taken in separating the homogeneous and particular solutions and in assigning integration constants. These problems are partially bypassed by the use of Laplace transforms, with their "built-in" automatic features.

The *i*th component of (4-1) reads

$$\dot{x}_i = a_{i1}x_1 + a_{i2}x_2 + \cdots + a_{in}x_n + b_{i1}u_1 + b_{i2}u_2 + \cdots + b_{im}u_m$$

and after Laplace transformation, we obtain

$$sX_i(s) - x_i(0) = a_{i1}X_1(s) + \cdots + a_{in}X_n(s) + b_{i1}U_1(s) + \cdots + b_{im}U_m(s)$$

By performing this operation for $i = 1, 2, \ldots, n$, we shall have a total of n linear transform equations. We introduce now the transform vectors

$$\mathbf{X}(s) \triangleq \begin{bmatrix} X_1(s) \\ X_2(s) \\ \cdot \\ \cdot \\ \cdot \\ X_n(s) \end{bmatrix} \quad \text{and} \quad \mathbf{U}(s) \triangleq \begin{bmatrix} U_1(s) \\ U_2(s) \\ \cdot \\ \cdot \\ \cdot \\ U_m(s) \end{bmatrix}$$

and can then write in compact form

$$sX(s) - \mathbf{x}_0 = \mathbf{A}X(s) + \mathbf{B}U(s) \tag{4-26}$$

Note: Accepted practice calls for the use of capital-letter symbols for Laplace-transformed variables. However, in multidimensional analysis, this collides with matrix symbols. Also, we would wish to use lowercase symbols for vectors. By writing $\mathbf{X}(s)$ instead of $\mathbf{X}$, a compromise is made and confusion can be avoided.

The *algebraic* vector equation (4-26) can now be rearranged as

$$sX(s) - AX(s) = x_0 + BU(s)$$

Therefore,

$$(sI - A)X(s) = x_0 + BU(s)$$

We wish to solve for $X(s)$, and we therefore premultiply both members of this equation by the inverse $(sI - A)^{-1}$ and obtain

$$IX(s) = X(s) = (sI - A)^{-1}x_0 + (sI - A)^{-1}BU(s) \tag{4-27}$$

The reader should note the striking resemblance between this expression and the one we obtain by Laplace transformation of the *scalar* equation (4-2):

$$X(s) = \frac{x_0}{s - a} + \frac{bU(s)}{s - a} = (s1 - a)^{-1}x_0 + (s1 - a)^{-1}bU(s)$$

The state vector $x(t)$ is clearly obtained by an inverse transformation of $X(s)$ in accordance with

$$x(t) = \mathscr{L}^{-1}[X(s)] = \mathscr{L}^{-1}[(sI - A)^{-1}x_0] + \mathscr{L}^{-1}[(sI - A)^{-1}BU(s)] \tag{4-28}$$

This solution obviously must be identical with the one obtained in Sec. 4-1 [Eq. (4-19)]. The first part of (4-28) must be the homogeneous solution as it will be the only remaining part if $u(t)$ [and therefore $U(s)$] vanishes. By comparison with Eq. (4-13), we then get

$$e^{At}x_0 = \mathscr{L}^{-1}[(sI - A)^{-1}x_0] = \mathscr{L}^{-1}[(sI - A)^{-1}]x_0$$

Note that whereas the expression within the brackets in the first step is an n-dimensional *vector*, in the second step it is an $n \times n$ *matrix*. By the inverse transform of a matrix, we shall understand the matrix of the inverse transforms of each element.

As a consequence of the last step, we thus obtain the following new formula for the matrix exponential:

$$e^{At} = \mathscr{L}^{-1}[(sI - A)^{-1}] \tag{4-29}$$

The importance of this new formula for e^{At} lies in the fact that it provides an *explicit* expression for the matrix exponential. This will be demonstrated with an example.

Example 4-4

Consider the example already treated in the previous section. We had

$$A = \begin{bmatrix} 1 & 0 \\ 1 & 1 \end{bmatrix}$$

In computing the inverse $(s\mathbf{I} - \mathbf{A})^{-1}$, we first find the adjugate

$$(s\mathbf{I} - \mathbf{A})^{+} = \begin{bmatrix} s - 1 & 0 \\ 1 & s - 1 \end{bmatrix}$$

and then the determinant

$$|s\mathbf{I} - \mathbf{A}| = (s - 1)^2$$

The inverse will therefore be

$$(s\mathbf{I} - \mathbf{A})^{-1} = \frac{1}{(s - 1)^2} \begin{bmatrix} s - 1 & 0 \\ 1 & s - 1 \end{bmatrix} = \begin{bmatrix} \dfrac{1}{s - 1} & 0 \\ \dfrac{1}{(s - 1)^2} & \dfrac{1}{s - 1} \end{bmatrix}$$

From (4-29), we then have

$$e^{\mathbf{A}t} = \begin{bmatrix} e^t & 0 \\ te^t & e^t \end{bmatrix}$$

(The actual inverse transforms have been obtained from a table.)   Note that if we express the exponentials in the above matrix in terms of their power series, we obtain

$$e^{\mathbf{A}t} = \begin{bmatrix} 1 + t + \dfrac{t^2}{2} + \cdots & 0 \\ t + t^2 + \cdots & 1 + t + \dfrac{t^2}{2} + \cdots \end{bmatrix}$$

This is in full agreement with the results previously obtained in Example 4-1. If we assume the same initial state as we did in Example 4-1, that is,

$$\mathbf{x}_0 = \begin{bmatrix} 1 \\ 1 \end{bmatrix}$$

we obtain the following *explicit* solution for $\mathbf{x}(t)$:

$$\mathbf{x}(t) = e^{\mathbf{A}t}\mathbf{x}_0 = \begin{bmatrix} e^t & 0 \\ te^t & e^t \end{bmatrix}\begin{bmatrix} 1 \\ 1 \end{bmatrix} = \begin{bmatrix} e^t \\ e^t(t + 1) \end{bmatrix}$$

4-4 EIGENVALUES AND STABILITY

In arriving at a solution by means of the formula (4-28), it is necessary to perform the inverse Laplace transformation of two transform vectors, each of which are obtained from a matrix-vector product containing as a factor the $n \times n$ matrix

$$(s\mathbf{I} - \mathbf{A})^{-1} = \frac{(s\mathbf{I} - \mathbf{A})^{+}}{|s\mathbf{I} - \mathbf{A}|} = \begin{bmatrix} \alpha_{11} & \cdots & \alpha_{1n} \\ & \cdots\cdots\cdots & \\ \alpha_{n1} & \cdots & \alpha_{nn} \end{bmatrix} \qquad (4\text{-}30)$$

The determinant $|s\mathbf{I} - \mathbf{A}|$ is an nth-order polynomial in s, and as the elements of the adjugate matrix $(s\mathbf{I} - \mathbf{A})^+$ are also polynomials in s of orders no higher than $n - 1$ (see definition of adjugate in Appendix A), it is clear that each element α_{ij} of the inverse $(s\mathbf{I} - \mathbf{A})^{-1}$ has a partial fraction decomposition of the type

$$\alpha_{ij} = \frac{a_1}{s - \lambda_1} + \frac{a_2}{s - \lambda_2} + \cdots + \frac{a_n}{s - \lambda_n} \tag{4-31}$$

where $\lambda_1, \lambda_2, \ldots, \lambda_n$ are the roots of the *characteristic* equation

$$|s\mathbf{I} - \mathbf{A}| = 0 \tag{4-32}$$

These roots are referred to as the n *eigenvalues* of the system. Sometimes the name *characteristic roots* or *values* is used. For our immediate purpose, let us assume that the eigenvalues are *distinct*, as is generally the case. (However, as was demonstrated in Example 4-4, it is not difficult to find systems having *multiple* eigenvalues.) Under this assumption, it is quite clear, therefore, that in the general case, each component of the homogeneous part of the $\mathbf{x}(t)$ vector will contain the n exponentials

$$e^{\lambda_1 t}, e^{\lambda_2 t}, \ldots, e^{\lambda_n t}$$

Note that we said *homogeneous;* i.e., we refer to the first part of Eq. (4-28). The second part, the particular part of the total solution, will in addition be influenced by the factor $\mathbf{U}(s)$.

If some of the eigenvalues are of the multiple type (of multiplicity q), then the partial fraction decomposition of α_{ij} will be

$$\alpha_{ij} = \frac{a_1}{s - \lambda_1} + \cdots + \frac{a_v}{(s - \lambda_v)^q} + \frac{a_{v+1}}{(s - \lambda_v)^{q-1}} + \cdots + \frac{a_n}{s - \lambda_n} \tag{4-33}$$

The homogeneous part of the $\mathbf{x}$ solution will now contain in addition to the exponentials $e^{\lambda_1 t}, e^{\lambda_2 t}, \ldots$, terms of the type

$$t^{q-1} e^{\lambda_v t}, t^{q-2} e^{\lambda_v t}, \ldots$$

(Compare Example 4-4, characterized by an eigenvalue $\lambda = 1$ of multiplicity 2.)

A few words should also be said about the case when some of the eigenvalues are not real. Whenever complex λ values appear, they *always* are present in conjugate complex pairs $\lambda_v = \sigma_v \pm j\omega_v$. The elements of the inverse matrix $(s\mathbf{I} - \mathbf{A})^{-1}$ therefore can be written

$$\alpha_{ij} = \frac{a_1}{s - \lambda_1} + \cdots + \frac{a_v + jb_v}{s - \sigma_v + j\omega_v} + \frac{a_v - jb_v}{s - \sigma_v - j\omega_v} + \cdots + \frac{a_n}{s - \lambda_n} \tag{4-34}$$

Note that the coefficients for the conjugate complex pair also are conjugate complex. This is necessary, of course, as α_{ij} must remain real for all s.

In addition to the real exponentials $e^{\lambda_1 t}, e^{\lambda_2 t}, \ldots$, the $\mathbf{x}$ solution will now contain the pair of conjugate exponentials

$$(a_v + jb_v) e^{(\sigma_v - j\omega_v)t} + (a_v - jb_v) e^{(\sigma_v + j\omega_v)t}$$

As the reader can easily verify, the sum of these two terms is a *real* term of the type

$e^{\sigma_v t} \sin(\omega_v t + \varphi_v)$

Should there finally be *multiple* conjugate complex eigenvalues of multiplicity q, we similarly can show that the solution must contain terms of the types

$t^{q-1} e^{\sigma_v t} \sin(\omega_v t + \varphi_v)$

$t^{q-2} e^{\sigma_v t} \sin(\omega_v t + \varphi_v)$

. . . .

We have now considered all possible varieties of eigenvalues and all types of associated response terms. It is possible at this time to draw an exceedingly important conclusion concerning the *stability* of a linear stationary system.

We first give the following definition of the term *stability:*

A linear time-invariant system described by the vector equation

$$\dot{\mathbf{x}} = \mathbf{A}\mathbf{x} + \mathbf{B}\mathbf{u}$$

is said to be stable if, undriven, its state tends to zero from any finite initial state $\mathbf{x}_0$.†

We can immediately give the following necessary and sufficient conditions for stability:

A linear time-invariant system is stable if and only if none of the n eigenvalues of **A** *is located in the right half of the s plane, including the* $j\omega$ *axis.*

This stability criterion is immediately arrived at from the previous study of the correlation between eigenvalues and system response. Note that the $j\omega$ axis must be included, because if some λ values should be located along it, we would have response terms present of the types

t^{q-1} or $t^{q-1} \sin(\omega_v t + \varphi_v)$

which obviously do not tend to zero for increasing t.

The situation is depicted in Fig. 4-1a, indicating the forbidden region for the eigenvalues.

In a practical situation, not only is it necessary to have a margin of safety, but one must also have a guarantee of sufficiently rapid decay of the transients. A practical stability requirement therefore could require an eigenvalue distribution as indicated in Fig. 4-1b.

The question of stability is of very great importance in control-system theory and practice. Self-sustained or growing oscillations are always a danger. The physical reason for the oscillations is the supply of external power into the

---

† It is possible to give various definitions of stability. The one we have chosen here is sometimes referred to as *asymptotic stability in the large*. For instance, instead of requiring that the state tend to zero, we could have been more lenient and specified only that it must not go to infinity. In linear theory, this is a fine point; a linear system would *always* be designed asymptotically stable. We must be more careful, however, in the case of nonlinear systems. A discussion will be given in Chap. 8.

closed control loop, as was indicated already in Fig. 1-1. Growing oscillations are, of course, a sign of increasingly powerful energy swings in the system, and these could only be maintained by a continuous supply of external energy.

In passing, it is of interest to mention a very important difference between linear and nonlinear systems with respect to their stability characteristics. The state of a stable linear system returns to the origin from *any* initial state in the entire finite state space. The stability of a nonlinear system, however, depends upon the initial state. For some initial states, the system returns to the origin; for other initial states, the system will either return to other points in the state

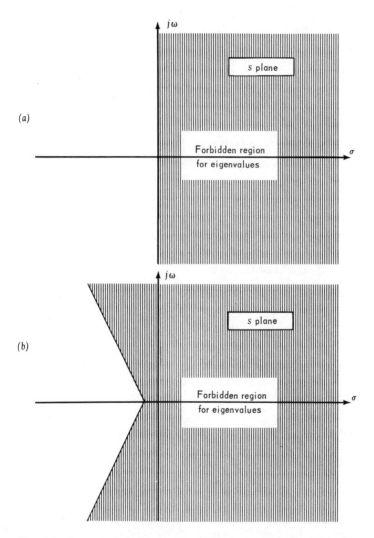

Fig. 4-1   For preserved stability, the eigenvalues must be located in the left side of *s* plane (*a*); for "practical" stability, even to a certain depth (*b*).

space or possibly grow to infinity. Indeed, much of the current effort in nonlinear stability theory centers around the problem of separating those regions of state space which are stable from those which are unstable. More will be said about these problems in Chap. 8.

4-5 TRANSFER MATRICES AND TRANSFER FUNCTIONS

Engineers often make use of block diagrams of various types when working with interconnected systems. Such diagrams are of great help in trying to visualize the role played by each component or subgroup of components making up the overall system.

With the block diagrams is always associated some highly specialized symbolic language by means of which the specialist at a glance obtains the necessary information about the function of the different blocks.

Transfer matrices and, in particular, transfer functions constitute such a symbolic language and have gained universal acceptance as a means for block representation of linear systems. Kalman[4] refers to this method for linear-system description as the "input-output" method (to be distinguished from the state-variable method presented in Chap. 3).

In order to demonstrate this method, let us for a moment consider the vector equation (4-27).

If we introduce the $n \times n$ matrix

$$\mathbf{T}_1(s) \triangleq (s\mathbf{I} - \mathbf{A})^{-1}$$

and also the $n \times m$ matrix

$$\mathbf{T}_2(s) \triangleq (s\mathbf{I} - \mathbf{A})^{-1}\mathbf{B}$$

then Eq. (4-27) may be written in a more compact form

$$\mathbf{X}(s) = \mathbf{T}_1(s)\mathbf{x}_0 + \mathbf{T}_2(s)\mathbf{U}(s) \tag{4-35}$$

The **T** matrices are referred to as *transfer-function matrices*, or *transfer matrices*, for short. They contain all information needed to obtain the full dynamic picture of the system.

Equation (4-35) can be displayed symbolically in block-diagram form as shown in Fig. 4-2. This is a signal-flow diagram where the "signals" consist of transform vectors. Should, in particular, the initial state vector be zero, then Eq. (4-35) reduces to

$$\mathbf{X}(s) = \mathbf{T}_2(s)\mathbf{U}(s) \tag{4-36}$$

(A system characterized by zero initial state is referred to as *inert*.)

Usually, we are more interested in the output vector **c** than the state **x**. If these two vectors are linearly related through the vector equation

$$\mathbf{c} = \mathbf{C}\mathbf{x}$$

then Laplace transformation yields†

$$\mathbf{C}(s) = \mathbf{C}\mathbf{X}(s) \tag{4-37}$$

By combining (4-36) and (4-37), we thus obtain

$$\mathbf{C}(s) = \mathbf{C}\mathbf{T}_2(s)\mathbf{U}(s) \triangleq \mathbf{G}_p(s)\mathbf{U}(s) \tag{4-38}$$

The overall transfer matrix $\mathbf{G}_p(s)$, relating the output $\mathbf{C}(s)$ directly with the control input $\mathbf{U}(s)$, is thus obtained by a multiplication of the individual cascaded transfer matrices shown in Fig. 4-3. One should note the order of the matrix multiplication. $\mathbf{G}_p(s)$ is the *plant-transfer matrix*.

$\mathbf{C}$ is a $p \times n$ matrix, and $\mathbf{T}_2(s)$ an $n \times m$ matrix. Consequently, the overall matrix $\mathbf{G}_p(s)$ is of dimension $p \times m$. *In the case of a single-input–single-output system, that is, $m = p = 1$, the overall transfer matrix reduces to a scalar, the so-called "transfer function."*

In working with linear multiple-input–multiple-output (MIMO) control systems, the transfer matrix is a very useful concept. It helps us with the "book-keeping" of all the dynamic elements in the system and permits us to manipulate and reduce the block diagrams in straightforward fashion and in a manner similar to that of the scalar case, with which the reader probably is already familiar. We shall exemplify in Chap. 7, where we shall use these methods in the design of a MIMO regulator (Example 7-9).

We must discourage the reader from using the above matrix approach in single-input–single-output (SISO) systems. As was pointed out earlier, the

† $\mathbf{C}(s)$ is a column *vector*, but $\mathbf{C}$ is a *matrix*.

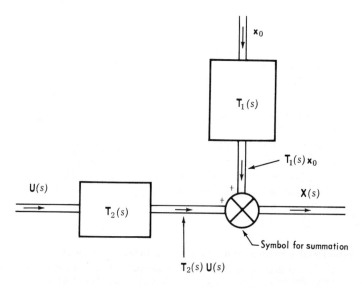

Fig. 4-2 Transfer matrices used for "input-output" description of linear time-invariant system.

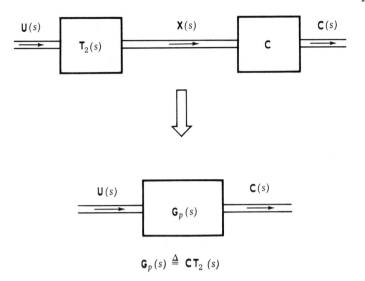

$$G_p(s) \triangleq CT_2(s)$$

Fig. 4-3 Definition of plant-transfer matrix $G_p(s)$.

transfer matrices reduce in these cases to scalars, which can be obtained much more simply by more direct means.   After all, the matrix methods represent the "sledge-hammer" approach to all problems of low dimensionality and simple objectives.

4-6 DERIVATION OF STATE MODELS FROM TRANSFER FUNCTIONS

In the previous section, we derived the transfer matrices from the Laplace-transformed version of the state differential equations.   It may sometimes be desirable to go the other way, i.e., to derive the state model from a knowledge of the transfer matrices or, more importantly, the transfer functions.   In actual engineering work, we often are forced to derive system dynamics *experimentally*. We measure the response of a system with various types of test inputs, either aperiodic inputs like steps or impulses or, perhaps more commonly, sinusoidal inputs with varying frequency (see also the discussion in Chap. 6 on *frequency transfer functions*).   We then try, in an optimum fashion, to fit the experimental data with a transfer function expressed as a ratio of polynomials in s.   From this transfer function, it is possible to derive a state model in a variety of ways.   Let us demonstrate with an example.

Example 4-5

Let us assume that we have performed measurements on the SISO plant shown in Fig. 4-4 and found that we can approximate it with a reasonable degree of accuracy with the transfer function

$$G_p(s) = \frac{C(s)}{U(s)} = \frac{2}{s^3 + 6s^2 + 11s + 6}$$

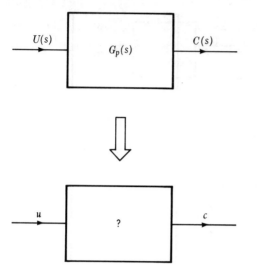

Fig. 4-4 Derivation of state model from transfer function.

Let us derive for this system a set of state equations based on this approximate model. The assumed model implies the following third-order differential equation relating the control force $u(t)$ with the output $c(t)$:

$$\dddot{c} + 6\ddot{c} + 11\dot{c} + 6c = 2u \tag{4-39}$$

We have pointed out before that there exists in every case an infinite number of vectors which qualify as candidates for *state* vectors. The simplest state model that can be derived from an equation of type (4-39) is the one we derive by choosing the derivatives themselves as state variables; that is,

$$\mathbf{x} = \begin{bmatrix} x_1 \\ x_2 \\ x_3 \end{bmatrix} \triangleq \begin{bmatrix} c \\ \dot{c} \\ \ddot{c} \end{bmatrix}$$

We then obtain directly from (4-39)

$$\begin{aligned}
\dot{x}_1 &= x_2 \\
\dot{x}_2 &= x_3 \\
\dot{x}_3 &= 2u - 6x_1 - 11x_2 - 6x_3
\end{aligned} \tag{4-40}$$

With this choice of state variables, we can write our model

$$\begin{aligned}
\dot{\mathbf{x}} &= \mathbf{Ax} + \mathbf{b}u \\
c &= \mathbf{Cx}
\end{aligned} \tag{4-41}$$

where

$$\mathbf{A} = \begin{bmatrix} 0 & 1 & 0 \\ 0 & 0 & 1 \\ -6 & -11 & -6 \end{bmatrix} \qquad \mathbf{b} = \begin{bmatrix} 0 \\ 0 \\ 2 \end{bmatrix} \qquad \mathbf{C} = \begin{bmatrix} 1 & 0 & 0 \end{bmatrix}$$

Another interesting state model can be obtained by first expanding the transfer function into partial fractions

$$\frac{C(s)}{U(s)} = \frac{2}{s^3 + 6s^2 + 11s + 6} = \frac{1}{s+1} + \frac{-2}{s+2} + \frac{1}{s+3}$$

Therefore,

$$C(s) = \frac{1}{s+1} U(s) + \frac{-2}{s+2} U(s) + \frac{1}{s+3} U(s) \tag{4-42}$$

We now define

$$X_1(s) \triangleq \frac{1}{s+1} U(s)$$

$$X_2(s) \triangleq \frac{-2}{s+2} U(s) \tag{4-43}$$

$$X_3(s) \triangleq \frac{1}{s+3} U(s)$$

By inverse transformation of these last expressions, we get

$$\dot{x}_1 + x_1 = u$$
$$\dot{x}_2 + 2x_2 = -2u \tag{4-44}$$
$$\dot{x}_3 + 3x_3 = u$$

Also from (4-42) and (4-43), we have

$$c = x_1 + x_2 + x_3 \tag{4-45}$$

Clearly, (4-44) and (4-45) constitute another state model of type (4-41), where

$$\mathbf{A} = \begin{bmatrix} -1 & 0 & 0 \\ 0 & -2 & 0 \\ 0 & 0 & -3 \end{bmatrix} \quad \mathbf{b} = \begin{bmatrix} 1 \\ -2 \\ 1 \end{bmatrix} \quad \mathbf{C} = [1 \ \ 1 \ \ 1]$$

We note an interesting feature characterizing this last model. The **A** matrix is *diagonal*, which means in effect that the three separate state equations are *decoupled* from each other. Also we note that the diagonal elements of **A** are identical with the three *eigenvalues*. This special form of state model is referred to as *canonical* and plays a particularly important role in control theory. We shall have reason to make use of it extensively in our discussions on the topics of controllability and observability in the next chapter.

It is instructive to illustrate the two different state models derived in the above example by means of block-diagram representations. Consider first the model defined by Eqs. (4-40). By inspection we confirm that it corresponds to the block diagram depicted in Fig. 4-5. Note that the transfer functions of the feedback

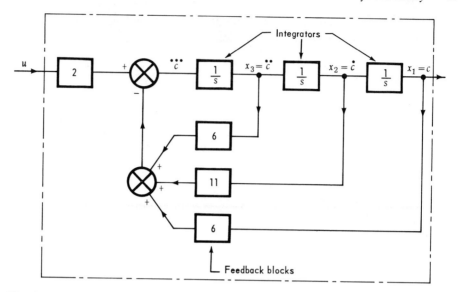

Fig. 4-5 Block-diagram representation of state model defined by Eq. (4-40).

blocks are identical with the coefficients of the defining differential equation (4-39), or the coefficients of the denominator polynomial of the plant-transfer function $G_p(s)$.

Next we turn our attention to the model defined by Eq. (4-44). By inspection we obtain the block diagram drawn in Fig. 4-6. The feedback blocks in this structure are identical with the eigenvalues of the system whereas the feedforward blocks contain the coefficients in the partial-fraction expansion of $G_p(s)$, that is, the residues at the poles of $G_p(s)$. The two block structures in Figs. 4-5 and 4-6 can be used directly for analog simulation of the system. More will be said about this in Chap. 12.

Before we leave the above example we shall make the following important observations.

*Both **A** matrices that we derived are characterized by identical eigenvalues.*

This statement is easily verified as we conclude that in both cases we obtain the characteristic equation

$$|s\mathbf{I} - \mathbf{A}| = s^3 + 6s^2 + 11s + 6 = 0 \tag{4-46}$$

The three eigenvalues ($\lambda_1 = -1$, $\lambda_2 = -2$, $\lambda_3 = -3$) that are derived from this equation are obviously also identical with the poles of the transfer function $G_p(s)$. None of these facts is really surprising as we already know that whatever model we use the resulting time response must be the same. In the next chapter we shall give a general proof of this "invariance of eigenvalues to a linear transformation."

In the example just treated the given plant transfer function was of the type

$$\frac{C(s)}{U(s)} = \frac{a_0}{s^n + b_{n-1}s^{n-1} + \cdots + b_0} = \frac{a_0}{(s - \lambda_1)(s - \lambda_2)\cdots(s - \lambda_n)} \tag{4-47}$$

i.e., it contained poles but no zeros. The corresponding differential equation is of the form

$$\frac{d^n c}{dt^n} + b_{n-1}\frac{d^{n-1}c}{dt^{n-1}} + \cdots + b_0 c = a_0 u \tag{4-48}$$

We sometimes refer to a plant of this type as being characterized by "denominator dynamics." The example proved that finding a state model in this case is a fairly simple task.

The situation is somewhat more complicated if the transfer function should contain both poles and zeros. Such a plant is said to have "numerator dynamics."

Consider the plant-transfer function

$$G_p(s) = \frac{a_m s^m + a_{m-1}s^{m-1} + \cdots + a_0}{s^n + b_{n-1}s^{n-1} + \cdots + b_0} = a_m \frac{(s - z_1)\cdots(s - z_m)}{(s - \lambda_1)\cdots(s - \lambda_n)} \tag{4-49}$$

(For physical reasons that will be discussed in Chap. 7, in practical cases we are only concerned with situations where $m < n$.)

The corresponding differential equation is therefore of the form

$$\frac{d^n c}{dt^n} + \cdots + b_0 c = a_m \frac{d^m u}{dt^m} + \cdots + a_0 u \tag{4-50}$$

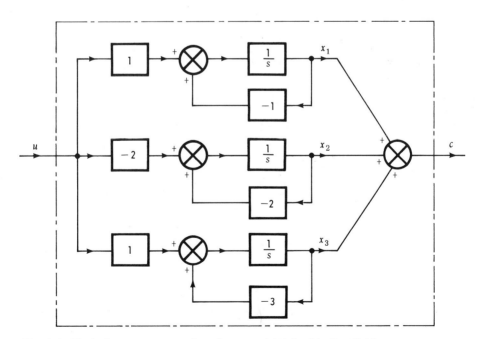

Fig. 4-6   Block-diagram representation of state model defined by Eq. (4-44).

Because this differential equation contains derivatives of u it is no longer possible to use the straightforward method earlier employed.

Example 4-6

Let us demonstrate by adding a zero to the transfer function in the previous example, i.e., we wish to find a state model for a plant characterized by

$$\frac{C(s)}{U(s)} = G_p(s) = \frac{s+4}{s^3 + 6s^2 + 11s + 6}$$

The corresponding differential equation is

$$\dddot{c} + 6\ddot{c} + 11\dot{c} + 6c = 4u + \dot{u} \tag{4-51}$$

If we were to define, as before, a state vector

$$\mathbf{x} = \begin{bmatrix} x_1 \\ x_2 \\ x_3 \end{bmatrix} \overset{\Delta}{=} \begin{bmatrix} c \\ \dot{c} \\ \ddot{c} \end{bmatrix}$$

we would fail to obtain our standard form (4-41). The student should verify this statement.

We shall instead define a state vector as follows:

$$
\begin{aligned}
x_1 &\overset{\Delta}{=} c \\
x_2 &\overset{\Delta}{=} \dot{c} \\
x_3 &\overset{\Delta}{=} \ddot{c} + ku
\end{aligned}
\tag{4-52}
$$

k is a constant and it is possible to assign a value to this constant so as to cause the derivative term of u to drop out. We see this by substitution of (4-52) into (4-51) which yields

$$\dot{x}_3 - k\dot{u} + 6(x_3 - ku) + 11x_2 + 6x_1 = 4u + \dot{u}$$

If we let k take on the value -1 we can obviously write this equation as follows:

$$\dot{x}_3 = -6x_1 - 11x_2 - 6x_3 - 2u \tag{4-53}$$

From the first two equations (4-52) we also have

$$
\begin{aligned}
\dot{x}_1 &= x_2 \\
\dot{x}_2 &= \ddot{c} = x_3 + u
\end{aligned}
\tag{4-54}
$$

The last three equations may be put into the vector form

$$\begin{bmatrix} \dot{x}_1 \\ \dot{x}_2 \\ \dot{x}_3 \end{bmatrix} = \begin{bmatrix} 0 & 1 & 0 \\ 0 & 0 & 1 \\ -6 & -11 & -6 \end{bmatrix} \begin{bmatrix} x_1 \\ x_2 \\ x_3 \end{bmatrix} + \begin{bmatrix} 0 \\ 1 \\ -2 \end{bmatrix} u \tag{4-55}$$

which then constitutes one possible solution to our problem.

4-7 SUMMARY

The most important solution methods of linear time-invariant multidimensional systems were presented. Perhaps the importance of the normal form did not become sufficiently obvious to the reader in Chap. 3. By now, however, he should have been impressed by its value, certainly as applied to linear systems. By starting from the normal vector form (4-1), which has a great formal likeness to the scalar equation (4-2), it is possible to derive a solution which likewise has a striking resemblance to the scalar solution. The same statement applies with respect to the solution method by means of Laplace transforms.

It was also demonstrated that transfer functions and matrices constitute an alternate method for representation of linear *time-invariant* systems. We hinted at (but did not exemplify) the usefulness of the transfer-matrix concept in analysis and synthesis of multiple-input–multiple-output control systems.

Finally, it was demonstrated that, just as we can derive transfer functions and matrices from the state models, we can also, in reverse, construct state models from the transfer functions. For linear time-invariant systems, state and transfer-function models thus represent alternative choices. The obvious question then is which of the two is to be preferred. The answer is that both have their usefulness—the particular problem at hand determines the preference of one to the other. In the next chapter we shall find, for instance, that the state model is a "natural" in dealing with the concepts of controllability and observability. In Chaps. 6 and 7 we shall find, on the contrary, that the transfer-function methods are well suited to the synthesis of servos.

Exercises

4-1 A linear time-invariant system is characterized by the system and distribution matrices

$$\mathbf{A} = \begin{bmatrix} 1 & 2 & 0 \\ 3 & 0 & -2 \\ 1 & -1 & 0 \end{bmatrix} \qquad \mathbf{B} = \begin{bmatrix} 1 & 1 \\ 0 & 1 \\ 0 & 0 \end{bmatrix}$$

(a) Compute the solution of the homogeneous equation, assuming the initial state vector

$$\mathbf{x}_0 = \begin{bmatrix} 1 \\ 0 \\ 1 \end{bmatrix}$$

Employ both the matrix exponential method (with the series truncated after the four first terms) and the eigenvalue approach. Compare the two solutions by plots.

b Assume then a control-force vector

$$\mathbf{u} = \begin{bmatrix} u_1 \\ u_2 \end{bmatrix}$$

Find the transfer matrix $\mathbf{T}_2(s)$ defined by Eq. (4-35). Using this matrix and assuming zero initial state, find *explicit* solutions for $\mathbf{x}(t)$ if the input vector $\mathbf{u}(t)$ has the value

$$\mathbf{u}(t) = \begin{bmatrix} t \\ \delta(t) \end{bmatrix}$$

$\delta(t)$ is a unit impulse occurring at $t = 0$.

4-2 Consider the oven depicted in Fig. 3-4. In some unit system, we have found that the $\mathbf{A}$ and $\mathbf{b}$ matrices have the values

$$\mathbf{A} = \begin{bmatrix} -0.2 & 0.1 \\ 0.1 & -0.1 \end{bmatrix} \qquad \mathbf{b} = \begin{bmatrix} 1 \\ 0 \end{bmatrix}$$

Find explicit solutions for the inside and jacket temperatures if a heat pulse of magnitude 2 units and duration 2 sec is applied.

4-3 Consider again the equation

$$\dot{\mathbf{x}} = \mathbf{Ax} + \mathbf{b}u$$

used in the previous exercise. In this problem, we shall assume that we have a free choice for u in the range

$$0 < u < \infty$$

(Note that we do *not* permit negative u values; that is, the oven jacket cannot be force-cooled.)

    a We now pose the following question: Is it possible to heat this oven from the initial state

$$\mathbf{x}_0 = \begin{bmatrix} 0 \\ 0 \end{bmatrix}$$

to the end state (after 20 sec)

$$\mathbf{x}(20) = \begin{bmatrix} 5 \\ 5 \end{bmatrix}$$

and then keep these two temperatures constant at these values? If it is possible, suggest a heat-up strategy plus a steady-state "hold" input that will do the job! Is the proposed solution unique?

    b Work problem *a* using the different end state

$$\mathbf{x}(20) = \begin{bmatrix} 5 \\ 3 \end{bmatrix}$$

    c Discuss what the solution to problem *b* would be if we provided the oven with two heating coils, one in the jacket and one in the inside space.

4-4 Derive a state model for a plant characterized by the transfer function

$$\frac{C(s)}{U(s)} = \frac{s}{s^2 + 1}$$

4-5 Consider a plant with two outputs c_1 and c_2 and two control inputs u_1 and u_2. It is characterized by the transfer matrix

$$\mathbf{G}_p(s) = \begin{bmatrix} 0 & \dfrac{1}{s+1} \\ \dfrac{1}{s+2} & \dfrac{1}{s+3} \end{bmatrix}$$

Derive a state model for this plant.

4-6 Consider the electrical network depicted in Fig. 4-7. We define the input and output voltages

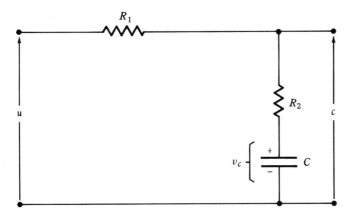

Fig. 4-7   Electrical "plant" characterized by "numerator dynamics."

respectively as u and c.   It is easy to prove that this "plant" has the transfer function

$$G_p(s) = \frac{C(s)}{U(s)} = \frac{R_2}{R_1 + R_2} \frac{s + 1/R_2C}{s + 1/(R_1 + R_2)C}$$

Evidently, we are here confronted with a system that has "numerator dynamics."   On the basis of the above transfer function, define a state model using the "k-coefficient method" exemplified in the text.   Also show that the state variable (this system is obviously one-dimensional) thus obtained will be proportional to the capacitor voltage.   Why is the last observation significant?

4-7 Clear up the following question concerning Eq. (4-19): In assuming a solution we settled on an integrand $e^{-A\tau}\mathbf{B}\mathbf{u}(\tau)$.   Why did we choose this particular product order?   After all, as this product contains three factors, $e^{-A\tau}$, $\mathbf{B}$, and $\mathbf{u}(\tau)$, we can conceive of six different products.   (In the scalar case, the product order is of no importance.)

4-8 Consider the mechanical system depicted in Figure 3-10.   You had developed the linearized perturbation equations around its two equilibrium positions in exercise 3-7.   Assume now the following simple numerical values:

$m_1 = m_2 = 1$ kilogram

$R = \frac{1}{2}L = 1$ meter

   Set also $g = 10$ met^2/sec

The equilibrium positions are thus characterized by

$\sin \varphi = 0.5$

   a Find the eigenvalues for both these positions and make your conclusions concerning the stability of the system.

   b Obtain the solution for the perturbation dynamics $\delta x(t)$ for the specific case when the pendulum is placed initially 2 degrees of arc off each of the equilibrium positions.

4-9 For the electric circuit in Figure 3-3 assume the following simple parameter values:

$C = 1$ farad

$L_1 = L_2 = 1$ henry

$R = 1.5$ ohm

  a Find the eigenvalues for the circuit and confirm its stability.   (Note that the characteristic equation is of third order but you can guess one root easily.)

  b Find the response (all three state variables) of this circuit for the case that the voltage source e_1 is a unit step and e_2 is zero.   (Zero e_2 means in effect that we have short-circuited this source.)   Plot your solutions!

4-10 Consider equations (3-4).   They are of the form

$$\dot{\mathbf{x}} = \mathbf{A}\mathbf{x} + \mathbf{b}u$$

This vector differential equation evidently describes the *open-loop* dynamics of the broom balancer, as no decision has yet been made as to control strategy.

  Let us now make such a decision.   Specifically let us assume proportional control in accordance with Eq. (2-8).   By substitution the differential equations now take on the form

$$\dot{\mathbf{x}} = \mathbf{A}_c\mathbf{x}$$

This vector equation evidently describes the *closed-loop* behavior of the broom balancer. The matrices $\mathbf{A}$ and $\mathbf{A}_c$ are of dimension 4×4 but most of their elements are zeros.

  a Find the four eigenvalues of the open-loop model and confirm its instability.

  b Explain why the closed-loop vector differential equation is *homogeneous*, i.e. is missing the forcing term.

  c Find the eigenvalues for the closed-loop system and confirm the response characteristics which we obtained in a different manner in section 2-4.1.

  d Explain the physical significance of the fact that both the open and closed-loop systems are characterized by double eigenvalues located in the origin of the *s*-plane.

  e Form the inverse matrix $(s\mathbf{I} - \mathbf{A}_c)^{-1}$ (which is not too difficult because of the simple $\mathbf{A}_c$ matrix) and by using Eq's. (4-13) and (4-29) and the initial state

$$\mathbf{x}_0 = \begin{bmatrix} \varphi_0 \\ 0 \\ 0 \\ 0 \end{bmatrix}$$

obtain a solution for $\mathbf{x}(t)$.

  Compare this solution with the ones you obtained in section 2-4.1.

References

1. R. Bellman, "Introduction to Matrix Analysis," McGraw-Hill Book Company, New York, 1960.

2. F. R. Gantmacher, "Matrix Theory," vols. I and II, Chelsea Publishing Company, New York, 1959.

3. R. E. Kalman, Y. C. Ho, and K. S. Narendra, Controllability of Linear Systems, *Contrib. Differential Equations*, **1**(2) (1961).

4. R. E. Kalman, Mathematical Description of Linear Dynamical Systems, *J. Control (SIAM)*, ser. A, **1**(2): 152–192 (1963).

chapter 5

CONCEPTS OF CONTROLLABILITY AND OBSERVABILITY

5-1 DEFINITIONS

In Chap. 2, we referred very briefly to a system characteristic that we vaguely spoke of as *controllability*. In this chapter, we shall examine more penetratingly the conditions that must be met in order for a system to be *controllable*. We shall discuss also the *dual* concept of *observability*.

It should be added that these concepts are quite new, having been introduced only recently by Kalman.[1-3]

Important interpretations and clarifications have been made by Gilbert, Ho, and others.[4,5] The late arrival of these ideas is in itself quite remarkable in view of the very fundamental nature of the problems they solve.

We shall begin our discussion by giving the following formal definition of *controllability*:

A system is said to be controllable if it is possible to find a control vector $\mathbf{u}(t)$ *which, in specified finite time* t_f, *will transfer the system between two arbitrarily specified finite states* $\mathbf{x}_0$ *and* $\mathbf{x}_f$.

We shall, in the following, refer to these two states as the *initial* and the *final* states, respectively.

Presently available theory provides the necessary and sufficient conditions for controllability for linear systems only, and therefore we shall concern ourselves only with such systems. Indeed, we shall restrict our discussions to linear time-invariant systems because this permits the use of simpler mathematics; we should not run the risk of obscuring the main course of our presentation with bulky formulas.

In physical terms, controllability implies simply that it is possible with the given set of control forces at hand to have our plant "under complete control"; i.e., we can change its state completely in accordance with our wishes. In view of the normal situation, where we have *fewer* control forces than we have state variables (in the broom-balancing system, we had four state variables but only one control force), it is certainly appropriate to question whether we have them all "under control." We have, in the past four chapters, encountered at least one system where we intuitively could predict noncontrollability (system *a* in Fig. 2-3).

Note that it is possible to make a noncontrollable system controllable by adding additional control forces. We certainly could make the double-broom system just referred to controllable by adding an additional force that attacks one of the brooms.

The controllability concept is extremely important from both a practical and a theoretical point of view. If we can confirm by the test methods to be presented in this chapter that a system is controllable, then we have a complete guarantee that it is possible to design a control system for the system in question. *However, we are given no hints about how to design it.*

From the definition and by use of Eq. (4-19), it follows that if a system is controllable, it must be possible to find a control vector **u** that satisfies the vector equation

$$\mathbf{x}_f = e^{\mathbf{A}t_f}\mathbf{x}_0 + e^{\mathbf{A}t_f} \int_0^{t_f} e^{-\mathbf{A}\tau}\mathbf{B}\mathbf{u}(\tau)\, d\tau \tag{5-1}$$

We will investigate in this chapter which conditions must be satisfied for this to be possible.

Before we proceed with this task, we shall point out that in the above definition we were concerned with the *state* controllability. In many instances, it is required to transfer not the state but the system *output* **c** between two specified values. The output, usually related to the state through the equation

$$\mathbf{c} = \mathbf{Cx}$$

is generally of lower dimensionality than the state, and the job of controlling the output is therefore generally an easier one.† The definition of *output* controllability is similar to the definition of *state* controllability given above. Usually, the modifiers "state" and "output" can be left out if it is clear from the context what type of controllability we are talking about.

Consider again the broom balancer. We had four state variables, φ, $\dot{\varphi}$, y, and $\dot{y}$, but only one output, the angular coordinate φ. It is conceivable that φ could be controlled, but not y; in which case, we would have a system that would be output-controllable but not state-controllable. (In reality, this system is both state- and output-controllable.)

It is appropriate to demonstrate these new concepts with some additional examples before we attempt to arrive at general conclusions.

Example 5-1

Our first example concerns a one-dimensional system

$$\dot{x} = ax + bu \qquad \text{with } b \neq 0 \tag{5-2}$$

---

† This statement does not apply in those cases where the output also is a function of the **u** vector [Eq. (3-17)].

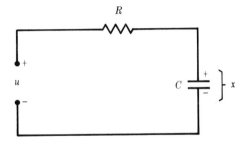

Fig. 5-1 Single-loop *RC* circuit used to demonstrate controllability in scalar case.

A specific physical system obeying this equation is shown in Fig. 5-1. With the capacitor voltage as state variable and the voltage source as control force, we obtain the following equation for this circuit:

$$\dot{x} = -\frac{1}{RC} x + \frac{1}{RC} u \tag{5-3}$$

This system is therefore completely controllable if it is possible to change the capacitor voltage between arbitrary finite levels x_0 and x_f in the arbitrarily specified time interval t_f. The feasibility of this becomes immediately clear if we make use of Eq. (5-1), which gives, in this case,

$$x_f = e^{at_f} x_0 + e^{at_f} \int_0^{t_f} e^{-a\tau} bu(\tau)\, d\tau$$

The question is: Can this equation be satisfied for arbitrary values of x_0, x_f, and t_f? We can answer this question in the affirmative if we can find a control force $u(\tau)$ in the interval $0 < \tau < t_f$ which renders a specified value to the integral

$$\int_0^{t_f} e^{-a\tau} bu(\tau)\, d\tau$$

A little thought reveals that *if no amplitude constraints* are put on u, this certainly is possible. Indeed, it is possible to execute the state transfer even if we restrict the control force to being *constant* throughout the interval.

In Fig. 5-2, we have indicated two workable control strategies, u_1 and u_2, resulting in the two different state trajectories T_1 and T_2. Obviously, we may find an *infinite* number of possible u strategies that would qualify.

Having thus confirmed that the system is completely controllable, one is faced with the additional (and generally more difficult) problem of choosing one of the possible strategies. It is obviously necessary to apply a more *selective criterion* if such a choice is to be possible. In the chosen example, we may, for instance, require that the state transfer take place with a minimum of power loss in the resistor.

The energy dissipated in the resistor is

$$W = \int_0^{t_f} Ri^2\, dt = RC^2 \int_0^{t_f} \dot{x}^2\, dt \tag{5-4}$$

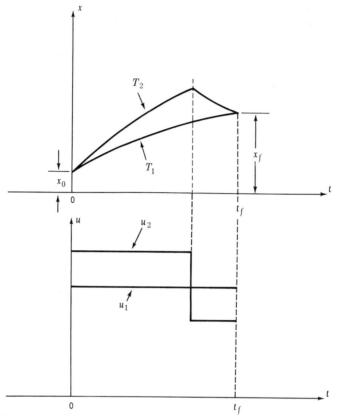

Fig. 5-2   Two possible control strategies for system in Fig. 5-1.

We intuitively feel that this energy restriction should sort out a specific *optimum strategy* among the infinite selection, and indeed this can be rigidly proved.   The problem thus posed is a typical *optimum-control problem*, the solution methods of which we shall discuss in Chap. 11.

Before we leave this example, we conclude that *all* one-dimensional systems of the form (5-2) are indeed completely controllable.   It is also worthwhile to mention that the stability (determined, in this case, by the sign of *a*) of the system has no direct influence on the controllability but certainly determines the success in *keeping* the system in the new state.

Example 5-2

In this example, we shall demonstrate a system which is *not* controllable.   Consider the two-dimensional system characterized by the vector equation

$$\begin{bmatrix} \dot{x}_1 \\ \dot{x}_2 \end{bmatrix} = \begin{bmatrix} a_{11} & 0 \\ 0 & a_{22} \end{bmatrix} \begin{bmatrix} x_1 \\ x_2 \end{bmatrix} + \begin{bmatrix} b_1 \\ 0 \end{bmatrix} u \tag{5-5}$$

The system depicted in Fig. 5-3 is represented by this vector equation.   In this case, we have

$$a_{11} = -\frac{1}{R_1 C_1} \qquad a_{22} = -\frac{1}{R_2 C_2} \qquad b_1 = \frac{1}{R_1 C_1}$$

The system is noncontrollable because the control force has no influence on x_2, which depends entirely on the initial state $x_2(0)$.   Those components of a state vector, in this case x_2, that are not in any way influenced by the control forces are referred to as "noncontrollable."

The reader may insist that, in view of nonexisting coupling between the two circuits in Fig. 5-3, noncontrollability is self-evident.   This is true, and the example was indeed chosen for this particular reason.   This example and the previous one were both clear-cut, leaving no doubt about the question of controllability.

In most instances, the situation is not this obvious, and we shall amplify this point by giving two additional examples.

Example 5-3

Consider a system satisfying the differential equations

$$\begin{bmatrix} \dot{x}_1 \\ \dot{x}_2 \end{bmatrix} = \begin{bmatrix} 2 & 0 \\ -1 & 1 \end{bmatrix} \begin{bmatrix} x_1 \\ x_2 \end{bmatrix} + \begin{bmatrix} 1 \\ -1 \end{bmatrix} u \tag{5-6}$$

or, fully written out,

$$\dot{x}_1 = 2x_1 + u$$
$$\dot{x}_2 = -x_1 + x_2 - u$$

Is this system controllable?   The question cannot be answered simply by inspection, as was possible in the previous examples.   Certainly, we can conclude from the first of the equations that x_1 is controllable.   But what about x_2?

By adding the two equations, we obtain

$$\dot{x}_1 + \dot{x}_2 = x_1 + x_2$$

By integration, using Eq. (4-6), we obtain

$$x_1(t) + x_2(t) = [x_1(0) + x_2(0)]e^t$$

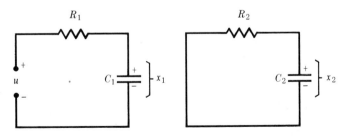

Fig. 5-3   Noncontrollable system.

We note from this last equation that $x_1(t_f)$ and $x_2(t_f)$ *cannot be specified independently,* which simply means that this system cannot be transferred between two arbitrarily chosen states. The system is therefore noncontrollable. We could in this case have expressed the situation as follows: The *sum* $x_1 + x_2$ is beyond the influence of the control force u.

Example 5-4

As a final example, consider the inertia wheel in Fig. 5-4.
Newton's law of acceleration yields

$$I\ddot{\varphi} = u \qquad u = \text{torque}; I = \text{moment of inertia}$$

By putting $I = 1$ (for simplicity) and introducing the state vector

$$\mathbf{x} = \begin{bmatrix} x_1 \\ x_2 \end{bmatrix} \triangleq \begin{bmatrix} \varphi \\ \dot{\varphi} \end{bmatrix}$$

we get the state model

$$\dot{x}_1 = x_2$$

$$\dot{x}_2 = u$$

or, in vector form,

$$\begin{bmatrix} \dot{x}_1 \\ \dot{x}_2 \end{bmatrix} = \begin{bmatrix} 0 & 1 \\ 0 & 0 \end{bmatrix} \begin{bmatrix} x_1 \\ x_2 \end{bmatrix} + \begin{bmatrix} 0 \\ 1 \end{bmatrix} u \qquad (5\text{-}7)$$

The reader is invited to draw his own conclusions concerning the controllability of this system at this time. We shall discuss it in detail later in the chapter.

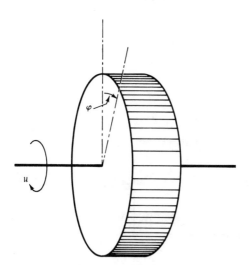

Fig. 5-4 Inertia wheel.

In the further discussion of controllability, it will prove very helpful to make use of some important characteristics of linear transformations. Therefore, we shall digress for the moment, but we shall return, better equipped, to pick up the interrupted story.

5-2 INVARIANCE OF THE EIGENVALUES TO A LINEAR TRANSFORMATION

In Chap. 3, we concluded that a specific choice of a set of state variables was not a unique choice. In a number of examples, we have demonstrated how the selection of state variables can be made conveniently on a physical basis; i.e., those system variables are selected that have an immediately recognizable physical meaning.

For some specific investigations, and the study of system controllability is one example, it may prove more instructive to base the choice on mathematical, rather than physical, convenience.

Consider the system

$$\dot{\mathbf{x}} = \mathbf{A}\mathbf{x} + \mathbf{B}\mathbf{u}$$

We shall assume that the $\mathbf{x}$ vector in this system has been chosen on a physical basis.

Of great theoretical interest are those new state variables $x_1^*, x_2^*, \ldots, x_n^*$ that may be defined through a *linear transformation* of the old ones

$$
\begin{aligned}
x_1 &= t_{11}x_1^* + t_{12}x_2^* + \cdots + t_{1n}x_n^* \\
&\cdots\cdots\cdots\cdots\cdots\cdots\cdots\cdots\cdots\cdots \\
x_n &= t_{n1}x_1^* + t_{n2}x_2^* + \cdots + t_{nn}x_n^*
\end{aligned}
\tag{5-8}
$$

or, in vector notation,

$$\mathbf{x} = \mathbf{T}\mathbf{x}^* \tag{5-9}$$

By substitution into our old system equation, we obtain the new one,

$$\dot{\mathbf{x}}^* = \mathbf{A}^*\mathbf{x}^* + \mathbf{B}^*\mathbf{u} \tag{5-10}$$

where

$$\mathbf{A}^* \overset{\Delta}{=} \mathbf{T}^{-1}\mathbf{A}\mathbf{T} \quad \text{and} \quad \mathbf{B}^* \overset{\Delta}{=} \mathbf{T}^{-1}\mathbf{B}$$

With respect to the *transformation matrix* $\mathbf{T}$, it is necessary to assume that it is nonsingular; that is, $|\mathbf{T}| \neq 0$. If this were not the case, then the inverse transformation would obviously not exist.

The great importance and usefulness of the $\mathbf{x}^*$ system are due to the following remarkable feature:

The eigenvalues of the $\mathbf{x}^*$ *system are identical to those of the* $\mathbf{x}$ *system.*

This invariance of the eigenvalues to a linear nonsingular transformation is easily proved, as follows:

The n eigenvalues $\lambda_1, \lambda_2, \ldots, \lambda_n$ of the $\mathbf{x}$ system are obtained (see Chap. 4) from the characteristic equation

$$|s\mathbf{I} - \mathbf{A}| = 0 \tag{5-11}$$

The n eigenvalues of the $\mathbf{x}^*$ system are similarly obtained from

$$|s\mathbf{I} - \mathbf{A}^*| = 0 \tag{5-12}$$

On account of the identity

$$\mathbf{I} = \mathbf{T}^{-1}\mathbf{I}\mathbf{T}$$

Eq. (5-12) can be written

$$|s\mathbf{T}^{-1}\mathbf{I}\mathbf{T} - \mathbf{T}^{-1}\mathbf{A}\mathbf{T}| = |\mathbf{T}^{-1}(s\mathbf{I} - \mathbf{A})\mathbf{T}|$$
$$= |\mathbf{T}^{-1}|\,|s\mathbf{I} - \mathbf{A}|\,|\mathbf{T}| = 0 \tag{5-13}$$

We have already assumed that $|\mathbf{T}|$ and therefore also $|\mathbf{T}^{-1}|$ are nonzero; therefore, Eq. (5-13) can be satisfied if and only if

$$|s\mathbf{I} - \mathbf{A}| = 0$$

The $\mathbf{x}^*$ system is characterized therefore by the same eigenvalues as the $\mathbf{x}$ system.

5-3 EIGENVECTORS AND NATURAL MODES

Assume, for simplicity, that the n eigenvalues are *distinct*. This assumption is slightly restrictive but will greatly simplify the mathematical proofs in the following. Furthermore, it can be shown that those systems possessing multiple eigenvalues can actually be approximated with arbitrary accuracy to a system having distinct eigenvalues.[6]

It was shown in Chap. 4 that the solution to the homogeneous system

$$\dot{\mathbf{x}} = \mathbf{A}\mathbf{x} \quad \text{with} \quad \mathbf{x}(0) = \mathbf{x}_0 \tag{5-14}$$

is composed of the exponential terms $e^{\lambda_1 t}, e^{\lambda_2 t}, \ldots, e^{\lambda_n t}$. We can therefore write

$$x_1(t) = e_{11}e^{\lambda_1 t} + \cdots + e_{1n}e^{\lambda_n t}$$
$$\cdots\cdots\cdots\cdots\cdots\cdots\cdots \tag{5-15}$$
$$x_n(t) = e_{n1}e^{\lambda_1 t} + \cdots + e_{nn}e^{\lambda_n}$$

where the coefficients e_{ij} indicate the contribution from each exponential term.

By introducing the n vector

$$\mathbf{e}^{\lambda t} \triangleq \begin{bmatrix} e^{\lambda_1 t} \\ \cdot \\ \cdot \\ \cdot \\ e^{\lambda_n t} \end{bmatrix} \tag{5-16}$$

and the $n \times n$ eigenvector matrix

$$\mathbf{E} \triangleq \begin{bmatrix} e_{11} & \cdots & e_{1n} \\ \cdots\cdots\cdots\cdots \\ e_{n1} & \cdots & e_{nn} \end{bmatrix} \tag{5-17}$$

we may write the **x** solution

$$\mathbf{x}(t) = \mathbf{E}e^{\lambda t} \tag{5-18}$$

We know that the solution of the n-dimensional vector equation (5-14) depends upon the n independently specifiable initial conditions $\mathbf{x}(0)$, and this means in effect that there are only n degrees of freedom for the n^2 elements e_{ij}. If it is possible, therefore, to find among these n^2 elements n linearly independent groups, then it is possible to express all **x** solutions in terms of these groups. There is an infinite number of choices that would be acceptable; a particularly interesting grouping is obtained if we settle for the *columns of* **E**. The n groups, or vectors, which we thus obtain will be referred to in the following as the *eigenvectors* $\mathbf{e}_1, \mathbf{e}_2, \ldots, \mathbf{e}_n$, defined by

$$\mathbf{e}_j \triangleq \begin{bmatrix} e_{1j} \\ \cdot \\ \cdot \\ \cdot \\ e_{nj} \end{bmatrix} \quad \text{for } j = 1, 2, \ldots, n \tag{5-19}$$

We note first from (5-15) that each eigenvector $\mathbf{e}_j$ is associated with one and only one eigenvalue λ_j. Actually, the **x** solution (5-15) can be written

$$\mathbf{x}(t) = \mathbf{e}_1 e^{\lambda_1 t} + \mathbf{e}_2 e^{\lambda_2 t} + \cdots + \mathbf{e}_n e^{\lambda_n t} \tag{5-20}$$

The eigenvectors can be computed easily if we realize that $\mathbf{e}_j e^{\lambda_j t}$ must be a solution to Eq. (5-14).† Consequently, it follows that

$$\lambda_j \mathbf{e}_j e^{\lambda_j t} = \mathbf{A} \mathbf{e}_j e^{\lambda_j t} \quad \text{for } j = 1, 2, \ldots, n$$

or upon division by $e^{\lambda_j t}$

$$\lambda_j \mathbf{e}_j = \mathbf{A} \mathbf{e}_j \quad \text{for } j = 1, 2, \ldots, n \tag{5-21}$$

Example 5-5

Find the eigenvectors for the system

$$\begin{bmatrix} \dot{x}_1 \\ \dot{x}_2 \end{bmatrix} = \begin{bmatrix} 1 & 2 \\ 4 & 3 \end{bmatrix} \begin{bmatrix} x_1 \\ x_2 \end{bmatrix}$$

First we compute the eigenvalues λ_1 and λ_2. We have

$$(\lambda - 1)(\lambda - 3) - 8 = 0$$

---

† If (5-20) is a solution to Eq. (5-14), certainly each term must also satisfy the equation.

which gives

$\lambda_1 = -1$

$\lambda_2 = 5$

Then we have, from (5-21),

$-1e_1 = Ae_1$

and

$5e_2 = Ae_2$

These two vector equations result in the two eigenvectors

$$e_1 = \begin{bmatrix} e_{11} \\ -e_{11} \end{bmatrix} \qquad e_2 = \begin{bmatrix} e_{12} \\ 2e_{12} \end{bmatrix}$$

Note that the lengths of the eigenvectors can be determined only after we specify the initial conditions. It is convenient to *normalize* the eigenvectors to unit length. These *unit eigenvectors* will be symbolized $\hat{e}_1$ and $\hat{e}_2$, and in our example, they are

$$\hat{e}_1 = \begin{bmatrix} \dfrac{1}{\sqrt{2}} \\ -\dfrac{1}{\sqrt{2}} \end{bmatrix} \qquad \hat{e}_2 = \begin{bmatrix} \dfrac{1}{\sqrt{5}} \\ \dfrac{2}{\sqrt{5}} \end{bmatrix}$$

The total **x** solution can then be written

$$x(t) = \alpha_1 \hat{e}_1 e^{-t} + \alpha_2 \hat{e}_2 e^{5t} \tag{5-22}$$

where the scalar coefficients α_1 and α_2 can be determined only upon specification of initial conditions. For instance, should we specify

$$x(0) = \begin{bmatrix} 1 \\ 1 \end{bmatrix}$$

then we can obtain α_1 and α_2 from (5-22) by letting $t \to 0$, i.e.,

$$\begin{bmatrix} 1 \\ 1 \end{bmatrix} = \alpha_1 \begin{bmatrix} \dfrac{1}{\sqrt{2}} \\ -\dfrac{1}{\sqrt{2}} \end{bmatrix} + \alpha_2 \begin{bmatrix} \dfrac{1}{\sqrt{5}} \\ \dfrac{2}{\sqrt{5}} \end{bmatrix}$$

Hence,

$$\alpha_1 = \frac{\sqrt{2}}{3}$$

$$\alpha_2 = \frac{2\sqrt{5}}{3}$$

resulting in the solution

$$\begin{bmatrix} x_1(t) \\ x_2(t) \end{bmatrix} = \begin{bmatrix} \frac{1}{3} \\ -\frac{1}{3} \end{bmatrix} e^{-t} + \begin{bmatrix} \frac{2}{3} \\ \frac{4}{3} \end{bmatrix} e^{5t}$$

The vector term $\mathbf{e}_j e^{\lambda_j t}$ of the total solution (5-20) is referred to as the jth *natural mode, or the natural mode associated with the jth eigenvalue* λ_j.

The total $\mathbf{x}$ solution therefore consists, in the general case, of contributions from all n modes. How much each mode contributes to the total solution depends entirely on the initial excitation.

In the example just treated, we note that we can "filter out" the second term of (5-22) completely (i.e., forcing α_2 to zero) by choosing an initial state $\mathbf{x}(0)$ proportional to $\hat{\mathbf{e}}_1$. Similarly, we could have filtered out the first term by specifying an initial-state vector proportional to $\hat{\mathbf{e}}_2$.

By introducing the n unit eigenvectors $\hat{\mathbf{e}}_1, \hat{\mathbf{e}}_2, \ldots, \hat{\mathbf{e}}_n$, we can write Eq. (5-20) as

$$\mathbf{x}(t) = \alpha_1 \hat{\mathbf{e}}_1 e^{\lambda_1 t} + \alpha_2 \hat{\mathbf{e}}_2 e^{\lambda_2 t} + \cdots + \alpha_n \hat{\mathbf{e}}_n e^{\lambda_n t} \tag{5-23}$$

The scalar coefficients α_j indicate the fractions that the different modes contribute to the total solution and *are functions of the initial state only.*

5-4 THE CANONICAL TRANSFORMATION

An extremely interesting and useful linear transformation is obtained if, for the transformation matrix $\mathbf{T}$ in Eq. (5-9), we choose the eigenvector matrix.

It does not really matter whether we use the normalized or nonnormalized eigenvectors for this purpose. Some notational simplifications are obtained by using the normalized vectors, and in order to distinguish the two, we introduce the notation

$$\hat{\mathbf{E}} \stackrel{\Delta}{=} [\hat{\mathbf{e}}_1 \quad \hat{\mathbf{e}}_2 \quad \ldots \quad \hat{\mathbf{e}}_n]$$

By using this $n \times n$ matrix, we obtain from (5-10)

$$\dot{\mathbf{x}}^* = \mathbf{A}^*\mathbf{x}^* + \mathbf{B}^*\mathbf{u} \quad \text{with } \mathbf{A}^* = \hat{\mathbf{E}}^{-1}\mathbf{A}\hat{\mathbf{E}} \quad \text{and} \quad \mathbf{B}^* = \hat{\mathbf{E}}^{-1}\mathbf{B} \tag{5-24}$$

[It is possible to show that the n eigenvectors $\hat{\mathbf{e}}_j$ are linearly independent and constitute what is referred to as a *basis* in n-space. This fact not only guarantees that the solution (5-23) is unique in terms of the eigenvectors but also gives us assurance that the $\hat{\mathbf{E}}$ matrix is nonsingular; i.e., the transformation (5-24) does really exist.]

In order to see what this transformation actually does for us, let us for a moment consider Eq. (5-21). By writing out this equation for $j = 1, 2, \ldots, n$, we obtain

$$\lambda_1 \hat{\mathbf{e}}_1 = \mathbf{A}\hat{\mathbf{e}}_1$$
$$\cdots\cdots\cdots \tag{5-25}$$
$$\lambda_n \hat{\mathbf{e}}_n = \mathbf{A}\hat{\mathbf{e}}_n$$

At this juncture, we introduce the *diagonal* $n \times n$ matrix $\mathbf{\Lambda}$, defined by

$$\mathbf{\Lambda} \triangleq \begin{bmatrix} \lambda_1 & & & 0 \\ & \lambda_2 & & \\ & & \cdot & \\ & & & \cdot \\ & & & \cdot \\ 0 & & & \lambda_n \end{bmatrix} \tag{5-26}$$

We note next that

$$\mathbf{\hat{E}\Lambda} = \begin{bmatrix} \lambda_1 \hat{e}_{11} & \cdots & \lambda_n \hat{e}_{1n} \\ \lambda_1 \hat{e}_{21} & \cdots & \lambda_n \hat{e}_{2n} \\ \cdots & \cdots & \cdots \\ \lambda_1 \hat{e}_{n1} & \cdots & \lambda_n \hat{e}_{nn} \end{bmatrix} \tag{5-27}$$

By using the relationships (5-25), we form now the following $n \times n$ matrix:

$$[\lambda_1 \hat{\mathbf{e}}_1 \quad \lambda_2 \hat{\mathbf{e}}_2 \quad \cdots \quad \lambda_n \hat{\mathbf{e}}_n] = [\mathbf{A}\hat{\mathbf{e}}_1 \quad \mathbf{A}\hat{\mathbf{e}}_2 \quad \cdots \quad \mathbf{A}\hat{\mathbf{e}}_n]$$

This equation may be written

$$\begin{bmatrix} \lambda_1 \hat{e}_{11} & \cdots & \lambda_n \hat{e}_{1n} \\ \lambda_1 \hat{e}_{21} & \cdots & \lambda_n \hat{e}_{2n} \\ \cdots & \cdots & \cdots \\ \lambda_1 \hat{e}_{n1} & \cdots & \lambda_n \hat{e}_{nn} \end{bmatrix} = \mathbf{A}[\hat{\mathbf{e}}_1 \quad \cdots \quad \hat{\mathbf{e}}_n] = \mathbf{A}\hat{\mathbf{E}}$$

By comparison with (5-27), we thus have

$$\mathbf{\hat{E}\Lambda} = \mathbf{A}\hat{\mathbf{E}} \tag{5-28}$$

Therefore,

$$\mathbf{\Lambda} = \hat{\mathbf{E}}^{-1}\mathbf{A}\hat{\mathbf{E}} \tag{5-29}$$

Equation (5-24) therefore can be written

$$\dot{\mathbf{x}}^* = \mathbf{\Lambda}\mathbf{x}^* + \mathbf{B}^*\mathbf{u} \tag{5-30}$$

If we write this vector equation in component form, we have

$$\dot{x}_i^* = \lambda_i x_i^* + i\text{th component of } (\mathbf{B}^*\mathbf{u}) \qquad \text{for } i = 1, 2, \ldots, n \tag{5-31}$$

The remarkable thing that has happened is that in the $\mathbf{x}^*$ *system, the state variables are completely decoupled from each other.* The new state variables $x_1^*, \ldots, x_n^*$ obtained through this transformation are referred to as the *canonical coordinates*, and the transformation through which they were obtained is called *canonical*.

A better physical appreciation of the situation is obtained if we note that the transformation

$$\mathbf{x} = \hat{\mathbf{E}}\mathbf{x}^*$$

actually can be written

$$\mathbf{x} = \hat{\mathbf{e}}_1 x_1^* + \hat{\mathbf{e}}_2 x_2^* + \cdots + \hat{\mathbf{e}}_n x_n^* \tag{5-32}$$

Upon comparison with (5-23), this expression reveals that the canonical coordinates are actually identical to the x coordinates or components in the basis $\hat{\mathbf{e}}_1, \hat{\mathbf{e}}_2, \ldots, \hat{\mathbf{e}}_n$.

Example 5-6

Let us perform a canonical transformation on the system defined by Eq. (5-6), which we had decided was noncontrollable. We have

$$\mathbf{A} = \begin{bmatrix} 2 & 0 \\ -1 & 1 \end{bmatrix} \qquad \mathbf{B} = \begin{bmatrix} 1 \\ -1 \end{bmatrix}$$

The eigenvalues are obtained therefore from the characteristic equation

$$(s - 2)(s - 1) = 0$$

Hence,

$$\lambda_1 = 2$$
$$\lambda_2 = 1$$

Equation (5-21) gives us the eigenvectors

$$2\hat{\mathbf{e}}_1 = \mathbf{A}\hat{\mathbf{e}}_1$$
$$1\hat{\mathbf{e}}_2 = \mathbf{A}\hat{\mathbf{e}}_2$$

From these two equations, we obtain the following two normalized eigenvectors:

$$\hat{\mathbf{e}}_1 = \begin{bmatrix} \dfrac{1}{\sqrt{2}} \\[2mm] -\dfrac{1}{\sqrt{2}} \end{bmatrix} \qquad \hat{\mathbf{e}}_2 = \begin{bmatrix} 0 \\ 1 \end{bmatrix}$$

Therefore,

$$\hat{\mathbf{E}} = \begin{bmatrix} \dfrac{1}{\sqrt{2}} & 0 \\[2mm] -\dfrac{1}{\sqrt{2}} & 1 \end{bmatrix} \qquad \text{and} \qquad \hat{\mathbf{E}}^{-1} = \begin{bmatrix} \sqrt{2} & 0 \\ 1 & 1 \end{bmatrix}$$

We confirm then by direct multiplication that

$$\mathbf{A}^* = \hat{\mathbf{E}}^{-1}\mathbf{A}\hat{\mathbf{E}} = \begin{bmatrix} 2 & 0 \\ 0 & 1 \end{bmatrix} = \mathbf{\Lambda}$$

Furthermore,

$$\mathbf{B}^* = \hat{\mathbf{E}}^{-1}\mathbf{B} = \begin{bmatrix} \sqrt{2} \\ 0 \end{bmatrix}$$

After the canonical transformation, the system (5-6) takes on the form

$$\begin{bmatrix} \dot{x}_1^* \\ \dot{x}_2^* \end{bmatrix} = \begin{bmatrix} 2 & 0 \\ 0 & 1 \end{bmatrix} \begin{bmatrix} x_1^* \\ x_2^* \end{bmatrix} + \begin{bmatrix} \sqrt{2} \\ 0 \end{bmatrix} u \tag{5-33}$$

In the next section we will demonstrate how by direct inspection of Eqs. (5-33) we can conclude that this system is noncontrollable.

In concluding this very brief discussion of canonical transformations, it is appropriate to remind the reader that all our derivations were based upon the assumption that the eigenvalues were distinct. However, they are permitted to be conjugate complex. Instead of trying at this time to complete the picture by investigating what effect multiple eigenvalues will have, we choose instead to return to our interrupted story of system controllability.

5-5 CRITERIA FOR CONTROLLABILITY

It is quite simple to determine the controllability of a system if its dynamic equations are transformed into their canonical form (5-30).

To understand this statement better, we shall write Eq. (5-30) in more detail:

$$\begin{bmatrix} \dot{x}_1^* \\ \dot{x}_2^* \\ \cdot \\ \cdot \\ \cdot \\ \dot{x}_n^* \end{bmatrix} = \begin{bmatrix} \lambda_1 & & & 0 \\ & \lambda_2 & & \\ & & \cdot & \\ & & & \cdot \\ 0 & & & \lambda_n \end{bmatrix} \begin{bmatrix} x_1^* \\ x_2^* \\ \cdot \\ \cdot \\ \cdot \\ x_n^* \end{bmatrix} + \begin{bmatrix} b_{11}^* & b_{12}^* & \cdots & b_{1m}^* \\ b_{21}^* & b_{22}^* & \cdots & b_{2m}^* \\ \multicolumn{4}{c}{\dotfill} \\ b_{n1}^* & b_{n2}^* & \cdots & b_{nm}^* \end{bmatrix} \begin{bmatrix} u_1 \\ \cdot \\ \cdot \\ \cdot \\ u_m \end{bmatrix} \tag{5-34}$$

The system is completely controllable if it is possible to transfer in finite time t_f each state variable x_i^* between arbitrarily specified states $x_i^*(0)$ and $x_i^*(t_f)$. *Because no coupling exists between the canonical state variables, we realize immediately that a necessary condition for controllability is that the matrix* **B*** *must have no zero rows.* Should one or several rows be zero, it would not be possible to influence the corresponding state variables by our control forces and the system would certainly not meet the conditions for controllability. Those state variables corresponding to zero rows are referred to as *noncontrollable*.

However, the fact that we can *influence* each state variable is certainly not a guarantee that we shall be able to *control* them. By "control," we mean "transfer between arbitrarily specified states in specified time." At a first glance, it would seem particularly impossible to control n state variables with a smaller number (m) of control forces.

Actually, it is possible to control any finite number of state variables by *one* control force only. If we can back up this statement with a proof, then in effect we have proven that the above-mentioned controllability criterion is both necessary and sufficient—because if we can do the job with *one* control force, we certainly can do it with several independent ones. What we actually are proposing to do then is to show that the system

$$
\begin{bmatrix} \dot{x}_1^* \\ \cdot \\ \cdot \\ \cdot \\ \dot{x}_n^* \end{bmatrix} = \begin{bmatrix} \lambda_1 & & 0 \\ & \cdot & \\ & & \cdot \\ 0 & & \lambda_n \end{bmatrix} \begin{bmatrix} x_1^* \\ \cdot \\ \cdot \\ \cdot \\ x_n^* \end{bmatrix} + \begin{bmatrix} b_1^* \\ \cdot \\ \cdot \\ \cdot \\ b_n^* \end{bmatrix} u
\tag{5-35}
$$

is indeed controllable, assuming that all the b_i^*'s are nonzero. (Of course, we still consider all eigenvalues distinct.) The set of equations (5-35) represents the physical system depicted in Fig. 5-5, and the reader may find it easier to think in terms of capacitor voltages than the abstract $\mathbf{x}^*$ vector. We are trying here to

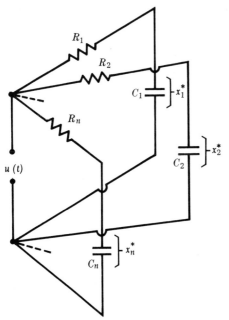

$$R_1 C_1 \neq R_2 C_2 \neq \cdots \neq R_n C_n$$

Fig. 5-5 Controllable system.

show that the n capacitor voltages may be changed in specified time t_f from n specified initial voltages to n likewise specified final voltages by one voltage source only. Any electrical engineer would consider this quite an accomplishment!

The system of equations (5-35) can be written in component form

$$\dot{x}_i^* = \lambda_i x_i^* + b_i^* u \qquad i = 1, 2, \ldots, n \tag{5-36}$$

Using Eq. (4-8), we integrate these equations one by one between 0 and t_f:

$$x_i^*(t_f) = e^{\lambda_i t_f} x_i^*(0) + e^{\lambda_i t_f} \int_0^{t_f} e^{-\lambda_i \tau} b_i^* u(\tau)\, d\tau \qquad i = 1, 2, \ldots, n \tag{5-37}$$

For the system to be controllable, we shall be able to find a $u(\tau)$ that satisfies *all* these n equations with arbitrarily assigned values to t_f, $x_i^*(0)$, and $x_i^*(t_f)$.

We note immediately that this requirement can be met if we can answer the following question in the affirmative: Can a $u(\tau)$ be found such that the n integrals

$$\int_0^{t_f} e^{-\lambda_i \tau} u(\tau)\, d\tau \qquad i = 1, 2, \ldots, n$$

assume n different arbitrarily specified values?

Because of the n *different* factors $e^{-\lambda_i \tau}$ (remember that the λ_i's were distinct), this certainly can be done. Indeed, there exists an infinite number of $u(\tau)$ that will do the job. The simplest solution is represented by a $u(\tau)$ function that is piecewise constant (see Fig. 5-6) and changes value $n - 1$ times in the interval $0 < \tau < t_f$. (The reader who has worked Exercise 4-3 has, in all probability, already tested this approach.)

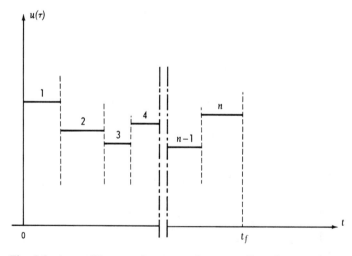

Fig. 5-6 A possible control strategy for controlling the system in Fig. 5-5.

Example 5-7

We concluded in the beginning of this chapter that the system represented by the differential equations (5-6) was noncontrollable. This finding should be confirmed by subjecting the system to a canonical transformation. Actually, we have done this already in Example 5-6, and the result was the canonical equation (5-33). We note that the $\mathbf{B}^*$ matrix has the form

$$\mathbf{B}^* = \begin{bmatrix} \sqrt{2} \\ 0 \end{bmatrix}$$

and as the second row is zero, we conclude that the canonical coordinate x_2^*, associated with the eigenvalue $\lambda_2 = 1$, cannot be *reached* by the control force. Only x_1^*, associated with $\lambda_1 = 2$, can be controlled.

It is interesting to note what happens if we compute the transfer function between input u and states x_1 and x_2 in this example. We obtain directly from (5-6)

$$\frac{X_1(s)}{U(s)} = \frac{1}{s-2} \qquad \frac{X_2(s)}{U(s)} = \frac{-1}{s-2}$$

The presence of the factor $(s-2)$ and the absence of any factor of the type $(s-1)$ indicate that whatever control force is employed, only the natural mode associated with $\lambda_1 = 2$ is being excited. The transfer-function description therefore overlooks the "hidden" second mode in the system.

The method (first suggested by Gilbert) that we have presented for testing the controllability of a system necessitates the transformation of the system into its canonical form. There exists a direct method due to Kalman[3] which considers the so-called "rank" of the $n \times nm$ matrix, which is obtained by grouping the $n \, n \times m$ matrices $\mathbf{B}$, $\mathbf{AB}$, $\mathbf{A^2B}$, ..., $\mathbf{A}^{n-1}\mathbf{B}$ into the new matrix

$$[\mathbf{B} \quad \mathbf{AB} \quad \mathbf{A^2B} \quad \dots \quad \mathbf{A}^{n-1}\mathbf{B}]$$

It is possible to show that the system is completely controllable only if the rank of this matrix equals n. The proof is very abstract and lacks all the physical "feel" of Gilbert's method; for this reason, it will not be included here.

5-6 OBSERVABILITY AND OBSERVERS

We pointed out several times previously that the state of a system does not necessarily equal its output. The p-dimensional output vector $\mathbf{c}$ is related in most instances to the state vector through the equation

$$\mathbf{c} = \mathbf{Cx} \tag{5-38}$$

In many problems of theoretical nature and also in practical instrumentation design, it is of great interest to know whether it is possible to obtain by measurement of the available output vector $\mathbf{c}$ all information about the system state. The question is particularly pertinent when the output vector $\mathbf{c}$ is of lower dimensionality than the state vector $\mathbf{x}$.

definition   *A system is said to be observable if measurements of the output* **c** *contain sufficient information to enable us to completely identify the state* **x**.

In systems that are not observable, one or several components of the state vector are "hidden" from observation.

The similarity between the concepts of controllability and observability should be apparent. In the one case, we are concerned about the possibility that one or several state components are beyond the influence of the input; in the other, we are asking ourselves if some of the state variables are shielded from observation through the available output.

The question of observability, like that of controllability, ties in very closely with the natural-mode interpretation of a linear system. We shall understand this better if we study what effect the canonical transformation

$$\mathbf{x} = \hat{\mathbf{E}}\mathbf{x}^*$$

has on the output relation (5-38). We obtain by substitution

$$\mathbf{c} = \mathbf{C}\hat{\mathbf{E}}\mathbf{x}^* \tag{5-39}$$

which we can write as

$$\mathbf{c} = \mathbf{C}^*\mathbf{x}^* \tag{5-40}$$

The new $p \times n$ matrix $\mathbf{C}^*$ is defined by

$$\mathbf{C}^* \triangleq \mathbf{C}\hat{\mathbf{E}} \tag{5-41}$$

We write Eq. (5-40) in component form, that is,

$$
\begin{aligned}
c_1 &= c_{11}^* x_1^* + c_{12}^* x_2^* + \cdots + c_{1n}^* x_n^* \\
c_2 &= c_{21}^* x_1^* + c_{22}^* x_2^* + \cdots + c_{2n}^* x_n^* \\
&\cdots\cdots\cdots\cdots\cdots\cdots\cdots\cdots \\
c_p &= c_{p1}^* x_1^* + c_{p2}^* x_2^* + \cdots + c_{pn}^* x_n^*
\end{aligned}
\tag{5-42}
$$

The necessary and sufficient condition for observability is that no component of $\mathbf{x}^*$ be missing in the above system. *We therefore conclude that complete observability necessitates that none of the columns of* $\mathbf{C}^*$ *be zero.* If any column is zero, the corresponding canonical coordinate is nondetectable and thus "hidden." A system that is nonobservable thus has dynamic modes which cannot be ascertained from measurements of the available output.

It is very instructive to divide the n natural modes of a system S into four subgroups (corresponding to four subsystems), as illustrated in Fig. 5-7. In the first group, we place those natural modes that are both controllable and observable; in the second group, those that are controllable but not observable. In the third subgroup, we find those natural modes that are observable but not controllable; and in the fourth group, those which are neither controllable nor observable. We note that the only link from input to output is via subsystem I. Indeed, if we compute the transfer matrix relating $\mathbf{C}(s)$ with $\mathbf{U}(s)$, then only those eigenvalues

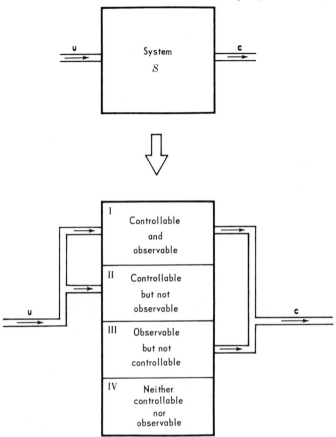

Fig. 5-7   Division of system on basis of controllable and observable
natural modes.

found in this subgroup will affect this matrix.   The transfer matrices of all the
remaining subsystems are zero.

  This means, in effect, that the transfer-function description of this system
tells us nothing about the dynamics of the subsystems II to IV.   For instance,
wild dynamics may take place in subsystem II under the influence of those control
forces that are coupled with the modes of this part while nothing is felt in the
output.   The lesson we should learn from this is that transfer-function descrip-
tions of systems should be viewed with a critical eye and one should make clear
from case to case whether important features and characteristics have been
overlooked.

Example 5-8

We shall demonstrate the concept of observability by means of a very simple
example.   In Chap. 3, we developed the mathematical model for the electrically

heated oven shown in Fig. 3-4. If x_1 and x_2 are taken to mean the jacket temperature and inside temperature, respectively, then we could write [see Eq. (3-29)] the temperature dynamics in the linear form

$$\dot{x} = Ax + bu \tag{5-43}$$

Let us assume that in some unit system, the **A** and **b** matrices have the simple numerical values

$$A = \begin{bmatrix} -0.2 & 0.1 \\ 0.1 & -0.1 \end{bmatrix} \quad \text{and} \quad b = \begin{bmatrix} 1 \\ 0 \end{bmatrix}$$

Output is provided via a thermocouple embedded in the jacket and indicating at all times the temperature x_1. We shall assume that the sensor has no thermal time constant; i.e., the output reading c is at all times equal to x_1. The output relationship is therefore

$$c = Cx \quad \text{with } C = [1 \quad 0] \tag{5-44}$$

We wish to exert control over *both* temperatures, but due to the fact that we have only *one* input and only *one* output, there is some doubt about the feasibility of this. It is, therefore, with good reason that we ask the following questions:

1. Is the system controllable? In other words, is it possible to control *both* the jacket and the inside temperatures by the *single* heat coil?
2. Is the system observable? In other words, is it possible to obtain from the *single* sensor information from which we can deduce *both* temperatures?

To find answers to these questions, we proceed to study the nature of the **B***and **C*** matrices. To that end, we first compute the eigenvalues.
We have

$$sI - A = \begin{bmatrix} s + 0.2 & -0.1 \\ -0.1 & s + 0.1 \end{bmatrix}$$

Solution of the characteristic equation $|sI - A| = 0$ results in the two eigenvalues

$$\lambda_1 = -\tfrac{1}{20}(3 + \sqrt{5}) = -0.2615$$
$$\lambda_2 = -\tfrac{1}{20}(3 - \sqrt{5}) = -0.0385$$

The two eigenvectors are then obtained from

$$-0.2615\hat{e}_1 = A\hat{e}_1$$
$$-0.0385\hat{e}_2 = A\hat{e}_2$$

These equations result in the $\hat{E}$ matrix

$$\hat{E} = [\hat{e}_1 \quad \hat{e}_2] = \begin{bmatrix} 0.854 & 0.526 \\ -0.524 & 0.848 \end{bmatrix}$$

Thus,

$$\hat{\mathbf{E}}^{-1} = \begin{bmatrix} 0.848 & -0.526 \\ 0.524 & 0.854 \end{bmatrix}$$

We are now fully equipped to compute the **B*** and **C*** matrices

$$\mathbf{B}^* = \hat{\mathbf{E}}^{-1}\mathbf{B} = \begin{bmatrix} 0.848 & -0.526 \\ 0.524 & 0.854 \end{bmatrix}\begin{bmatrix} 1 \\ 0 \end{bmatrix} = \begin{bmatrix} 0.848 \\ 0.524 \end{bmatrix}$$

$$\mathbf{C}^* = \mathbf{C}\hat{\mathbf{E}} = \begin{bmatrix} 1 & 0 \end{bmatrix}\begin{bmatrix} 0.854 & 0.526 \\ -0.524 & 0.848 \end{bmatrix} = \begin{bmatrix} 0.854 & 0.526 \end{bmatrix}$$

None of the rows of **B*** or any column of **C*** is zero, and thus we conclude that the temperature state of the oven is both controllable and observable.

It must be stressed that just because we have concluded that a system is observable, we have not solved the problem of *how* to "observe" it. *Observability guarantees only that it is theoretically possible to reconstruct the state vector* **x** *from observations of the output vector* **c**. Note the similarity between observability and controllability in this respect. We remember that controllability also guarantees only that control is possible, but no clue is given as to how.

It is tempting to use the relationship

$$\mathbf{c} = \mathbf{Cx}$$

and as **c** is assumed known from observations, we then formally obtain

$$\mathbf{x} = \mathbf{C}^{-1}\mathbf{c}$$

However, the $p \times n$ matrix **C** does not possess an inverse, and this approach obviously is not successful when the order of **c** is less than **x**.

It should be pointed out that in most practical control systems, we are concerned with controlling only those components of the state vectors that are directly available for observation.

For example, in our introductory example in Chap. 2, we concluded that the total state vector was four-dimensional, but we were interested in controlling only one of its components. However, there are situations where one would wish to control the *whole* state of a system, or at least more state-vector components than could be observed directly through sensors. In such a situation, one must, by one means or another, reconstruct the "missing" state components. A device or system designed for this purpose is called an *observer*. Several types of observers have been proposed.

Clearly, the obvious approach would be to build a *model* of the actual system, either by hardware or by computer simulation, and then drive this model (Fig. 5-8) by the same control-force vector **u** as controls the real system. The model should be so designed that all its state vectors are available for direct measurements. This straightforward approach has one serious drawback—the model will not record disturbances that affect the state of the real system.

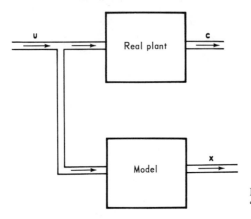

Fig. 5-8 An electronic model used as "observer."

Another method, often used in practical situations, is reconstruction of state components by means of differentiators. In the introductory example of Chap. 2, we proposed to use proportional-plus-derivative control, and assuming that only the position coordinate φ is available for measurement, it is theoretically possible to obtain the velocity $\dot{\varphi}$ by differentiation of φ. If the φ signal is not too badly contaminated with noise, this usually is practically possible. (In Chap. 9, it is shown how this can be achieved by means of a so-called *rate gyro*.) As a differentiator is characterized by the transfer function $T(s) = s$, it has a tendency to accentuate beyond tolerance high-frequency noise.

Luenberger[7] in a recent dissertation discusses the problem of constructing observers and also gives a state-of-the-art report.

5-7 EFFECT OF MULTIPLE EIGENVALUES

All our previous discussions were based on the assumption that all n eigenvalues of the system matrix **A** were distinct. There are important situations where this assumption does not apply, i.e., where the system is characterized by *multiple* eigenvalues. For example, the system in Example 5-4 has a double eigenvalue in the origin of the s plane.

Example 5-9

We shall demonstrate the effects of multiple eigenvalues on the simple second-order mechanical system depicted in Fig. 5-9. The system consists of two platforms P_1 and P_2 coupled to each other and to a fixed support (ground) via springs and dashpot dampers. In order not to end up with expressions that are too complicated, we shall neglect the platform masses. Furthermore, we assume unity values for the spring constants and also for one of the dashpot coefficients. One of the dashpots is assumed to have an adjustable coefficient k. We define the platform displacements as our state variables x_1 and x_2 and proceed first to establish a state model for our system.

Force balance on each platform requires that†

$$u = x_1 - x_2 + \dot{x}_1 - \dot{x}_2 = x_2 + k\dot{x}_2 \tag{5-45}$$

and therefore we obtain immediately

$$\dot{x}_1 = -x_1 + \frac{k-1}{k} x_2 + \frac{k+1}{k} u$$

$$\tag{5-46}$$

$$\dot{x}_2 = -\frac{1}{k} x_2 + \frac{1}{k} u$$

or

$$\dot{\mathbf{x}} = \mathbf{A}\mathbf{x} + \mathbf{b}u$$

where

$$\mathbf{A} = \begin{bmatrix} -1 & \dfrac{k-1}{k} \\ 0 & -\dfrac{1}{k} \end{bmatrix} \quad \text{and} \quad \mathbf{b} = \begin{bmatrix} \dfrac{k+1}{k} \\ \dfrac{1}{k} \end{bmatrix}$$

† Note that because we have neglected the platform masses, the control force u will be felt *immediately* by the lower platform.

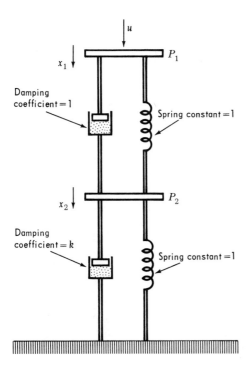

Fig. 5-9 A double-platform system.

From the characteristic equation $|sI - A| = 0$, we then obtain the eigenvalues

$$\lambda_1 = -1$$

$$\lambda_2 = -\frac{1}{k}$$

We next make Eq. (5-46) subject to a canonical transformation. We could employ the general method outlined in Sec. 5-4 but in order to vary the approach, we shall use the method outlined in Example 4-5. For that purpose, we Laplace-transform (5-46) and form the transfer ratios $X_1(s)/U(s)$ and $X_2(s)/U(s)$. We obtain

$$\frac{X_1(s)}{U(s)} = \frac{1}{s+1} + \frac{1/k}{s+1/k}$$

$$\frac{X_2(s)}{U(s)} = \frac{1/k}{s+1/k}$$

(5-47)

We then define

$$X_1^*(s) \overset{\Delta}{=} \frac{U(s)}{s+1}$$

$$X_2^*(s) \overset{\Delta}{=} \frac{U(s)}{s+1/k}$$

(5-48)

The latter equations can be written

$$(s+1)X_1^*(s) = U(s)$$

$$\left(s + \frac{1}{k}\right)X_2^*(s) = U(s)$$

which, after inverse transformation, yield

$$\dot{x}_1^* + x_1^* = u$$

$$\dot{x}_2^* + \frac{1}{k}x_2^* = u$$

(5-49)

or, in matrix form,

$$\begin{bmatrix} \dot{x}_1^* \\ \dot{x}_2^* \end{bmatrix} = \begin{bmatrix} -1 & 0 \\ 0 & -\frac{1}{k} \end{bmatrix} \begin{bmatrix} x_1^* \\ x_2^* \end{bmatrix} + \begin{bmatrix} 1 \\ 1 \end{bmatrix} u$$

(5-50)

This is obviously our sought canonical form

$$\dot{x}^* = \Lambda x^* + B^* u$$

We note that the B^* matrix has no zero rows, and we conclude therefore that the platform displacements are controllable. *However, this is true only if $k \neq 1$, that is, if the two eigenvalues are distinct.*

Let us see what happens if we now adjust k to unity so that both eigenvalues become equal. *As a result, the two canonical equations* (5-49) *become identical:*

$$\dot{x}_1^* + x_1^* = u$$
$$\dot{x}_2^* + x_2^* = u \tag{5-51}$$

and the control force has no possibility of distinguishing between the identical modes.

What really happens is better understood if we subtract the two equations (5-51):

$$(\dot{x}_1^* - \dot{x}_2^*) + (x_1^* - x_2^*) = 0 \tag{5-52}$$

In words: *The difference* $(x_1^* - x_2^*)$ *is beyond the influence of the control force.*

A still better picture is obtained if we consider what happens with the *physical* variables x_1 and x_2. By combining (5-47) and (5-48), we have

$$X_1(s) = X_1^*(s) + \frac{1}{k} X_2^*(s)$$

$$X_2(s) = \frac{1}{k} X_2^*(s)$$

or, in the time domain,

$$x_1 = x_1^* + \frac{1}{k} x_2^*$$

$$x_2 = \frac{1}{k} x_2^* \tag{5-53}$$

From these equations, we can easily solve for x_1^* and x_2^*, and upon substitution into (5-52), we get, for $k = 1$,

$$(\dot{x}_1 - 2\dot{x}_2) + (x_1 - 2x_2) = 0 \tag{5-54}$$

which we can readily integrate to

$$x_1 - 2x_2 = [x_1(0) - 2x_2(0)]e^{-t} \tag{5-55}$$

This proves that the two platform displacements x_1 and x_2 cannot be *independently* specified; i.e., the system is *uncontrollable*. A particularly simple situation is created if we arrange so that the initial displacements satisfy the equation

$$x_1(0) - 2x_2(0) = 0$$

Under this condition $x_1 = 2x_2$ whatever control force u we apply; i.e., the lower platform faithfully follows (with half amplitude) the upper one.

The example demonstrates that eigenvalue coincidence profoundly affects the controllability of a system. When multiple eigenvalues have been confirmed, one must proceed with greater caution in making statements concerning both controllability and observability. The analysis is complicated by the fact that, *in general,*† it is no longer possible to diagonalize the **A** matrix, which means in effect that the natural modes cannot be completely decoupled from each other (Example 5-9 actually is an exception to this rule). The best we can do is effect a transformation of **A** into a so-called *Jordan canonical matrix*

$$\mathbf{J} = \mathbf{T}^{-1}\mathbf{AT} \tag{5-56}$$

having the following properties:

1. All diagonal elements are the eigenvalues of the matrix **A** (and also of **J**).
2. All other elements are zero except possibly those elements above the diagonal adjacent to two equal eigenvalues, which are unity.

For example, assume that we have found that the 3×3 matrix **A** has an eigenvalue λ of multiplicity 3. Then the Jordan canonical matrix can have one but only one of the following three forms:

$$\begin{bmatrix} \lambda & 0 & 0 \\ 0 & \lambda & 0 \\ 0 & 0 & \lambda \end{bmatrix} \qquad \begin{bmatrix} \lambda & 0 & 0 \\ 0 & \lambda & 1 \\ 0 & 0 & \lambda \end{bmatrix} \qquad \begin{bmatrix} \lambda & 1 & 0 \\ 0 & \lambda & 1 \\ 0 & 0 & \lambda \end{bmatrix}$$

Example 5-4 (Cont.)

We shall demonstrate how controllability can be ascertained in systems where the natural modes cannot be decoupled from each other, and we shall for that purpose return to Example 5-4 (the inertia wheel in Fig. 5-4). We had derived the state equations for this system and arrived at the **A** matrix

$$\mathbf{A} = \begin{bmatrix} 0 & 1 \\ 0 & 0 \end{bmatrix}$$

As we can write **A** as

$$\mathbf{A} = \begin{bmatrix} \lambda & 1 \\ 0 & \lambda \end{bmatrix}$$

we draw the following conclusions:

1. The system is characterized by a double eigenvalue $\lambda_1 = \lambda_2 = 0$.
2. The **A** matrix is already expressed as a Jordan form.
3. Because of this, the two state variables already chosen (position and velocity) actually represent the two natural modes in this system. [For this reason, we should symbolize them with *starred* symbols, but for simplicity, let us continue with the symbols we already used in Eq. (5-7)].

† Diagonalization is guaranteed only if **A** is *symmetric*.

The state equations read

$$\dot{x}_1 = x_2$$

$$\dot{x}_2 = u$$

and the question is now whether it is possible to find a $u(\tau)$ in the interval $0 < \tau < t_f$ that will transfer *both* x_1 and x_2 between specified states. We note that the velocity coordinate x_2 is decoupled from x_1, and we therefore certainly can effect any velocity transfer that we wish.

The situation is more doubtful with respect to the position coordinate x_1, *which does not explicitly depend upon the control force but is coupled with x_2.*

Actually, it is possible to find a control force that will *simultaneously* meet the end requirements imposed upon both state variables. Indeed, an infinite number of solutions exists. We shall demonstrate the simplest solution as applied to our inertia wheel. To that end, let us first impose the following boundary conditions on x_1 and x_2:

$$\mathbf{x}(0) = \begin{bmatrix} 0 \\ 0 \end{bmatrix} \qquad \mathbf{x}(t_f) = \begin{bmatrix} -1 \\ +1 \end{bmatrix}$$

We shall further assume a control interval t_f of 1-sec duration. The control strategy (= torque) that we shall use is shown in Fig. 5-10c and consists of two constant segments, $-a$ and b, with one switching at $t = t_s$. Thus, the velocity trajectory will consist of two straight-line segments, and the position trajectory of two parabolic sections. We thus have three free parameters, a, b, and t_s, which we can vary, and we shall prove that a proper choice of these parameters results in the desired state transfer.

First, we determine the requirement for proper velocity transfer. As the graph in Fig. 5-10b is the integral of the one in Fig. 5-10c, we obtain directly

$$x_2(1) = 1 = -at_s + b(1 - t_s)$$

Therefore,

$$b = \frac{1 + at_s}{1 - t_s} \tag{5-57}$$

We now have reduced the number of free parameters to two, a and t_s. They must be chosen so that the position trajectory ends up in -1. We note that this trajectory must be the integral of the one in Fig. 5-10b, and by simple analysis, this leads to the equation

$$x_1(1) = -1 = \tfrac{1}{2} - (1 + a)\frac{t_s}{2} \tag{5-58}$$

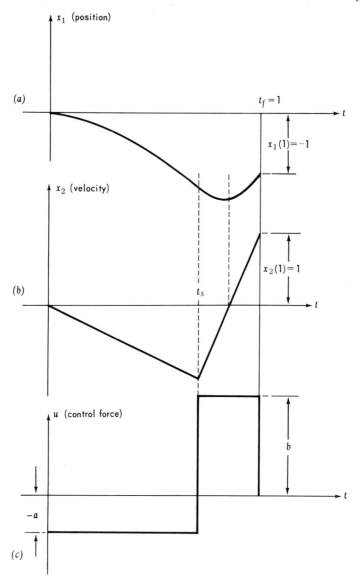

Fig. 5-10   A possible control strategy for inertia wheel in Fig. 5-4.

which can be written

$$t_s = \frac{3}{1 + a} \tag{5-59}$$

We now have reduced the choice of free parameters to one only.   We have still a partly free choice of a.   Only one restriction must be imposed upon this parameter—*it must be large enough so that t_s, that is, the switching moment, will lie within the control interval.*

For example, we could choose the control strategy characterized by the set of parameters

$$a = 3$$

$$t_s = \frac{3}{1+3} = 0.75$$

$$b = \frac{1 + 3 \times 0.75}{1 - 0.75} = 13.0$$

It is interesting to note that we can find an infinite number of possible control strategies of the piecewise linear type shown in Fig. 5-10c.

5-8 SUMMARY

The concepts of controllability and observability are fundamental in the theory of control. We demonstrated these concepts with a number of physical systems and found that they have a close relation to the natural-mode interpretation of a linear system. A simple and, from a physical viewpoint, attractive method was presented by means of which we can test by inspection whether a system is controllable and/or observable.

The test procedure is somewhat complicated in those cases which are characterized by multiple eigenvalues because the natural modes may then be coupled with each other. We exemplified how such situations can be handled.

We limited our discussion to linear systems for the simple reason that controllability and observability of nonlinear systems are a practically unknown field.

It is important to realize that in controllability studies, we always tacitly assume that the control-force vector **u** is *unbounded.* If we therefore have confirmed that a system is controllable, *in theory* we can transfer the system between arbitrarily specified states in *as short a time as we please.*

Clearly, *in practice* we must obey physical constraints on the control-force components (and also on the state variables, of course).

This then means that if we specify the control interval t_f, we can expect to find limitations on those states to which our system can be transferred. We can only transfer the states to the *reachable set.* More will be said about this in Chap. 11, in connection with time-optimal systems.

Exercises

5-1 The electrical network depicted in Fig. 5-11 has, for the parameter values given in the figure, an impedance, as felt by the source *u*, which is purely resistive *for all frequencies.* Is the system controllable?

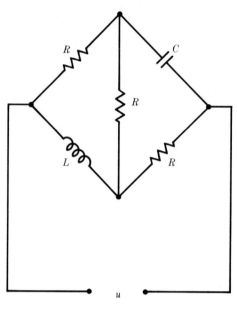

$$R = L = C = 1$$

Fig. 5-11   Noncontrollable electric circuit.

5-2 Study the controllability of the two systems in Fig. 2-3.   Neglect the mass of the carriage as it does not have any important effect.

What would happen in system *a* if you chose nonidentical brooms?

5-3 Consider the two networks depicted in Fig. 5-12*a* and *b*.   As shown in the text they are both controllable individually.   With the assigned parameter values the networks have the transfer functions given in the figure.

If we cascade the networks as shown in Fig. 5-12*c* a second-order plant is obtained.

If an isolation amplifier (having unity gain, infinite input, and zero output impedance) is placed between the networks, the overall transfer function is simply obtained by multiplication of the individual transfer functions.   In the process the zero of network *a* will cancel the pole of network *b*.   Demonstrate that this, in effect, means that the compound network is noncontrollable. Choose capacitor voltages as state variables!

5-4 Consider the system depicted in Fig. 5-9.   How would you choose the initial state $\mathbf{x}(0)$ for this system if you wished that only the natural mode associated with the eigenvalue $-1/k$ would be present in the response?

The system is assumed uncontrolled; that is, $u = 0$.   Also limit the study to the case $k \neq 1$.

5-5 By using the test method described in the text, prove that the system depicted in Fig. 3-9 is controllable.   For simplicity, use the following simple numerical data:

Sectional area: 1 m² (same for both vessels)
Valve resistance: 100 sec/m²

Then solve the following paradox: We specify that the state be transferred between

$$\mathbf{x}_0 = \begin{bmatrix} 1 \\ 1 \end{bmatrix} \quad \text{and} \quad \mathbf{x}_f = \begin{bmatrix} 0 \\ 0 \end{bmatrix}$$

in some time interval t_f.   Quite clearly, this state transfer is impossible to achieve.   Why?   This fact seems to contradict our earlier findings in respect to controllability.   Explain!

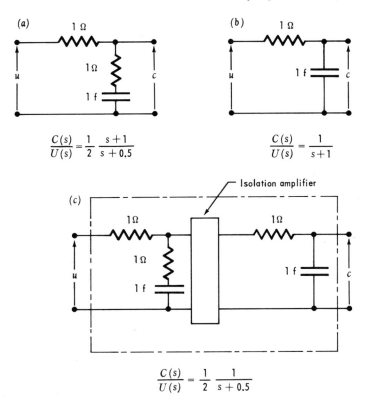

$$\frac{C(s)}{U(s)} = \frac{1}{2}\frac{s+1}{s+0.5}$$

$$\frac{C(s)}{U(s)} = \frac{1}{s+1}$$

$$\frac{C(s)}{U(s)} = \frac{1}{2}\frac{1}{s+0.5}$$

Fig. 5-12   Systems individually controllable may lose controllability when interconnected.

5-6 Interconnect the two networks in Fig. 5-12 *without using the isolation amplifier.*

   a Find the two natural modes for the two-loop circuit thus obtained by using the two separate methods presented in the text.

   b Consider for a moment the circuit non-controlled, i.e. put $u = 0$. If arbitrary initial charges are assigned to the two capacitors the subsequent transients will, in general, contain contributions from both natural modes. Determine how you should assign these charges in order to filter out one or the other of the modes. (The problem makes an interesting demonstration example on an analog computer.)

   c It is possible to find a control force u that will excite a response containing only one of the two natural modes. Consider for simplicity the circuit initially inert. (You should give this question considerable thought.)

5-7 If all friction forces are neglected the dynamics of the spring-mass system in Fig. 3-2a will be governed by the differential equation

$$\ddot{y} = \frac{k}{m}y = 0$$

   The reader is familiar with the fact that the solution of this differential equation reveals that the mass will perform undamped oscillations of frequency $\omega = \sqrt{\frac{k}{m}}$ rad/sec. Let us now interpret the dynamics of this system in terms of natural modes. We define first a state vector

$$\mathbf{x} = \begin{bmatrix} x_1 \\ x_2 \end{bmatrix} \triangleq \begin{bmatrix} y \\ \dot{y} \end{bmatrix}$$

and obtain then the system state model

$$\begin{bmatrix} \dot{x}_1 \\ \dot{x}_2 \end{bmatrix} = \begin{bmatrix} 0 & 1 \\ -\omega^2 & 0 \end{bmatrix} \begin{bmatrix} x_1 \\ x_2 \end{bmatrix}$$

By using equation (4-32) we obtain next the complex eigenvalues

$$\lambda_1 = j\omega \qquad \lambda_2 = -j\omega$$

and from Eq. (5-21) the likewise complex eigenvectors

$$\hat{\mathbf{e}}_1 = \frac{1}{1 - \omega^2} \begin{bmatrix} 1 \\ j\omega \end{bmatrix} \qquad \hat{\mathbf{e}}_2 = \frac{1}{1 - \omega^2} \begin{bmatrix} 1 \\ -j\omega \end{bmatrix}$$

In accordance with (5-23) we may thus write the **x**-solution in terms of the natural modes:

$$\begin{bmatrix} x_1 \\ x_2 \end{bmatrix} = \frac{\alpha 1}{1 - \omega^2} \begin{bmatrix} 1 \\ j\omega \end{bmatrix} e^{j\omega t} + \frac{\alpha_2}{1 - \omega^2} \begin{bmatrix} 1 \\ -j\omega \end{bmatrix} e^{-j\omega t}$$

a Prove that the scalar coefficients α_1 and α_2 must by necessity be *conjugate complex* numbers the real part of which depends upon the initially specified position $x_1(0)$, and the imaginary part upon the initial velocity $x_2(0)$. *Hint:* Remember that $\mathbf{x}(t)$ must be a *real* function.
   b Find the **x**-solution in terms of $x_1(0)$ and $x_2(0)$.
   c Why would it be physically impossible to "filter out" one natural mode in this case?
   d Extend those discussions to the system in Fig. 3-2b. Prove in particular that the four eigenvalues are of the form

$$\left.\begin{array}{c} \lambda_1 \\ \lambda_2 \end{array}\right\} = \pm j\omega_1 \qquad \left.\begin{array}{c} \lambda_3 \\ \lambda_4 \end{array}\right\} = \pm j\omega_2$$

Show also that by proper choice of initial conditions we now can filter out the natural modes *in pairs*, i.e. the response will contain only one of the two frequencies ω_1 and ω_2. Demonstrate this fact on an analog computer.

References

1. R. E. Kalman, On the General Theory of Control Systems, *Proc. Intern. Congr. Auto. Control,* 1st, London, **1**: 481–492 (1961).
2. R. E. Kalman, Contributions to the Theory of Optimal Control, *Bol. Soc. Mat. Mex.,* 102–119 (1960).
3. R. E. Kalman, Mathematical Description of Linear Dynamical Systems, *J. Control (SIAM),* ser. A, **1**(2): 152–192 (1963).
4. E. G. Gilbert, Controllability and Observability in Multivariable Control Systems, *ibid.,* 128–151.
5. R. E. Kalman, Y. C. Ho, and K. S. Narendra, Controllability of Linear Dynamical Systems, *Contrib. Differential Equations,* **1**: 189–213 (1961).
6. R. Bellman, "Introduction to Matrix Analysis," McGraw-Hill Book Company, New York, 1960.
7. D. G. Luenberger, Determining the State of a Linear System with Observers of Low Dynamic Order, Institute in Engineering Economic Systems CCS-1, Stanford University.

chapter 6

LINEAR SERVOMECHANISMS— THE ANALYSIS PROBLEM

6-1 DEFINITION

This chapter and the next will be devoted to the study of a class of control systems of great practical and historical significance—the so-called *servomechanisms*, or *servos*, for short. As we pointed out in the introductory chapter, the early investigations of the dynamics of "slaving" mechanisms constituted the beginning of control engineering. Since coming of age, the theory of servomechanisms has not stagnated but has, in fact, in recent years been subject to a renewed interest spurred by the demand for high-precision servos for aerospace applications. This interest has been directed mainly toward nonlinear servo design. We shall in this chapter discuss the most useful analysis methods available for the study of *linear* servomechanisms.

By "analysis," we shall mean the problem of investigating a *given* system. In other words, system structure and parameters are known, and we wish to study the performance of this system under specified conditions. In the next chapter, we shall discuss the synthesis problem. By "synthesis," we shall mean the problem of finding a system that will meet a certain set of performance specifications (PS). We feel that the powerful *root-locus technique* is basically a synthesis rather than an analysis tool, and consequently, we have postponed discussion of it until the next chapter.

Scores of books on servomechanisms have been published since World War II, and the reader is in particular urged to consult the classic works by James, Nichols, and Phillips[1] and Truxal[2] for a more detailed exposition of linear servo theory than can be afforded here.

Here, and in the chapters to follow, we shall attempt to classify control systems on the basis of the specific control objectives for which they are designed. In the introductory chapter, we stated that the basic problem in control engineering is to determine an input **u** that imparts upon the output **c** a certain desired behavior.

A control system is referred to as a servo if the output $c(t)$ *is designed to follow as closely as possible a given reference signal* $r(t)$.

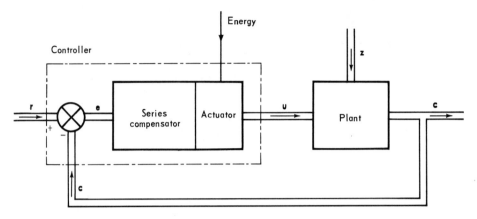

Fig. 6-1   Typical servo structure with series compensation.

In the special case where the reference signal **r**(*t*) is *constant*, we talk about a *regulator* rather than a servo.

For example, based on this definition, the broom balancer discussed in Chap. 2 is actually a regulator. The control objective was, as the reader may remember, to keep the output φ as close as possible to the vertical reference.

We define an *error vector*

$$\mathbf{e}(t) \triangleq \mathbf{r}(t) - \mathbf{c}(t) \tag{6-1}$$

and are then able to judge the quality of the servo by its ability to minimize in some sense this error vector. We shall postpone until the next chapter a more detailed discussion of those criteria most frequently used in judging servo performance.

The vast majority of linear servomechanism designs culminate in one or the other of the two feedback structures depicted in Figs. 6-1 and 6-2. As will be demonstrated in this and the next chapter, both of these structures exhibit the classical advantages of feedback:

1. Good static accuracy
2. Reduced sensitivity to disturbances, internal as well as external
3. Shortened response time

The controller portions of the overall systems incorporate:

1. The *actuator*, which supplies the control forces **u**. This is the "brute-force" portion of the controller.
2. The *comparator-compensator*, which constitutes the "brain" of the system.

The actuator requires external power for its operation and may, in some instances, be an inseparable part of the plant itself. The block diagrams therefore are not intended to show the true physical division between the different parts of the system but rather the functional division.

The comparator-compensator portion of the controller usually consists of *passive* networks, the main functions of which are to shape the dynamics of the signals before they enter the actuator portion. Quite often, it is necessary to include *active* networks (integrators, for instance) in the compensator design. Depending upon the placement of these networks, we distinguish between *series* (or *cascade*) and *feedback* compensation.

As we have already pointed out, our attention will be directed, in this and the next chapter, toward servos with *linear* controllers only. Furthermore, most of the material in these two chapters will concern *single-input–single-output* (SISO) systems only. Here are the reasons:

1. Most systems encountered in real life are of this type.
2. A great amount of knowledge exists for SISO systems. Our most useful synthesis methods are applicable only to servos in this category.

In formulating the mathematical models for linear servomechanisms, we could conceivably use either the *state-variable* or the *input-output* (transfer-function) method outlined in Chap. 4. For both historical and practical reasons, the latter method *completely* dominates the scene. Our most powerful synthesis method, the root-locus technique, is particularly well suited for system description in terms of transfer functions.

In spite of this, we shall proceed with a demonstration of *both* techniques as applied to system structures of the basic types shown in Figs. 6-1 and 6-2.

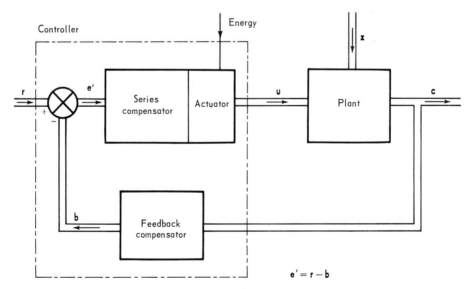

$$e' = r - b$$

Fig. 6-2 Typical servo structure with series and/or feedback compensation.

We feel that this is not a waste of time but rather serves to widen our horizons, and furthermore, as was pointed out in the previous chapter, the state-variable method on occasion gives a more *complete* description of the system dynamics than does the transfer-function method.

6-2 STATE-VARIABLE DESCRIPTION OF SERVOMECHANISMS

In demonstrating this approach, we shall start out with two equations that fully characterize the plant:

$$\dot{x} = Ax + Bu$$
$$c = Cx \tag{6-2}$$

(We have not included any disturbance input z, as this would not add any appreciable value to our demonstration.)

These equations may be said to represent the *open-loop* description of the system. The simplest assumption† we can make about the controller is that it produces a set of control forces that are proportional to the error in a vector sense, that is,

$$u = K_1 e \tag{6-3}$$

K_1 is an $m \times p$ constant matrix. We shall refer to this control strategy as *proportional control*.

By using the relationship (6-1), we now can eliminate u and e, and after some manipulation, we obtain the following set of equations describing the *closed-loop* dynamics of the overall system:

$$\dot{x} = (A - BK_1 C)x + BK_1 r$$
$$c = Cx \tag{6-4}$$

We note that these equations are of the same form as the open-loop equations (6-2). The closed-loop system is characterized by the new *closed-loop system and distribution matrices*

$$A_c \overset{\Delta}{=} A - BK_1 C$$

and

$$\tag{6-5}$$

$$B_c \overset{\Delta}{=} BK_1$$

The reference input r plays the same role in the closed-loop system as does u in the open-loop configuration.

---

† This assumption is, of course, not a prerequisite for using state models. We use it for reasons of simplicity only.

If, in particular, the reference input is zero, that is, $\mathbf{r} = \mathbf{0}$, then the system of Eqs. (6-4) reduces to

$$\dot{\mathbf{x}} = \mathbf{A}_c\mathbf{x}$$
$$\mathbf{c} = \mathbf{C}\mathbf{x} \tag{6-6}$$

For example, Eqs. (2-9) fall within this category. (See also Exercise 4–10.)

Example 6-1

Consider the servomechanism sketched in Fig. 6-3. The position coordinate φ of an inertia load I (a radar antenna, for instance) can be controlled, via a gear train, by a d-c motor. The torque of the motor can be varied in both magnitude and direction by means of the control voltage u obtained from the output of an amplifier feeding directly into the motor field.

We may wish to slave either the output position φ (*target* antenna) or the velocity $\dot{\varphi}$ (*scanning* antenna) to some desired reference. In the latter case, we talk about a *velocity servo*. In Fig. 6-3 is shown how both of these objectives can be met. To obtain a position servo, we put the switch S in position B and compare the reference voltage r with the pick-off voltage from the potentiometer PM. A velocity servo is obtained if, instead, we use the voltage from the *tachometer generator TM* for comparison.† In both cases, we form an error voltage, which

† A tachometer generator outputs a voltage proportional to its speed.

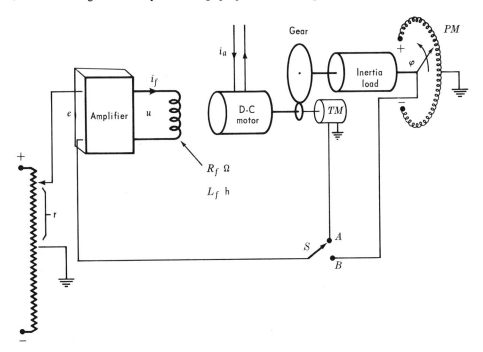

Fig. 6-3 Velocity or position control of inertia load.

is fed directly into the amplifier. If this amplifier has a constant gain K_1, we then in effect have *proportional control*.

Unfortunately, as will be shown later in this chapter, the proposed position servo does not work because of instability, and therefore we limit our immediate attention to the velocity servo. We first construct the open-loop mathematical model.

We shall assume that the armature current i_a is kept constant by external means; the torque of the motor will then be proportional to the field current i_f (assuming linear magnetic characteristics). Furthermore, if we neglect all mechanical damping torques (windage plus friction), the motor torque will be proportional to the acceleration; that is,

$$i_f \sim \ddot{\varphi} \tag{6-7}$$

The proportional constant in (6-7) must be a function of the motor characteristics, gear ratio, and moment of inertia. We lump all these data into one constant K_2 and obtain

$$K_2 i_f = \ddot{\varphi} \tag{6-8}$$

For the field circuit, we obtain directly

$$u = R_f i_f + L_f \dot{i}_f \tag{6-9}$$

A convenient choice of state vector is

$$\mathbf{x} = \begin{bmatrix} x_1 \\ x_2 \\ x_3 \end{bmatrix} \overset{\Delta}{=} \begin{bmatrix} i_f \\ \varphi \\ \dot{\varphi} \end{bmatrix} \tag{6-10}$$

In terms of this state vector, the *open-loop* model is obtained directly from Eqs. (6-8) and (6-9), which yield

$$\begin{bmatrix} \dot{x}_1 \\ \dot{x}_2 \\ \dot{x}_3 \end{bmatrix} = \begin{bmatrix} -\dfrac{R_f}{L_f} & 0 & 0 \\ 0 & 0 & 1 \\ K_2 & 0 & 0 \end{bmatrix} \begin{bmatrix} x_1 \\ x_2 \\ x_3 \end{bmatrix} + \begin{bmatrix} \dfrac{1}{L_f} \\ 0 \\ 0 \end{bmatrix} u \tag{6-11}$$

The antenna velocity $\dot{\varphi}$ is our output. As the tachometer voltage is proportional to $\dot{\varphi}$ and as we are actually comparing this *voltage* (not $\dot{\varphi}$) with the reference input r, we find it more convenient actually to use this voltage directly as our output:

$$c \overset{\Delta}{=} K_3 \dot{\varphi} = [0 \quad 0 \quad K_3]\mathbf{x} \tag{6-12}$$

The constant K_3 has the dimension volts per radians per second and is a function of both tachometer characteristics and gear ratio.

From the last equation, we note that

$$\mathbf{C} = [0 \quad 0 \quad K_3] \tag{6-13}$$

We then turn our attention to the *closed-loop* model. In accordance with Eq. (6-5), we first form the $\mathbf{BK_1C}$ matrix

$$\mathbf{BK_1C} = \begin{bmatrix} \dfrac{1}{L_f} \\ 0 \\ 0 \end{bmatrix} K_1 [0 \quad 0 \quad K_3] = \begin{bmatrix} 0 & 0 & \dfrac{K_1K_3}{L_f} \\ 0 & 0 & 0 \\ 0 & 0 & 0 \end{bmatrix}$$

Therefore,

$$\mathbf{A_c} = \mathbf{A} - \mathbf{BK_1}\,\mathbf{C} = \begin{bmatrix} -\dfrac{R_f}{L_f} & 0 & -\dfrac{K_1K_3}{L_f} \\ 0 & 0 & 1 \\ K_2 & 0 & 0 \end{bmatrix} \tag{6-14}$$

We then compute the closed-loop distribution matrix

$$\mathbf{B_c} = \mathbf{BK_1} = \begin{bmatrix} \dfrac{K_1}{L_f} \\ 0 \\ 0 \end{bmatrix} \tag{6-15}$$

The closed-loop dynamics therefore is obtained from the following system of equations:

$$\begin{bmatrix} \dot{x}_1 \\ \dot{x}_2 \\ \dot{x}_3 \end{bmatrix} = \begin{bmatrix} -\dfrac{R_f}{L_f} & 0 & -\dfrac{K_1K_3}{L_f} \\ 0 & 0 & 1 \\ K_2 & 0 & 0 \end{bmatrix} \begin{bmatrix} x_1 \\ x_2 \\ x_3 \end{bmatrix} + \begin{bmatrix} \dfrac{K_1}{L_f} \\ 0 \\ 0 \end{bmatrix} r \tag{6-16}$$

By employing the analysis techniques presented in Chap. 4, we are now able to explore fully the dynamic characteristics of the system. For instance, we can study the stability of the velocity servo by finding the three eigenvalues from the equation

$$|s\mathbf{I} - \mathbf{A_c}| = 0 \tag{6-17}$$

Assuming that the system is stable, we then can study the response $\mathbf{x}$ to some input r. Of course, we are particularly interested in how well the component x_3 follows r. It is customary in servo analysis to apply certain standard input functions (test inputs) and record the corresponding responses (see Sec. 6-5) in order to study the follow-up characteristics.

If the system is a speed *regulator* rather than a *servo*, that is, $r = $ const, we may wish to know how well the system returns to its set point from some initial offset. (The reader may remember that this was indeed the method we employed in judging the efficiency of the broom balancer in Chap. 2.)

From a computational point of view, the chosen system is particularly simple. We note that the second column of the A_c matrix is zero, which means that both x_1 and x_3 are decoupled from x_2. This simplifies considerably the computation of the eigenvalues, as we may *partition* the three-dimensional system into the following two subsystems, the first of which is completely decoupled from the second:

$$\begin{bmatrix} \dot{x}_1 \\ \dot{x}_3 \end{bmatrix} = \begin{bmatrix} -\dfrac{R_f}{L_f} & -\dfrac{K_1 K_3}{L_f} \\ K_2 & 0 \end{bmatrix} \begin{bmatrix} x_1 \\ x_3 \end{bmatrix} + \begin{bmatrix} \dfrac{K_1}{L_f} \\ 0 \end{bmatrix} r \tag{6-18}$$

$$\dot{x}_2 = x_3 \tag{6-19}$$

The latter subsystem has the eigenvalue

$$\lambda_2 = 0 \tag{6-20}$$

The eigenvalues λ_1 and λ_3 of the first subsystem are obtained from

$$\begin{vmatrix} s + \dfrac{R_f}{L_f} & \dfrac{K_1 K_3}{L_f} \\ -K_2 & s \end{vmatrix} = 0$$

which yields

$$\left.\begin{matrix} \lambda_1 \\ \lambda_3 \end{matrix}\right\} = -\frac{R_f}{2L_f} \pm \sqrt{\frac{R_f^2}{4L_f^2} - \frac{K_1 K_2 K_3}{L_f}} \tag{6-21}$$

These eigenvalues, located in the left half of the s plane, are most important as they govern the dynamics of x_3, that is, the velocity of the servo. We note, for instance, that the state variables x_1 and x_3 (field current and velocity) making up the first subsystem are stable, whereas x_2 (position) is inherently unstable since x_2 does not tend to zero from an arbitrary initial offset, something that both x_1 and x_3 would do (assuming $r = 0$, of course).†

Equation (6-21) also gives additional valuable hints to the designer about this control system. Of all the five parameters which determine the magnitudes of the eigenvalues, only K_1, the amplifier gain, is easily adjusted. We note that by varying K_1 throughout the range $0 \rightarrow \infty$, we can most significantly affect the values of λ_1 and λ_3 and thereby the type of response. Very low gain results in eigenvalues which are negative and real, located in the s plane, as shown in

---

† The reader should confirm these findings with the physics. Why is x_2 unstable?

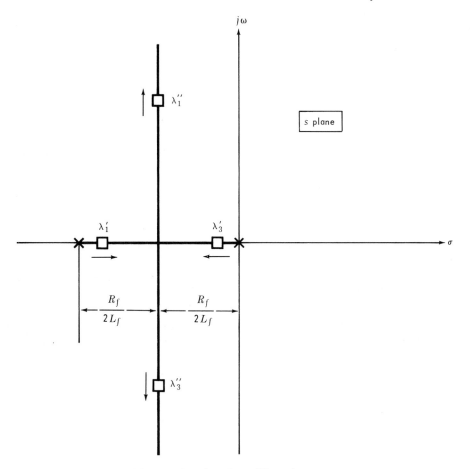

Fig. 6-4   Eigenvalue position as a function of amplifier gain.

Fig. 6-4 (marked λ_1' and λ_3').   The corresponding response is overdamped and sluggish (due to the term $e^{\lambda_3 t}$).   By increasing the gain, the eigenvalues move toward each other and "collide" at the point

$$s = -\frac{R_f}{2L_f}$$

which happens when the gain has such a value that the radical vanishes, that is, when

$$K_1 = \frac{R_f{}^2}{4L_f K_2 K_3}$$

We shall refer to this gain value as the *critical gain* $K_{1\mathrm{cr}}$.

   If the gain is increased still further, the eigenvalues turn conjugate complex (λ_1'' and λ_3'' in the figure) and move in opposite directions along the line

$$s = -\frac{R_f}{2L_f} \pm j\omega$$

The response turns more "vigorous" but also oscillatory, with increasing frequency but constant damping coefficient. Figure 6-5 shows the velocity response to a reference step input. Two plots corresponding to two different K_1 values are shown. The response plots correspond approximately to the two eigenvalue locations shown in Fig. 6-4. (The reader may compare the effects of changing gain in this example with those of the broom-balancing system in Chap. 2.)

   The two eigenvalues λ_1 and λ_3 in this example will move, for increasing gain, along the boldface lines in Fig. 6-4, referred to as *closed-loop root loci* (*locus* in singular). Such loci evidently give the system designer very valuable, qualitative information regarding the closed-loop system response. Construction of root loci is actually a very popular and important design method that will be discussed further in the next chapter.

   Before we leave this example, we wish to point out one additional important piece of information that we can easily obtain from the closed-loop differential equation (6-18). For a constant reference input $r = r^0$, it would be of interest

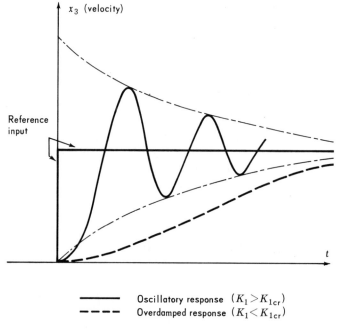

Fig. 6-5 Response as a function of loop gain.

to know the steady-state output $c = c^0$. This gives us a good idea of the *static follow-up capability* of the servo. From Eq. (6-18), we get

$$
\begin{bmatrix} 0 \\ 0 \end{bmatrix} = \begin{bmatrix} -\dfrac{R_f}{L_f} & -\dfrac{K_1 K_3}{L_f} \\[2ex] K_2 & 0 \end{bmatrix} \begin{bmatrix} x_1^{\,0} \\[1ex] x_3^{\,0} \end{bmatrix} + \begin{bmatrix} \dfrac{K_1}{L_f} \\[1ex] 0 \end{bmatrix} r^0
$$

Therefore,

$$
x_1^{\,0} = 0
$$

$$
x_3^{\,0} = \frac{r^0}{K_3}
$$

From (6-12), we thus get

$$
c^0 = K_3 \frac{r^0}{K_3} = r^0
$$

Our servo gives perfect static follow-up.

This result may seem somewhat strange at first glance. Perfect follow-up means zero steady-state error, which means zero field current ($x_1^{\,0} = 0$) and, therefore, zero motor torque. However, the reader is reminded that we assumed zero windage and friction losses for the moving parts, and therefore no torque is needed to maintain constant velocity.

6-3 TRANSFER-FUNCTION DESCRIPTION OF LINEAR SERVOS

The application of state-variable techniques to the theory of servo mechanisms is of relatively recent origin. It has been prompted by dire necessity, as the control engineers more and more frequently resort to nonlinear system designs in order to meet increasingly stringent performance specifications. For instance, as will be shown in later chapters, most optimum controllers are inherently nonlinear.

The "classic" theory of servomechanisms was concerned exclusively with linear systems, and transfer-function presentation became standard. The historic reason for this probably was that many of the early studies were performed by electrical engineers who already had adopted transfer-function analysis methods in their work with communication networks. Also, the transfer-function method has certain advantages over the state-variable method.

We shall now proceed to present the linear *p*-dimensional servo by means of transfer-function description. For our demonstration purposes, we shall choose the structure shown in Fig. 6-2, as it is more general than the one in Fig. 6-1.

Using the symbols introduced in Fig. 6-2 and the transfer matrices already introduced in Chap. 4, we obtain directly the following set of transform equations:

$$\mathbf{E}'(s) = \mathbf{R}(s) - \mathbf{B}(s)$$
$$\mathbf{B}(s) = \mathbf{H}(s)\mathbf{C}(s)$$
$$\mathbf{U}(s) = \mathbf{G}_s(s)\mathbf{E}'(s) \tag{6-22}$$
$$\mathbf{X}(s) = \mathbf{T}_2(s)\mathbf{U}(s) + \mathbf{FZ}(s)$$
$$\mathbf{C}(s) = \mathbf{CX}(s)$$

We introduced the matrices $\mathbf{H}(s)$ and $\mathbf{G}_s(s)$, describing, respectively, the transfer characteristics of the feedback compensators and the series portion of the controller. The set of Eqs. (6-22) becomes considerably more meaningful if tied together to the block diagram in Fig. 6-6. If we leave out the disturbance-input vector $\mathbf{Z}(s)$, the diagram reduces to the one shown in Fig. 6-7. Here, for brevity, we have introduced the plant-transfer matrix $\mathbf{G}_p(s)$ defined in Eq. (4-38), which directly relates the output $\mathbf{C}(s)$ with the control force $\mathbf{U}(s)$. We can achieve still greater simplicity by introducing the *open-loop transfer matrix*

$$\mathbf{G}(s) \overset{\Delta}{=} \mathbf{G}_p(s)\mathbf{G}_s(s) \tag{6-23}$$

$\mathbf{G}(s)$ relates the output vector $\mathbf{C}(s)$ directly with the "error" vector $\mathbf{E}'(s)$. The diagram reduces now to the one in Fig. 6-8.

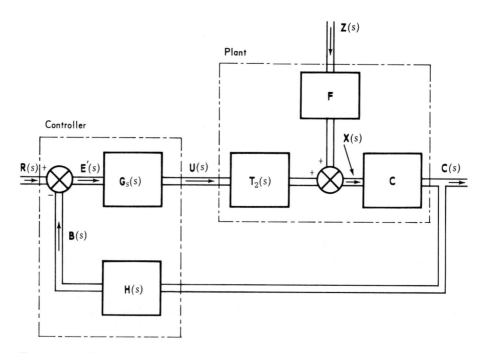

Fig. 6-6　Transfer-matrix description of system in Fig. 6-2.

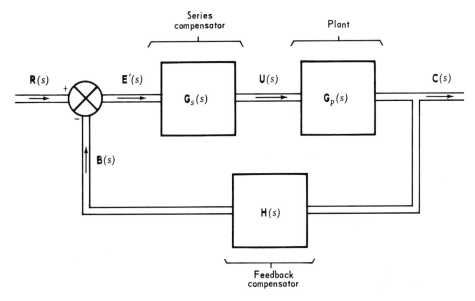

Fig. 6-7 Reduction of block diagram in Fig. 6-6.

If the system were of the *unity-feedback type,* i.e., if the feedback-transfer matrix $\mathbf{H}(s)$ equaled $\mathbf{I}$, then we finally would obtain the simple block diagram of Fig. 6-9.

For the block diagram of Fig. 6-8, we have

$$\mathbf{C}(s) = \mathbf{G}(s)[\mathbf{R}(s) - \mathbf{B}(s)] = \mathbf{G}(s)[\mathbf{R}(s) - \mathbf{H}(s)\mathbf{C}(s)]$$

which we may write

$$[\mathbf{I} + \mathbf{G}(s)\mathbf{H}(s)]\mathbf{C}(s) = \mathbf{G}(s)\mathbf{R}(s)$$

Solving for $\mathbf{C}(s)$ yields

$$\mathbf{C}(s) = [\mathbf{I} + \mathbf{G}(s)\mathbf{H}(s)]^{-1}\mathbf{G}(s)\mathbf{R}(s) \qquad (6\text{-}24)$$

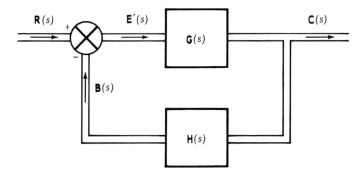

Fig. 6-8 Further reduction of block diagram in Fig. 6-7.

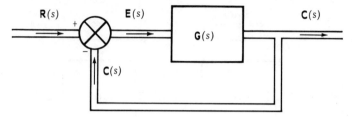

Fig. 6-9   Unity-feedback servo.

At this juncture, we shall define the *closed-loop transfer matrix*

$$\mathbf{G}_c(s) \overset{\Delta}{=} [\mathbf{I} + \mathbf{G}(s)\mathbf{H}(s)]^{-1}\mathbf{G}(s) \tag{6-25}$$

By means of this matrix, we can express directly the output $\mathbf{C}(s)$ in terms of the reference input $\mathbf{R}(s)$

$$\mathbf{C}(s) = \mathbf{G}_c(s)\mathbf{R}(s) \tag{6-26}$$

The whole closed-loop structure thus reduces to the single block of Fig. 6-10.

We should take note of the following features in connection with these block-diagram reductions:

1. The order of the factors is very important in the matrix products.
2. In the successive reductions, we lose information about the internal signal structure. The end product, Fig. 6-10, is very simple, but it provides information only about the output signal.

In the SISO case, that is, $p = 1$, the matrices $\mathbf{G}(s)$, $\mathbf{H}(s)$, and $\mathbf{G}_c(s)$ reduce to *scalars* $G(s)$, $H(s)$, and $G_c(s)$, and the vector equation (6-24) reduces to the *scalar* equation

$$C(s) = \frac{G(s)}{1 + G(s)H(s)} R(s) \tag{6-27}$$

We shall demonstrate the transfer-function method by two examples. In the first example, we shall choose a two-input–two-output system, and in the second example, we shall return to the velocity servo that we have already treated from a state-variable point of view.

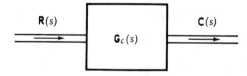

Fig. 6-10   Final reduction of servo block diagram.

Example 6-2

In this example, we shall construct a model for the regulator proposed in Exercise 2-2. The system was intended as an improved version of the broom balancer. Not only do we wish to keep the broom angle at $\varphi = 0$, but also we desire that the carriage position y be kept equal to some reference value, which here, for simplicity, we shall assume to be $y = 0$.

We had proposed a proportional-control strategy [Eq. (2-31)] which we restate for easy reference:

$$u = k_1\varphi + k_2 y \tag{6-28}$$

(It should be pointed out that there is no guarantee that this is a workable choice, but we are not at present so concerned about this possibility.)

Equation (6-28) determines the transfer matrix $\mathbf{G}_s(s)$. For the description of the plant $\mathbf{G}_p(s)$, we need to refer to Eqs. (2-7), which, as the reader will remember represented the linearized model of the broom-carriage assembly. In order not to clutter up our expressions unnecessarily, we shall make use in the following analysis of the simple numerical values:

$$m = M = L = 1$$
$$g = 9.81 \text{ m/sec}^2 \approx 10 \qquad I = \tfrac{1}{3}mL^2 = \tfrac{1}{3}$$

By Laplace transformation of Eqs. (2-7) and (6-28), we obtain

$$\tfrac{4}{3}s^2\Phi(s) + s^2 Y(s) - 10\Phi(s) = 0$$
$$s^2\Phi(s) + 2s^2 Y(s) = U(s) \tag{6-29}$$
$$U(s) = k_1\Phi(s) + k_2 Y(s)$$

The first two equations yield the relationships between the input to and the output from the plant:

$$\Phi(s) = \frac{3}{60 - 5s^2} U(s)$$

$$Y(s) = \frac{30 - 4s^2}{s^2(60 - 5s^2)} U(s)$$

or, in matrix form,

$$\mathbf{C}(s) \triangleq \begin{bmatrix} \Phi(s) \\ Y(s) \end{bmatrix} = \begin{bmatrix} \dfrac{3}{60 - 5s^2} \\[2ex] \dfrac{30 - 4s^2}{s^2(60 - 5s^2)} \end{bmatrix} U(s) \tag{6-30}$$

Therefore,

$$\mathbf{G}_p(s) = \begin{bmatrix} \dfrac{3}{60 - 5s^2} \\[2ex] \dfrac{30 - 4s^2}{s^2(60 - 5s^2)} \end{bmatrix} \tag{6-31}$$

From the third of Eqs. (6-29), we can obtain the transfer matrix $\mathbf{G}_s(s)$:

$$U(s) = k_1 \Phi(s) + k_2 Y(s) = [k_1 \quad k_2] \begin{bmatrix} \Phi(s) \\ Y(s) \end{bmatrix} \tag{6-32}$$

As we note that

$$\mathbf{E}(s) = \mathbf{R}(s) - \mathbf{C}(s)$$

and as $\mathbf{R}(s) = \mathbf{O}$, we get

$$\mathbf{E}(s) = -\mathbf{C}(s) = \begin{bmatrix} -\Phi(s) \\ -Y(s) \end{bmatrix}$$

Therefore, Eq. (6-32) yields

$$U(s) = [-k_1 \quad -k_2] \begin{bmatrix} -\Phi(s) \\ -Y(s) \end{bmatrix} = [-k_1 \quad -k_2]\mathbf{E}(s) \tag{6-33}$$

Consequently,

$$\mathbf{G}_s(s) = [-k_1 \quad -k_2] \tag{6-34}$$

We now can assemble the block diagram in Fig. 6-11. Note that, in this particular case, the control-force vector is one-dimensional but all other vectors are two-dimensional. If we desire more detailed signal-flow information than this diagram affords, we can construct the block diagram in Fig. 6-12, which is obtained directly from Fig. 6-11 but which shows each component of the vectors $\mathbf{R}(s)$, $\mathbf{E}(s)$, and $\mathbf{C}(s)$ separately.

From this type of block diagram, we can of course obtain all the simpler systems that result from assigning special values to the different parameters.

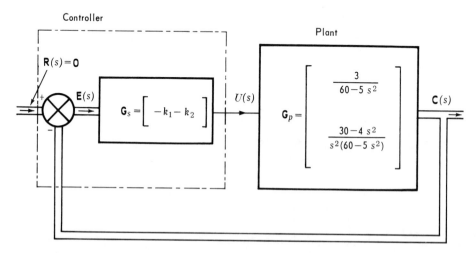

Fig. 6-11   Block diagram of the MIMO servo proposed in Fig. 2-12.

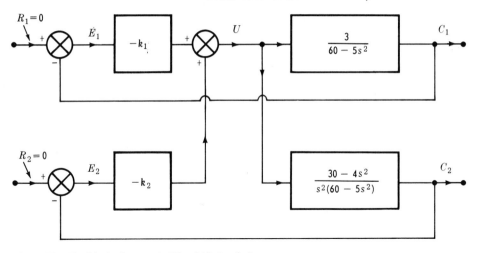

Fig. 6-12   The block diagram in Fig. 6-11 detailed.

For example, if we put $k_1 = 0$, the SISO system of Fig. 6-13 results.   Of course, we can further reduce the block diagram of Fig. 6-11 by eliminating $U(s)$.   By using Eq. (6-23), we obtain a representation of the type shown in Fig. 6-9, where the open-loop transfer matrix equals

$$\mathbf{G}(s) = \begin{bmatrix} \dfrac{3k_1}{5s^2 - 60} & \dfrac{3k_2}{5s^2 - 60} \\[2ex] \dfrac{k_1(4s^2 - 30)}{s^2(60 - 5s^2)} & \dfrac{k_2(4s^2 - 30)}{s^2(60 - 5s^2)} \end{bmatrix}$$

Example 6-3

In this example, we wish to demonstrate the transfer-function approach to a SISO system, and we choose the velocity servo (Fig. 6-3) which we already have analyzed by means of state variables.   We restate first the differential equations characterizing this system.

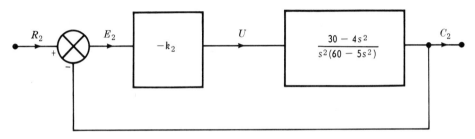

Fig. 6-13   For $k_1 = 0$, the MIMO servo in Fig. 6-12 reduces to a SISO servo.

If, as before, we use the tachometer voltage as our output c, we have (with the switch in position A)

$$r - c = e \tag{6-35}$$

From Eqs. (6-8) and (6-12), we also get

$$K_2 i_f = \ddot{\varphi} = \frac{1}{K_3} \dot{c} \tag{6-36}$$

As before, we have for the field circuit

$$K_1 e = u = R_f i_f + L_f \dot{i}_f \tag{6-37}$$

After Laplace transformation and elimination of $U(s)$ and $I_f(s)$, we obtain

$$R(s) - C(s) = E(s)$$
$$\frac{C(s)}{E(s)} = G(s) = \frac{K_1 K_2 K_3}{s(R_f + sL_f)} \tag{6-38}$$

Note that there was no need for resorting to matrix methods in arriving at these relations. We could, of course, have used the general formula (6-23) for deriving $G(s)$, but this would have necessitated our computing the matrix $\mathbf{T}_2(s)$ (4-35), involving an inversion of a 3×3 matrix. Again, we find reason to stress that matrix methods should never be employed in scalar problems.

The transform equation (6-38) can be assembled into the block diagram in Fig. 6-14.

From Eq. (6-27), we finally compute the closed-loop transfer function $G_c(s)$:

$$G_c(s) = \frac{G(s)}{1 + G(s)} = \frac{K_1 K_2 K_3}{K_1 K_2 K_3 + s(R_f + sL_f)} \tag{6-39}$$

The output c is obtained by an inverse transformation of $C(s)$

$$c = \mathscr{L}^{-1}[C(s)] = \mathscr{L}^{-1}[G_c(s)R(s)] \tag{6-40}$$

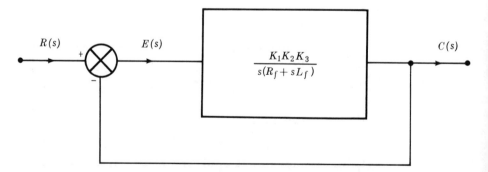

Fig. 6-14   Transfer-function description of velocity servo in Fig. 6-3.

In order to make use of the Laplace-transform tables, it is necessary to find the poles of $G_c(s)$, and this is clearly tantamount to finding the roots of the *characteristic* equation

$$1 + G(s) = 0 \tag{6-41}$$

This equation yields the roots

$$\left.\begin{aligned}\lambda_1\\\lambda_2\end{aligned}\right\} = -\frac{R_f}{2L_f} \pm \sqrt{\frac{R_f{}^2}{4L_f{}^2} - \frac{K_1 K_2 K_3}{L_f}}$$

We note that these roots are identical to the eigenvalues λ_1 and λ_3 (6-21) which we earlier obtained from the equation

$$|s\mathbf{I} - \mathbf{A}_c| = 0$$

This, of course, must be expected, as the solution (6-40) must be identical with the solution for x_3 that can be obtained from Eq. (6-16).

It is interesting to note a very important difference between the solution obtained via the transfer-function method and the one we obtained by means of the state-variable method. The transfer-function approach neglects completely the third eigenvalue $\lambda_2 = 0$, which means that the solution (6-40) gives no *explicit* information concerning the position coordinate φ ($= x_2$). The reason for this should be clear from the discussions in the previous chapter, where it was pointed out that the transfer function does not necessarily carry along all information regarding the total dynamics of a system.

6-4 FREQUENCY-RESPONSE TECHNIQUES

In Appendix B, we show that it is possible to characterize dynamic phenomena in either the *time* or the *frequency* domains.

The control engineer is wise to recognize this fact because situations frequently arise when frequency analysis methods have definite advantages to offer over time-domain or "transient-response" analysis methods.

In our discussions so far, we have made exclusive use of state-variable and transfer-function analysis methods, both of which must be classified primarily as time-domain analysis methods.† Modern textbooks on control theory have placed strong emphasis on Laplace-transform methods and transient analysis, and certainly there are good reasons for this approach. However, it is interesting to observe that the early contributors to the theory of servos used frequency-response techniques almost exclusively. The pendulum thus has made a full swing.

---

† It can be argued that it is not correct to classify Laplace-transform and transfer-function methods as time-domain methods. Some authors would disagree violently and point to the fact that the Laplace operator *s* can be considered a "complex frequency." The whole matter is simply a point of view. One can use Laplace transforms for a whole lifetime without mentioning the term "frequency response"—for the sole purpose of solving linear differential equations (the way we have used them so far in this book). Certainly, this is a time-domain analysis.

We feel that a balanced usage of the two types of analysis tools is to be recommended, and therefore we shall devote this section to a presentation of the basic features of the frequency-response technique.

First, let us discuss what the motivations are for using these methods in the first place. Consider for this purpose the linear system in Fig. 6-15. If it is possible adequately to describe this system by a transfer function $T(s)$ (or system matrix **A**, if we use state variables) *and* if, in addition, the input signal is also well defined (step function, pulse, etc.), then the output $o(t)$ may be obtained most conveniently by the inverse transformation

$$o(t) = \mathscr{L}^{-1}[I(s)T(s)] = \frac{1}{2\pi j} \int_{-\infty}^{+\infty} I(s)T(s)e^{st}\, ds \tag{6-42}$$

Today, most undergraduate students are well versed in these operations and are assisted by well-stocked Laplace-transform tables.

Assume, however, that neither the input signal nor the system can be handled this easily. Then, obviously, the above approach fails. This is actually the case in many practical situations. Consider first the input signal. In many, perhaps most, practical servo systems, the reference signal $r(t)$ is of *random* rather than *deterministic* origin. In describing such signals, we obviously should make use of as much information as is available. Unfortunately, in many cases, not much information is available, and whatever information there is *is not in a form suitable for Laplace-transform description.* It turns out, as a fact of life, that the most significant identification of various random signals can be made (and measured) on the basis of their *spectral composition.* For instance, the most meaningful description of a voice signal makes use of the relative amplitude distribution in the frequency band. Similar situations are common in the area of control. For instance, we may wish to design a servo that will faithfully follow a random reference signal which we are able to identify only to the extent of its frequency distribution. The situation may be complicated further by the fact that the random reference signal is contaminated with random noise. If we know, or can at least estimate, the frequency distribution of this noise and if this distribution luckily does not overlap the signal distribution, then by proper design and by working in the frequency domain, we may obtain a servo that responds properly to the useful signal but filters out the noise.

In the examples just described, our choice of the frequency-response method was due to the characteristics of the signals with which we were forced to work. In all such cases, we must match the system description to the signal description, and this, then, is where the *frequency-transfer function* enters the picture. This situation is, of course, particularly prevalent in the field of communication engineering.

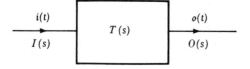

Fig. 6-15 A linear time-invariant stable system.

In control engineering, we sometimes find it necessary to adopt frequency-response techniques for a different reason than the one just outlined. For many engineering systems, it is just plain impossible (or at least associated with great practical obstacles) to obtain a mathematical model. We may be forced to determine the system characteristics *by experiment*, and very often such experiments can be performed most effectively by subjecting the system to a *sinusoidal* input. For instance, assume that we wish to design a frequency-control system for a large interconnected electric-power system. In such a system, the frequency is controlled by manipulation of the power input from one or several power stations, in a manner very similar to the speed control of an automobile by means of changing the power output from the engine. Due to its complexity, size, and changing character, it is quite difficult to establish an accurate model for such a system. It is also practically impossible to have the system available for test because it must be operated on a 24-hr basis. It is possible, however, to test the system *while in operation* by injecting a test input (= power injection) superimposed upon the normal inputs and recording the resulting output (frequency change), which is, of course, also superimposed upon the normal output. To obtain meaningful results, it is necessary to choose inputs of such a nature that the resulting responses can be easily detected. Sinusoidal input signals satisfy these requirements. Not only is it practically feasible to change the power output of a station sinusoidally, but it is possible by means of refined statistical (correlation) methods to filter out that particular frequency component in the output with great accuracy; and the longer the measuring time we are permitted to use, the greater the accuracy. By varying the frequency of the input variations, one can obtain the system response as a function of frequency. This type of measurement technique is also often used for chemical processes for which mathematical model building is inherently very difficult.

These, then, are the major reasons why frequency-response techniques are employed. Some other advantages can also be gained. For instance, the classic stability criterion, named after its discoverer, Nyquist, can be used only in conjunction with frequency-response data. In all fairness, it must be added that this criterion has lost some of its popularity since the introduction of root-locus techniques.

6-4.1 FREQUENCY-TRANSFER FUNCTIONS

We now proceed to present some basic concepts that will prove useful in our further discussions. First, we shall define the concept of *frequency-transfer function* (FTF).

Consider the linear system in Fig. 6-15. We shall assume that the system is *stable*, which means, as we have shown earlier, that the transfer function $T(s)$ has no poles in the right side of the s plane, including the $j\omega$ axis.

We now apply a harmonic input to the system, consisting of one single spectral component of frequency ω, that is,

$$i(t) = i_0 \cos \omega t \tag{6-43}$$

having the transform

$$I(s) = \frac{i_0 s}{s^2 + \omega^2}$$

The output can thus be obtained from

$$o(t) = \mathcal{L}^{-1}\left[T(s)\frac{i_0 s}{s^2 + \omega^2} \right]$$

$$= \mathcal{L}^{-1}\left(\frac{A_1}{s + j\omega} + \frac{A_2}{s - j\omega} + \frac{A_3}{s - p_1} + \frac{A_4}{s - p_2} + \cdots \right)$$

where $p_1, p_2, \ldots$ are the poles of $T(s)$. Therefore,

$$o(t) = A_1 e^{-j\omega t} + A_2 e^{j\omega t} + A_3 e^{p_1 t} + A_4 e^{p_2 t} + \cdots \tag{6-44}$$

Let us now limit our attention to the *steady-state* value of this output. Because of our assumption of stability, all terms $e^{p_i t}$ must vanish, and in steady state, only the first two terms of (6-44) will remain; that is,

$$o_{ss}(t) = A_1 e^{-j\omega t} + A_2 e^{j\omega t} \tag{6-45}$$

(The subscript ss refers to "steady state.")

The amplitudes A_1 and A_2 can be computed as

$$A_1 = \frac{i_0 s}{s - j\omega} T(s)\Bigg]_{s = -j\omega} = \frac{i_0}{2} T(-j\omega)$$

$$A_2 = \frac{i_0 s}{s + j\omega} T(s)\Bigg]_{s = +j\omega} = \frac{i_0}{2} T(j\omega)$$

Therefore,

$$o_{ss}(t) = \frac{i_0}{2} T(-j\omega)e^{-j\omega t} + \frac{i_0}{2} T(j\omega)e^{j\omega t}$$

$$= i_0 |T(j\omega)| \frac{e^{-j\omega t}e^{-j\underline{/T(j\omega)}} + e^{j\omega t}e^{j\underline{/T(j\omega)}}}{2}$$

$$= i_0 |T(j\omega)| \cos\left[\omega t + \underline{/T(j\omega)}\right] \tag{6-46}$$

In the derivation of (6-46), we have made use of the equalities

$$T(\pm j\omega) = |T(j\omega)|\, e^{\pm j\underline{/T(j\omega)}}$$

The complex frequency function $T(j\omega)$ is referred to as the *frequency-transfer function* (FTF) of the system.

Equation (6-46) tells us that a stable linear time-invariant system subjected to a harmonic input signal will, in steady state, have a harmonic output signal of the same frequency as the input but with the amplitude magnified in the ratio $|T(j\omega)|$ and with the phase advanced with the amount $\underline{/T(j\omega)}$.

Formula (6-46) gives us information about the output signal in the simple case of one spectral input component only. If several input frequencies are present, then we can obtain the output by superposition because our system is linear. In the general case where the input function $i(t)$ is an *aperiodic* function, there is an infinite number of frequencies present, each of infinitesimal amplitude.

In Appendix B, Eq. (B-14) informs us that the spectral composition of an aperiodic signal is given by

$$i(t) = \frac{1}{\pi} \int_0^\infty |I(j\omega)| \cos [\omega t + \underline{/I(j\omega)}] \, d\omega \tag{6-47}$$

This equation tells us that the input contains an infinite number of cosinusoids, each of amplitude

$$\frac{|I(j\omega)|}{\pi} \, d\omega$$

By superposition, the output signal will thus be

$$o(t) = \frac{1}{\pi} \int_0^\infty |I(j\omega)| \, |T(j\omega)| \cos [\omega t + \underline{/I(j\omega)} + \underline{/T(j\omega)}] \, d\omega \tag{6-48}$$

As $|I(j\omega)|$ and $|T(j\omega)|$ are *even* and $\underline{/I(j\omega)}$ and $\underline{/T(j\omega)}$ *odd* functions of ω, it is simple to reduce this integral to the more compact form

$$o(t) = \frac{1}{2\pi} \int_{-\infty}^{+\infty} I(j\omega) T(j\omega) e^{j\omega t} \, d\omega \tag{6-49}$$

We note (compare Appendix B) that the output signal actually has been obtained by an inverse Fourier transformation of the transform function $I(j\omega)T(j\omega)$. Note the similarity between (6-49) and (6-42).

We shall find the FTF very useful as a means of predicting system response and specifying performance. Before we investigate those matters any further, we shall demonstrate with two examples how FTF is computed, and also we shall discuss two very convenient graphical methods for its display.

Example 6-4

Consider as a first example the *RC* network shown in Fig. 6-16.

We quite easily obtain the transfer function

$$T(s) = \frac{E_{out}(s)}{E_{in}(s)} = \frac{1}{1 + sRC}$$

We then get, for the FTF,

$$T(j\omega) = \frac{1}{1 + j\omega RC}$$

Hence,

$$|T(j\omega)| = \frac{1}{\sqrt{1 + (\omega RC)^2}}$$

$$\underline{/T(j\omega)} = -\tan^{-1}(\omega RC)$$

The *gain* $|T(j\omega)|$ and *phase* $\underline{/T(j\omega)}$ are plotted versus the radian frequency ω in Fig. 6-16.

In dealing with amplification factors or gains, it is customary in frequency analysis to use the *decibel* (db), arbitrarily defined by the relation

$$\text{db} \triangleq 20 \log \frac{\text{output amplitude}}{\text{input amplitude}}$$

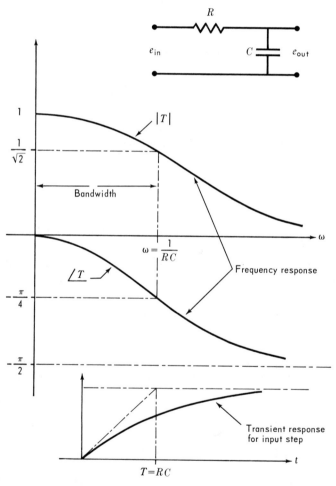

Fig. 6-16 Frequency and step responses for *RC* circuit.

We thus have

$$\text{db} \triangleq 20 \log |T(j\omega)| \tag{6-50}$$

If the gain is larger than unity (db > 0), the signal is evidently *amplified*; if less than unity (db < 0), the signal is *attenuated*.

In the present problem, the signal is obviously attenuated. Between the frequencies $\omega = 0$ and $\omega = 1/RC$, the signal will experience an attenuation in the ratio $1:\sqrt{2}$, or 3 db approximately, and we arbitrarily define this frequency range as the system *bandwidth* (BW):

$$\text{BW} \triangleq \frac{1}{2\pi}\frac{1}{RC} \quad \text{cps} \tag{6-51}$$

The product RC is recognized as the *time constant* T of the circuit [compare Eq. (5-3)] and constitutes a measure of the *speed* or *rise time*† T_R of a system—in this particular case a measure of how fast the output will attain steady state after a step-input voltage (see Fig. 6-16).

From Eq. (6-51), we obviously can conclude that the bandwidth of this system is inversely proportional to the time constant or rise time; that is,

$$\text{BW} \sim \frac{1}{T_R} \tag{6-52}$$

a relationship which not only is true for this system but has general applicability.

Example 6-5

Consider the velocity servo discussed in the previous section. The open-loop transfer function is, according to Eq. (6-38),

$$G(s) = \frac{K_0}{s(1 + sT)}$$

where, for brevity, we have introduced

$$K_0 \triangleq \frac{K_1 K_2 K_3}{R_f}$$

$$T \triangleq \frac{L_f}{R_f}$$

The open-loop FTF thus has the value

$$G(j\omega) = \frac{K_0}{j\omega(1 + j\omega T)} = \frac{K_0}{\omega\sqrt{1 + (\omega T)^2}} e^{-j(\pi/2 + \tan^{-1}\omega T)} \tag{6-53}$$

$|G(j\omega)|$ and $\underline{/G(j\omega)}$ are plotted versus ω in Fig. 6-17.

---

† There exist several definitions of rise time. One is given in the next chapter.

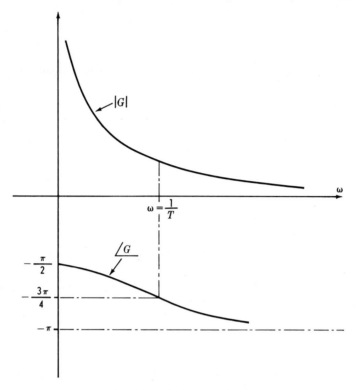

Fig. 6-17   Open-loop FTF for velocity servo in Fig. 6-3.

6-4.2 BODE PLOTS

Bode and Nyquist have suggested more practical plotting methods of the FTF than those used in Figs. 6-16 and 6-17.   Let us first discuss Bode's method, which is particulaïly suited to those cases where the FTF appears in the form

$$T(j\omega) = K \frac{(1 + j\omega T_1)(1 + j\omega T_2) \cdots}{(j\omega)^N (1 + j\omega T_a)(1 + j\omega T_b) \cdots} \tag{6-54}$$

The systems discussed in the above two examples evidently fall within this category.

By taking the logarithm of (6-54), we obtain

$$\ln [T(j\omega)] = \ln (|T|\, e^{j\underline{/T}}) = \ln |T| + j\underline{/T}$$

$$= \ln K + \tfrac{1}{2} \ln [1 + (\omega T_1)^2] + j \tan^{-1} (\omega T_1) + \cdots$$

$$- N \ln \omega - jN \frac{\pi}{2} - \tfrac{1}{2} \ln [1 + (\omega T_a)^2] - j \tan^{-1} (\omega T_a) - \cdots$$

By comparing the real and imaginary parts of this equation, we obtain the following two expressions for the *gain* of FTF, expressed in db, and the *phase*, expressed in radians:

Gain:

$$20 \log |T| = 20 \log K + 10 \log [1 + (\omega T_1)^2] + \cdots$$
$$- 20N \log \omega - 10 \log [1 + (\omega T_a)^2] - \cdots \quad (6\text{-}55)$$

Phase:

$$\underline{/T} = \tan^{-1}(\omega T_1) + \cdots - N\frac{\pi}{2} - \tan^{-1}(\omega T_a) - \cdots \qquad (6\text{-}56)$$

It is particularly simple to plot these functions on a semilog plotting paper (Fig. 6-18). On such a paper, the function $-20N \log \omega$ will simply be a straight line with a negative slope of $-20N \log 2 \approx -6N$ db per *octave*. If we had used a *decade* frequency scale (1, 10, 100, . . .), then the negative slope would have been $-20N \log 10 = -20N$ db per decade.

The terms of the form $\pm 10 \log [1 + (\omega T)^2]$ are also handled very conveniently. We note that if $\omega T \gg 1$, that is, $\omega \gg 1/T$, then this term approaches the asymptote $\pm 20 \log (\omega T)$. This is obviously a straight line with the slope ± 6 db per octave intersecting the 0-db level at the frequency $\omega = 1/T$, referred to as the *break frequency*. If $\omega T \ll 1$, that is, $\omega \ll 1/T$, then the term approaches

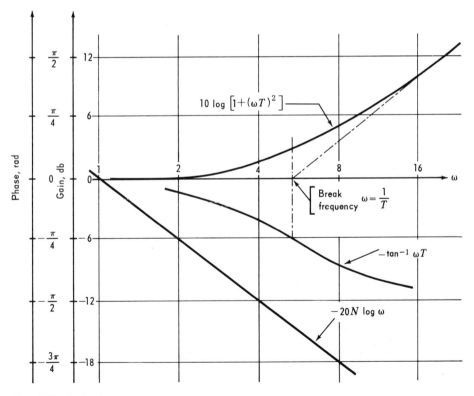

Fig. 6-18   Bode plots.

the asymptote $\pm 10 \log 1$, which is obviously the abscissa axis.   Right at the break frequency, the term equals $\pm 10 \log 2 \approx \pm 3$ db.   The total plot is shown in Fig. 6-18.   To obtain the overall gain, one only has to add up terms which consist basically of straight-line segments.   The phase angles of these terms, $\pm \tan^{-1}(\omega T)$, are also plotted in the graph.   *It is important to note that the total gain and the total phase of $T(j\omega)$ are obtained simply by summing up terms of the basic types shown in Fig. 6-18.*   Having settled for a certain frequency, decibel, and angle scale, we actually can construct plastic templates which can be used in constructing very rapidly the overall FTF.

6-4.3 NYQUIST DIAGRAMS

An obvious disadvantage of the Bode plot is that it takes two separate graphs to plot the FTF, one for the gain and one for the phase.

These inconveniences may be avoided by the use of the *Nyquist diagram.* This diagram has found great usage in servo design and analysis; indeed, it is probably the most popular and time-tested of all analytical tools available to the control engineer.   Not only is a Nyquist diagram very easily constructed, but it also provides a great deal of information concerning the nature of response, relative stability, and steady-state errors of a linear servo system.   We wish to

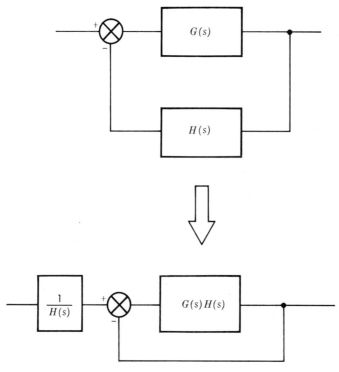

Fig. 6-19   Equivalence between unity- and nonunity-feedback servos.

discuss the main features of this analytical tool, and we shall proceed to do so in reference to a unity-feedback system of the configuration shown in Fig. 6-9. We shall limit our attention to a single-input–single-output system.

The choice of a unity-feedback system does not exclude the use of these methods with systems having dynamic elements in the feedback path, as it is possible to reduce such a system to a unity-feedback system, as demonstrated in Fig. 6-19.

The Nyquist method leans heavily on the theory of *conformal mapping*.

Let us point out very briefly the basic features of this theory. Consider for that purpose a function $G(s)$, where $s = \sigma + j\omega$ is the complex independent variable. For every point s in the s plane, we find a corresponding point $G(s)$ in the $G(s)$ plane. We use the terminology that the function G *maps* the point in the s plane onto the $G(s)$ plane. Likewise, a path P and a closed region R in the s plane are mapped into a corresponding path P' and closed region R' in the $G(s)$ plane, as demonstrated in Fig. 6-20. The two regions may, in general, look quite different; indeed, if the function $G(s)$ is *multivalued*, the mapping will be *overlapping*, as indicated by the region A'.

Consider now a *small* step Δs away from the point s_0 in the s plane. In the $G(s)$ plane, this corresponds to the *small* step $\Delta G(s)$ away from the point $G(s_0)$. We shall now assume that our function $G(s)$ is *analytic* in a region that includes s_0. By that, we mean that the function must possess a *derivative* $G'(s_0)$, defined by

$$G'(s_0) \overset{\Delta}{=} \lim_{\Delta s \to 0} \left[\frac{\Delta G(s)}{\Delta s} \right] \tag{6-57}$$

Specifically, the limit value will exist *and be independent of the direction of the step Δs*. The vast majority of those $G(s)$ functions that we shall be interested in are analytic throughout the entire s plane, with the possible exception of a few isolated (singular) points where the $G(s)$ function itself "blows up," i.e., in the poles of $G(s)$.

Assuming analyticity, we now can write Eq. (6-57) as

$$\Delta G(s) \approx G'(s_0) \, \Delta s \tag{6-58}$$

(We use the approximate sign because we shall consider small but *finite* steps.)

Equation (6-58) is a *complex* equation, and therefore we must require equality of both magnitude and phase; that is,

$$|\Delta G(s)| = |G'(s_0)| \, |\Delta s| \tag{6-59}$$

$$\underline{/\Delta G(s)} = \underline{/G'(s_0)} + \underline{/\Delta s}$$

These two equations, properly interpreted, reveal that the mapping is *conformal*. The first equation tells us that a *small* region around s_0 is linearly magnified with the scale factor $|G'(s_0)|$, whereas the second equation informs us that a rotation through the angle $\underline{/G'(s_0)}$ has taken place. Conformality implies, for instance, that a small square in the s plane maps into a small square in the $G(s)$ plane. In general, the squares are of different size and are differently oriented with respect to the coordinate axes.

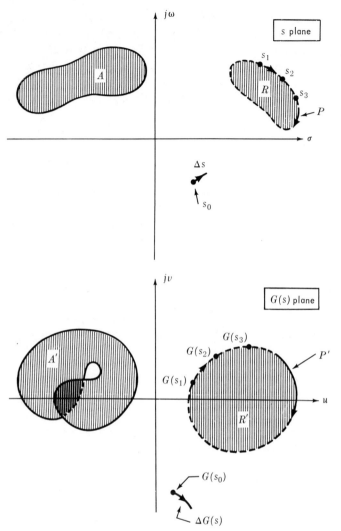

Fig. 6-20 Mapping of points, paths, and regions in s plane onto $G(s)$ plane.

After this very brief detour into the complex domain, let us pick up our interrupted story on Nyquist plots. Let us do it with reference to a specific example.

Example 6-6

Consider the transfer function plotted in the previous example:

$$G(s) = \frac{K_0}{s(1 + sT)}$$

The corresponding FTF

$$G(j\omega) = \frac{K_0}{j\omega(1 + j\omega T)}$$

was found [Eq. (6-53)].   If we now let ω vary from 0 to ∞, we obviously proceed in the s plane from origin to ∞ along the $j\omega$ axis.   In the $G(s)$ plane, we correspondingly proceed along the map of the $j\omega$ axis.   The actual shape of this map is shown in Fig. 6-21 and is obtained directly from (6-53).   We note specifically that for *small* ω values,

$$|G(j\omega)| \to \frac{K_0}{\omega} \to \infty$$

$$\underline{/G(j\omega)} \to -\frac{\pi}{2}$$

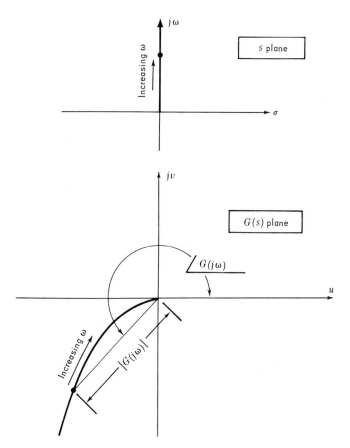

Fig. 6-21   Mapping of $j\omega$ axis onto the $G(s)$ plane utilizing the mapping function $G(s) = K_0/s(1 + sT)$.   The resulting map is called a *Nyquist plot.*

and for *large* ω values,

$$|G(j\omega)| \to \frac{K_0}{\omega^2 T} \to 0$$

$$\underline{/G(j\omega)} \to -\pi$$

The plotting is simplified by using so-called *polar* graph paper.

Example 6-7

Consider as a second example the system of Example 6-6, but connected as a *position* rather than as a velocity servo. With reference to Fig. 6-3, this means that the feedback voltage is obtained from the potentiometer *PM* rather than from the tachometer generator *TM*.

As our output now is φ rather than $\dot{\varphi}$, it is simple to confirm that the open-loop transfer function now will be of the form

$$G(s) = \frac{K_0}{s^2(1 + sT)} \tag{6-60}$$

Therefore,

$$|G(j\omega)| = \frac{K_0}{\omega^2 \sqrt{1 + (\omega T)^2}} \tag{6-61}$$

$$\underline{/G(j\omega)} = -\pi - \tan^{-1}(\omega T)$$

The corresponding Nyquist diagram is drawn in Fig. 6-22.

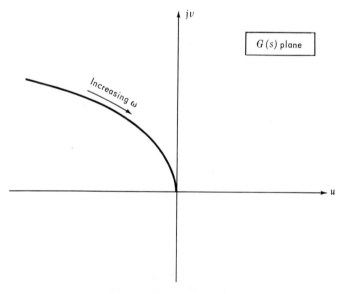

Fig. 6-22 The Nyquist plot of system having $G(s) = K_0/s^2(1 + sT)$.

6-4.4 THE NYQUIST STABILITY THEOREM

Diagrams of the types shown in Figs. 6-21 and 6-22 are most useful in the area of stability study.   Indeed, it is possible to predict the stability of a servo from direct observation of its Nyquist diagram.   For instance, Fig. 6-21 tells us that the velocity servo is stable for all values of the open-loop gain K_0.   (This fact was confirmed, of course, in our earlier analysis of this system.)   On the other hand, the Nyquist diagram in Fig. 6-22 of the corresponding position servo indicates instability for all values of the open-loop gain.

In making these observations, we made use of the famous *Nyquist stability criterion*.†   This criterion informs us not only about the stability or instability of a system but, more importantly, about the *degree* of stability.   Because of the great importance of this criterion, we wish to discuss the main features of the underlying theory.   We shall present a simplified proof based on the theory of conformal mapping.

We first make the following very fundamental observation:

If the region R, consisting of the entire right half of the s plane (including the jω axis), is mapped onto the G(s) plane and if the resulting region R' includes the point G(s) = −1, then the corresponding servo system is unstable.   If the point −1 is not included in R', the system is stable.

proof: Stability requires that all roots of the characteristic equation

$$G(s) + 1 = 0$$

are located in the left half of the s plane.   If, on the contrary, the system were unstable, this equation would have to have *at least* one root in the right half of the s plane, i.e., within the region R.   If this were the case, then there would have to exist at least one s value within this same region that would satisfy the equation

$$G(s) = -1$$

This is possible, of course, only if the point $G(s) = -1$ is located *inside* the region R'.

The value of this theorem is enhanced by the fact that it usually is sufficient to complete only partially the mapping referred to above.   We shall demonstrate this by the following examples.

Example 6-8

Again we make use of the open-loop transfer function for the previously described velocity servo,

$$G(s) = \frac{K_0}{s(1 + sT)}$$

Using this function as a mapping function, we shall first map the right half of the s plane onto the $G(s)$ plane.

---

† Nyquist's original paper[1] is a true classic, and anybody who wants to consider himself a control engineer should not be ignorant of its contents.

In mapping a region, we find it more convenient to study how the *contours* of that region are being mapped.   In this case, we choose the contour shown in Fig. 6-23.   As the $G(s)$ function is nonanalytic at the origin, we choose to bypass this point in the s plane by going around it in a small semicircle of radius r.   Also, because $G(s)$ vanishes for $s = \infty$, we prefer to consider a contour of finite dimension, and this then explains the outer semicircle of radius R.   Note that $G(s)$ is analytic on the inside and on the borders of the chosen region.   Also, by letting

$$R \to \infty$$

$$r \to 0$$

the chosen region actually will coincide with the right half of the s plane.

We save ourselves 50 percent of the mapping job by realizing that $G(s)$ is a conjugate complex function, which means that the map will be symmetric around the abscissa axis in the $G(s)$ plane.   We perform the actual mapping in the following three steps:

step 1   Move from point 1 to point 2 in the s plane by going along the circle $s = re^{j\varphi}$ in counterclockwise direction between $\varphi = 0° \to 90°$.

step 2   Move from point 2 to point 3 by going along the line $s = j\omega$ from jr to jR.

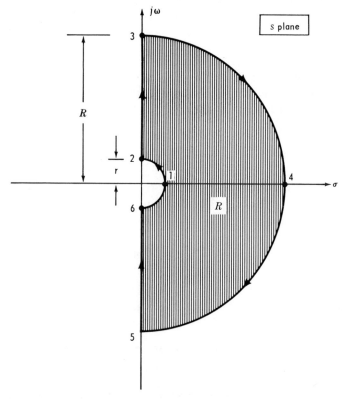

Fig. 6-23   Mapping contour used in Example 6-8.

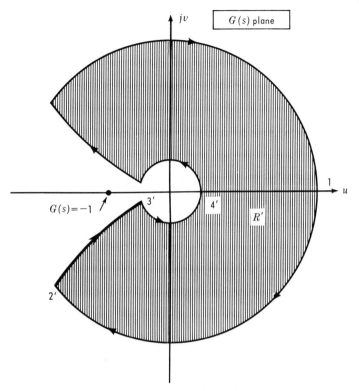

jv

G(s) plane

1   u

$G(s) = -1$ 3'

4'

R'

2'

Fig. 6-24   The map of the contour shown in Fig. 6-23.   Mapping function is $G(s) = K_0/s(1 + sT)$.

step 3   Move between points 3 and 4 by going along the circle $s = Re^{j\varphi}$ in clockwise direction between $\varphi = 90° \to 0°$.

We proceed to discuss each step in full detail.

step 1   We have, along the little semicircle,

$$G(s) = \frac{K_0}{re^{j\varphi}(1 + Tre^{j\varphi})} \approx \frac{K_0}{re^{j\varphi}} = \frac{K_0}{r} e^{-j\varphi}$$

When we complete a counterclockwise quarter turn on the little circle in the s plane, we evidently complete a clockwise quarter turn along a circle with a large radius K_0/r, in the $G(s)$ plane.

step 2   We now get

$$G(s) = \frac{K_0}{j\omega(1 + j\omega T)} = G(j\omega)$$

Evidently in this step we go along the "Nyquist plot" shown in Fig. 6-21 from $G(jr)$ to $G(jR)$.

step 3   Now we have

$$G(s) = \frac{K_0}{Re^{j\varphi}(1 + TRe^{j\varphi})} \approx \frac{K_0}{TR^2 e^{j2\varphi}} = \frac{K_0}{TR^2} e^{-j2\varphi}$$

Therefore, a clockwise quarter turn around the big circle in the s plane corresponds to a counterclockwise half turn around a small circle of radius K_0/TR^2 in the $G(s)$ plane.

In summarizing, we conclude that the contour 1-2-3-4 in the *s* plane maps into the contour 1′-2′-3′-4′ in the *G(s)* plane, as shown in Fig. 6-24. Note also that the inside of the *s*-plane contour lies to the right with respect to our travel direction. We therefore must find the inside of the mapped region to the right of our path in the *G(s)* plane. Because of conformality, the two 90° right-hand sharp turns at points 2 and 3 must correspond to 90° right-hand sharp turns at points 2′ and 3′.

Utilizing the previously mentioned symmetry feature, we then can complete the total map.

Before we discuss the results obtained, let us for comparison also use the mapping function *G(s)* of (6-60), i.e., the transfer function for the position servo.

We may perform the mapping in this case using techniques similar to those in the previous example. The result is shown in Fig. 6-25.

In comparing the two maps in Figs. 6-24 and 6-25, we draw the following conclusions:

1. The map in Fig. 6-25 includes the point −1, whereas the map in Fig. 6-24 does not. Therefore, the velocity servo is stable, but the position servo is unstable.

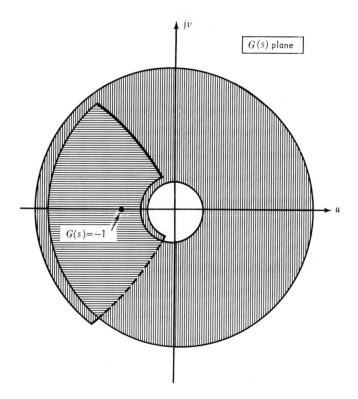

Fig. 6-25 The contour shown in Fig. 6-23 mapped by function $G(s) = K_0/s^2(1 + sT)$.

2. The question of inclusion or noninclusion of the point −1 seems in both cases to be a matter of the specific nature of the frequency transfer function $G(j\omega)$ (boldface in both maps).

The latter point is extremely important because it means, in effect, that we can draw the proper conclusions concerning the stability of a system based upon information of $G(j\omega)$ only, without need for the time-consuming mapping procedure. It is sufficient to make a polar plot of the open-loop FTF, and on the basis of its relation to the critical point $G(s) = -1$, we can determine directly whether or not the system is stable.

Nyquist stability theorem specifically states:

Plot $G(\pm j\omega)$ *for all positive frequencies. If the point* $G(s) = -1$ *lies completely "outside" the resulting curve, the system is stable; if not, it is unstable.*

It is necessary to make a couple of remarks concerning the theorem.

remark 1 By "outside," we shall mean the region to the left of the plot of $G(+j\omega)$ when we move in increasing ω direction. This is easily understood if we note from Fig. 6-23 that when we move from 2 → 3, we have the stable s plane region to the left.

remark 2 The theorem holds only for $G(s)$ functions that are analytic in the entire right-hand s plane. Should $G(s)$ have singular points in this part of the s plane, then we must exclude these in our mapping† (see Exercise 6-1).

In Fig. 6-26 are shown four typical situations. In all four cases, the solid plot refers to $G(+j\omega)$, with the arrow indicating increasing frequency. The dotted plot is the symmetrical $G(-j\omega)$. Case *d* depicts a so-called *conditionally stable* system, which we may make unstable either by increasing or decreasing the loop gain.

6-4.5   RELATIVE STABILITY; GAIN AND PHASE MARGINS

The Nyquist diagram tells us not only *if* a specific system is stable but also *how* stable it is. This matter of degree is very essential from the designer's viewpoint as it gives him an opportunity to estimate directly from the polar plot the effect of specific parameter changes. Consider the two different systems shown in Fig. 6-27a and *b*. We shall assume that the eigenvalue or closed-loop pole configurations of the two systems are the ones indicated in the s planes. (These configurations actually apply to the velocity servo discussed earlier.)

Obviously system *a* is "more stable" than system *b* as its closed-loop poles are located deeper inside the left-half of the s plane. By mapping the gridnets of the s plane onto the $G(s)$ plane, we notice the effects on the Nyquist plot. The closer the eigenvalues are to the $j\omega$ axis, the closer the $G(j\omega)$ plot will be to the critical point −1.

The degree of stability has a profound effect on the *closed-loop* FTF

$$G_c(j\omega) = \frac{G(j\omega)}{1 + G(j\omega)}$$

† The physical meaning of $G(s)$ poles in the right-half of the s plane is that the open-loop system, i.e., the plant plus series compensator, is *unstable*.

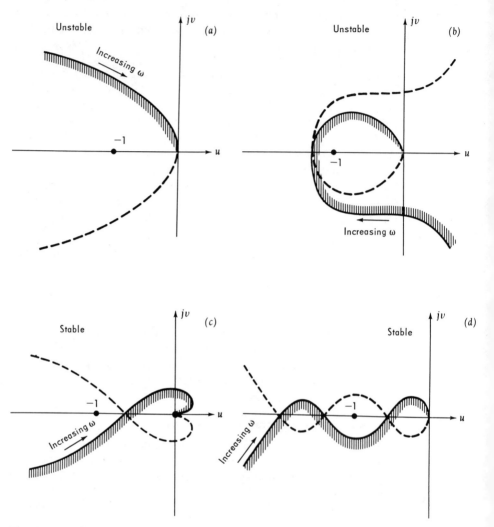

Fig. 6-26 Typical Nyquist plots.

As demonstrated in Fig. 6-28, this ratio may conveniently be obtained directly from the Nyquist diagram. Note that the denominator expression $1 + G(j\omega)$ assumes quite small values for frequencies around $\omega = \omega_p$ (peak frequency) when the Nyquist plot passes close to the critical point -1. This means that the closed-loop FTF is characterized by a *resonance* peak ("M-peak") for $\omega = \omega_p$. The two graphs in Fig. 6-28 demonstrate this for the two different systems the Nyquist plots of which were shown in Fig. 6-27.

A certain measure of the degree of stability can be obtained by means of the *gain* and *phase margins*. The gain margin (GM) is defined as the gain increase

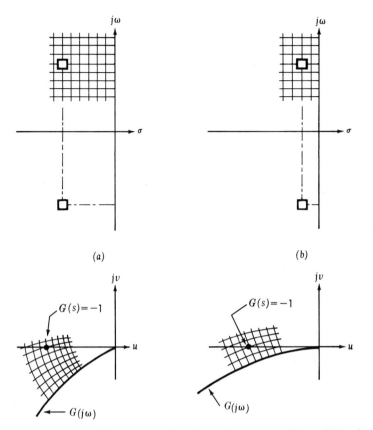

Fig. 6-27 Correlation between closed-loop eigenvalue position and Nyquist plot.

needed to drive the system into instability. With reference to Fig. 6-29, this means

$$\text{GM} \triangleq \frac{1}{a} - 1 \tag{6-62}$$

(Other definitions of GM are found in the literature, and therefore care should be exercised when using this quantity.)

The phase margin (PM) is defined in association with the *crossover frequency* ω_{co}, that is, the frequency at which the open-loop gain equals unity. We have (see Fig. 6-29)

$$\text{PM} \triangleq \underline{/G(j\omega_{co})} - 180° \tag{6-63}$$

In most cases, a satisfactory phase margin (say, 45°) automatically guarantees a good gain margin, and vice versa. However, cases exist, as

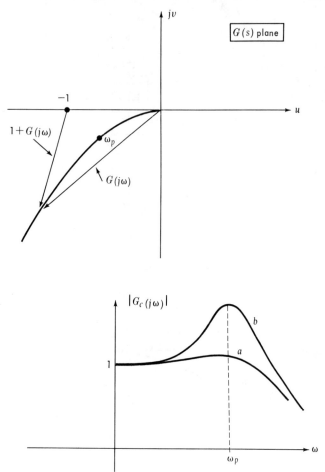

Fig. 6-28 Correlation between Nyquist plot and closed-loop FTF.

demonstrated by the two graphs in Fig. 6-30, where the specification of one does not necessarily satisfy the requirements for the other.

It should also be pointed out that the concept of gain margin is rather useless for a *conditionally stable system*. Such a system obviously can be driven into instability by either increasing or decreasing the gain. (See also the system in Fig. 7-39.)

6-5 SENSITIVITY AND ERROR ANALYSIS

The quality of a servomechanism or a regulator must be judged on the basis of its ability to keep the error below a specified minimum level when it is used under normal operating conditions. The presence of an error usually can be attributed to a number of factors; we shall enumerate the three most important ones:

1. *Change in the reference input.* (This does not apply to a regulator.) Most often, these changes are of random character, which makes the job of the servo more difficult than would be the case if the changes were predictable. Even if the reference input is fully deterministic in nature, unavoidable errors will result. (It is more difficult to take aim at a running rabbit than at a sitting duck.)

2. *Parameter variations.* The components making up the servo may change due to aging, deterioration, damage, and other factors. The servo should be so designed as to minimize, if possible, the effects of such changes. The best means to counteract the effects of structural variations in the system is the feedback principle itself.

3. *Loading effects.* This is a very important factor. Every servomechanism, with the possible exception of instrument servos, is required to do its job against the opposition of various "loading forces." For instance, the positioning of a radar antenna must be done with required precision in spite of wind forces acting on the disk.

We shall proceed by discussing the most useful error-analysis methods in each of these cases.

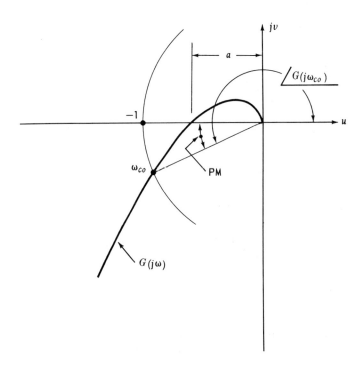

Fig. 6-29   Definition of GM and PM in terms of Nyquist plot.

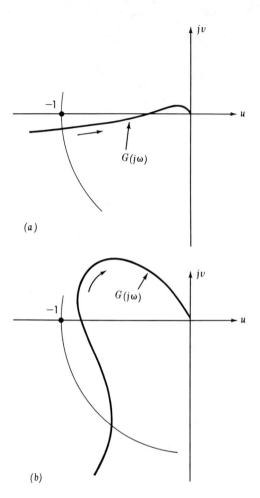

(a)

(b)

Fig. 6-30 These Nyquist plots show that it is sometimes necessary to specify *both* GM and PM. In case (*a*) GM but not PM is satisfied, in case (*b*) the opposite is true.

6-5.1 ERRORS DUE TO REFERENCE-INPUT CHANGES

We shall investigate specifically a unity-feedback system. The methods discussed could also be used for the case where the feedback channel contains dynamic elements, but by limiting our attention to the unity-feedback case, we should be able to get the essential problem illuminated with the least effort. In this case, we obtain the error-transfer function

$$E(s) = \frac{1}{1 + G(s)} R(s) \tag{6-64}$$

As we might expect, the error will be a function of the type of reference input $r(t)$. It is customary, in judging the error-reducing capability of a specific system, to compare the *steady-state* error produced by different types of test inputs. We are, in other words, concerned with the *static* accuracy of the system.

Two different types of inputs are generally used:

1. Sinusoidal input

$$r = r_0 \sin \omega t$$

2. *m*th-order parabolic input

$$r = r_0 \left(\frac{t}{t_0}\right)^m \qquad m \geqslant 0$$

The motivation for a sinusoidal test input has been discussed earlier in this chapter. The choice of the second type of test input is motivated by a specific feature of the *m*th-order parabola (Fig. 6-31). For different values of *m* (we chose integer values only), this input is characterized, in increasing order, by constant *magnitude*, constant *rate*, constant *acceleration*, and so on, and each additional step in the *m* scale therefore represents a tightening in the follow-up requirements of the servo.

The steady-state errors for the above test inputs can now be computed.

1. For the sinusoidal test input, we get, by using Eq. (6-46),

$$e_{ss} = \frac{1}{|1 + G(j\omega)|} r_0 \sin\left[\omega t + \left/\frac{1}{1 + G(j\omega)}\right.\right] \tag{6-65}$$

2. For the *m*th-order parabola, we get, by using the final-value theorem,

$$e(\infty) = \lim_{s \to 0}\left[s \frac{1}{1 + G(s)} \frac{r_0 m!}{t_0{}^m s^{m+1}}\right] \tag{6-66}$$

$$= \lim_{s \to 0}\left[\frac{1}{1 + G(s)} \frac{r_0 m!}{t_0{}^m s^m}\right]$$

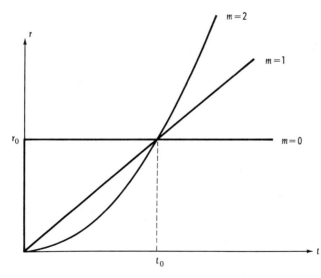

Fig. 6-31   Parabolic test inputs in the cases *m* = 0, 1, and 2.

Note that in deriving Eqs. (6-65) and (6-66), we have tacitly assumed that the servo is stable.

We observe from the last expression that if a servo is to be able to follow an mth-order parabola input *perfectly*, i.e., with zero static error, its open-loop transfer function must contain the factor s^{m+1} in its denominator; i.e., it must have at least $m + 1$ integrators in the forward loop. If the number of integrators is less than $m + 1$, the static error will be either constant or infinite. The situation is summarized in Table 6-1, the entries of which are obtained directly from Eq. (6-66). The table is based upon an open-loop transfer function of the type

$$G(s) = K_0 \frac{(1 + sT_1)(1 + sT_2) \cdots}{s^N(1 + sT_a)(1 + sT_b) \cdots} \tag{6-67}$$

We make the following important observation:

In order to reduce the static error for a specified parabolic input, the obvious solution would be to increase the number of integrators in the open loop. *However, as a result of the attendant increase in phase shift, this would tend to make the system unstable.*

Table 6-1   The static error in the case of parabolic input shown as a function of N and m

Order of input, m	Number of integrators, N		
	0	1	2
0	$\dfrac{r_0}{1 + K_0}$	0	0
1	∞	$\dfrac{r_0}{K_0 t_0}$	0
2	∞	∞	$\dfrac{2r_0}{K_0 t_0{}^2}$

This follows directly from the Nyquist stability criterion and was demonstrated quite clearly in the case of the position servo versus the velocity servo. Remember that the position servo differed from the velocity servo only in terms of the number of open-loop integrators.

Example 6-9

We wish to show the actual error situation for the velocity servo characterized by

$$G(s) = K_0 \frac{1}{s(1 + sT)}$$

1. The amplitude of the frequency error for the servo is obtained from (6-65):

$$|E(j\omega)| = \frac{1}{|1 + K_0[1/j\omega(1 + j\omega T)]|} r_0$$

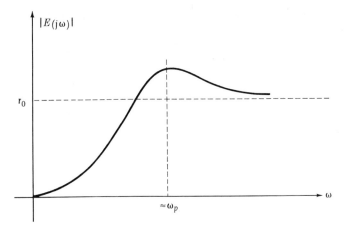

Fig. 6-32   Frequency error for servo in Example 6-9.

Therefore,

$$|E(j\omega)| = \frac{\omega\sqrt{1 + (\omega T)^2}}{\sqrt{(K_0 - \omega^2 T)^2 + \omega^2}}\, r_0$$

Note that we may obtain quite conveniently the error versus frequency directly from the Nyquist plot. As shown in Fig. 6-32, the error has a peak at approximately (but not exactly) the peak frequency $\omega = \omega_p$, and the closer to the critical point the Nyquist diagram runs, the sharper the peak.

2. From Table 6-1, we find that the velocity servo (as was shown in Sec. 6-2) has a perfect follow-up to a step input but a constant nonzero static error for a ramp input. Should we desire to reduce the static error to zero even for this input, we would find it necessary to add one integrator *and, at the same time, compensate for the lost stability.* Such synthesis procedures will be discussed in the next chapter.

6-5.2 ERRORS DUE TO PARAMETER AND LOAD CHANGES

We indicated earlier that parameter and load changes are the second and third major error sources in servos. It is very essential that these effects be understood, predicted, and, if possible, neutralized.

In attempting to analyze these effects, we often encounter difficulties in the form of differential equations with *time-variant* parameters. Such equations, although linear, cannot be solved with the great ease that characterizes linear time-invariant equations; however, in most practical cases, it is possible to obtain acceptable approximate solutions.

We have seen earlier in this chapter that when disturbances z enter the system in a *linear time-invariant* fashion, we may represent them as special inputs entering the control loop in the block-diagram representation (Fig. 6-6). The effects of such inputs on the output c can, of course, be computed in a manner quite similar to the computation of the effects due to the reference input r.

Even in those cases where parameter and load changes do not enter the system differential equations in a time-invariant way, it is possible, *with certain approximations*, to use the same techniques for studying their effects.

As all practical servomechanisms will be subject to disturbances in one form or other and as it is, as a rule, necessary to *desensitize* the system against these disturbances to a specified degree, all servo designs must be checked with respect to their disturbance sensitivity. It is useful in this connection to introduce a *sensitivity measure* S_x^c, defined as the ratio (often expressed in percent) between the percentage of change in the output c and the percentage of change in a parameter x.

Example 6-10

We demonstrate with an example the analysis procedures useful in this type of situation. Figure 6-33 depicts a simple voltage regulator. A d-c machine supplies power to the load resistor R_L, and it is required to keep the terminal voltage c constant. The voltage is controlled automatically by means of adjustment of the field current i_f via the amplifier. We wish to study the effects on the controlled variable c of the following possible occurrences:

1. Changes in the reference voltage source V
2. Variations of the amplifier gain K
3. Changes in generator speed n
4. Load variations

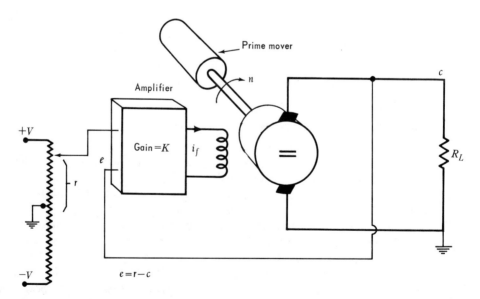

Fig. 6-33 Simple voltage regulator.

In an actual system, all the above parameter changes inevitably will occur. The first three would probably be relatively small, in terms of percentages, except, of course, in those cases where complete component failure would occur. The load variations, on the other hand, would be of a different magnitude. Quite probably, the voltage regulator would be expected to function properly in the total load range, 0 to 100 percent output. This would correspond to R_L values in the range

$$R_{\min} < R_L < \infty$$

where $R_{\min}$ is the load-resistance value resulting in full (100 percent) output current from the generator.

All these parameter changes will unavoidably affect the output voltage c. It is essential to know to what degree (and, in particular, if) it is possible to desensitize the system to these changes.

The first step in our sensitivity analysis is to establish a mathematical model of the regulator. We obtain, in this case, the following set of differential equations:

$$r - c = e$$
$$Ke = R_f i_f + L_f \dot{i}_f \tag{6-68}$$
$$K_e n i_f = c + \frac{c}{R_L} R_i = \left(1 + \frac{R_i}{R_L}\right) c \triangleq f_L c$$

The first two equations are self-explanatory. The last equation expresses the fact that the generator emf, $K_e n i_f$, must equal the sum of the terminal voltage c and the internal voltage drop ($=$ the product of internal resistance R_i and armature current c/R_L). For brevity, we have defined, in the last equation, a load factor

$$f_L \triangleq 1 + \frac{R_i}{R_L}$$

that evidently is a function of the load R_L.

The Eqs. (6-68) are linear, and if, in addition, all parameters are time-invariant, then we may, after Laplace transformation, represent the voltage regulator with the block diagram shown in Fig. 6-34. The open-loop gain K_0 and time constant T_0 are defined by

$$K_0 \triangleq \frac{KK_e n}{R_f f_L}$$
$$T_0 \triangleq \frac{L_f}{R_f} \tag{6-69}$$

We note, in passing, that this is indeed quite a crude regulator. In accordance with our discussions in the previous section, it is unable to eliminate the static error, even for a step input.

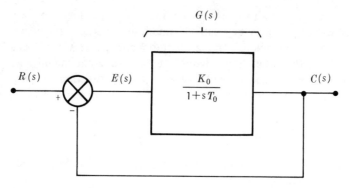

Fig. 6-34 Transfer-function model of the voltage regulator in Fig. 6-33.

In order to study the effects of the above-mentioned parameter changes, we proceed as follows:

Initially, the regulator is assumed to be in a steady state, indicated by the superscript (^{0}) and directly obtained from the Eqs. (6-68):

$$r^0 - c^0 = e^0$$
$$K^0 e^0 = R_f i_f^0 \qquad\qquad (6\text{-}70)$$
$$K_e n^0 i_f^0 = c^0 f_L^0$$

Next, we introduce the four different parameter variations (symbolized by the prefix δ) that we earlier agreed could conceivably occur:

$$r = r^0 + \delta r$$
$$K = K^0 + \delta K$$
$$n = n^0 + \delta n \qquad\qquad (6\text{-}71)$$
$$f_L = f_L^0 + \delta f_L$$

As a result of these variations, the system variables e, c, and i_f will undergo the changes

$$e = e^0 + \delta e$$
$$c = c^0 + \delta c \qquad\qquad (6\text{-}72)$$
$$i_f = i_f^0 + \delta i_f$$

We now introduce all these changes into our mathematical model (6-68), and the result is the set of *time-variant* linear differential equations

$$r^0 + \delta r - (c^0 + \delta c) = e^0 + \delta e$$

$$(K^0 + \delta K)(e^0 + \delta e) = R_f(i_f^0 + \delta i_f) + L_f \frac{d}{dt}(i_f^0 + \delta i_f) \qquad (6\text{-}73)$$

$$K_e(n^0 + \delta n)(i_f^0 + \delta i_f) = (f_L^0 + \delta f_L)(c^0 + \delta c)$$

These equations do not possess simple solutions in the form of elementary functions. Indeed, approximate solution methods represent the only practical approach.

In the specific case where we can assume with certainty that the parameter variations are *small in terms of percentages*, it is possible to simplify the equations to a considerable degree. Small parameter variations result in small variable changes, and it is possible, therefore, without too great a loss of accuracy, to neglect all second-order terms in the above equations. By observing the identities (6-70), we obtain in this case the following set of approximate equations:

$$\delta r - \delta c = \delta e$$

$$K^0 \, \delta e + e^0 \, \delta K \approx R_f \, \delta i_f + L_f \frac{d}{dt} (\delta i_f) \tag{6-74}$$

$$K_e n^0 \, \delta i_f + K_e i_f^0 \, \delta n \approx f_L^0 \, \delta c + c^0 \, \delta f_L$$

These equations are linear, with *time-invariant* parameters, and may thus easily be handled by means of transform calculus. Before we proceed, a comment is appropriate concerning the assumptions that made these simplifications possible. With reference to Eqs. (6-71), we can confidently assume that the first three variations, δr, δK, and δn are small. But what about δf_L? We had stated earlier that the regulator must function properly within the total load range 0 to 100 percent. As we had earlier mentioned, this means, in effect, that the load resistance R_L will be permitted to vary between

$$R_{\min} < R_L < \infty$$

This, then, corresponds to a variation of the load factor f_L throughout the range

$$1 + \frac{R_i}{R_{\min}} > f_L > 1$$

In a normal machine of this type, the internal resistance R_i usually is no larger than 5 to 10 percent of $R_{\min}$. Larger values are not permitted in view of the power losses. This means that f_L will vary throughout the range

$$1.10 > f_L > 1.00$$

and we conclude therefore that even δf_L is a small quantity. We can therefore with confidence make use of the simplified Eqs. (6-74), which after Laplace transformation take on the form

$$\Delta R - \Delta C = \Delta E$$

$$K^0 \, \Delta E + e^0 \, \Delta K \approx (R_f + sL_f) \, \Delta I_f \tag{6-75}$$

$$K_e n^0 \, \Delta I_f + K_e i_f^0 \, \Delta N \approx f_L^0 \, \Delta C + c^0 \, \Delta F_L$$

We have made use here of the notation

$$\Delta X \triangleq \mathscr{L}(\delta x)$$

These transform equations can be translated into the block diagram of Fig. 6-35, which gives the reader a better feel for the physics of the situation. We note first that the block diagram is the same as the one in Fig. 6-34; i.e., if we combine the three separate transfer functions in the forward path, we obtain the overall open-loop transfer function defined by Eq. (6-69). The four parameter variations enter as disturbance inputs at various points in the system. We may use this diagram to obtain the effects of any one of these inputs alone or all of them simultaneously.

As an example, we shall make use of the block diagram to study the effects on the output due to speed changes. No other parameter variations are assumed, and if thus ΔR, ΔK, and ΔF_L are zero, the diagram of (6-35) will simplify to the extent shown in Fig. 6-36. From this diagram, we find that

$$(\Delta C G_1 + K_e i_f^0 \, \Delta N) G_2 = \Delta C$$

Therefore,

$$\Delta C = \frac{G_2}{1 - G_1 G_2} K_e i_f^0 \, \Delta N = \frac{G_2}{1 + G} K_e i_f^0 \, \Delta N \tag{6-76}$$

where G is the open-loop transfer function defined in Fig. 6-34.

Equation (6-76) tells us that the effect on the output of the speed variation ΔN is determined by the transfer function shown in Fig. 6-37.

Let us, for example, compute the static (= steady-state) error in the output δc^0 that would result from a step change in the generator speed.

If this step change has the magnitude δn^0, we get

$$\Delta N = \frac{\delta n^0}{s}$$

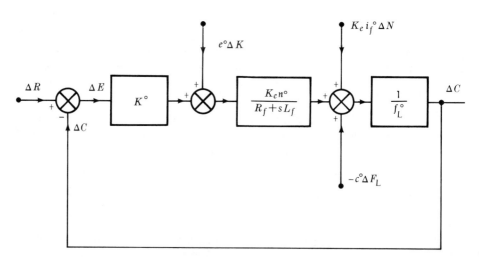

Fig. 6-35   The model in Fig. 6-34 with disturbance inputs added.

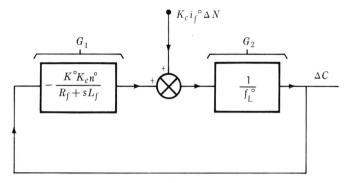

Fig. 6-36 Model used for analysis of the effects of speed drop.

By using the final-value theorem and employing diagram 6-37, we get

$$\delta c^0 = \lim_{s \to 0} \left[s \frac{\delta n^0}{s} \frac{K_e i_f{}^0 G_2}{1 + G} \right]$$

$$= \lim_{s \to 0} \left[\delta n^0 \frac{K_e i_f{}^0 (1/f_L{}^0)}{1 + K^0 K_e n^0 / (R_f + s L_f)(1/f_L{}^0)} \right]$$

$$= \delta n^0 \frac{K_e i_f{}^0 (1/f_L{}^0)}{1 + K^0 K_e n^0 / R_f f_L{}^0}$$

In view of Eq. (6-70), this last expression can be reduced to

$$\delta c^0 = \delta n^0 \frac{c^0/n^0}{1 + c^0/e^0}$$

The ratio c^0/e^0 obviously is the *static* open-loop gain K_0 [defined in Eq. (6-69)], and we therefore obtain

$$\frac{n^0 \, \delta c^0}{c^0 \, \delta n^0} = \frac{\delta c^0/c^0}{\delta n^0/n^0} = S_n{}^c = \frac{1}{1 + K_0} \tag{6-77}$$

For example, assume an open-loop gain $K_0 - 100$. For the sensitivity $S_n{}^c$ we then would obtain

$$S_n{}^c = \frac{1}{1 + 100} = 0.01$$

In words: An open-loop gain of 100 would reduce the effect of a 10 percent speed drop to a mere 0.1 percent drop in the regulator voltage. This is what feedback does for us.

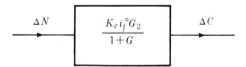

Fig. 6-37 The diagram of Fig. 6-36 reduced to one single block.

6-5.3 CONCEPTS OF OUTPUT IMPEDANCE AND COMPLIANCE

In the example just treated, the output load could be caused to change by variation of a system parameter R_L. In other cases, the load is caused by external inputs. For example, in the servo depicted in Fig. 6-3, the output member may be directly subject to torques caused, for instance, by wind forces. This would simply mean that an additional term would be added to Eq. (6-8), which would therefore preserve its *time-invariant* character. Therefore, the sensitivity analysis in such cases (in respect to load changes) actually would be simpler than in the time-variant case. The external load would also in this case enter into our block diagram as an external "disturbance" input.

It is customary to specify the maximum permissible effects caused by these load inputs in terms of the following two measures:

1. Output impedance Z
2. Compliance Q

The output impedance is, in analogy with electrical impedances, a frequency-domain specification. The load input thus is assumed to vary sinusoidally, and the resulting sinusoidal variation of the output is computed (or recorded, if we measure the quantity experimentally). *The complex ratio between the output and load input is defined as the output impedance.*†

For example, consider our voltage regulator. From the diagram (Fig. 6-35), we first find the transfer function relating the load input ΔF_L with the output ΔC (see Fig. 6-38a). This is left as an exercise for the reader.

We then obtain directly

$$Z \triangleq \frac{\Delta C(j\omega)}{\Delta F_L(j\omega)} = \frac{c^0/f_L^0}{1 + G(j\omega)}$$

An ideal servo obviously should have $Z = 0$ at all frequencies. This is, however, impossible to achieve physically.

Note that the unit of the output impedance differs from case to case. In the present case, the unit of Z must be determined from the units of c and f_L and will clearly be volts. It is more practical to define a "per-unit" impedance $Z_{\text{p.u.}}$, a concept familiar to most electrical students. It is obtained, as shown in Fig. 6-38b, by defining the impedance as the ratio between the dimensionless *normalized* outputs and the load inputs. The per-unit impedance will always be dimensionless.

The compliance measure Q is the time-domain counterpart of output impedance and is defined as the ratio between the output change and the load input, assuming *static* (step-input) variations. It is obvious, therefore, that the

---

† *Impedance* is a concept usually associated with electric-circuit theory, having the physical unit volts per ampere. Note, however, that our definition of output impedance gives it a *general* meaning. Compare also Exercise 6-3.

(a)

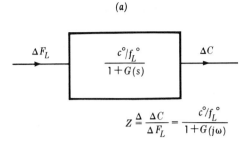

$$Z \triangleq \frac{\Delta C}{\Delta F_L} = \frac{c^\circ / f_L^{\,\circ}}{1 + G(j\omega)}$$

(b)

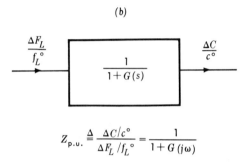

$$Z_{\text{p.u.}} \triangleq \frac{\Delta C / c^\circ}{\Delta F_L / f_L^{\,\circ}} = \frac{1}{1 + G(j\omega)}$$

Fig. 6-38   Definition of output impedance.

compliance actually can be obtained from the output impedance Z by letting $\omega \to 0$, that is,

$$Q \triangleq Z(j0)$$

We may consider Q as the "d-c" output impedance.

For example, let us use the Q measure to determine the static-voltage drop in our voltage regulator as a result of a suddenly applied 100 percent load.†

Our per-unit impedance equals, in accordance with Fig. 6-38*b*,

$$Z_{\text{p.u.}} = \frac{1}{1 + G(j\omega)}$$

For the static case, we compute our d-c impedance or compliance

$$Q_{\text{p.u.}} = \frac{1}{1 + G(j0)} = \frac{1}{1 + K_0} \qquad \text{per unit}$$

Let us assume, as before, that the static open-loop gain is 100.   Hence,

$$Q_{\text{p.u.}} = 0.01 \text{ p.u. or 1 percent}$$

How shall we interpret this result?

† Such a treatment would most certainly also cause a speed drop.   Let us disregard this side effect. If we wish to account for it, we may do so by using the method earlier outlined.

Let us assume for sake of argument that the 100 percent sudden load change corresponds to a 10 percent change in our load factor f_L. The 0.01 value of the per-unit compliance thus tells us that the static percentage change in the output voltage will be

$$0.01 \times 10 \text{ percent} = 0.1 \text{ percent}$$

We also may express the situation as follows: If we open the feedback loop and subject the generator to a 100 percent load, its terminal voltage will drop 10 percent statically. If we do the same with the feedback loop closed, the drop will be only 0.1 percent.

Exercises

6-1 Consider the broom balancer in Chap. 2.

    a Put the linearized version in the block diagram form depicted in Fig. 6-39. In particular, prove that the plant transfer function is of the form

$$G_p(s) = \frac{a}{s^2 - b^2}$$

Find a and b.

    Determine also $G_s(s)$ in both the PPD and pure P cases.

    b Note that the unstable plant has a pole in $s = b$ and $G(s)$ is therefore nonanalytic in this point. Map the right-hand s plane onto the $G(s)$ plane using a contour as indicated in Fig. 6-39. Note that $G(s)$ is analytic within this contour. Find the relationship of $G(s) = -1$ in respect to the mapped region and confirm the stability conditions we already found by other means in Chap. 2.

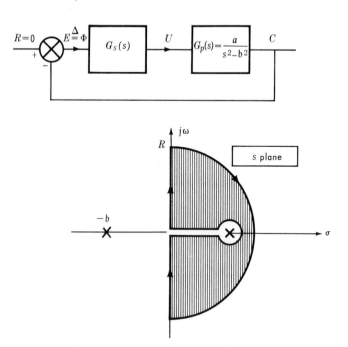

Fig. 6-39 Transfer-function model of broom balancer in Chap. 2.

6-2 A unity-feedback servo is characterized by the open-loop transfer function

$$G(s) = \frac{K_0}{s(1 + s)^2}$$

It is desired to limit the static steady-state error for the ramp input $r(t) = t$ to a value not in excess of 0.25. Is this requirement consistent with the requirement for stability? Make use of a Nyquist plot.

6-3 Consider the broom balancer again. Use PPD control and compute the output impedance and compliance measure for a system having the following data (for symbols, see Chap. 2; all units are in MKS):

$L = 1$

$m = M = 1$

$k_1 = k_2 = 100$

(Put $g = 10$ for simplicity.)

It is assumed that the wind force z is horizontal and attacks the broom at CG.

Why does the constant k_2 affect the value of the output impedance but not the value of the compliance? (Compare Exercise 2-3.)

6-4 Assume that the open-loop transfer function $G(j\omega)$ is represented graphically in the form of a Bode plot. How would you interpret stability from such a diagram using the Nyquist criterion presented in the text?

6-5 The spring-mass system in Fig. 3-2a is being controlled by a force u. The system is lightly damped (not indicated in the figure), and we find that the differential equation describing the system is

$$\ddot{y} + 0.1\dot{y} + 10y = u$$

Assume now that the control force is sinusoidal

$$u = 3 \sin \omega t$$

Use the concept of FTF and compute the largest possible amplitudes y_{max} and the frequency at which they occur. Plot the FTF versus frequency.

(Those among the readers who are electrical engineers may try to define a Q value similarly, as is being done for lightly damped electric circuits.†)

6-6 A servo is characterized by the open-loop transfer function

$$G(s) = \frac{K(1 + s)^2}{s^2(1 + 2s)(1 + 0.2s)^2}$$

Prove that the system is conditionally stable for a certain range of the gain K.

References

1. H. M. James, N. B. Nichols, and R. S. Phillips, "Theory of Servomechanisms," McGraw-Hill Book Company, New York, 1947.
2. John G. Truxal, "Control System Synthesis," McGraw-Hill Book Company, New York, 1955.
3. H. W. Bode, "Network Analysis and Feedback Amplifier Design," D. Van Nostrand Company, Inc., Princeton, N.J., 1945.
4. H. Nyquist, Regeneration Theory, *Bell System Tech. J.*, **11**: 126–147 (1932). The paper appears in a recent Dover publication, "Mathematical Trends in Control Theory," edited by Bellman and Kalaba.

† This Q measure, often used to evaluate the "goodness" of electric resonance circuits, should not be confused with the compliance measure Q introduced in the present chapter.

chapter 7

LINEAR SERVOMECHANISMS— THE SYNTHESIS PROBLEM

7-1 PERFORMANCE SPECIFICATIONS

In this chapter, we shall continue our discussion of linear servomechanisms. Having devoted the entire previous chapter to an exposé of the more useful analysis procedures, it is only natural that we should complete our coverage of servos with a presentation of the most important synthesis techniques available to the designer. It is not possible, within our condensed format, to cover this topic exhaustively, since, in the strictest sense, there exist as many synthesis methods as there are control-system designers. This state of affairs is basically due to the fact that the vast majority of those servomechanisms that actually are being built are being designed to meet specifications that are not in a true sense *optimal*. This terminology will be defined shortly; for the moment, it will suffice to note that a *nonoptimal*, or *suboptimal*, set of specifications usually can be met by a number of different designs, often an infinite number, or in other words, a given set of specifications does not necessarily lead to a unique solution.

The choice of synthesis method, indeed the whole philosophy of control-system design, is intimately tied in with the choice of *performance criterion or criteria*. It is appropriate, therefore, to start this chapter with an exposition and comparison of the different types of criteria presently in use.

It should be pointed out as a matter of great interest that emphasis (or maybe *overemphasis* would be a better word) at certain times on specific control criteria has had a very profound effect on the research efforts in control theory. A classic example is the time-optimal criterion, specifying a system that will in minimum time execute a transfer between two specified system states. For several years, the research in the area of time-optimal control systems overshadowed all other efforts and probably delayed the developments in other, certainly equally important fields.

We have earlier, on several occasions, lightly touched on the topic of performance specifications. Let us summarize now the most important considerations on the basis of which a specific set of performance specifications (PS) should be selected. (We sometimes shall find it more convenient to refer to *figure of merit* or *control criterion* when we find that the set reduces to a single scalar number.)

1. *The PS should adequately, concisely, and unambiguously spell out the requirements imposed upon the control system.*
2. *The PS chosen should not be more stringent than sound engineering judgment deems necessary.*
3. *A specific figure of merit should not be chosen on the basis of mathematical tractability alone.*

Each of the above points merits a few comments. Consider first objective 1. When writing down the minimum requirements that a specific control system should meet, one should make an effort to limit attention to only those characteristics that truly affect the usefulness for the specific job intended. Overspecification results in ambiguity. For instance, it is not possible independently to specify bandwidth and rise time of a system, as the values of these two parameters are dependent on each other. Overspecification also tightens the design requirements unnecessarily and results in a more expensive design. If in the case of a regulator, for instance, we are concerned only with the static errors, then we should not unnecessarily require a specific transient response, as this might necessitate the inclusion of a compensating network that would shape the response but contribute nothing to the static accuracy.

The second point concerning the stringency requirement is very appropriate, particularly in this, the age of "optimum control." Let us, in this connection, define this concept, as it has great bearing on our choice of PS. It is obvious that the less restrictive the performance specs chosen, the easier it is to satisfy them, as our choice of system configuration and control strategy is widened. Indeed, it is this leniency in PS that actually so often permits us to choose a linear design and also makes it possible to satisfy the performance requirements with a number of different system solutions. Should the PS now be tightened to such an extent that we accept only that design which will give us the *optimum* performance in some defined sense, we then, in effect, have called for the *optimum-control system* for this specific application. Minimum-fuel, maximum-range, minimum-power-loss control systems are but a few examples of systems where we tolerate only the *best* solution possible. It lies in the nature of things that in most of these examples, there is one, *and only one*, system that will do; i.e., the design of the optimum controller is *unique*. And it must be added, difficult. Only in rare instances does the optimum-control strategy turn out to be linear. Not only does the optimum-control requirement result in great analytical difficulties, but, perhaps more important, the actual hardware implementations become quite difficult to accomplish. In view of these very real difficulties, one should be very critical of the need for an optimum solution. Would not a suboptimal design meet the real objectives? It should be added that there are many modern engineering control problems with solutions which are utterly dependent upon an optimally applied control vector. The motivations for optimum-control theory are thus strong.

Optimum control is meaningless without an *optimum criterion*. It is true that one easily can settle for a meaningful figure of merit in a number of engineering problems, but it is equally true that in many other instances it is a hopeless task to define what one should mean by "best." The reader can verify the truth of this statement by performing the following little experiment: Ask three different persons on which basis they would like to judge the excellence of the performance of the broom balancer discussed in Chap. 2. Then note the number of different answers.

After these generalities, we shall now present and compare the specific PS that have been found useful in linear servo design. We may divide these into the following three subgroups:

1. Frequency-domain specifications
2. Time-domain specifications
3. Specifications on statistical bases

Of these three, time- and frequency-domain specifications are completely dominant and will be discussed in detail in the following sections. Statistical specifications are beyond our present scope.

7-1.1 FREQUENCY-DOMAIN SPECIFICATIONS

In the previous chapter, we gave the motivation for using frequency-domain data presentation. We shall deal here with the specifications that relate to the relationships between the sinusoidal inputs and outputs of a servo. The control literature contains references to dozens of frequency-domain specifications, of which the more common are:

Bandwidth
Phase margin (and crossover frequency)
Gain margin
M peak (and peak frequency)
Deviation ratio
Error-constant–bandwidth ratio
Output impedance
Gain-bandwidth product

It is quite clear that all these specifications are not mutually exclusive. For instance, as was pointed out in the previous chapter, gain and phase margin and M peak are all measures of relative system stability.

Guided† by Air Force rules,[3] we recommend the following set of PS:

Bandwidth BW
M peak M_p
Peak frequency ω_p
Output impedance Z

---

† The United States Air Force should, of course, not be the rule setter. However, we feel that their praxis in this matter is worth adopting.

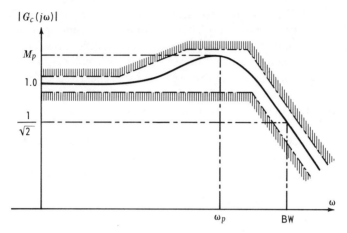

Fig. 7-1   Frequency-domain performance specifications.

All these system parameters were discussed in Chap. 6.   The first three are summarized in Fig. 7-1.   This figure also shows the Air Force method of specifying the accepted tolerances in BW, M_p, and ω_p (the nonshaded area).

Each of these four specifications will be discussed briefly.

Bandwidth BW

BW is probably the most significant PS as it gives indication of the speed of response of a servo and is therefore a measure of the signal reproducibility.   The higher the BW, the faster the servo and the better the signal reproduction. [Remember formula (6-52), which told us that the speed of response is proportional to BW.]   However, noise rejection and price considerations require low BW. The choice of BW is thus a compromise affair that will differ from case to case.

M Peak M_p and Peak Frequency ω_p

These are stability specifications.   Note that they do not apply to all systems. An overdamped system does not exhibit a resonance peak.   There is a correlation between M_p and the "settling time" (see under time-domain specs), i.e., the time required for transient oscillations to die out.   The higher the M_p, the longer the settling time.   A too high M peak can be particularly dangerous should the system input contain considerable energy on and around the peak frequency. In such cases, large destructive amplitudes may result.   (Note the similarity between the M_p measure and the Q measure used in electric resonance circuits.)

Output Impedance Z

A maximum specification on Z will guarantee that the servo will perform properly over the expected load range.   It is particularly important to realize that Z will vary with frequency, and it is therefore necessary to specify its *peak* value.   The corresponding time-domain specification, compliance, is obviously not sufficient to predict intolerable output oscillations that could result from periodic load variations if applied at a frequency corresponding to peak impedance.

It should be stressed that the impedance specifications make sense only in those cases where, in reality, we can expect load fluctuations. Let us remember objective 2: "Never specify more requirements than necessary."

7-1.2 TIME-DOMAIN SPECIFICATIONS

Probably the most common of all PS are those that relate the transient output of a system to a test input, usually in the form of a step function. Conceivably, one could specify time-domain PS in terms of many various types of test inputs, and it is therefore appropriate to give some of the reasons why we chose this particular one:

1. A step is easy to apply and is sufficiently drastic.
2. No physical system is capable of following a step completely.
3. A large amount of information is available in the literature relating to this type of test input.
4. From a knowledge of the step-function response, it is possible to compute the response for any arbitrary input.

The last fact is demonstrated in Fig. 7-2. We wish to compute the response at time t for the general input function $i(\tau)$, assuming that we know, either from analysis or from experiment, the response $g(\tau)$ for a unit step input applied at $t = 0$. The input function $i(\tau)$ can be considered composed of the infinitesimal step functions shown shaded in the figure.

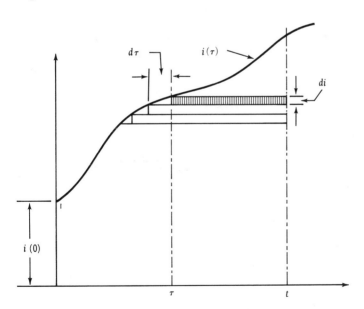

Fig. 7-2 A general signal $i(\tau)$ can be considered as composed of elementary step functions.

By superposition, we obtain the output at time t from all these step functions of amplitude di plus the initial step of magnitude $i(0)$:

$$o(t) = i(0)g(t) + \int_0^t g(t - \tau)\,di = i(0)g(t) + \int_0^t g(t - \tau)\frac{di}{d\tau}\,d\tau$$

$$= i(0)g(t) + \int_0^t g(t - \tau)i'(\tau)\,d\tau$$

(7-1)

As in the case of frequency-domain PS, we find that the literature abounds with suggested figures of merit. Using again the Air Force recommendations, we shall settle for the following set of PS, which, with a maximum of five scalar quantities, quite adequately "boxes in" the transient response:

1. Delay time T_D
2. Rise time T_R
3. Percentage overshoot PO
4. Settling time T_S
5. Final (static) value of error FVE

Each of these quantities is indicated in Fig. 7-3, which depicts a fairly typical response picture. Not all of these PS necessarily apply to a specific case.

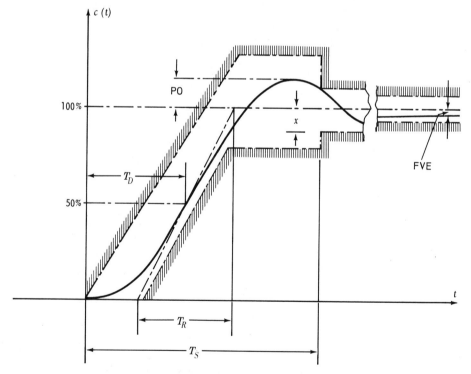

Fig. 7-3   Time-domain performance specifications.

For instance, an overdamped system does not have an overshoot (just as it had no M peak in the frequency domain).

Note that the above set of PS ignores loading effects. The Air Force recommendations put this job up to the "output impedance," a frequency-domain specification. However, we feel that we would obtain a better symmetry between time- and frequency-domain PS if we included here the d-c output impedance, and we thus will add this sixth item to the above list:

6. Compliance Q

(Note that we may consider a step input the limit case as the frequency of the sinusoidal input approaches zero.)

The concepts of both "compliance" and "static error" have been adequately covered in the previous chapter. Therefore, we shall limit the following comments to the first four of the above PS.

Delay Time T_D

This quantity is a measure of the "delay" of the servo and is defined as the time interval between the application of the input step and the moment when a *substantial* output is observed, usually defined as 50 percent of the step amplitude. The delay time is closely associated with the second item in the set of PS, the rise time.

Rise Time T_R

This quantity expresses the *sharpness of the leading edge* of the output. Several definitions exist—the one suggested here is based upon the rate of the pulse increase at the moment the output pulse "arrives," i.e., at time T_D. Both delay and rise time are closely related to the bandwidth specification in the frequency domain.

Overshoot PO and Settling Time T_S

These two quantities specify the degree of stability of the servo. They therefore are closely associated with M peak and peak frequency in the frequency domain. T_S is defined as the time it takes for the output to settle down within a specified x percent of the final value.

The shaded area in Fig. 7-3 shows how to specify tolerances on the above PS.

In addition to the above set of PS (and we refer here to both frequency- and time-domain specs), we must design our servo to meet all *sensitivity specifications* that may be imposed. No general recommendations are possible here, but we have exemplified in the previous chapter how these matters can be handled.

The performance specifications discussed so far (of both the frequency- and time-domain varieties) are characterized by one obvious disadvantage—the designer must *simultaneously* meet *several* more or less hard-to-satisfy design limits. Indeed, in trying to "box in" the system response within limits of the types shown in Figs. 7-1 and 7-3, the only way out is via *trial-and-error* synthesis methods.† To remedy this situation, time-domain criteria have been proposed which, due to their intrinsic simplicity, permit more direct synthesis procedures. These criteria all have one characteristic in common—they incorporate, in one single figure of merit *I*, all those pertinent factors that (in the opinion of the proponent) determine the quality of the servo.

The error *e* certainly is the one single factor that is most likely to influence such a figure of merit. As the *duration* of the error also must play a role, one finds that the most meaningful of these figures of merit or indices of performance are of the form

$$I = \int_0^\infty F(e,t)\, dt \tag{7-2}$$

In many systems it would be unrealistic not to include in the performance index the *cost of the control effort u*, and the figure of merit in such cases would then attain the form

$$I = \int_0^\infty F(e,u,t)\, dt \tag{7-3}$$

The two most popular error criteria are the so-called Integral of Squared Error (ISE) and Integral of Time multiplied by Absolute Error (ITAE) criteria, defined by, respectively,

$$I = \int_0^\infty e^2\, dt \tag{7-4}$$

$$I = \int_0^\infty t\,|e|\, dt \tag{7-5}$$

The first criterion, tolerant to *small* but punitive to *large* error, has the *advantage of analytical simplicity*. The second criterion is lenient to the (unavoidable) errors which appear immediately after the application of the step input but penalizes late errors. The ITAE criterion has the advantage of being quite selective,[5] but it suffers the disadvantage of being hard to use due to analytical difficulties. All criteria of this type can be applied only to systems having zero FVE. For other systems, the integrals fail to converge. Another obvious shortcoming of these and similar *mathematical* criteria is that they actually may violate some of the more *practical* PS earlier discussed. For instance, neither the ISE nor the ITAE gives any guarantee that tight limits on, say, overshoot are observed. This is, of course, the price we pay for analytical simplicity.

† The term "trial and error" best describes the methods to be discussed. It is hoped that the engineer who for 20 years has *designed* servos and now is told that he has actually synthesized "by trial and error" will not be offended. We must remember that most engineering design is in reality of the trial-and-error type. This is the only way open, considering how the design specifications usually are stated. It also should be added that this is the design method that *really* requires skill, experience, and intuition in the right mixture.

7-1.3 SPECIFICATION ON STATISTICAL BASIS

Statistical specification of control systems and, more generally, design on a statistical basis are not presently and probably never will be of great importance in comparison with deterministic design techniques. However, there are occasions when all our deterministic design methods fail simply because we lack the necessary system and signal data. If it is possible to describe the data by statistical methods and if it is possible to assign some meaningful statistical performance measure, then we still may be able to tackle the task. However, even in the most elementary situations, statistical design involves fairly complex procedures, of both a theoretical and a practical (hardware) nature. It is felt that a discussion of these matters should be postponed until we have gained a fuller understanding of deterministic control theory.

7-2 CLASSIFICATION OF SYNTHESIS METHODS

We have already hinted at the fact that there exists today a great variety of synthesis methods. As we have set for ourselves the ambitious objective of covering all the essential aspects of contemporary deterministic control, it is necessary, indeed, to try to bring some measure of order into the picture; and therefore we shall make an attempt to classify the synthesis procedures available to today's control engineer. Such a classification will help us at the same time to discern some of the distinctive differences between what we may call the "classic" and the "modern" control.

On the basis of their fundamental character, we shall divide existing synthesis methods into *direct* and *indirect* methods.

Under these two main headings, we can distinguish three different approaches: *trial-and-error, analytical,* and *optimal* design (see Table 7-1). The trial-and-error

Table 7-1 Classification of synthesis methods

Approach	Indirect design methods	Direct design methods	
I	Trial and error		⎫
II	Analytical		⎬ classical
III		Optimal	⎭ modern

and the analytical approaches can be considered as "classical" design methods; the optimal-control-system design approach is often referred to as "modern control." The analytical procedures may also be viewed as a transitory stage, both historically and methodologically. Actually, the choice of the name "analytical" is a rather unfortunate one, as it may convey the wrong idea that the other methods are nonanalytical.   The name was adopted[6] before the age of optimum control and is by now thoroughly entrenched in the minds of control people.

We shall proceed with a brief identification of each of the above design techniques.

7-2.1   THE TRIAL-AND-ERROR SYNTHESIS TECHNIQUE

This is the oldest of control-system design techniques and is still very popular. Most of today's control engineers use this method exclusively, and the vast majority of the control systems operating today are designed by trial and error. Of the approximately one hundred textbooks on control theory published before 1966, all except about half a dozen cover trial-and-error design almost exclusively.

Actually, we are not really discussing *one* technique, but a whole spectrum of techniques, and the basic feature of all these techniques is that the design starts out from an elaborate but suboptimal set of PS, usually of the type depicted in Figs. 7-1 and 7-3.   The designer seeks to satisfy all the system requirements by choosing a design by "trial."   This choice usually is based upon experience, intuition, and common engineering judgment.   The choice usually settles on a linear configuration, and the designer proceeds then to check, by linear analysis, that the selected system fulfills all the PS.   Usually it does not, and the designer is therefore forced to reexamine his choice, perhaps change configuration or (at best) readjust parameter settings, and finally check again, by analysis, that the PS are met.   If the designer is very good, or very lucky, this procedure converges very rapidly to an acceptable design solution.

If, however, he is born under an unlucky star, it will never converge, not even after trying out a number of different configurations.   He may actually have run headlong into one of the main obstacles of this type of approach—the inconsistent set of PS.   It is quite likely that a set of PS of the type shown in Figs. 7-1 and 7-3 cannot be met by a physically realizable system, and the designer, who does not know whether the fault is his own or lies in the set of PS, faces a frustrating situation.

On the other hand—and this explains the popularity of the approach—if the PS are consistent, no other method will result in an acceptable solution with less analytical effort.   As the reader will remember, our selection of a PPD controller for the broom balancer in Chap. 2 was actually a simple example of design by trial and error.

Figure 7-4 shows a flow-diagram representation of this design method. It should be added that one of the most powerful tools in this type of design work is the electronic analog computer.   The most time-consuming part of the trial-and-error procedure is the analysis check of PS, once a readjustment of parameters has been made.   Such a check can be made in a few seconds or minutes by means of an analog computer, and this then permits the designer to check out a much larger number of possible designs.   Particularly fast design checks are possible if the computer is provided with *fast integrators* and *repetitive-operation* switching equipment.   (See further discussions of usage of analog computers in Chap. 12.)

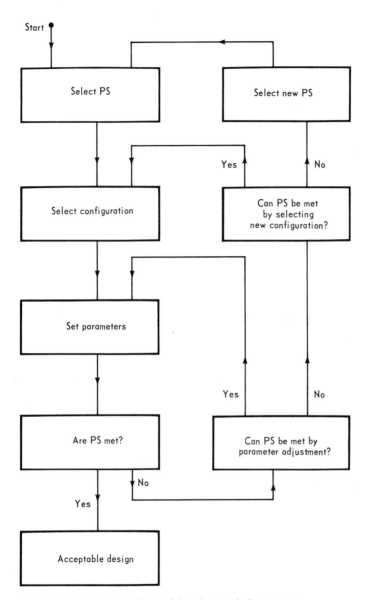

Fig. 7-4   A flow graph of the trial-and-error design process.

In most cases, the trial-and-error synthesis procedures center around the very specific configurations shown in Figs. 6-1 and 6-2. The final acceptable design crystallizes into either a *series* (cascade) *compensator* or a *feedback* compensator, which may consist of either passive or active, mostly electric, networks.

In summary, here are the pros and cons that characterize this design method:

advantages

1. Relatively simple mathematical tools suffice.
2. Vast amounts of experience have accumulated.
3. The method is well adapted for use in conjunction with analog computers.
4. Linear designs usually can be accepted.

disadvantages

1. Inconsistent PS can be encountered.
2. The design is not optimal.
3. The method is suitable mostly (but not always) for single-input–single-output systems.

Later in this chapter, we shall discuss this design method in greater detail.

We hope that this brief classification has not given the impression that design by trial and error is all art, no science. Later design examples will demonstrate that this design method is art *and* science. After all—is not this *true engineering*?

7-2.2 ANALYTICAL DESIGN METHODS

The point of departure in the analytical control-system design procedure is a PS consisting of a *single figure of merit*. The ISE figure of merit is very common, but other performance indices can be used as well. With respect to the choice of PS, this design method therefore is identical to optimum synthesis procedures. The similarities cease, however, right there. Whereas a designer of an optimum system places no restrictions on system configuration, the analytical designer must obey certain constraints in this respect. Actually, most proponents of the analytical method[6] use the configurations that were preferred by trial-and-error designers. Within the limits of these constraints, the analytical designer now proceeds as follows (we choose the configuration in Fig. 6-1 as an example and shall concern ourselves only with the scalar case):

1. The system configuration in Fig. 6-1 is replaced by its closed-loop equivalent $G_c(s)$, shown in Fig. 6-10, where

$$G_c(s) = \frac{G_s(s)G_p(s)}{1 + G_s(s)G_p(s)} \tag{7-6}$$

2. A figure of merit and a "desired output" c_d are chosen. (Generally, by not requiring c_d to equal the reference input r, we have, in effect, eased the restrictions on the system.)
3. A $G_c(s)$ is now chosen such that the figure of merit is minimized.

Steps 1 and 2 are simple enough—the difficulties start in step 3. And these are real difficulties. For instance, if we choose the ISE figure of merit (the "error" is here defined as $c - c_d$), then we can prove that the optimum or "best" choice for $G_c(s)$ can be *implicitly* solved from the so-called *Wiener-Hopf integral equation* (Ref. 6, Chap. 5).   Integral equations are not easily solved, and furthermore, even if we could obtain a solution, we still know only $G_c(s)$.   There still remains the problem of choosing and physically realizing a compensator $G_s(s)$ which will, in accordance with Eq. (7-6), render $G_c(s)$ an optimum.

The analytical-design approach is tremendously simplified if, at the outset, the controller configuration is fixed.   The problem then reduces to a relatively simple search for those controller parameter values which minimize the index of performance.   (See Examples 7-1 and 7-2.)

It should be remembered that neither the trial-and-error nor the analytical design techniques represent optimal designs.   As, in addition, both techniques in most cases lead to solutions of the same configuration, their relative values must be compared on the basis of the PS which they utilize and the amount of mathematical complexity which they require.

The analytical design methods never have "sold" well.   The average control engineer evidently has not felt that the high price in mathematical complexity has been worth paying for the dubious return in system performance.

The general feeling seems to be that if very sophisticated mathematical methods must be employed in control-system design, one might as well "go all the way" to the truly optimal design procedures and get the maximum possible payoff.   We subscribe to the same philosophy, and our coverage of this technique will therefore be very light.

7-2.3 OPTIMUM-CONTROL-SYSTEM DESIGN

Considerably more attention will be paid in later chapters of this book to *optimum* control.   At this time, we wish to give a very brief and general identification of this, the most modern of all design methods, in order to complete the present classification.

Optimum control is the most direct of all design methods.   It starts out with an index of performance that as adequately as possible incorporates all the factors that add to the cost of the performance.   Optimum-control design methods utilize, as we shall see, almost exclusively state-variable, rather than transfer-function, system description, and therefore the index of performance, as a rule, will be expressed as a scalar function I of the state and control-force vectors

$$I = \int_0^{t_f} F(\mathbf{x},\mathbf{u}) \, dt \tag{7-7}$$

The only constraints imposed upon the solution are those that relate to the physical restrictions on the magnitudes of the components of $\mathbf{x}$ and $\mathbf{u}$.   Thus, no a priori assumptions are made as to system configuration or linearity of the control strategy.

By observing the above magnitude constraints, a $\mathbf{u}$ solution is sought (we shall refer to it as $\mathbf{u}_{opt}$) which optimizes the chosen I criterion.   Simultaneously we must observe

1. The system differential equation

$$\dot{\mathbf{x}} = \mathbf{f}(\mathbf{x},\mathbf{u})$$

2. Possibly some prescribed *initial* and *final* states $\mathbf{x}(0)$ and $\mathbf{x}(t_f)$

    The only inconsistency that one may encounter in the above problem statement lies in the prescription of the final state $\mathbf{x}(t_f)$. One must make sure that the system is controllable and that the prescribed state is reachable.

    The problem of finding the *optimum-control strategy* $\mathbf{u}_{opt}$ is, in general, not an easy one. There are, however, several approaches available, all of the *variational* type. Only in very simple systems and for very simple I criteria is it possible to obtain *explicit* solutions for $\mathbf{u}_{opt}$. In most practical cases, one must be content with a *numerical* solution generated by a digital computer, which is incorporated as part of the system. One of the advantages of this numerical approach is that one is not limited to only those I criteria which result in analytical convenience.

    We summarize in the following tabulation all those characteristics that have contributed to making "optimum control" a popular and exciting area of modern control technology.

1. It supplies the unique† solution that, in the chosen sense, is truly optimal.
2. It incorporates all the advantages of the modern digital computer. It leaves the computational drudgery to the computer, giving the designer more time to devote to analytical problems.
3. It can be applied to nonlinear and time-variant systems.
4. It is the *only* technique that can handle with any success multiple-input–multiple-output systems.‡

    Finally, we point out that the search for optimum-design methods initiated a wide range of research activities that have contributed immeasurably to our knowledge and understanding of fundamental aspects of control theory.

    We must not forget that optimal control is characterized by some serious disadvantages. We already have pointed out that it may be difficult to implement the optimum strategy into hardware. The computational requirements may also be so severe that the computer cost may render the optimum solution practically nonfeasible.

7-3 CLASSICAL DESIGN OF SINGLE-INPUT— SINGLE-OUTPUT SERVOMECHANISMS

We intend to devote the remaining part of this chapter to a review of those two design methods that rightfully deserve to be referred to as classical—the "trial-and-error" and "analytical" synthesis approaches. As generalizations are difficult to come by in any trial-and-error technique, we shall make an attempt to find typical demonstration examples instead.

---

† In rare instances, the optimum-control strategy is not characterized by uniqueness.
‡ The statement does not apply in those rare cases where analytical solutions exist.

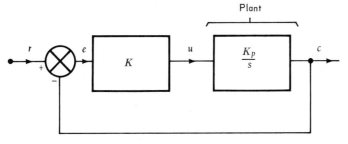

Fig. 7-5   Simple first-order system used in Example 7-1.

7-3.1 THE ANALYTICAL APPROACH—TWO EXAMPLES

Example 7-1

First, we shall synthesize two servomechanisms by making use of the analytical approach.   The first system is depicted in block-diagram form in Fig. 7-5.   The plant is exceedingly simple, consisting of a simple integrator.   We propose to use proportional control for simplicity, and our synthesis problem thus is reduced to finding a proper gain setting K.   To obtain a better physical feel for what we are doing, we can consider the level regulator shown in Fig. 7-6.   The controller, i.e., the pump, controls the fluid level c by supplying fluid at the rate of u ft^3/sec to the container.   If the container cross section is A, we have

$$u = A\dot{c}$$

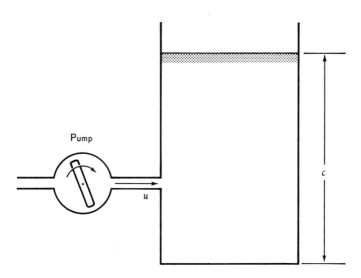

Fig. 7-6   Physical process having a plant transfer function of the integrator type.

Therefore,

$$\frac{C(s)}{U(s)} = \frac{1}{As} \triangleq \frac{K_p}{s} \tag{7-8}$$

If we further assume, in order to preserve linearity, that the pump rate is proportional to the level error,† that is,

$$u = Ke$$

then this regulator will be represented properly by the model in Fig. 7-5.

The open-loop transfer function is

$$G(s) = \frac{KK_p}{s}$$

and the closed-loop transfer-function representation is therefore

$$G_c(s) = \frac{G(s)}{1 + G(s)} = \frac{KK_p/s}{1 + KK_p/s} \triangleq \frac{K_c}{s + K_c} \tag{7-9}$$

where, for brevity, we have introduced

$$K_c \triangleq KK_p \tag{7-10}$$

The output response to a unit input step is obviously

$$c(t) = 1 - e^{-K_c t} \tag{7-11}$$

In deciding upon proper gain setting, we need a figure of merit I which in some meaningful manner measures the performance of the regulator. We shall demonstrate the different design solutions that we arrive at by using two different performance indices of the types (7-2) and (7-3).

case 1 Try $I = \displaystyle\int_0^\infty e^2 \, dt$ (ISE criterion). As the error $e = e^{-K_c t}$, we thus obtain

$$I = \int_0^\infty e^{-2K_c t} \, dt = \frac{1}{2K_c} = \frac{1}{2K_p K} \tag{7-12}$$

The variation of I versus gain setting is shown in graph in Fig. 7-7. We conclude that the higher the gain we choose, the "better" the system gets.

This result may satisfy a mathematician, but a control engineer should feel a little uncomfortable about it. There is obviously something wrong with the ISE criterion in this case. Increasing the gain means, in effect, increasing the pump size, and if we chose the gain that the ISE criterion tells us we should, we would need quite a pump.

---

† It is much more probable that one would design this controller with *maximum-effort* pumping action.

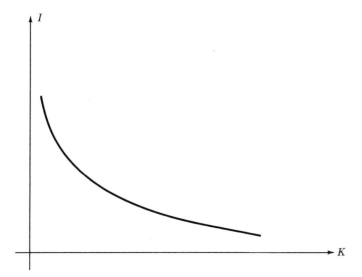

Fig. 7-7   The I measure as a function of K in case 1.

Sound engineering judgment tells us that we must include in our figure of merit the "cost" of the control effort. We can do this in many ways; in this case, we shall select:

case 2

$$I = \int_0^\infty (e^2 + \alpha u^3) \, dt \tag{7-13}$$

where $\alpha > 0$.

Before we proceed to find a new design based on this more elaborate criterion, let us explain each part of it. We note that, as in the previous case, the error still is penalized in ISE sense. The second term represents the cost of the control effort. This cost figure would certainly be most realistic if chosen proportional to pump power. The power rating of a pump depends upon many factors, such as flow rate and pressure difference. We shall assume here that the pressure difference is zero; power is then only needed for accelerating the fluid. The power is thus equal to kinetic energy (mass × velocity^2) imparted per second. We have

Mass $\sim u$

Velocity $\sim u$

Therefore,

Power $\sim u^3$

The proportional constant is included in the α factor, which must serve also as a weighting factor expressing the ratio between control and error costs.

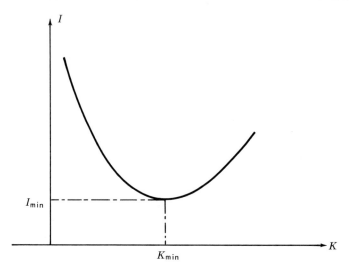

Fig. 7-8   *I* as a function of *K* in case 2.

Using as before the error obtained from Eq. (7-11), we now obtain a new *I* figure:

$$I = \int_0^\infty (e^2 + \alpha K^3 e^3)\, dt = \frac{1}{2K_c} + \frac{\alpha K^3}{3K_c} = \frac{1}{K_p}\left(\frac{1}{2K} + \frac{\alpha K^2}{3}\right) \tag{7-14}$$

The graph in Fig. 7-8 depicts the variation of *I* versus *K*. We note that the index of performance is minimized if the gain setting is chosen

$$K_{\min} = \sqrt[3]{\frac{3}{4\alpha}} \tag{7-15}$$

which we shall define therefore as our "best" choice. Of course, it is still up to the designer to decide on a proper α value. Indeed, this simple example was chosen in order to demonstrate how many rather arbitrary decisions will have to be made by somebody before a final design can be reached. In summarizing, we conclude that decisions had to be made in regard to:

1. System configuration
2. General type of PS
3. Cost of error
4. Cost of control

Example 7-2

As a second example of analytic synthesis, we shall complete our design of the broom balancer, which, as the reader may remember, we left half-finished (see Chap. 2). We had concluded that an "acceptable" response was obtained by introducing derivative control, which resulted in artificial damping of the system. We never settled the question, however, of *how much* damping we should build into the system. We shall now try to decide upon a choice by applying a reasonable figure of merit.

As this particular system was classified as a *regulator* rather than a *servo*, its performance should be judged upon its ability to return to its set point ($\varphi = 0$) rather than upon its ability to follow a changing input, as it will never be used in this way.

Equation (2-24) was derived on this assumption; it gives the φ dynamics following an initial arbitrary offset φ_0. We shall restate the equation for easy reference

$$\ddot{\varphi} + 2\alpha\dot{\varphi} + \omega^2\varphi = 0 \qquad\qquad (7\text{-}16) = (2\text{-}24)$$

The parameter ω determines the speed of response and can be adjusted by the motor gain [Eq. (2-11)]. The derivative feedback, and thus the damping, is controlled by adjusting the parameter α [Eq. (2-25)]. The graphs in Fig. 7-9 indicate the change of response when α is varied throughout the range

$$0 < \alpha < \infty$$

[Note that the response for $\alpha = \infty$ is obtained very simply from (7-16) by neglecting all terms except the second one, that is,

$$2\alpha\dot{\varphi} = 0$$

Hence,

$$\varphi = \text{const} = \varphi_0]$$

We decide again to choose a criterion which will penalize the "error" (φ, in this case) and its duration, and we select for that purpose the ISE criterion. We make the observation from the graphs in Fig. 7-9*a* and *e* that for very small and very large damping, the ISE figure of merit must approach ∞. The intermediate graphs (Fig. 7-9*b* to *d*) seem to indicate a *finite* figure of merit for finite nonzero α values.

It is reasonable to assume, therefore, that a specific α value should result in a minimization of the figure of merit, and we set out to find this optimum value α_{opt}.

Equation (7-16) has already been integrated [Eq. (2-26)]:

$$\varphi = \varphi_0 \frac{\omega}{\omega_0} e^{-\alpha t} \sin\left(\omega_0 t + \tan^{-1}\frac{\omega_0}{\alpha}\right) \qquad\qquad (7\text{-}17) = (2\text{-}26)$$

where

$$\omega_0 \overset{\Delta}{=} \sqrt{\omega^2 - \alpha^2}$$

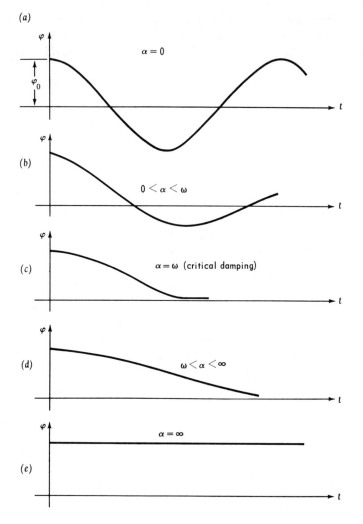

Fig. 7-9 The response of the broom balancer as a function of velocity damping factor α.

and φ_0 equals the initial offset. We note that this equation holds true even for the *overdamped* case, i.e., for $\alpha > \omega$, if we observe the identities

$$\sin jx = j \sinh x$$

$$\tan^{-1} jx = j \tanh^{-1} x$$

We next compute, in ISE sense, the figure of merit

$$I = \int_0^\infty \varphi^2 \, dt$$

By introducing the φ solution (7-17) into this integral and performing the required integration, we obtain the following remarkably simple expression for the performance measure:

$$I = I(\alpha,\omega) = \frac{\varphi_0{}^2}{\omega} \frac{1 + 4(\alpha/\omega)^2}{4(\alpha/\omega)} \qquad (7\text{-}18)$$

(Again, this equation holds true for both underdamped and overdamped cases.)

We have plotted I versus the relative (or normalized) damping ratio α/ω in Fig. 7-10. As we predicted, I will experience a minimum

$$I_{min} = \frac{\varphi_0{}^2}{\omega}$$

for an $\alpha = \alpha_{opt}$ that occurs in the middle of the underdamped region. The minimum is quite flat—a variation of α throughout the range -50 to $+100$ percent of α_{opt} results only in a maximum 20 percent increase in the figure of merit. This seems to indicate that the ISE criterion has rather poor selectivity in this case. We can also interpret this to mean that the α setting is not too important. The reader is free to pick his own interpretation.

We note that we can reduce the I_{min} to an arbitrary degree by increasing ω, that is, by speeding up the response. This, of course, will take place at the cost

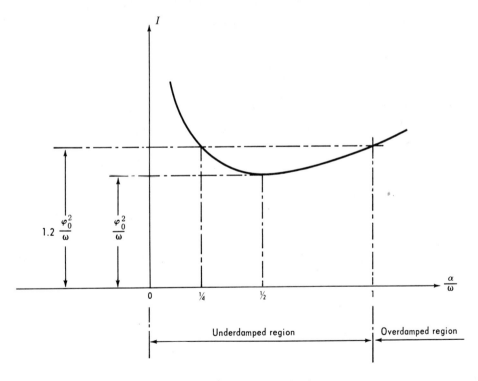

Fig. 7-10 The ISE measure as a function of damping ratio α/ω.

of increased control effort and increased motor size. If this is an important consideration in the speed range we are interested in, then we must include the cost of control in our figure of merit in a manner similar to that which was demonstrated in the previous example.

The two examples just treated have confirmed a certain directness characterizing the analytical design method. Once we have selected a system configuration and a figure of merit, we proceed in a straightforward, direct fashion to obtain the optimum parameter settings. The only difficulties we may run into are of a purely computational nature. As long as we work with deterministic signals and quadratic criteria (like ISE), the mathematics, as a rule, turns out to be simple. If we had used the ITAE criterion (see Exercise 7-1) in the last example, we would have obtained a better selectivity but at a computational price.

We shall proceed to discuss trial-and-error synthesis methods, but for the moment we shall digress in order to present a very necessary design tool—the root-locus technique.

7-3.2 THE ROOT-LOCUS METHOD (RLM)

The RLM, introduced by Evans[7] in 1948, won early popular acclaim and has since become our most important synthesis technique for single-input–single-output linear servomechanisms. The RLM is a mixed graphical-analytical procedure that has been used with surprising success even in the study of moderately nonlinear systems and systems with slowly time-varying parameters. The method is particularly suited for synthesis in those cases where the performance specifications are given in the time domain, but as it is very simple to obtain all important frequency-response data directly from a root-locus plot, the RLM can also be employed when the PS are given in the frequency domain. The basic idea underlying the RLM is very simple. We have learned how the closed-loop eigenvalues or the poles of the closed-loop transfer function

$$G_c(s) = \frac{G(s)}{1 + G(s)H(s)}$$

completely determine the response of the servomechanism. It would therefore prove extremely valuable if we possessed a *simple* method whereby we could keep track of the changing positions of these poles in the s plane as we, during our synthesis process, try out various parameter choices. The RLM will do just that. More specifically, by means of this method we can find the traces ($=$ loci) in the s plane of the eigenvalues as they, under the influence of changing parameter values, move in distinct patterns (root loci) across the s plane.

Actually, we already have encountered an example of how such loci may be found—we are referring to Fig. 6-4, which depicts the movements in the s plane of the eigenvalues of the velocity servo characterized by the open-loop transfer function

$$G(s) = \frac{K}{s(1 + sT)}$$

subject to variations of the open-loop gain factor K. The example is far from representative, as it was possible to obtain these loci by *direct solution* of the second-order characteristic equation

$$1 + G(s) = 0$$

For instance, it would turn out to be a problem of an entirely different magnitude to find in this manner the root loci for the third-order system

$$G(s) = \frac{K}{s^2(1 + sT)}$$

By comparison, making use of the techniques we are about to present, we find it about as easy to construct the root loci for a third-, or higher-, order system as for a second-order one. This *elimination of the dimensionality barrier* is one of the reasons for the popularity of the RLM.

Before we enter into the details of root-locus construction, it is appropriate to discuss some of the uses we can make of the information obtained from such loci. It turns out that if we possess full information concerning the location of the closed-loop poles and zeros, we can obtain directly not only the time response but also the frequency response for a system. Furthermore, it is possible from the pole-zero configuration to draw some extremely valuable conclusions concerning the relative importance of the different eigenvalues.

Time Response from Root-locus Plot

Consider first the relationship between the transient response of a servo and its closed-loop pole-zero configuration. For the system depicted in Fig. 6-8 (only the scalar case is considered), it will be assumed that the n closed-loop eigenvalues (or poles) λ_j and m zeros z_i are known and that we therefore can express the closed-loop transfer function $G_c(s)$ in the following form:

$$G_c(s) = \frac{G(s)}{1 + G(s)H(s)} = K_c \frac{(s - z_1)(s - z_2) \cdots (s - z_m)}{(s - \lambda_1)(s - \lambda_2) \cdots (s - \lambda_n)}$$

$$= K_c \frac{\prod\limits^{m} (s - z_i)}{\prod\limits_{n} (s - \lambda_j)} \tag{7-19}$$

The n eigenvalues λ_j must all be located in the left half of the s plane for preservation of stability.

Note that the closed-loop gain constant K_c is *not* an independent variable (as is the case with the open-loop gain) but actually can be expressed in terms of the z_i's and the λ_j's. For instance, if we assume that this system has a zero FVE for a unit-step input, then K_c can be computed as follows:

As we know that $c(t)$ must approach unity as t approaches ∞, we get, by using the final-value theorem,

$$c(\infty) = 1 = \lim_{s \to 0} \left[s \frac{1}{s} \frac{G(s)}{1 + G(s)H(s)} \right] = K_c \frac{\prod\limits^{m} (-z_i)}{\prod\limits_{n} (-\lambda_j)}$$

Therefore,

$$K_c = \frac{\prod\limits^{n}(-\lambda_j)}{\prod\limits^{m}(-z_i)} \tag{7-20}$$

Equation (7-19) thus yields

$$G_c(s) = \frac{\prod\limits^{n}(-\lambda_j) \prod\limits^{m}(s - z_i)}{\prod\limits^{m}(-z_i) \prod\limits^{n}(s - \lambda_j)} \tag{7-21}$$

From this formula, we are able to obtain a very useful expression for the response of the system to a step input. If we assume that the eigenvalues λ_j are distinct, we get

$$C(s) = \frac{1}{s} G_c(s) = \frac{1}{s} + \frac{A_1}{s - \lambda_1} + \frac{A_2}{s - \lambda_2} + \cdots + \frac{A_n}{s - \lambda_n} \tag{7-22}$$

Therefore,

$$c(t) = 1 + \sum_{k=1}^{n} A_k e^{\lambda_k t} \tag{7-23}$$

The amplitudes A_k are obtained from Eq. (7-22) by first multiplying Eq. (7-22) by the factor $(s - \lambda_k)$ and then letting s approach λ_k.

This procedure yields

$$A_k = -\frac{\prod\limits^{n}_*(-\lambda_j) \prod\limits^{m}(\lambda_k - z_i)}{\prod\limits^{m}(-z_i) \prod\limits^{n}_*(\lambda_k - \lambda_j)} \tag{7-24}$$

(The symbol $\prod_*$ defines the product over all j except $j = k$.)

This formula permits us to obtain the response of a system *directly*, once its closed-loop pole-zero configuration is known.

Example 7-3

Consider, for instance, the system depicted in Fig. 7-11, having one closed-loop zero and three closed-loop poles, the latter located as follows:†

$$\lambda_1 = -2 + j2$$
$$\lambda_2 = -2 - j2$$
$$\lambda_3 = -1$$

The response of this system to a step input will thus be

$$c(t) = 1 + A_1 e^{(-2+j2)t} + A_2 e^{(-2-j2)t} + A_3 e^{-t}$$

† Disregard the vectors $v_1 \ldots v_4$, which relate to Example 7-4.

Using formula 7-24, we obtain the amplitudes A_1, A_2, and A_3:

$$A_1 = -\frac{(2+j2)1}{3}\frac{(-2+j2+3)}{(-2+j2+2+j2)(-2+j2+1)} = \frac{1}{30} + j\frac{7}{30}$$

$$A_2 = -\frac{(2-j2)1}{3}\frac{(-2-j2+3)}{(-2-j2+2-j2)(-2-j2+1)} = \frac{1}{30} - j\frac{7}{30}$$

$$A_3 = -\frac{(2-j2)(2+j2)}{3}\frac{(-1+3)}{(-1+2-j2)(-1+2+j2)} = -\frac{16}{15}$$

The time response will thus be

$$c(t) = 1 + (\tfrac{1}{30} + j\tfrac{7}{30})e^{(-2+j2)t} + (\tfrac{1}{30} - j\tfrac{7}{30})e^{(-2-j2)t} - \tfrac{16}{15}e^{-t}$$
$$= 1 + (\tfrac{1}{15}\cos 2t - \tfrac{7}{15}\sin 2t)e^{-2t} - \tfrac{16}{15}e^{-t}$$

Frequency Response from Root-locus Plot

The closed-loop frequency response of a system having the closed-loop transfer function (7-19) is uniquely determined from the FTF

$$G_c(j\omega) = \frac{G(j\omega)}{1 + G(j\omega)H(j\omega)} \tag{7-25}$$

By utilizing Eq. (7-21), we obtain directly the closed-loop FTF

$$G_c(j\omega) = \frac{\prod\limits^{n}(-\lambda_j)\prod\limits^{m}(j\omega - z_i)}{\prod\limits^{m}(-z_i)\prod\limits^{n}(j\omega - \lambda_j)} \tag{7-26}$$

We make the following two observations:

1. When ω approaches zero the closed-loop FTF approaches unity. This of course is a consequence of the fact that we derived Eq. (7-21) under the assumption of zero FVE.

2. For all physical systems, we must of necessity require that

$$\lim_{\omega \to \infty} G_c(j\omega) \to 0$$

This evidently requires that $n > m$; that is, the number of closed-loop poles must exceed the number of closed-loop zeros.†

Example 7-4

Find the closed-loop FTF for the system having the pole-zero configuration depicted in Fig. 7-11.

We obtain directly from Eq. (7-26)

$$G_c(j\omega) = \frac{1(2 - j2)(2 + j2)}{3}\frac{v_4}{v_1 v_2 v_3}$$

† If the reader ever encounters a case where this does not occur, it means that the mathematical model is inaccurate for high frequencies.

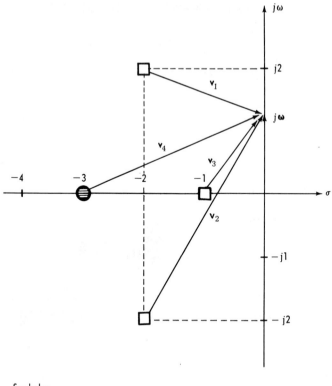

Symbols:

☐   Closed-loop pole or eigenvalue

⬿   Closed-loop zero

Fig. 7-11   Pole-zero configuration for the system in Example 7-3.

The four vectors $\mathbf{v}_1 \cdots \mathbf{v}_4$ are defined in Fig. 7-11.   By letting the vector **jω** vary from **j0** through **j∞** we obviously can obtain graphically the total frequency response of the system.

If the conjugate complex pole pair in Fig. 7-11 is moving close to the *jω* axis a very important relationship between the frequency and the time response of the system becomes apparent.   In the *time response*, the slightly damped oscillatory term of frequency $\omega = 2$ becomes dominant, resulting in long settling time. In the *frequency response*, we obtain due to the vector $\mathbf{v}_1$ a very pronounced M peak at a frequency $\omega_p \approx 2$.   If the pole pair were actually to coincide with the *jω* axis we would clearly get $M_p = \infty$ and $\omega_p = 2$.

Dominant Poles

The above example demonstrated that a slightly damped pole pair dominates the response of a servo simply through slow decay.   This usually is never permitted to occur as the performance specifications as a rule put limits on either M peak or settling time.

The designer often will eliminate the undesired influence of a particular pole or pole pair by simply removing it sufficiently far from the remaining pole cluster with a resulting *reduction in amplitude* of the corresponding response term. We confirm this effect directly from Eq. (7-24). Assume that the pole with the effect we wish to eliminate is λ_k. If λ_k is sufficiently far from the rest of the poles we have

$$|\lambda_k| \gg |\lambda_j| \qquad \text{for } j = 1 \ 2, \ldots, n; \text{ except } j = k$$

Equation (7-24) then yields

$$A_k \sim \frac{1}{\lambda_k^{n-m}} \tag{7-27}$$

We earlier agreed that $n > m$, and we thus conclude from Eq. (7-27) that the importance of amplitude A_k diminishes as λ_k is pushed farther and farther away.

It should be noted that the importance of λ_k is being reduced not only because of vanishing amplitude but also because of *fast decay*.

Example 7-5

Consider the closed-loop pole configuration in Fig. 7-12, which, as the reader will remember, represents the overdamped velocity servo discussed in Chap. 6 (Fig. 6-4). We compute the amplitudes using Eq. (7-24)

$$A_1 = \frac{\lambda_2}{\lambda_1 - \lambda_2}$$

$$A_2 = \frac{\lambda_1}{\lambda_2 - \lambda_1}$$

Therefore,

$$\frac{A_1}{A_2} = -\frac{\lambda_2}{\lambda_1}$$

that is, the relative magnitude of the two components is inversely proportional to the distance to the origin of the eigenvalues. Consider, for instance, the numerical case

$$\lambda_1 = -1$$
$$\lambda_2 = -5$$

The exact response for a unit-step input will be

$$c(t) = 1 - 1.25e^{-t} + 0.25e^{-5t}$$

By including only the dominant term, we obtain an *approximate* expression

$$c(t) \approx 1 - 1.25e^{-t}$$

A comparison between the approximate and exact responses is shown in Fig. 7-12, and the graph records that the agreement is good except around $t = 0$.

We note, by the way, that just as the dominant pole shapes the time response, it also determines the main features of the frequency response. It is suggested that the reader demonstrate this in the present example.

The fact that those poles located closest to the origin generally are the main contributors to the system response is utilized quite frequently in the early phases of the synthesis process. It permits the designer to obtain a fairly good approximation of the response by simply taking into account a very few of the poles of the total pole configuration.

It is possible to *tabulate* the unit-step response for a number of often encountered, simple pole-zero configurations. The graphs in Fig. 7-13 are examples. These curves depict the response to a unit-step input for a servo

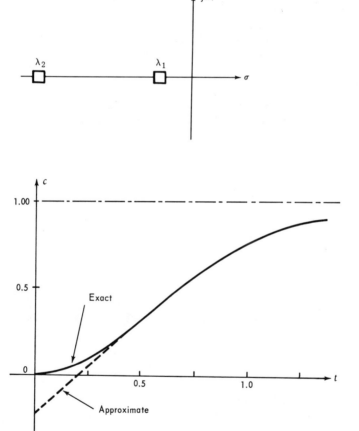

Fig. 7-12   Example showing the relative importance of poles.

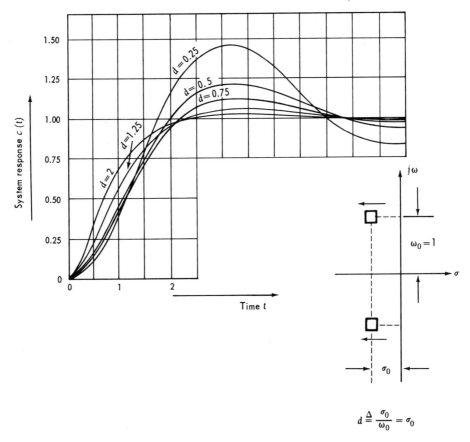

Fig. 7-13 Example of tabulated "response." The graph depicts the step-function response for a system having the *closed-loop* pole configuration shown in the figure. The response is given for five different σ_0 values and for "normalized" $\omega_0 = 1$.

characterized by a conjugate complex pole pair, as shown in the figure.† The different graphs correspond to various positions of the pole pair as they move to the left into the stable half of the *s* plane. The curves have been *normalized*; i.e., the imaginary pole part ω_0 has been set to unity. In this way, it is easy to extend their usage to other value pairs. For example, assume that we wish to know the time response for a system characterized by a complex pole pair

$$\lambda_{1,2} = \sigma_1 \pm j\omega_1 = -20 \pm j10$$

† These curves are borrowed from a report by Elgerd and Stephens.[8] The report contains 25 curve sheets covering a variety of pole-zero configurations, from one single pole to a configuration consisting of three poles and two zeros. A copy of the report can be obtained from Florida Engineering and Industrial Experiment Station, College of Engineering, University of Florida, Gainesville, Fla.

First, we compute the parameter d:

$$d = \frac{20}{10} = 2.0$$

We therefore use the curve labeled $d = 2$.   However, the time scale in the graph corresponds to $\omega_0 = 1$, and as we now have

$$\omega_1 = 10\omega_0$$

we must speed up all the readings with a factor of 10.

Curves of this type can be of great assistance in the early design stages to give a *rough estimate* of the time response.   We shall exemplify later in this chapter.

Construction of Root Loci

In summarizing the findings on the previous pages, we conclude that knowledge of the location of the closed-loop poles λ_j and zeros z_i permits us to obtain direct information concerning the closed-loop

1. Time response
2. Frequency response
3. Possible pole dominance, which allows certain approximations in the time and frequency domains

Note that all factors contained in the two fundamental formulas (7-24) and (7-26) may be represented as *vectors* in the s plane, as was demonstrated in Fig. 7-11.   This fact evidently permits us to perform all associated computations quickly (but with a few percent inaccuracy) based on data obtained *graphically*. We already have mentioned that the root-locus method gives us information concerning the eigenvalues in *graphical* form; this method is therefore particularly useful in combination with the above formulas.   We shall proceed now with a presentation of the basic features of this method.

The "roots" that the method refers to are the roots of the characteristic equation

$$1 + G(s)H(s) = 0 \tag{7-28}$$

We shall prefer, however, to refer to them as the closed-loop poles or eigenvalues λ_j.

In what follows, we shall assume that both transfer functions $G(s)$ and $H(s)$ are expressed as ratios of the form

$$K \frac{\prod (s - \text{zeros})}{\prod (s - \text{poles})}$$

As it will be necessary to refer to "poles" and "zeros" repeatedly in our following discussions and as it is of the utmost importance that we do not confuse the poles and zeros of the three different transfer functions G, H, and G_c, we shall settle first for an unambiguous choice of terminology and symbols.   Table 7-2 summarizes our choice.   Note that in assigning symbols to the H and G poles, we have made no distinction between them.   This also applies to the G and H zeros.   The reason is that the characteristic equation (7-28), which will

Table 7-2   Definition of pole and zero symbols

Transfer functions	Mathematical symbol	Graphical symbol	Name
$G_c(s)$			
Poles	λ	□	Closed-loop poles or eigenvalues
Zeros	z	◎	Closed-loop zeros
$G(s)$			
Poles	P	×	G poles
Zeros	Z	○	G zeros
$H(s)$			
Poles	P	×	H poles
Zeros	Z	○	H zeros

serve as the starting point for our search for the root loci, contains G and H in form of the *product GH*. It obviously does not matter whether the poles or zeros belong to G or H. In such cases, where a distinction is unnecessary, we shall use the terminology "*HG* poles" P and "*HG* zeros" Z.

However, in determining the position of the closed-loop *zeros*, it *is* important to distinguish between the two. If we pay proper attention to this one exception (see rule 1 below), we should not run into any difficulties with our choice of notation.

The locations of the closed-loop poles and zeros are functions of $G(s)$ and $H(s)$. The zeros z_i will, as a rule, be *fixed*, whereas the poles will *move* along the above-mentioned root loci as we vary the parameters in the loop. The actual procedures for pinpointing these fixed zero positions and for the construction of the root loci will be given now in the form of a set of rules.

Determining the position of the z_i's is the simplest part of our job, and we shall devote the first in our series of rules to this task.

rule 1   *The closed-loop zeros z_i coincide with the G zeros and the H poles.*

The statement of the rule is proved directly by examining the expression for the closed-loop transfer function

$$G_c(s) = \frac{G(s)}{1 + H(s)G(s)} = \frac{K_G \dfrac{\prod (s - G \text{ zeros})}{\prod (s - G \text{ poles})}}{1 + K_H \dfrac{\prod (s - H \text{ zeros})}{\prod (s - H \text{ poles})} K_G \dfrac{\prod (s - G \text{ zeros})}{\prod (s - G \text{ poles})}}$$

$$= \frac{K_G \prod (s - G \text{ zeros}) \prod (s - H \text{ poles})}{\prod (s - G \text{ poles}) \prod (s - H \text{ poles}) + K_G K_H \prod (s - G \text{ zeros}) \prod (s - H \text{ zeros})}$$

We thus confirm the necessity of carefully distinguishing between the H and G functions in this case.   All the following rules will be concerned with the problem of constructing the loci for the eigenvalues; therefore, from now on, we may combine these two transfer functions into *one* inseparable block *HG*.

rule 2   *The root loci will always be symmetrical with respect to the σ axis.   Sections of the σ axis may constitute part of the loci.*

This rule follows as an immediate consequence of the fact that the eigenvalues obtained from the characteristic equation (7-28) are either real or conjugate complex or are a combination of both.

rule 3   *The general character of the root loci is obtained by satisfying the angular part of Eq. (7-28). The specific positions of the eigenvalues λ_j along the loci are determined from the modular part.*

Equation (7-28) can be written

$$K \frac{\prod\limits^{q} (s - Z)}{\prod\limits^{n} (s - P)} = -1 \tag{7-29}$$

where K is the total open-loop gain and n and q represent the number of *HG* poles and zeros, respectively.   (Note that, in general, $q \neq m =$ the number of closed-loop zeros.)   This equation is *complex*, and therefore we can separate it into two parts:

1. The *modular* part

$$K \frac{\prod\limits^{q} |s - Z|}{\prod\limits^{n} |s - P|} = 1 \tag{7-30}$$

2. The *angular* part

$$\sum^{q} \underline{/s - Z} - \sum^{n} \underline{/s - P} = -\pi + v2\pi \tag{7-31}$$

v is a positive integer that can assume the values

$$v = 0, 1, 2, \ldots, n - q - 1$$

The eigenvalues must satisfy *both* Eqs. (7-30) and (7-31).   We note, however, that the modular equation can be satisfied for *any* s value in the s plane by proper adjustment of K.   We therefore must rely on the angular equation for our locus search.   It is quite clear that only along certain curves (loci) in the s plane can we find s values that satisfy the angular requirements.   Once these are found, we can use the modular equation to pinpoint exactly *where* on the loci a specific gain setting K places the eigenvalues.

The situation is exemplified in Fig. 7-14, showing the search for the root loci for a system having two *HG* poles and one *HG* zero.   We note first that

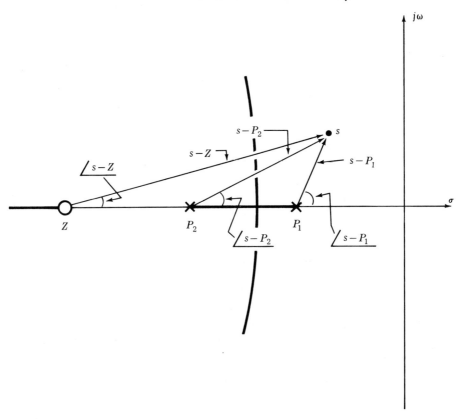

Fig. 7-14   Search of root loci for system having two open-loop poles and one zero.

wherever we place the point *s*, we can assign a *K* value that satisfies the modular equation

$$K \frac{|s - Z|}{|s - P_1| \, |s - P_2|} = 1$$

However, the angular equation

$$\underline{/s - Z} - \underline{/s - P_1} - \underline{/s - P_2} = -\pi$$

is much more selective.

We immediately conclude, however, that the boldface portions of the negative σ axis must satisfy the latter equation.   Generally, these portions of the root loci are always the easiest to find and can be identified by direct inspection.

It also seems reasonable that, apart from these portions of the real axis, we are able to satisfy the angular requirements along a curve of the type shown boldface in the figure.   It is more time-consuming to find the exact nature of these portions.   The procedure is a trial-and-error one, as follows:

1. Select a point s_1 that seems a reasonable choice.
2. Measure the three angles $\underline{/s_1 - Z}$, $\underline{/s_1 - P_1}$, and $\underline{/s_1 - P_2}$.
3. If the angles satisfy the angular equation, the choice was good and we can proceed with a new point.
4. If the angular equation is not satisfied, make an appropriate correction in s_1 and test again.

As a rule, this type of search converges very fast and is indeed one of the main selling points of the RLM.

rule 4   *There are a total of n root-locus branches, each starting from one of the n HG poles for a gain setting that approaches zero.*

We note that for vanishing K, the modular equation (7-30) can be satisfied only if *any one* of the n vector magnitudes $|s - P|$ is permitted to approach zero.   Low-magnitude K values therefore place the eigenvalues close to *each* of the *HG* poles.

Take, for example, the pole-zero configuration depicted in Fig. 7-14.   We already have concluded that the portion of the σ axis that is located between the two poles P_1 and P_2 constitutes part of the loci.

By application of rule 4, we thus conclude that the two eigenvalues λ_1 and λ_2 start out their s-plane journey in the fashion depicted in Fig. 7-15.

rule 5   *For very high loop gain, the root loci will either approach any one of the q HG zeros or end up in infinity.*

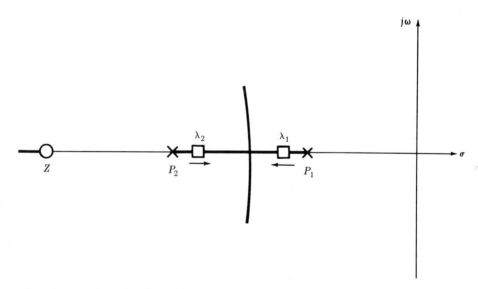

Fig. 7-15   The eigenvalues λ_1 and λ_2 must start their s-plane journey from the open-loop poles P_1 and P_2.

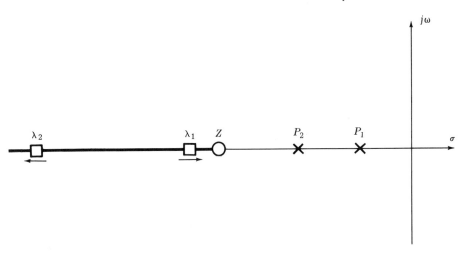

Fig. 7-16 The eigenvalues must end their *s*-plane journey either in the zero or in infinity.

The first part of this rule is verified directly from the modular equation (7-30). However, as there are only q zeros, the remaining $n - q$ root-locus branches must end up elsewhere. We note that for high gain values, Eq. (7-30) can be satisfied not only by forcing the factors $s - Z$ to zero *but also* by letting all the factors in both numerator and denominator take on very large values.† In other words, those loci which do not end up on the zeros Z must tend to infinity.

rule 6 *Those n-q loci which tend to infinity will do so along straight-line asymptotes.*

For large s, the angular equation (7-31) tends to

$$(n - q)\underline{/s} \to \pi - \nu 2\pi \qquad \nu = 0, 1, 2, \ldots, n - q - 1$$

The loci therefore must tend to infinity along asymptotes forming the *constant* angles

$$\underline{/s} = \frac{\pi - \nu 2\pi}{n - q} \qquad \nu = 0, 1, \ldots, n - q - 1 \tag{7-32}$$

with the positive σ axis. The asymptotes are thus straight lines.

For example, the system depicted in Fig. 7-14 has *one* asymptote forming a 180° angle with the positive σ axis. As there is only one locus tending to infinity and as we must obey rule 2, the negative σ axis is not only the asymptote but also the locus. Figure 7-16 depicts the asymptotic behavior of the eigenvalues as K tends to infinity.

rule 7 *All asymptotes must pass through the "center of gravity" (CG) of the HG pole-zero cluster. The CG is computed on the basis that all poles have the mass +1 and all zeros the mass −1.*

† Note that the denominator of the modular equation is of higher order than the numerator.

For a proof, consider the picture in Fig. 7-17. We draw lines from a point *s* far out on the asymptote to each of the *n* poles and *q* zeros. The angular equation (7-31) must be satisfied for the point *s*, which means, in effect, that we must require

$$\alpha_1 + \alpha_2 + \cdots + \alpha_n - (\beta_1 + \beta_2 + \cdots + \beta_q) = 0$$

The α's and β's are defined in Fig. 7-17.

As all these angles are *small*, we can write this equation in terms of the distances a_ν and b_μ (also defined in the figure), which are proportional to α_ν and β_μ, respectively. Thus,

$$a_1 + a_2 + \cdots + a_n - (b_1 + b_2 + \cdots + b_q) = 0 \qquad (7\text{-}33)$$

The asymptote must pass through the pole-zero cluster in such a way that this equation is satisfied. Equation (7-33) can be written

$$0 = \sum_{\nu=1}^{n}(+1)a_\nu + \sum_{\mu=1}^{q}(-1)b_\mu$$

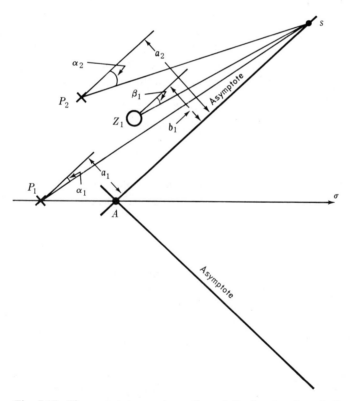

Fig. 7-17 The asymptotes must pass through the "center of gravity" of the open-loop pole-zero cluster.

The right side equals the total moment of all the "masses" of the poles and zeros with respect to the asymptote, and this moment equals zero only if the asymptote passes through the center of gravity.

rule 8   *The angle measured relative to the σ axis at which a locus leaves a pole P_k will be referred to as "angle of departure" φ_{dep}. It can be computed from the formula*

$$\varphi_{dep} = \pi + \sum_{i=1}^{q} \underline{/P_k - Z_i} - \sum_{j=1}^{n} {}_* \underline{/P_k - P_j} \tag{7-34}$$

(The symbol Σ_* implies summation over all j except $j = k$.)

For a proof consider a point s_1 located on the locus leaving the pole P_k. The "angle of departure" equals

$$\varphi_{dep} = \lim_{s_1 \to P_k} (\underline{/s_1 - P_k})$$

The formula (7-34) is obtained directly from Eq. (7-31) after the indicated limit process has been performed.

Quite often one encounters systems having double poles on the real axis. Such a double pole will serve as the starting point for *two* locus branches. The angles of departure for these loci are either 0 and π or $\pm\pi/2$. The proof is left as an exercise for the reader.

rule 9   *The angle at which a locus arrives at a zero Z_k will be referred to as "angle of arrival" φ_{arr}. It can be computed from the formula*

$$\varphi_{arr} = -\pi + \sum_{j=1}^{n} \underline{/Z_k - P_j} - \sum_{i=1}^{q} {}_* \underline{/Z_k - Z_i} \tag{7-35}$$

The proof is performed in a fashion similar to that for Eq. (7-34).

rule 10   Our final rule concerns the determination of so-called "breakaway points," i.e., points on the σ axis where the loci enter or return from the complex region of the s plane. As it would be awkward to state this rule concisely, we shall instead illustrate the procedure with a simple example. Consider for this purpose the pole-zero configuration depicted in Fig. 7-14. We concluded that the two loci of this system start out as indicated in Fig. 7-15 and end up as shown in Fig. 7-16. The *only* way for this to be possible is for the root loci to make a swing out into the complex s plane, as shown in Fig. 7-18. In order to obtain an accurate picture, it is important to establish the exact location of the two breakaway points A and B. We shall demonstrate by fixing the exact position of point B. To that end, let us consider a point s_1 adjacent to the real axis at a distance x from origin. For this point to be on the locus, we must require the following relationship between the small angles α_1, α_2, and α_3:

$$\alpha_1 - \alpha_2 - (\pi - \alpha_3) = -\pi$$

Therefore,

$$\alpha_1 + \alpha_3 = \alpha_2$$

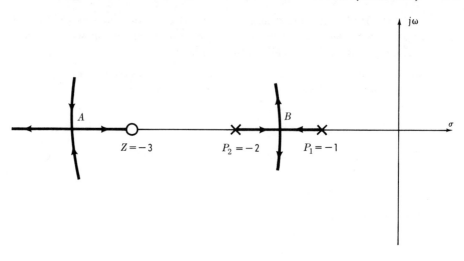

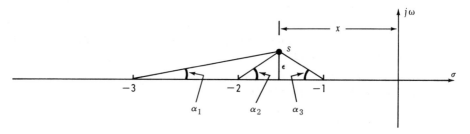

Fig. 7-18 Search for the breakaway points.

As these angles are small, we may replace the angles by the tangents

$$\frac{\epsilon}{3-x} + \frac{\epsilon}{x-1} = \frac{\epsilon}{2-x}$$

or

$$\frac{1}{3-x} + \frac{1}{x-1} = \frac{1}{2-x} \tag{7-36}$$

We solve this equation and obtain

$$x = 1.59$$

which fixes the breakaway point *B*. The exact position for *A* ($x = 4.41$) is obtained in a similar manner.

In this particular example, the equation for *x* is of second order. In the more general case, this would not be true, but as equations of the type (7-36) are quite simple to solve by trial and error, this poses no serious problem.

As we shall find opportunity to make use of the RLM in most of the synthesis problems in the next section, we shall postpone until then any further demonstration of the usage of the above rules.

7-3.3 SYNTHESIS BY TRIAL AND ERROR

Having defined "trial-and-error" synthesis in Sec. 7-2.1, we shall enter now into a more detailed discussion of this, the most common and probably also most useful and therefore most important of the known synthesis techniques. We already have indicated that in the great majority of actual design cases, the problem usually boils down to a suitable choice of either a *series* or a *feedback* compensator, as depicted in Figs. 6-1 and 6-2. We also have hinted at the usefulness of a *simulator* or an analog computer to speed up the actual design work. It is worthwhile to point out at this time that the role played by the analog computer is important indeed but that the computer, however sophisticated, is to be considered *only as a computational aid*. The human designer is entirely on his own when it comes to making the important decisions about performance specs, system structure, and type of controller.

The trial-and-error procedure should not, of course, be an aimless search for a "lucky-shot" type of solution. On the contrary, although the method is empirical in nature, it taxes heavily all the ingenuity and total system know-how that the designer possesses.

As we are concerned in this chapter only with *linear* systems, we shall limit our attention to those designs that render the controllers linear. It is appropriate at this time to remind the reader about the difference in the terms "controller" and "compensator," which will be used repeatedly in the following examples.

Controller is defined (Figs. 1-1, 6-1, and 6-2) as the totality of the control system, exclusive of the controlled plant with its output sensors. It contains, as its *active* part, the *actuator* (motor, hydraulics, etc.) that supplies the control forces and, as its *passive* part, the *compensators* (*filters, compensating networks, or equalizers*) that shape the system response.

The choice of the active components is usually quite limited since they, as a rule, are determined by the nature of the controlled plant. For instance, if our controlled plant is an aircraft, we have no choice but to select hydraulic actuators.

On the other hand, the system designer has at his disposal an almost limitless choice of passive components. Whether to use electrical, mechanical, pneumatic, or hydraulic compensators is a matter that has to be decided upon from case to case. Componentry lies outside the scope of this treatise; however, we cannot entirely divorce theory from practice. It is quite clear that the physical nature of the signals throughout the system constitutes an extremely important factor in the choice of components. The *availability* of these signals is also important and is quite often determining for the choice of series versus feedback compensation. The choice falls, in the majority of cases, on *electrical* components. Even in those cases where the signals are not electrical in nature, we often prefer to

No.	Network	Transfer function $\dfrac{E_{out}(s)}{E_{in}(s)}$	Pole-zero configuration
1	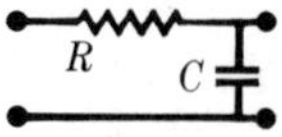 R C	$\dfrac{1}{T} \cdot \dfrac{1}{s+1/T}$ $T \triangleq RC$	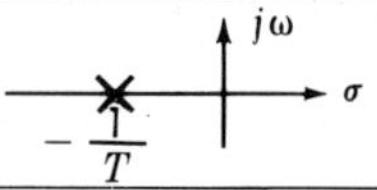 (pole at $-\frac{1}{T}$)
2	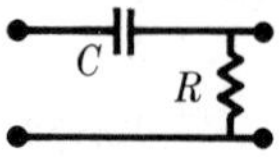 C R	$\dfrac{s}{s+1/T}$ $T \triangleq RC$	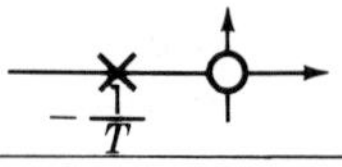 (pole at $-\frac{1}{T}$, zero at origin)
3	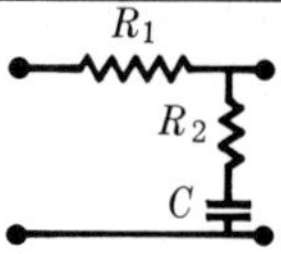 R_1 R_2 C	$\dfrac{1}{\alpha} \cdot \dfrac{s+1/T}{s+1/\alpha T}$ $\alpha \triangleq 1 + \dfrac{R_1}{R_2}$ $T \triangleq R_2 C$	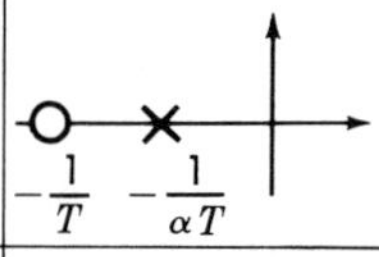 (zero at $-\frac{1}{T}$, pole at $-\frac{1}{\alpha T}$)
4	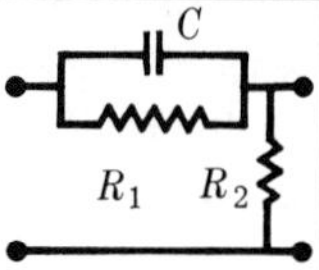 C R_1 R_2	$\dfrac{s+1/\alpha T}{s+1/T}$ $\alpha \triangleq 1 + \dfrac{R_1}{R_2}$ $T \triangleq C \dfrac{R_1 R_2}{R_1+R_2}$	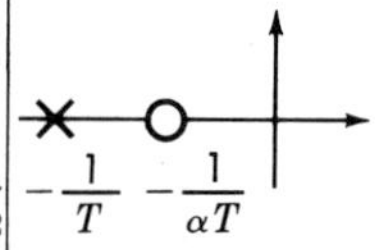 (pole at $-\frac{1}{T}$, zero at $-\frac{1}{\alpha T}$)
5	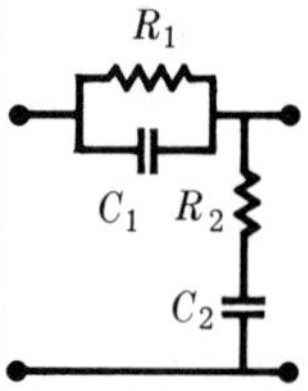 R_1 C_1 R_2 C_2	$\dfrac{(s+1/T_1)(s+1/T_2)}{(s+1/T_a)(s+1/T_b)}$ $T_1 \triangleq R_1 C_1$ $T_2 \triangleq R_2 C_2$ $T_{12} \triangleq C_1 R_2$ $\dfrac{1}{T_a T_b} \triangleq \dfrac{1}{T_1 T_2}$ $\dfrac{1}{T_a} + \dfrac{1}{T_b} \triangleq \dfrac{1}{T_1} + \dfrac{1}{T_2} + \dfrac{1}{T_{12}}$	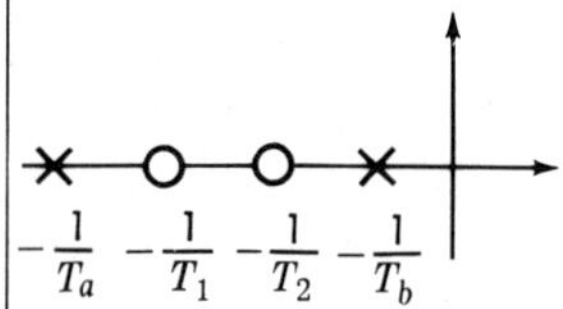 (poles at $-\frac{1}{T_a}$, $-\frac{1}{T_b}$; zeros at $-\frac{1}{T_1}$, $-\frac{1}{T_2}$)

Fig. 7-19   A selection of simple *RC* compensation networks and their transfer functions.

transform them by means of *transducers* into electrical signals for reasons of simplified transmission, increased reliability, reduced component weights, and maximum accuracy.   To this we can add that it is far more convenient to compensate electrical signals than any other physical variety.   The table in Fig. 7-19 contains the most commonly used electrical equalizers together with their transfer functions and corresponding pole-zero configurations.   A surprisingly large number of practical compensation jobs can be accomplished with the entries in this table.   (Note that the transfer functions in the table are computed on the basis of zero output current.)

   The following set of synthesis problems will demonstrate some of the more important aspects of synthesis by trial and error.   In an actual situation, the designer would quite probably be in a position to make use of an analog computer, thereby bypassing much of the numerical drudgery that we must either tackle or, in serious cases, only imply.   As the severity of the performance specifications directly determines the difficulty of design, we start with a problem characterized by very light PS. This first example should really be considered as an introductory example on the usage of RLM.

Example 7-6

Consider the mechanical system in Fig. 7-20. We wish to control the position c of a mass m constrained by a spring and damped by a dashpot arrangement. We shall assume that the hydraulic actuator is very fast compared with the plant, the latter being *underdamped* and represented by the transfer function

$$\frac{C(s)}{U(s)} = G_p(s) = \frac{1}{s^2 + 4s + 5} = \frac{1}{(s + 2 + j)(s + 2 - j)} \tag{7-37}$$

that is, the two plant poles are *conjugate complex*. The designer must base his design upon the following data:

1. The position c and velocity $\dot{c}$ are available in the form of electrical signals. (The student should give this matter some thought. Discuss some possible transducers that would do these jobs.)
2. The hydraulic actuator is being driven directly from an electrical amplifier.
3. The only PS stipulated is that the servo must follow with zero FVE a ramp input.

In view of the nature of the plant transfer function (no integrating element) and the necessity of meeting the PS, the designer has no choice (see Table 6-1) but to include a *double* integrator in the controller. He realizes that in spite of the fact that the plant itself is stable, this extra 180° phase shift will cause severe stability problems. To counteract this, the designer tries to find some means to increase the stability *with least effort*. Knowing that rate feedback generally improves stability (remember how we stabilized the broomstick) and in view of the fact that the velocity $\dot{c}$ is *available*, he makes, on a more or less intuitional basis, the attempt to feed back the signal

$$b = c + \alpha\dot{c} \tag{7-38}$$

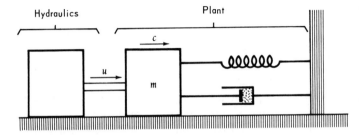

Fig. 7-20 A hydraulically controlled plant.

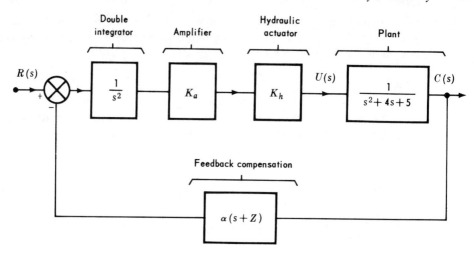

Fig. 7-21 Preliminary design for closed-loop control of the plant in Fig. 7-20.

where α determines the strength of the rate feedback. We thus obtain

$$B(s) = (1 + \alpha s)C(s) \overset{\Delta}{=} H(s)C(s)$$

where

$$H(s) \overset{\Delta}{=} 1 + \alpha s = \alpha\left(s + \frac{1}{\alpha}\right) \overset{\Delta}{=} \alpha(s + Z) \tag{7-39}$$

We conclude that the rate feedback resulted in an H zero, the distance to the origin of which, Z, is inversely proportional to the strength of the rate feedback. In addition to this design parameter, the designer has also control over the amplifier gain K_a, and his next concern is to check whether, by proper choice of these two parameters, he can preserve the stability of the system. In Fig. 7-21, we have summarized the preliminary design structure; and if by K we define the total loop gain

$$K \overset{\Delta}{=} \alpha K_a K_h \tag{7-40}$$

then the characteristic equation of this system reads

$$K\frac{s + Z}{s^2(s^2 + 4s + 5)} + 1 = 0 \tag{7-41}$$

We make the following observations:

1. The equation is of the fourth order, and therefore any classical solution methods are, from a practical viewpoint, unthinkable. Note that at this point in our design, we do not seek some specific set of eigenvalues for a specific set of α and K_a values. *We are instead more concerned about the general behavior of the eigenvalues for the whole practical range of these parameter values.*

2. The total loop gain $K = \alpha K_a K_h = K_a K_h / Z$ depends evidently upon the position of the compensation zero. If we increase the *rate* feedback, i.e., decrease the Z value, then we obviously must decrease K_a just in order to keep the total loop gain K constant.

The total open-loop pole-zero configuration is depicted in Fig. 7-22, where also each pole and zero is properly identified. We have tentatively placed the zero at $\sigma = -1$. Now we shall proceed to construct the root loci for this system, and we shall do this by adding piece to piece, using the set of rules given in the previous section. The results are presented in Fig. 7-22. We approach the

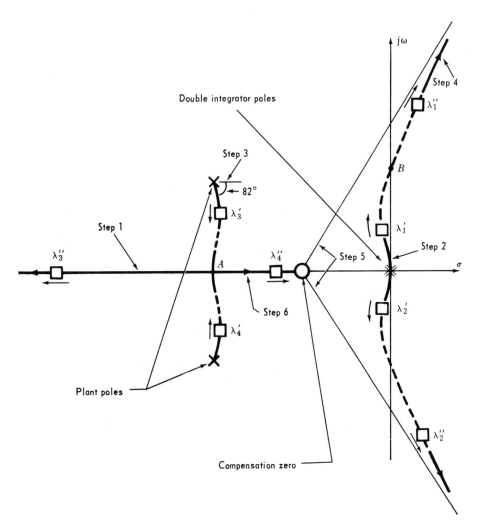

Fig. 7-22   Root loci for system in Fig. 7-21.

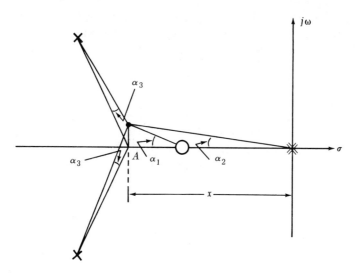

Fig. 7-23   Search for breakaway point.

problem in the following order:

step 1   Using rule 2, we find that the part of the σ axis between $-\infty$ and -1 constitutes part of the loci.

step 2   Making use of rule 8, we obtain the angles of departure for the two loci leaving the double pole in origin. *Note that these loci bend to the left into the stable s plane!* Why?

step 3   Making use of rule 8 again, we find the angles of departure for the plant poles $\varphi_{\mathrm{dep}} = -82°$.

step 4   In accordance with rule 6, we have three asymptotes with the angles 60°, 180°, and $-60°$.

step 5   From rule 7, we find that these asymptotes must intersect the σ axis at $\sigma = -1$.

step 6   Rule 5 tells us that one locus must approach the compensation zero. Obviously, because of the findings in step 1, this must occur from the left along the σ axis.

The above results are all incorporated in boldface into Fig. 7-22. It does not require too much imagination to complete the root-locus diagram on the basis of this skeleton information. (This has been done in dotted boldface.) Note that the two points A and B must be determined in order to have an accurate picture. To find the last point, we use the method we employ for finding any point on the root loci, i.e., the application of the angular equation (7-31). The breakaway point A must be sought by using the method of rule 10. The small angles in Fig. 7-23 evidently must satisfy the equation

$$2\alpha_2 - \alpha_1 - 2\alpha_3 = 0$$

and if we express these angles in terms of the distances involved, we get

$$\frac{2}{x} - \frac{1}{x-1} - \frac{2(2-x)}{(2-x)^2 + 1} = 0$$

This equation must be solved by trial and error, and in this case, due to the simple pole-zero distances chosen, the solution is exactly

$$x = 2$$

We conclude from the final appearance of the root-locus diagram that relatively low loop gains result in a stable system. Corresponding eigenvalue positions are marked $\lambda'_1, \ldots, \lambda'_4$, of which the pair λ'_1 and λ'_2 is the dominant one. These poles are lightly damped, and if we cared to compute the actual time response from formula (7-23), we should find a considerable overshoot. If we limit our attention to these two dominant poles only, we can get a fast estimate of the transient response from the curves in Fig. 7-13.

As no restrictions have been imposed upon the relative stability, we conclude that the design is satisfactory for these low gain settings. Very high gains drive the system into instability, as indicated by the eigenvalues marked $\lambda''_1, \ldots, \lambda''_4$. It is of interest to investigate how the zero position Z influences the shape of the root loci. The diagrams in Fig. 7-24a to c depict the variations of the root loci for increasing rate feedback.

Moving the zero closer to origin obviously improves the stability of the system. (The reader may find it of interest to construct the loci for the two limit cases $Z = 0$ and $Z = \infty$.)

It is interesting to note that we easily could have preserved the stability of this system by *series* rather than feedback compensation had we not had available the rate signal. This would have necessitated the inclusion of a *lead network*† (for instance, No. 4 in Fig. 7-19) in the series—or, for that matter, in the feedback path. Figure 7-25 shows the effect on the root loci. The idea here is to push the compensation pole so far to the left that it has no appreciable effect on the *dominant* eigenvalues. *Note that, as far as the dominant poles are concerned, the diagrams of Figs. 7-22 and 7-25 are almost identical.* Note also that inclusion of the extra pole increases the order of the system from four to five, adding one additional but noninfluential eigenvalue λ_5.

Example 7-7

In our next example, we shall tighten the performance specifications considerably. We could have used the previous system for illustration, but in order to obtain some variety, we shall choose a different one. As the reader may remember, we left some unfinished business in the previous chapter. We concluded that the position servo in Fig. 6-3 was hopelessly unstable but suggested at the time no remedy for this situation. We wish to attend to this matter now and shall first settle for the following specific system data:

motor: Field circuit parameters are

$$R_f = 20 \, \Omega \qquad L_f = 2.0 \text{ henrys}$$

---

† As the zero in this network dominates the pole, the angle $\underline{/\,T(j\omega)}$ will be positive; i.e., the output *will lead* the input.

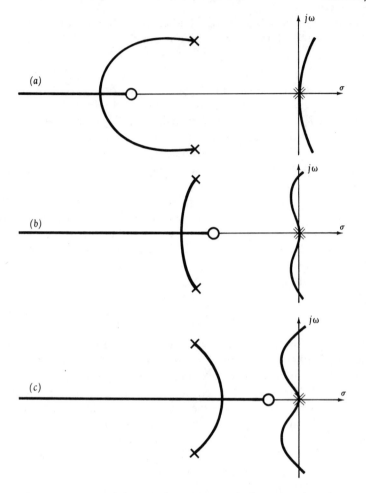

Fig. 7-24   Sketch of the variation of the root loci as a function of the position of the compensation zero.

Torque constant: 1 amp in the field winding produces a shaft torque of 5.0 newton-m.

load + gear train: The motor speed is geared down in ratio 10 : 1. The load inertia (including gear plus motor, referred to the low-speed side) is

$$I = 10 \text{ kg-m}^2$$

output potentiometer (PM): When the output position φ varies between $\pm\pi$ rad, the potentiometer voltage varies between ±100 volts.

We shall define the pick-off voltage from the output pot as our servo output c and, similarily, the pick-off voltage from the reference pot as our reference input *r.* In terms of these variables, we can now establish the following mathematical model:

motor + load:

$$10\ddot{\varphi} = 10\left(\frac{\pi}{100}\,\ddot{c}\right) = 10 \times 5i_f$$

Thus,

$$\ddot{c} = \frac{500}{\pi}\,i_f \tag{7-42}$$

[This corresponds to Eq. (6-8).]

field circuit:

$$u = 20i_f + 2\dot{i}_f \tag{7-43}$$

amplifier:

$$K_1 e = K_1(r - c) = u \tag{7-44}$$

If we Laplace-transform these equations, we obtain directly the block diagram in Fig. 7-26*a*, which is reducible to the one in Fig. 7-26*b*. We construct the root loci for this uncompensated system, as shown in Fig. 7-27, and conclude immediately that it is hopelessly unstable, thus confirming the conclusion we drew earlier from the Nyquist plot in Fig. 6-25.

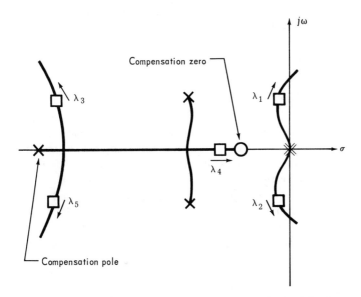

Fig. 7-25　Root loci for system in Fig. 7-21; the rate feedback has been replaced by a series-compensation lead network.

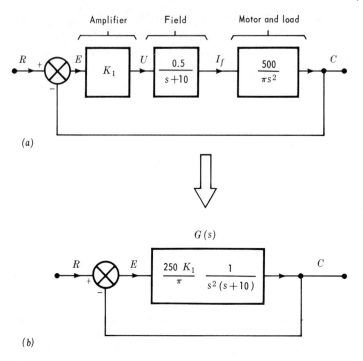

Fig. 7-26 Transfer-function representation of the position servo in Fig. 6-3.

In this example, we wish not only to stabilize the inherently unstable system but also to prescribe that it meet the following PS:

1. FVE $= 0$ for both step and ramp inputs
2. PO $=$ less than 8 percent
3. $T_D =$ less than 0.75 sec

As we have a tachometer generator coupled to the system (see Fig. 6-3), it makes sense to utilize it for rate feedback for stabilization purposes. The tachometer generator is assumed to output 1.0 volt per rpm (this is its rating), but we shall use only a fraction, α, of this voltage for feedback. The compensated system will thus have a feedback signal b obtained as depicted in Fig. 7-28. (Note that it is important to choose a polarity such that terminal A is positive with respect to B for positive velocity; that is, $\dot{c} > 0$.)

We obtain the proper expression for the feedback signal b in the following manner:

The velocity on the low-speed side of the gear is

$$\frac{\pi}{100}\dot{c} \qquad \text{rad/sec}$$

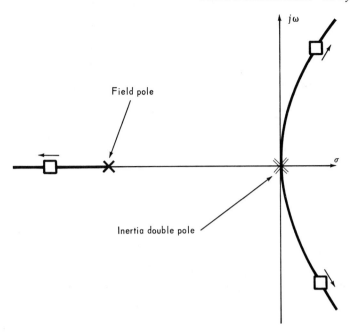

Fig. 7-27   Root loci for system in Fig. 7-26.

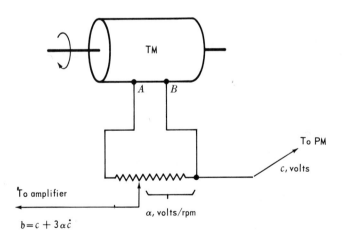

Fig. 7-28   Addition of tachometric feedback.

or

$$\frac{\pi}{100} \dot{c} \frac{30}{\pi} = 0.3\dot{c} \quad \text{rpm}$$

The speed on the motor side is thus

$3\dot{c}$ rpm

and the voltage picked off from the voltage divider thus equals $3\alpha\dot{c}$ volts.
The total feedback signal b is thus

$$b = c + 3\alpha\dot{c} = 3\alpha\left(\dot{c} + \frac{1}{3\alpha}c\right) \tag{7-45}$$

Therefore,

$$B(s) = 3\alpha\left(s + \frac{1}{3\alpha}\right)C(s) \tag{7-46}$$

The compensated system therefore can be represented by the block diagram in Fig. 7-29.
We have

$$HG = K\frac{s + 1/3\alpha}{s^2(s + 10)}$$

where $\tag{7-47}$

$$K \triangleq \frac{750\alpha K_1}{\pi}$$

and again our compensation results in a zero, the effect of which on the root loci we now wish to study.

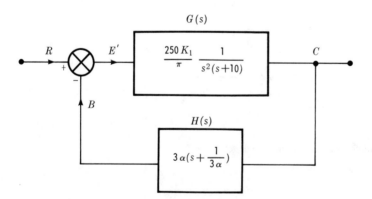

Fig. 7-29   Block diagram of position servo with rate feedback added.

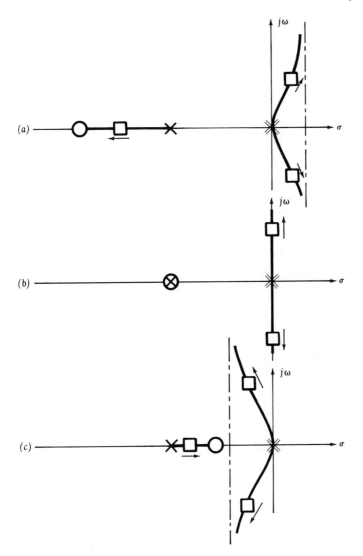

Fig. 7-30 Stable response can be obtained only if the compensation zero is placed to the right of the field pole.

To get a feel for the situation and, in particular, to obtain a rough idea of the possibilities of this type of compensation, we first *sketch* the approximate appearance of the loci for different zero positions. The results are shown in Fig. 7-30a to c. With the zero far away from origin, i.e., for vanishing α, we shall of course approach the *uncompensated* system. This is confirmed in Fig. 7-30a. When the zero is pushed closer to origin, its effect is felt more and more, and the "unstable" portions of the loci are bent over to the left side of the s plane. We

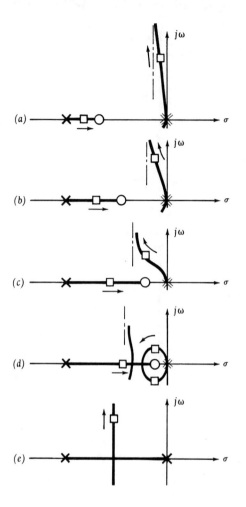

Fig. 7-31 The effect of zero location on the root loci in the stable case.

note that stable operation† is guaranteed for

$$\frac{1}{3\alpha} < 10 \quad \text{or} \quad \alpha > \frac{1}{30} \tag{7-48}$$

or when the zero is placed to the *right* of the field pole. The interesting α range is thus

$$\tfrac{1}{30} < \alpha < 1$$

and we sketch the root loci for some different zero locations in this range. The results are shown in Fig. 7-31*a* to *e*. Note that it is possible actually to bend the loci down to the σ axis (Fig. 7-31*d*) and thus obtain a system that is *not oscillatory*.

† Figure 7-30*b* depicts the limit case.

Note also that when $\alpha \to \infty$,† that is, when the rate feedback completely dominates the position feedback, we should in the limit obtain a *velocity* servo rather than a *position* servo. This is confirmed, as the root loci in Fig. 7-31*e* actually are similar to the ones for the *velocity servo*, shown in Fig. 6-4.

The reader should take stock of the fact that all the above findings have been obtained by means of very rough sketching of the loci. At this stage in our synthesis process, we are more interested in obtaining a *feel* for the system dynamics than in wasting time on accurate computations that would have little success in rendering an acceptable response. We are better off "boxing in" the design parameters within reasonable ranges before embarking upon detailed computations.

We are now at a stage where we had better judge the *consistency* of the given specs; i.e., we should make an assessment as to our success in meeting the given set of PS with the compensation chosen. We shall discuss each item of the specs separately.

1. The FVE requirement certainly can be met as our *G* function contains a *double* integrator.
2. The PO requirement should not be hard to meet in view of Fig. 7-31*c* and *d*. Indeed, we could have specified *zero* PO and still met it.
3. Whether the speed requirement T_D can be met is a question that must be given a little more attention. In view of the overshoot stipulation, it seems reasonable to assume that we can tolerate a compensation in the zero range

$$-4 < Z < -1$$

corresponding to a root-locus configuration of the type shown in Fig. 7-31*c* and *d*. The closed-loop pole-zero configuration in this case (compare rule 1) consists of three poles, one real and two conjugate complex, and we thus can obtain a fairly good time-response estimate‡ by using curves of the type presented in Fig. 7-13. Note that if we push the real pole too close to origin (which we do if we use too strong a rate feedback), we obtain too sluggish a response. The estimates confirm that we can expect to meet the maximum specification on T_D easily.

Having thus concluded that we are on the right track, we must finish our design by fixing a pair of design parameters that render an acceptable response.

Had we been forced to conclude that our chances for success were very slim, this would have been the right time to reevaluate the situation, choose a different compensation scheme, and start all over.

† This is physically impossible in our case as our particular arrangement permits only α values less than 1.
‡ If no tabulated response is available, we must compute a few sample responses or obtain it from computer simulation.

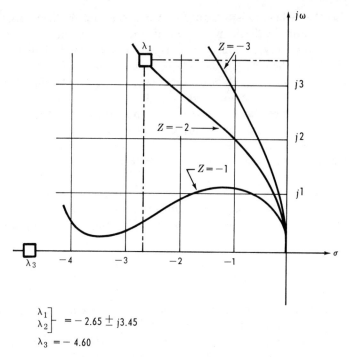

$$\left.\begin{matrix} \lambda_1 \\ \lambda_2 \end{matrix}\right\} = -2.65 \pm j3.45$$

$$\lambda_3 = -4.60$$

Fig. 7-32   Root loci for three specific compensations.

For the final part of our design, it becomes necessary to leave the sketching stage and construct the root loci as accurately as our means permit us.   This we have done in Fig. 7-32 for the following three values of the zero location:

$$Z = -1$$
$$Z = -2$$
$$Z = -3$$

As a first trial, we rather arbitrarily choose an eigenvalue on the locus corresponding to $Z = -2$:

$$\left.\begin{matrix} \lambda_1 \\ \lambda_2 \end{matrix}\right\} = 2.65 \pm j3.45$$

The eigenvalue λ_1 is shown in Fig. 7-32.   It takes a loop gain of $K = 43$ to place the eigenvalue in this position.   For this gain, we then also determine the position $\lambda_3 = -4.6$ for the third eigenvalue, also indicated in the figure.

By the use of formulas (7-23) and (7-24), we can compute the response

$$c(t) = 1 - 1.21e^{-4.6t} + e^{-2.65t}(0.21 \cos 3.45t - 1.43 \sin 3.45t)$$

The response is plotted in Fig. 7-33. By direct measurement, we obtain

$PO \approx 5$ percent

$T_D \approx 0.6$ sec

These values are well within the specified margins, and therefore we shall accept this design as final. It remains to summarize the values of the design parameters that did the job.

1. Tachometric feedback. From Eq. (7-46), we have

$$-Z = 2 = \frac{1}{3\alpha}$$

Therefore, we obtain the potentiometer setting

$$\alpha = 0.17$$

2. Amplifier gain. From Eq. (7-47), we have

$$43 = \frac{750\alpha K_1}{\pi}$$

Therefore,

$$K_1 = 1.1$$

(It would seem unnecessary even to include an amplifier in the loop as we have just concluded that its gain should be ≈ 1. However, remember that the device serves not only as a voltage booster but also as an impedance matcher. The reference and output potentiometers plus the tachometer generator are high-impedance circuits which tolerate no current drain. The amplifier therefore must have very high input impedance. At the same time, its output impedance must be low as it is feeding into the field circuit of the motor.)

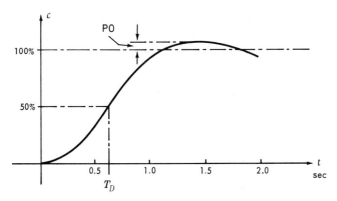

Fig. 7-33 Step response for the eigenvalue combination shown in Fig. 7-32.

In neither of the two previous synthesis examples did the PS include any limits on the output impedance. We were concerned basically with obtaining an acceptable response to a reference input. A specification on the output impedance necessitates the observance of certain limits on the response resulting from inputs other than the reference input. Clearly then, this means a tougher job for the designer as he now is forced to keep an eye on two different responses at the same time. The situation is complicated by the fact that when he tries to compensate for one, he affects the other, possibly in an undesired direction.

Example 7-8

We shall demonstrate this situation by turning our attention again to the position servo that we just finished work on in our previous example. We shall assume now that the output member of this servo is subject to loading torques τ, the effects of which we wish to cancel. For instance, the output member may be an antenna disk, and we wish to eliminate as much as possible the position errors due to wind forces.

In order to stress our point, we shall impose a rather severe restriction on the servo:

The compliance Q must be zero. In addition, its response characteristics should be at least of the same quality as already specified in Example 7-7.

We note that the servo already designed certainly does not meet these compliance specs. Zero Q means that a static torque applied to the output member will cause zero output displacement. If a static torque were applied to our servo from Example 7-7, an error position and error voltage of such magnitude would result that the resulting motor torque would exactly balance out the disturbance torque. The important thing to realize is that *an error is absolutely required in order to establish this balance.* It is true that we could reduce this error by increasing the loop gain, but these efforts would take us far out on the root-locus branches in Fig. 7-31, and we would then violate the response requirement which we have tried so laboriously to meet.

Anyway, no gain increase would be enough to meet the zero-Q requirement. Obviously, we shall have to take a different approach.

We start our investigation by determining in what way and where the disturbance torque will enter into our block diagram. To ascertain this, it becomes necessary to return to Eqs. (7-42) to (7-44), from which we derived our block diagram. The load torque τ will affect the first of these equations, which now will change to

$$10 \frac{\pi}{100} \ddot{c} = 50i_f + \tau \tag{7-49}$$

We Laplace-transform this equation and obtain

$$s^2 \frac{\pi}{10} C(s) = 50I_f(s) + T(s) \tag{7-50}$$

where $T(s) \triangleq \mathscr{L}[\tau(t)]$.

The block diagram of Fig. 7-29 will therefore have to be modified to the extent shown in Fig. 7-34. From this diagram, we can easily obtain the transfer function between the T input and C output as follows:

We have, for $R = 0$,

$$C = G_2\left(I_f + \frac{T}{50}\right)$$

and

$$I_f = -G_1 HC$$

By elimination of I_f, these equations yield

$$C = \frac{G_2}{1 + G_1 G_2 H}\frac{T}{50} = \frac{G_2}{1 + GH}\frac{T}{50}$$

The transfer function G was defined in Fig. 7-26b. Note that we also can write this last equation in the form

$$\frac{C}{T} = \frac{1}{G_1}\frac{G}{1 + GH}\frac{1}{50} = \frac{1}{G_1}\frac{C}{R}\frac{1}{50} \qquad (7\text{-}51)$$

In other words, we have expressed the transfer ratio C/T in terms of the transfer ratio C/R.

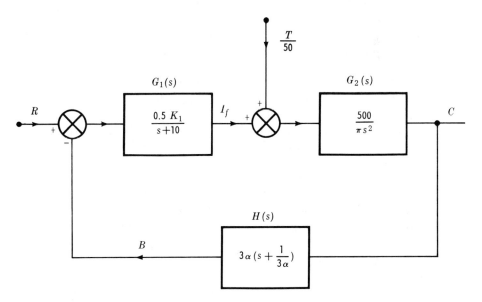

Fig. 7-34   Block diagram showing disturbance input.

From this last equation, we obtain directly an expression for the output impedance Z:

$$Z = \frac{C(j\omega)}{T(j\omega)} = \frac{1}{50G_1(j\omega)} \frac{G(j\omega)}{1 + G(j\omega)H(j\omega)} \tag{7-52}$$

The compliance Q is obtained by letting ω approach zero in this expression, and as

$$\lim_{\omega \to 0} \left[\frac{G(j\omega)}{1 + G(j\omega)H(j\omega)} \right] = 1 \tag{7-53}$$

we get

$$Q = \frac{1}{50G_1(j0)} = \frac{1}{2.5K_1} \tag{7-54}$$

We have thus confirmed that Q is nonzero but that, as we already have indicated, we can reduce it by increasing the gain K_1.

Equation (7-52) also gives us hints about what must be done to reduce Q to zero. Two possibilities are open. Make either

$$\lim_{\omega \to 0} \left[\frac{G(j\omega)}{1 + G(j\omega)H(j\omega)} \right] = 0$$

or

$$\lim_{\omega \to 0} [G_1(j\omega)] = \infty$$

We realize immediately that the first result can be obtained by an added s^{-1} factor in the H function. The same factor added to the G_1 function would give the second result. We therefore draw the following important conclusion:

Zero compliance should be obtained by adding an integrator to either the H or the G_1 function.

Note that we use the form "should," implying that there is no certainty that this approach will work, the reason being that the added integrator may make the system *unstable*. Should this be the case, then we know from the previous chapter that we have no right to define an FTF. In other words, it makes no sense to talk about an output impedance (including compliance) for an unstable system.

It is interesting, by the way, to note that the *double* integrator that we already have in our plant (Fig. 7-34) does not help us. The integrator must be added *before* the point of entrance of the disturbance input to be of any help. We decide to add it just before the amplifier K_1, and after this addition, we have

$$H(s)G(s) = K \frac{s + 1/3\alpha}{s^3(s + 10)} \tag{7-55}$$

A few comments are appropriate at this juncture concerning the practical problem of designing an integrator. There are many schemes to obtain integrating action by mechanical, pneumatic, hydraulic, and electrical means. In our case, we would need an electrical integrator. Such devices are of basic concern in electronic simulators, and they will be discussed in Chap. 12.

Before we proceed to investigate the effect of the added integrator on the loop stability, let us discuss from a *physical* point of view why this integrator results in $Q = 0$. We earlier concluded that we need a motor torque to balance out the load torque. Such a torque can be obtained only if we have a field current. This requires, in turn, that the amplifier K_1 have a nonzero output voltage u. The question now is: How do we obtain a nonzero amplifier output with *zero* error voltage? Here is where the integrator will work the trick. An integrator, placed before the amplifier, may provide a nonzero output *with zero input*. What actually happens, of course, is that after the application of the load torque, we do have an error for a while. This error is integrated and the integrator output increases, with the effect that the load torque is balanced out, the error is reduced, and *if the overall loop is stable*, the system settles down to an equilibrium position characterized by zero error, nonzero field current, and a motor torque which exactly balances out the load torque.

Evidently "stability" is the key word, and thus our most pressing problem is to determine whether the tachometric feedback is able to handle the additional $90°$ phase shift introduced by the added integrator. In Fig. 7-35 are sketched the root loci corresponding to the HG function given in Eq. (7-55). We note that the triple pole in origin causes two of the three loci which start at origin to take off into the unstable half of the s plane at angles of $\pm 60°$. The zero will bend

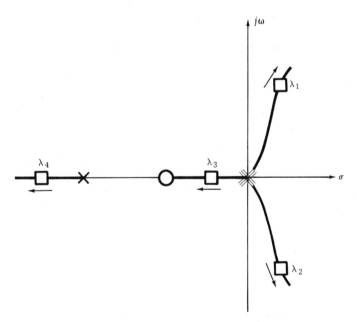

Fig. 7-35 Uncompensated system is unstable for all gain values.

these loci back slightly but not enough to get them back into the stable portion of the *s* plane. It is simple to confirm that this single zero is not able to do the job alone, even if we place it very close to origin, i.e., even if we provide very strong rate feedback.

The added integrator has therefore totally destroyed the loop stability. We can only confirm regretfully that "the operation was successful, but the patient died."

The root-locus plot in Fig. 7-35 indicates that we should be able to bend the two unstable locus branches into the left *s* plane if we place an additional zero at about the place of the old one. This can be done in several ways—for instance, we may introduce a lead network of type 4 in Fig. 7-19. We are free to place the pole and zero wherever we desire—generally, the pole should be pushed as far aside as possible to let the zero dominate. In order not to have too many different angles to keep track of, we have placed the new zero on top of the old "tacho-metric" zero and the new pole on top of the old "field pole." The total pole-zero configuration therefore consists of:

A triple pole at origin
A double pole at $s = -10$
A double zero at $s = -Z$

The added lead network results in an overall loop-transfer function

$$H(s)G(s) = K \frac{(s + Z)^2}{s^3(s + 10)^2} \tag{7-56}$$

The root-locus diagram for this fifth-order system is shown in Fig. 7-36. The two important conjugate complex eigenvalues λ_1 and λ_2 will still take off into the unstable *s* plane for low values of the loop gain. However, when increasing the gain above the value K_1', all five eigenvalues will be found in the stable *s* plane. For very high gain ($> K_1''$), the system again turns unstable.

Our design obviously has led to a so-called *conditionally* stable system. There is, of course, nothing wrong with such a system. With a properly chosen gain, it works well—the question is: Does it work sufficiently well to meet our standards? To find this out, we have no choice but to tackle the detailed computational work head on. We note from rule 1 that our final design has five *closed-loop* poles and one zero. We probably can discard with little error the eigenvalues λ_4 and λ_5 in Fig. 7-36. The conclusion is that the three eigenvalues λ_1, λ_2, and λ_3 plus the one closed-loop zero are the truly dominating ones, and we may be able to obtain a fairly accurate response picture by considering this simplified pole-zero configuration.

We have taken an easier approach. We put the system on the analog computer and tested out a few reasonable parameter values. The recordings in Fig. 7-37*a* to *c* are the results.† We shall describe each of these and also relate the results to the root-locus plot in Fig. 7-36.

---

† The author gratefully acknowledges the assistance of Mr. Alexandre G. Cerveira, a graduate student at the University of Colorado.

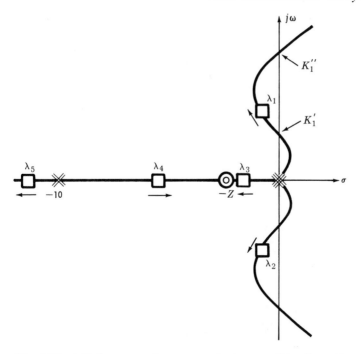

Fig. 7-36 Added compensation zero results in a conditionally stable system.

First, we point out that *all* graphs are obtained for a lead-compensation network that has its zero placed on top of the tachometric compensation zero. Both are placed at $s = -1$. The compensation pole is placed on top of the field pole at $s = -10$.

Recordings in Fig. 7-37a

The recordings depict c responses for reference step inputs. The three computer runs correspond to the following gain settings:

1. $K_1 = 0.90$
2. $K_1 = 6.5$
3. $K_1 = 16$

With reference to the root-locus plot in Fig. 7-36, these gains lie within the ranges

$$0.90 < K_1' < 6.5 < K_1'' < 16$$

As we can expect, response 1 will be unstable at a relatively low frequency and response 2 will be stable and 3 unstable at a relatively high frequency. Note also that the oscillatory component in the stable response (2) dies out rather slowly, the reason being that the corresponding complex root pair λ_1 and λ_2 is relatively poorly damped (Fig. 7-36).

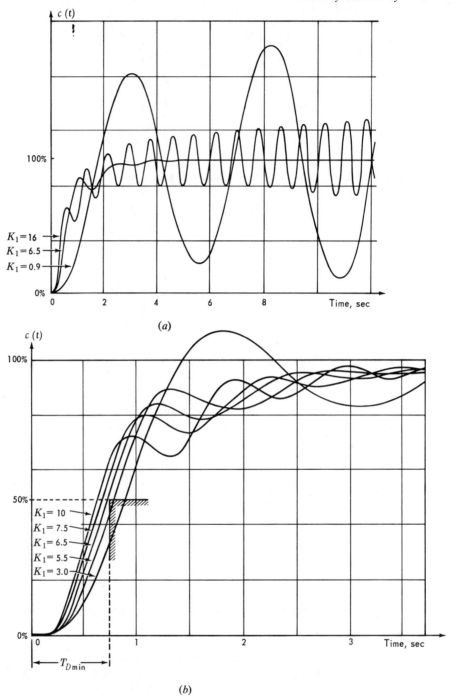

Fig. 7-37 Step responses for the system finally selected.

Recordings in Fig. 7-37b

All five graphs depict c responses to unit-reference step inputs. They are all recorded for amplifier gains in the *stable* range

$$K_1' < K_1 < K_1''$$

We note that all gains above $K_1 = 6.5$ satisfy the speed requirement $T_D < 0.75$ sec. We note also that overshoot is no problem. However, there is a tendency for slow settling (due both to the relatively sluggish eigenvalue λ_3 and to the poorly damped pair λ_1 and λ_2).

Recordings in Fig. 7-37c

This recording shows (in a different time scale) the response for $K_1 = 6.5$, which we shall settle for as an acceptable response. In this graph, we also have shown

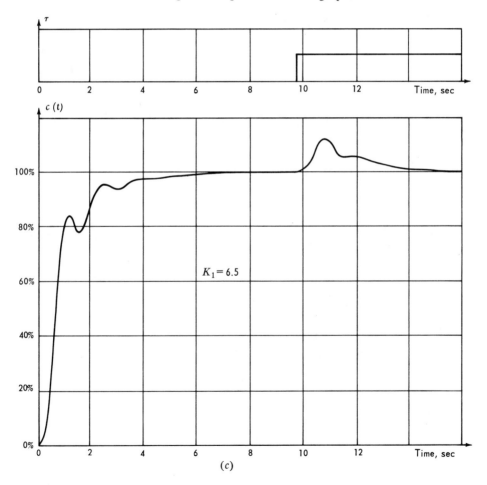

(c)

The different graphs are discussed in text.

the response for a suddenly applied loading step τ. We note that after an initial excursion, the output settles down to a static value corresponding to FVE = 0, that is, the compliance $Q = 0$.

We summarize the parameter values that will satisfy the PS:

1. Amplifier:

$K_1 = 6.5$

2. Tachometric feedback:

$$-Z = \frac{1}{3\alpha} = 1.0 \quad \text{yielding } \alpha = 0.33$$

3. Lead network: We settled for

Zero at $s = -1$

Pole at $s = -10$

From the table in Fig. 7-19, we then get

$$10 = 1 + \frac{R_1}{R_2} \quad \text{and} \quad T = \frac{1}{10} = C\frac{R_1 R_2}{R_1 + R_2}$$

This results in a lead network having the approximate parameter values shown in Fig. 7-38.

In Fig. 7-39, we summarize the transfer functions for the final design.

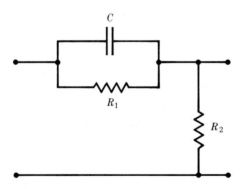

$C = 10\ \mu\text{f}$
$R_1 = 100\ \text{k}\Omega$
$R_2 = 10\ \text{k}\Omega$

Fig. 7-38   Lead network for series compensation.

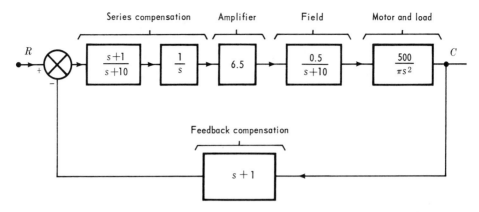

Fig. 7-39   Final design.

We shall mention briefly two design methods which must be classified as trial and error although they employ a somewhat more direct synthesis approach than exemplified in our previous examples.   They are sometimes referred to as the *cancellation* and *algebraic* techniques.

Let us consider the cancellation method first, and let us discuss it in connection with the previous design example, Example 7-6.   The basic idea of this method is to try to shape the overall response of the system by proper cancellation of undesired poles and/or zeros of the open-loop transfer function.

Consider, for example, the system discussed in Example 7-6.   The total open-loop pole configuration, after inclusion of the necessary double integrator in origin, would be the one shown in Fig. 7-40a.   Quite clearly, as the root loci indicate, this system must be compensated in some way, and we have already given one solution.   However, theoretically we could approach the problem in the following way: Let us try to *cancel* the poles that evidently give us trouble, i.e., the plant poles (note that we are *not* permitted to cancel the poles in the origin because that would violate the PS).   We obviously can do this most simply by placing two zeros on top of the poles.   This leaves us with a reduced system having only the double pole in origin and a root-locus situation, as depicted in Fig. 7-40b.   This is not sufficient from a stability viewpoint, so we add, for example, one additional zero at $s = -2$ and obtain a root-locus diagram as depicted in Fig. 7-40c.   This gives us an acceptable closed-loop response—indeed, a very excellent one.   Note, however, that to achieve this design, we need a compensation network with the transfer function

$$G_s(s) = (s + 2)(s^2 + 4s + 5) = s^3 + 6s^2 + 13s + 10 \qquad (7\text{-}57)$$

This is the crux of the matter, as obtaining such a compensation network is *practically impossible*.   Let us try to justify this statement.

Network synthesis is beyond the scope of this book, but we must point out the following facts concerning design of compensation networks.   Assume that

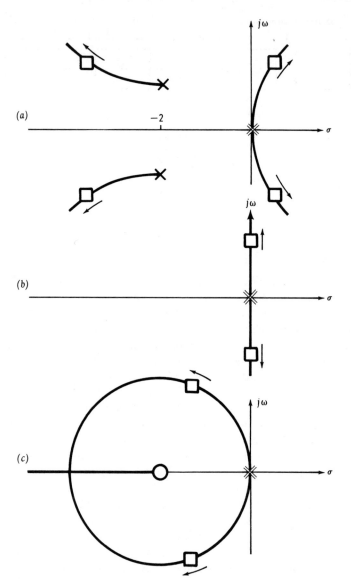

Fig. 7-40 Cancellation compensation.

we are asked to design a network characterized by a transfer function expressable as a *rational* function in *s*, that is,

$$G_s(s) = \frac{N(s)}{D(s)} \tag{7-58}$$

For example, in the present case we have

$$N(s) = s^3 + 6s^2 + 13s + 10$$

$$D(s) = 1$$

The first appropriate question we should ask is whether it is *physically possible* to design such a network. This question can be answered in the affirmative *if we are permitted to use both active and passive components.*

If we can use *only passive* devices (capacitors, resistors, springs, dashpots, etc.), it is, in general, not possible. Only certain types of rational functions are physically realizable. Network theory tells us which.

However, even if it is theoretically possible to design a given network, it may turn out that the resulting network *is useless from a practical point of view.* This is particularly true if the rational function (7-58) is *improper*, that is, if $N(s)$ is of higher order in *s* than $D(s)$. In such a situation, we can write

$$G_s(s) = a_1 s^m + a_2 s^{m-1} + \cdots + \frac{N_1(s)}{D(s)}$$

where the ratio N_1/D is now proper. We note that this means that we now need *m cascaded differentiators* in our compensator. For example, in our particular example [Eq. (7-57)], we would need three! A differentiator is characterized by the following serious drawbacks:

1. Noise amplification
2. Plant saturation for drastically changing error signals (a step input would command a differentiator to output an impulse)

We therefore can draw the conclusion that although a *mathematical* cancellation of the type suggested in Fig. 7-40c works beautifully, there is not a chance that it can be put into hardware. The mistake that we made was to attempt the *impossible—to completely annul the inherent dynamics of the plant we were about to control.* It takes infinite forces (impulses) to do that, and that is exactly what the mathematics told us to build into our compensation network. In attempting the cancellation method, it is necessary to take a "softer" approach. In particular, it is necessary to keep an eye on the *physical* requirements at each step to be sure that no physical limitations have been violated.

For example, if we plan to use only *passive* components in our compensation network, then we could say right at the outset in the previous example that it is impossible to even try to cancel the complex pole pair. An *approximate* cancellation is the best we can hope to accomplish. If active components are employed, then we must always be aware of the possibility of signal *saturation*. As a general statement about cancellation compensation, we can say that the problem is dumped in the lap of the designer of the compensation network.[4]

The "algebraic" compensation technique is, in many respects, quite similar to the cancellation procedure. Whereas the cancellation method aimed at shaping the *open-loop* pole-zero configuration to achieve a configuration in accordance with the designer's wishes, the algebraic method goes one step further and takes aim directly at the *closed-loop* configuration. Actually, on the surface, this type of approach would seem to be the most logical of them all. Consider the structure in Fig. 6-7, and for sake of simplicity, let us assume a scalar case with $H(s) = 1$.

From the expression for the closed-loop transfer function

$$G_c = \frac{G_s G_p}{1 + G_s G_p}$$

we solve directly for G_s:

$$G_s = \frac{G_c}{G_p(1 - G_c)}$$

As G_p is known, and *if we specify G_c*, the transfer function for the series-compensation network can be obtained *directly* and explicitly. This would seem to be a very attractive and straight-to-the-point approach. It has, however, the same drawbacks as the cancellation method since it generally results in too severe specifications for the compensation network. We note from the expression for G_s that if we want to avoid differentiators in the compensation network, then we must be very careful in our specification of G_c. This means, in effect, that our output response cannot be selected arbitrarily but is, indeed, subject to severe limitations. Even if we can find a response (and this search must be performed by trial and error) which results in an acceptable G_s function, we still are faced with the problem of *synthesizing a compensating network which satisfies this transfer function.*

We have concluded that what at a first glance looked like a very direct and attractive synthesis procedure bogs down in the end in perhaps as much trial and error as our previously discussed method. When the transfer functions involved are fairly simple, the algebraic method, due to its mathematical directness, has advantages that sometimes can be utilized profitably. An example will be given in the next section, where it will be used in synthesizing a compensation network for a multiple-input–multiple-output servo.

7-4 SYNTHESIS OF MULTIPLE-INPUT–MULTIPLE-OUTPUT LINEAR SERVOS

In this final section of the chapter, we wish to discuss briefly the synthesis of linear multiple-input–multiple-output (MIMO) servomechanisms. In the previous chapter (Sec. 6-3), we developed the transfer-matrix description for such systems, and we also gave an example of a specific physical system (Fig. 6-11) that falls within this category.

In principle, the problem of synthesizing a MIMO controller is very similar to the SISO case. The synthesis problem can be stated as follows:

A plant is given, and it is assumed that its transfer matrix $\mathbf{G}_p(s)$ is known.† Find a series compensator $\mathbf{G}_s(s)$ or a feedback compensator $\mathbf{H}(s)$ or a combination of both that will result in desired closed-loop performance. The problem of compensation is compounded, of course, by:

1. The multiplicity of inputs and outputs
2. The interaction between the different inputs

The first observation that we can make and which, of course, has a tremendous bearing on the synthesis problem is that we no longer can rely on performance specifications of the type used for SISO systems. Consider, for example, a two-dimensional system with two inputs r_1 and r_2 and two outputs c_1 and c_2. Assume that we wish to use time-domain PS in judging the performance of this servo. The problem that now presents itself is how to relate the system responses to the test step inputs. Should we apply step inputs to the two channels separately or simultaneously? Clearly three possibilities exist, and the output picture would, in general, look different in all three cases. It makes a lot of practical sense to strive for a system characterized by *noninteraction* between the various channels.

For instance, in the two-dimensional case just mentioned, it would probably be most desirable if a change in the reference input r_1 gave response in c_1 only —the same thing being true about r_2 and c_2.

MIMO systems are well represented in the process-control area, and quite often they are of the *regulator* type; i.e., they are used when it is desired to set the different reference inputs $r_1, r_2, \ldots, r_p$ at constant values and then hope that the system will maintain the corresponding outputs *accurately* at those values. If noninteraction were achieved, it would be so much easier to perform these settings, as manipulating one input would not affect the other ones.

We summarize here four different PS that dominate in the judgment of MIMO systems:

1. Requirement for noninteraction
2. Requirement for static accuracy
3. Requirement for stability
4. Requirement for insensitivity to disturbances

We shall touch lightly upon each of these items.

† For symbols, see block diagram in Fig. 6-7.

7-4.1 NONINTERACTION

Consider the closed-loop transfer matrix, defined by Eq. (6-25),

$$\mathbf{G}_c = \begin{bmatrix} G_{c11} & \cdots & G_{c1p} \\ \cdots\cdots\cdots\cdots \\ G_{cp1} & \cdots & G_{cpp} \end{bmatrix}$$

The elements off the main diagonal in this matrix determine the degree of interaction between the different reference inputs.   To obtain complete decoupling between the p different inputs, we obviously must require that $\mathbf{G}_c$ be *diagonal*, that is, that

$$G_{cij} = 0 \qquad \text{for } i \neq j \tag{7-59}$$

It is easy to prove that a *necessary* and *sufficient* condition for noninteraction in a unity-feedback system is that the open-loop transfer matrix

$$\mathbf{G} = \begin{bmatrix} G_{11} & \cdots & G_{1p} \\ \cdots\cdots\cdots\cdots \\ G_{p1} & \cdots & G_{pp} \end{bmatrix}$$

also *be diagonal*.   [G is defined by Eq. (6-23).]

proof: From Eq. 6-25, we have (assuming $\mathbf{H} = \mathbf{I}$)

$$\mathbf{G}_c = (\mathbf{I} + \mathbf{G})^{-1}\mathbf{G}$$

By solving for **G**, we get

$$\mathbf{G} = \mathbf{G}_c(\mathbf{I} - \mathbf{G}_c)^{-1} \tag{7-60}$$

We had concluded that $\mathbf{G}_c$ must be *diagonal*; therefore, $\mathbf{I} - \mathbf{G}_c$ must also be *diagonal*

$$\mathbf{I} - \mathbf{G}_c = \begin{bmatrix} 1 - G_{c11} & & & 0 \\ & 1 - G_{c22} & & \\ & & \cdot & \\ & & & \cdot \\ & & & & \cdot \\ 0 & & & 1 - G_{cpp} \end{bmatrix}$$

By inversion, we then have

$$(\mathbf{I} - \mathbf{G}_c)^{-1} = \begin{bmatrix} \dfrac{1}{1 - G_{c11}} & & & 0 \\ & \dfrac{1}{1 - G_{c22}} & & \\ & & \cdot & \\ & & & \cdot \\ & & & & \cdot \\ 0 & & & \dfrac{1}{1 - G_{cpp}} \end{bmatrix}$$

And upon performing the multiplication called for in (7-60), we finally obtain

$$\mathbf{G} = \begin{bmatrix} \dfrac{G_{c11}}{1 - G_{c11}} & & 0 \\ & \cdot & \\ & & \cdot \\ & & \cdot \\ 0 & & \dfrac{G_{cpp}}{1 - G_{cpp}} \end{bmatrix} \qquad (7\text{-}61)$$

The **G** matrix is obviously diagonal, with elements G_{ii} obtainable from the equation

$$G_{ii} = \frac{G_{cii}}{1 - G_{cii}} \qquad i = 1, 2, \ldots, p \qquad (7\text{-}62)$$

We shall return to and make use of these relations later.

7-4.2 STATIC ACCURACY

Now we shall study the conditions that must be satisfied in order to achieve perfect static accuracy. We would wish that for *constant* reference input, the error vector

$$\mathbf{e}(t) = \mathbf{r}(t) - \mathbf{c}(t)$$

would approach zero, that is,

$$\lim_{t \to \infty} \mathbf{e}(t) = \mathbf{0}$$

As we have

$$\mathbf{E}(s) = \mathbf{R}(s) - \mathbf{C}(s) = \mathbf{R}(s) - \mathbf{G}_c(s)\mathbf{R}(s) = [\mathbf{I} - \mathbf{G}_c(s)]\mathbf{R}(s)$$

we realize, by application of the final-value theorem, that a necessary condition for zero FVE is

$$\lim_{s \to 0} [\mathbf{G}_c(s)] = \mathbf{I} \qquad (7\text{-}63)$$

This condition can be realized in a number of ways by proper design of either $\mathbf{G}_s$ or $\mathbf{H}$. Consider, for example, the case of unity feedback, that is, $\mathbf{H} = \mathbf{I}$. We have, in this case,

$$\mathbf{G}_c = (\mathbf{I} + \mathbf{G})^{-1}\mathbf{G}$$

If we now impose the requirement (7-63) upon this expression for $\mathbf{G}_c$, we obtain

$$\lim_{s \to 0} [\mathbf{I} + \mathbf{G}(s)] = \lim_{s \to 0} [\mathbf{G}(s)]$$

Therefore,

$$\mathbf{I} + \mathbf{G}(0) = \mathbf{G}(0) \tag{7-64}$$

This requirement places no constraints on the elements off the main diagonal of the $\mathbf{G}$ *matrix, but it stipulates that each of the p-diagonal elements* $G_{ii}(s)$ *must approach* ∞ *for vanishing s.*

We can also formulate the requirement as follows: *Each of the diagonal elements of the open-loop transfer matrix* $\mathbf{G}$ *must contain at least one integrator.*

7-4.3   STABILITY

We obtain the time response of the MIMO system by performing the inverse Laplace transform

$$\mathbf{c}(t) = \mathcal{L}^{-1}[\mathbf{C}(s)] = \mathcal{L}^{-1}[\mathbf{G}_c\mathbf{R}(s)] = \mathcal{L}^{-1}[(\mathbf{I} + \mathbf{GH})^{-1}\mathbf{GR}(s)]$$

As

$$(\mathbf{I} + \mathbf{GH})^{-1} = \frac{1}{|\mathbf{I} + \mathbf{GH}|}(\mathbf{I} + \mathbf{GH})^{+}$$

we realize that *each* component of the *p*-dimensional column vector

$$(\mathbf{I} + \mathbf{GH})^{-1}\mathbf{GR}(s)$$

will contain the factor $|\mathbf{I} + \mathbf{GH}|$ in the denominator. Therefore, in applying Heaviside's expansion theorem, it will be necessary to obtain all roots of the *characteristic equation*

$$|\mathbf{I} + \mathbf{GH}| = 0 \tag{7-65}$$

These, then, are the *eigenvalues* of the closed-loop system.

Equation (7-65) is, of course, the MIMO equivalent to the SISO equation

$$1 + GH = 0$$

For the unity-feedback case, the characteristic equation reduces to

$$|\mathbf{I} + \mathbf{G}| = 0 \tag{7-66}$$

Stability is preserved, as before, if *all* eigenvalues are located in the left side of the *s* plane. The characteristic equation will be particularly simple in the *case of noninteracting control*. Then we have

$$
\mathbf{I} + \mathbf{G} =
\begin{bmatrix}
1 + G_{11} & & & 0 \\
& 1 + G_{22} & & \\
& & \cdot & \\
& & & \cdot \\
& & & \cdot \\
0 & & & 1 + G_{pp}
\end{bmatrix}
$$

Therefore, the characteristic equation will read

$$|\mathbf{I} + \mathbf{G}| = (1 + G_{11})(1 + G_{22}) \cdots (1 + G_{pp}) = 0 \tag{7-67}$$

which evidently is satisfied for

$$1 + G_{ii} = 0 \qquad i = 1, 2, \ldots, p$$

Each of the *p* noninteracting control channels obviously is behaving, from an eigenvalue point of view, like an isolated SISO system.

7-4.4 SENSITIVITY ANALYSIS

Consider the block diagram in Fig. 6-6. If we put $\mathbf{R}(s) = \mathbf{0}$ and if we introduce the transformed disturbance vector $\mathbf{Z}'(s)$, defined by

$$\mathbf{Z}'(s) \stackrel{\Delta}{=} \mathbf{FZ}(s) \tag{7-68}$$

then we can put the diagram in the form shown in Fig. 7-41. This diagram permits us to predict the influence the disturbance $\mathbf{Z}'(s)$ will have on the output $\mathbf{C}(s)$.

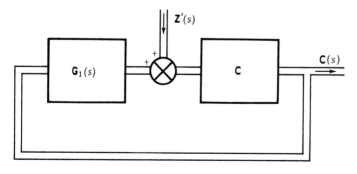

$$\mathbf{G}_1(s) \stackrel{\Delta}{=} - \mathbf{T}_2(s) \cdot \mathbf{G}_s(s) \cdot \mathbf{H}(s)$$

Fig. 7-41   Block diagram used for computing the effect of disturbances.

We obtain directly from this diagram

$$C(s) = [I - CG_1(s)]^{-1}CZ'(s) = [I + G(s)H(s)]^{-1}CZ'(s) \qquad (7\text{-}69)$$

It is interesting to note that if the system has been designed for noninteraction between the **r** components, it is not necessarily noninteracting with respect to the different disturbance inputs. This follows as a consequence of the fact that although $(I + GH)^{-1}$ is diagonal, this does not generally apply to the matrix $(I + GH)^{-1}C$.

Example 7-9

We shall demonstrate some of the important aspects of synthesis of MIMO servos by completing the design of a two-dimensional position regulator. The plant, consisting of two spring-coupled platforms P_1 and P_2, is shown in Fig. 7-42. We wish to control the individual positions of each platform, and we thus

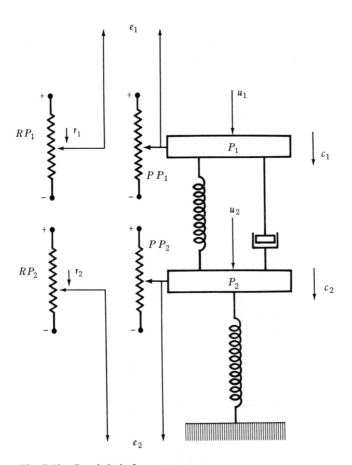

Fig. 7-42 Coupled-platform system.

define these two positions as our two output components, that is,

$$\mathbf{c} = \begin{bmatrix} c_1 \\ c_2 \end{bmatrix}$$

Each output component is sensed as an electric d-c voltage from the position potentiometers PP_1 and PP_2.

The reference inputs r_1 and r_2 are set on the reference potentiometers RP_1 and RP_2. The two difference voltages e_1 and e_2 are obviously direct indicators of the two error positions $r_1 - c_1$ and $r_2 - c_2$.

We shall assume that the actual "brute-force" job is done by two independent control forces u_1 and u_2, obtained, for instance, from two fast hydraulic actuators. These actuators are being controlled via impedance-matching electrical amplifiers from the two error voltages e_1 and e_2. Our design should result in a control strategy telling in specific terms just *how* u_1 and u_2 should be utilized to achieve the specific control job we wish to accomplish.

It is necessary at this time to settle for a set of performance specifications. We shall require that our completed servo be able to perform within the following limits:

1. The system should be noninteracting with respect to the two different reference inputs.
2. The speed of each channel will be of "the order of 0.1 sec."
3. Zero static error in each channel.
4. Zero compliance in each channel.

Before we proceed with the design, it is necessary to comment on each of the above items:

1. The requirement for noninteraction means that a change in the r_1 setting will result in an immediate response of the position of platform P_1 *but without anything happening with the other platform.* The same must also be true with respect to r_2 and c_2. *Is this requirement consistent with the physics of the system?* Yes. The second control force u_2 must be told by the controller to *exactly* counteract the forces that are transmitted via the spring and dashpot. As no limitations have been assumed about the hydraulic actuators, this definitely should be feasible. Note, however, that we could not have required noninteraction if we had only *one* control force available (the system depicted in Fig. 6-12 can therefore never be made noninteracting).
2. The "speed-of-response" requirement also should be feasible in view of no restriction on the control forces. The question of how we should interpret the statement "of the order of 0.1 sec" will be answered later.
3. Zero static error in each control channel should not be beyond the possibilities of the system in view of the completely unrestricted control-force vector **u**.
4. Each platform will be subject to external loads, and it is necessary that these loads be exactly counteracted for zero compliance. From what we learned in a previous example, this definitely means integrators in each channel in view of the fact that we do not tolerate any static errors.

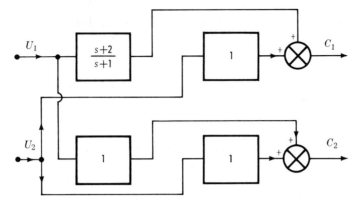

Fig. 7-43   Plant model of platform system.

The next topic on our agenda is the establishment of a linear model of our plant.   We shall assume that spring, dashpot, and control forces are comparatively large in relation to inertia forces, and in addition we shall set all spring and dashpot coefficients equal to unity in order not to clutter up our expressions and obscure important matters.

By requiring balance between all forces acting on each platform, we get:

For P_1 $u_1 = \underset{\substack{\text{spring} \\ \text{force}}}{(c_1 - c_2)} + \underset{\substack{\text{damping} \\ \text{force}}}{(\dot{c}_1 - \dot{c}_2)}$

For P_2 $u_2 = c_2 - (c_1 - c_2) - (\dot{c}_1 - \dot{c}_2)$

$$(7\text{-}70)$$

Laplace transformation yields

$$U_1 = C_1 - C_2 + sC_1 - sC_2$$
$$U_2 = 2C_2 - C_1 + sC_2 - sC_1$$

$$(7\text{-}71)$$

We may write these two equations in vector form:

$$\begin{bmatrix} C_1 \\ C_2 \end{bmatrix} = \begin{bmatrix} \dfrac{s+2}{s+1} & 1 \\ 1 & 1 \end{bmatrix} \begin{bmatrix} U_1 \\ U_2 \end{bmatrix}$$

$$(7\text{-}72)$$

or

$$\mathbf{C}(s) = \mathbf{G}_p(s)\mathbf{U}(s)$$

The interaction between the two control forces and the two outputs is shown in Fig. 7-43.   We shall now make an attempt to solve our problem by means of the unity-feedback structure in Fig. 7-44.   The problem is basically one of attempting to find a series compensator $\mathbf{G}_s$ that will result in an overall system that meets the specifications imposed upon the servo.   In principle, we could attack this problem in a manner similar to that demonstrated with several examples in the previous section dealing with SISO systems.   However, synthesis methods based entirely on trial and error have very little success when applied to multidimensional systems.   The reason is simply that we have too many variables to keep track of.   In the present problem, we must try to select the four different elements of $\mathbf{G}_s$ to satisfy a set of *four* performance specifications.   It is absolutely necessary to resort to synthesis techniques that will enable us to make use of the bookkeeping ability of the matrix methods.

This gives us no choice but to adopt some of the direct "algebraic" methods that we briefly introduced in the previous section.   It is also worthwhile to point out that, whereas we usually have quite a latitude in selecting the parameters for the compensating networks for SISO systems (this was particularly well demonstrated in Example 7-8), the requirement for noninteraction puts extremely exacting specifications on the different elements of the compensating matrix in the MIMO case.

After these sobering reflections, we return to our problem.

By combining Eqs. (6-23) and (6-25), we obtain (for $\mathbf{H} = \mathbf{I}$)

$$\mathbf{G}_c = (\mathbf{I} + \mathbf{G}_p\mathbf{G}_s)^{-1}\mathbf{G}_p\mathbf{G}_s$$

This matrix equation tells us how the closed-loop response depends upon the open-loop transfer matrices.   We solve this equation for $\mathbf{G}_s$:

$$\mathbf{G}_s = \mathbf{G}_p^{-1}\mathbf{G}_c(\mathbf{I} - \mathbf{G}_c)^{-1} \qquad (7\text{-}73)$$

(Note that the order of multiplication is important.)

This equation is the counterpart to the SISO equivalent

$$G_s = \frac{G_c}{G_p(1 - G_c)}$$

Just as, in the SISO case, we could assign a desired value to G_c and (because G_p is known) solve for the required G_s, we now can assign a $\mathbf{G}_c$ matrix and, because $\mathbf{G}_p$ is known, compute directly the required compensation $\mathbf{G}_s$.

There is one important difference—the inverse $\mathbf{G}_p^{-1}$ must exist.   In our present problem, it does [compare Eq. (7-72)], but it is not difficult to conceive of situations where it would not.   For instance, if we had only *one* control force, then the $\mathbf{G}_p$ matrix would reduce to a column matrix, which does not have an

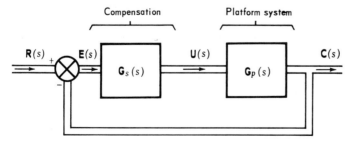

Fig. 7-44   Suggested closed-loop structure.

inverse. Equation (7-73) is a *matrix* equation, and the full equivalence is established only if all p^2 elements of each side are equal. Therefore, the equation actually represents p^2 *scalar* equations. As there are exactly p^2 unknowns (the elements of $\mathbf{G}_s$), the problem has a unique solution. Of course, as in the SISO case, we have no guarantee that these p^2 scalar transfer functions can be synthesized easily.

In our specific example, we shall attempt a solution by stipulating the closed-loop transfer matrix

$$\mathbf{G}_c = \begin{bmatrix} \dfrac{10}{s+10} & 0 \\ 0 & \dfrac{10}{s+10} \end{bmatrix} \tag{7-74}$$

We make this choice for the following reasons:

1. The matrix is *diagonal*; therefore, the first of the four PS would be satisfied.
2. $\mathbf{G}_c(0) = \mathbf{I}$, and because of Eq. (7-63), we therefore would satisfy the static-accuracy requirement.
3. Both G_{c11} and G_{c22} are of the form

$$\frac{1}{1 + sT}$$

where $T = 0.1$ sec, and therefore the response *in each channel* to a unit step would be of the exponential type with a time constant of 0.1 sec. We thus would satisfy the third of the four PS, the one relating to speed of response.

At this point, we cannot predict whether the fourth item of the PS, the zero-compliance requirement, will be met. This must be ascertained later.

We can determine $\mathbf{G}_s$ directly from (7-73) by substituting the assumed value for $\mathbf{G}_c$ into the matrix equation. This is an unattractive approach as we need to perform the matrix inversion $\mathbf{G}_p^{-1}$. We circumvent this difficulty by premultiplying both sides by $\mathbf{G}_p$; that is,

$$\mathbf{G}_p\mathbf{G}_s = \mathbf{G} = \mathbf{G}_c(\mathbf{I} - \mathbf{G}_c)^{-1} \tag{7-75}$$

We already concluded that the *open-loop* matrix $\mathbf{G}$ must be diagonal, and from Eqs. (7-61) and (7-74), we therefore get

$$\mathbf{G} = \begin{bmatrix} G_{11} & 0 \\ 0 & G_{22} \end{bmatrix} = \begin{bmatrix} \dfrac{10}{s} & 0 \\ 0 & \dfrac{10}{s} \end{bmatrix}$$

By then introducing our $\mathbf{G}_p$ matrix [Eq. (7-72)], we get directly from (7-75)

$$
\begin{bmatrix} \dfrac{10}{s} & 0 \\[2ex] 0 & \dfrac{10}{s} \end{bmatrix} = \begin{bmatrix} \dfrac{s+2}{s+1} & 1 \\[2ex] 1 & 1 \end{bmatrix} \begin{bmatrix} G_{s11} & G_{s12} \\[1ex] G_{s21} & G_{s22} \end{bmatrix} \tag{7-76}
$$

This matrix equation represents the four scalar equations

$$
\frac{10}{s} = \frac{s+2}{s+1} G_{s11} + G_{s21}
$$

$$
0 = \frac{s+2}{s+1} G_{s12} + G_{s22} \tag{7-77}
$$

$$
0 = G_{s11} + G_{s21}
$$

$$
\frac{10}{s} = G_{s12} + G_{s22}
$$

We solve these with little difficulty and obtain

$$
\mathbf{G}_s = \begin{bmatrix} 10\,\dfrac{s+1}{s} & -10\,\dfrac{s+1}{s} \\[3ex] -10\,\dfrac{s+1}{s} & 10\,\dfrac{s+2}{s} \end{bmatrix} \tag{7-78}
$$

By adding this compensation matrix in front of the plant matrix (see Fig. 7-43), we obtain an overall system as depicted in Fig. 7-45.

At this juncture, we ask an appropriate question: Can the four transfer functions constituting the $\mathbf{G}_s$ matrix be considered practically feasible?

As each one is of the type

$$
\frac{sK_1 + K_2}{s} = K_1 + \frac{K_2}{s}
$$

we can answer this question in the affirmative. Actually, this type of compensation is very common, particularly in the area of process control. The transfer function consists of a proportional term K_1 and an integral term K_2/s and is referred to as "proportional-plus-integral" (PPI) compensation; it can be instrumented easily by means of electrical, mechanical, hydraulic, or pneumatic devices.[13]

What remains to be checked is whether the stipulated compliance requirements are met by the system thus obtained. To investigate this, we apply disturbance forces z_1 and z_2 to each platform. This simply means that u_1 and

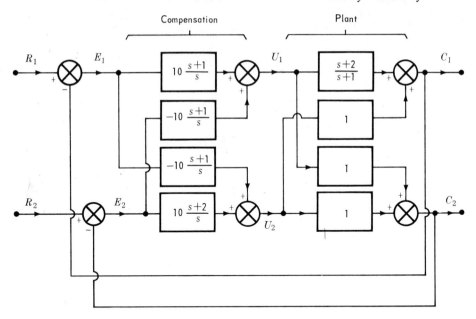

Fig. 7-45   Final design of platform controller.

u_2 in Eq. (7-70) will be replaced by $u_1 + z_1$ and $u_2 + z_2$, respectively, and we therefore conclude that the "disturbance-input" block diagram must look as shown in Fig. 7-46.

It is left as an exercise for the reader to confirm from this diagram and Eq. (7-69) that the stipulated Q values are indeed met.

7-5 SUMMARY

The last two chapters were devoted to design of linear servomechanisms. Major emphasis was directed toward "classical" design techniques of the "trial-and-error" variety.

The performance specifications applicable in each case will determine the design methods to be used. In most practical cases, these specifications preclude the use of any other design procedures but the trial-and-error type. For this reason alone, we must conclude that classical design is here to stay.

In the design examples that we used for demonstration purposes, we started from a set of specifications based upon desired response characteristics. It is important to realize, however, that in reality the designer has to meet additional practical design constraints, e.g., limits on size, weight, and price and component-failure rates.

In all but the simplest cases, the designer relies on modern computational aids. We exemplified the use of analog computers. In Chap. 12, we shall discuss more penetratingly the usage of computers in design.

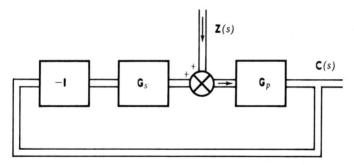

Fig. 7-46 The effects of disturbance forces can be predicted from this diagram.

Finally, it must be understood that classical designs cover a much wider spectrum of design techniques than we have been able to discuss in this book. Personal preference enters as a very important factor. The reader probably has realized by now that we are "sold" on root-locus techniques.

Exercises

7-1 The diagram in Fig. 7-10 was computed using the ISE criterion. On the basis of this criterion, the "best" choice of the damping coefficient α turned out to be

$$\alpha_{\text{opt}} = \tfrac{1}{2}\omega$$

What result would the ITAE criterion give? (A digital computer is helpful in performing the integration called for.)

▲ **7-2** Consider the thrust-propelled missile shown in Fig. 7-47. It is supposed to travel a vertical trajectory. It is acted upon by three basic forces:

1. Gravity force mg attacking in CG
2. Thrust T attacking in rear center
3. Aerodynamic forces attacking in the center of pressure CP

The last force can be resolved into two components:

1. The "drag" D, acting axially
2. The "lift" L, acting perpendicularly

The thrust T is set at a value in excess of $D + mg$, with the result that the missile is accelerating upward. In any particular point of the trajectory, the lift force is a function of the angle of attack; and if the angles are small enough, the lift is linearly dependent on α, that is,

$$L = k_L \alpha$$

(Note that the coefficient k_L varies along the trajectory. It is a function of both velocity and air pressure.) We can exert control of α by changing the direction of the thrust force through an angle δ. We shall assume that this is accomplished by hydraulically gimbaling the entire thrust engine.

    a Investigate how a change in δ affects the angle α. Specifically, compute the plant transfer function

$$G_p(s) = \frac{A(s)}{\Delta(s)}$$

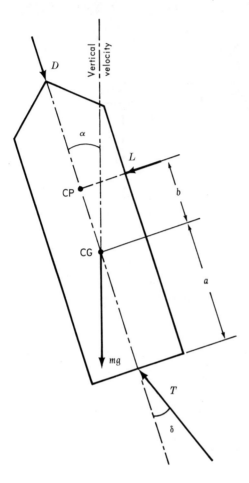

Fig. 7-47   Thrust-propelled vehicle.

where

$$A(s) \overset{\Delta}{=} \mathscr{L}[\alpha(t)] \quad \text{and} \quad \Delta(s) \overset{\Delta}{=} \mathscr{L}[\delta(t)]$$

For your analysis, make the following assumptions:

1. All angles are small.
2. All dynamics take place in the paper plane (pitch plane) only.   (Of course, the missile will perform dynamics in the two other coordinates, yaw and roll, also, but if the pitch and yaw angles are small and if the missile has rotational symmetry, the three modes of dynamics are "decoupled.")

3. Consider the missile a "rigid body" having a moment of inertia I kg-m² with respect to CG.
   b Suggest a control system ("autopilot") that will keep the output α as close to the vertical reference as possible.
   c Actually, a liquid-fuel missile is far from "rigid."   For one thing, its fuel load will slosh in the tanks.   A good model of a sloshing mass of fuel is obtained by replacing it with a spring-constrained mass m_0 performing transversal oscillations.   Compute the transfer function

$$G_p(s) = \frac{A(s)}{\Delta(s)}$$

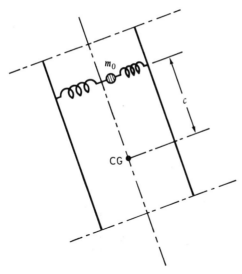

Fig. 7-48 Sloshing-fuel model.

in the presence of one of these oscillating masses. How will this affect the root loci of your system in problem b? You can make the assumption that $I \gg m_0 c^2$. (For symbols, see Fig. 7-48.)

7-3 Consider the system the pole-zero configuration of which is shown in Fig. 7-22. If the compensation zero at $s = -Z$ is pushed too far to the left, the system will be unstable for *all* loop gains K. Give the minimum Z value for which this would occur.

7-4 Construct the root loci for the broom-carriage position-control servo depicted in Fig. 6-13.

Can you conceive of a compensation scheme that will stabilize this system? We shall assume that we have an accelerometer available that produces an electrical signal proportional to the carriage acceleration $\ddot{y}$.

7-5 Figure 7-49 shows a liquid (H_2O) process consisting of two series-connected vessels. We wish to control the level c of the downstream vessel by controlling the input flow u by means of the control valve V. There are three disturbance inputs, each of which is beyond our control and the effects of which we must counteract:

$z_1 = $ inflow to upstream vessel

$z_2 = $ inflow to downstream vessel

$z_3 = $ pressure head back of throttle valve T_2

LC is a "level controller" which senses the error e in the controlled level and commands a change in the inflow u. The basic problem is to determine a suitable transfer function G_s for LC; that is, we wish to determine

$$G_s = \frac{U(s)}{E(s)}$$

so that the regulator performs in accordance with the PS. We introduce the following variables:

$u, q_1, q_2, z_1, z_2 = $ flows, expressed in m³/sec
A_1 and $A_2 = $ vessel areas, expressed in m²
c and $h = $ vessel levels, expressed in m
$z_3 = $ pressure, expressed in m H_2O

a Write the equations for this process. For the flow through the throttle valves, assume the relations

$$R_1 q_1 = h$$

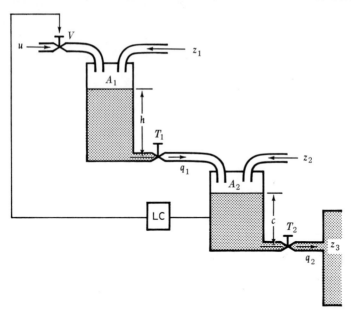

Fig. 7-49   A level controller.

and

$$R_2 q_2 = c - z_3$$

where R is the valve "resistance" expressed in meter head/meter³ per second, or second/meter².

    b Consider a process characterized by the numerical values

$$R_1 = R_2 = 100 \text{ sec/m}^2$$

$$A_1 = A_2 = 1 \text{ m}^2$$

The process is in *steady state*, characterized by the following data:

$$z_1 = z_2 = u = 0.01 \text{ m}^3/\text{sec}$$

$$z_3 = 0.5 \text{ m}$$

Compute the constant heads h and c.

    c We wish to keep the level c at the value computed in problem *b*, in spite of the fact that z_1, z_2, and z_3 change with the amounts δz_1, δz_2, and δz_3. Give a detailed block diagram for the closed-loop process, indicating all four inputs.

    d Suggest a suitable level controller LC for the regulator to meet the following PS:

1. Zero compliance with respect to all three disturbance inputs and zero FVE with respect to the reference input.
2. For a step change in the reference input of 10 cm, we wish the output to settle down to within 1 cm of the new steady-state level in less than 60 sec.

    We assumed in problem *d* that there were no limitations on either u or h. If we now assume that

$$0 < u < 0.025 \text{ m}^3/\text{sec}$$

and

$0 < h < 2.5$ m

will the controller which you designed in problem *d* be acceptable?

7-6 For the MIMO system we designed in Sec. 7-4, we never were concerned about the possibility of instability.   Why?

Assume now that we compensate the system *inaccurately*.   For instance, we found that the element G_{s22} of the compensation matrix $\mathbf{G}_s$ was supposed to equal

$$G_{s22} = 10\,\frac{s+2}{s} = 10 + \frac{20}{s}$$

Because of error in compensation, we obtain instead the value

$$G_{s22} = 10 + \frac{K}{s} \qquad \text{where } K \neq 20$$

Prove that incorrect K values may lead to instability.   Specifically, determine how many percent we can be off before the system becomes unstable.

7-7 Consider the servo depicted in Fig. 7-50.   It has a plant characterized by the transfer function

$$G_p = \frac{1}{s(s+10)}$$

a Use the algebraic synthesis method and determine the necessary compensation transfer function needed if we use

1. Series compensation
2. Feedback compensation

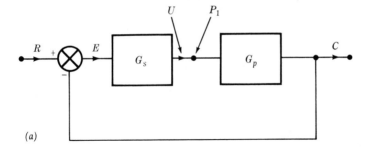

(a)

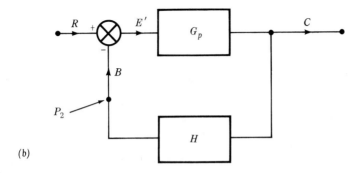

(b)

Fig. 7-50   Examples of algebraic design.

In both cases, we wish to get an output

$$c(t) = 1 - e^{-t}$$

for a unit-step input.

b Compute the signals appearing at the points marked P_1 and P_2 in the block diagrams and criticize your designs on the basis of your findings.

7-8 Consider the system in Fig. 2-3*b*, for which you wrote the dynamic equations in Exercise 3-1. It is desired to keep *both* "brooms" vertical by means of the control force *u* applied by a motor in the carriage. Suggest a workable control strategy!

In order to avoid expressions that are too messy, assign the following simple numerical data for each broom:

Length = 1 m

Mass = 2 kg

Neglect the carriage mass.

Hint: Assume a control strategy of the type $u = k_1\varphi_1 + k_2\dot{\varphi}_1 + k_3\varphi_2 + k_4\dot{\varphi}_2$, and then use Routh stability criterion to settle for proper parameter values.

▲ **7-9** Work out in as much detail as your background knowledge permits a control system for the pilot centrifuge sketched in Fig. 3-7.

The following specifications should be met by your design:

1. The centrifuge speed n_{max} must correspond to a centrifugal acceleration of 15 g.
2. The control loop must be stable throughout the complete test run, with a gain margin of at least 100 percent and a phase margin of 45°.
3. The acceleration and deceleration periods are each of $\frac{1}{2}$-min duration. In view of this, it is deemed necessary that the control loop should have a speed "of the order of 1 sec."

The centrifuge data are:

$L = 10$ m (see Fig. 3-7).

$I = 10^5$ kg-m², including motor plus gear, as measured on the centrifuge side of the gear train [Eq. (3-49)].

It is estimated that the windage torque $(k_w\dot{\varphi}^2)$ equals 25 percent of the inertia torque $(I\ddot{\varphi})$ at full speed.

You probably will find that the best drive arrangement will be a d-c motor connected in so-called Ward-Leonard configuration.

Your design should include:

1. Choice of system configuration
2. Calculation of motor size
3. Estimate of system parameters
4. Loop compensation

References

1. W. C. Schultz and V. C. Rideout, Control System Performance Measures: Past, Present, and Future, *IRE Trans. Auto. Control*, **AC-6**(1) (1961).
2. J. Zaborszky, The Development of Performance Criteria for Automatic Control Systems, *AIEE, Inst. Tech. Group Auto. Control*, **I**(2) (1962).
3. J. E. Gibson et al., Specification and Data Presentation in Linear Control Systems, *Rept.* AFMDC-TR-60-2, Purdue University, Lafayette, Ind.
4. John G. Truxal, "Control System Synthesis," McGraw-Hill Book Company, New York, 1955.
5. D. Graham and R. C. Lathrop, The Synthesis of Optimum Transient Response: Criteria and Standard Forms, *Trans. AIEE*, **72**, pt. 2: 278–288 (November, 1953).

6. G. C. Newton, L. A. Gould, and J. F. Kaiser, "Analytical Design of Linear Feedback Controls," John Wiley & Sons, Inc., New York, 1957.

7. W. R. Evans, Graphical Analysis of Control Systems, *Trans. AIEE,* **67**: 547–551 (1948).

8. O. I. Elgerd and W. C. Stephens, Effect of Closed-loop Transfer Function Pole and Zero Locations on the Transient Response of Linear Control Systems, *Trans. AIEE, Appl. Ind.,* **42** (1959).

9. J. Zaborszky, Integrated *s*-plane Synthesis Using 2-way Root Locus, *Trans. AIEE,* pt. I: 797–801 (January, 1957).

10. John Peschon, "Disciplines and Techniques of Systems Control," Blaisdell Publishing Co., New York, 1964. (Chapter III is devoted to multivariable systems.)

11. H. K. Chatterjee, Multivariable Process Control, *Trans. IFAC Conf.,* 1st, London, 831–836 (1961).

12. R. J. Kavanagh, Multivariable Control System Synthesis, *Trans. AIEE,* **77**, pt. II: 425–429 (1958).

13. D. P. Eckman, "Automatic Process Control," John Wiley & Sons, Inc., New York, 1950.

chapter 8

NONLINEAR
CONTROL SYSTEMS

8-1 INTRODUCTION

On the basis of that very fundamental physical property, the *superposition principle*, we have divided systems into two main groups:

1. Linear systems, for which the principle applies
2. Nonlinear systems, for which it does not

So far we have concerned ourselves exclusively with linear and, in addition, time-invariant systems. We should by now be impressed by the ease with which such systems can be handled analytically. The specific examples given in the previous chapter should also have convinced us of their practical usefulness as applied to the area of control.

This chapter will be devoted to a presentation of nonlinear theory as it applies to the control-systems area. At the outset, we should point out that our knowledge of nonlinear-system behavior is very limited as compared with the situation in the linear field. Actually, we are quite inadequately equipped to handle any but the very simplest classes of nonlinear systems, and all those methods that we do possess suffer severely from *lack of generality*. It is probably safe to say that at present we are analytically equipped to solve *accurately* only rather trivial problems.

It must be added that there exists a vast amount of accumulated knowledge concerning the solution of *special* nonlinear differential equations. However, the control engineer rarely, if ever, is helped much by this fact, since he is, as a rule, unable to arrange the equations pertaining to his very special system into a form that is identifiable with a known nonlinear differential equation. At first glance, this would seem to be a rather regrettable state of affairs. It would be convenient, no doubt, for the analyst to possess a solution method that would serve him as faithfully as the Laplace-transform method does in the case of linear time-invariant equations. Most certainly, such a panacea will never be found—the infinite variety of nonlinear functions forever precludes this possibility. However, this absence of a predictable behavior pattern makes the area of nonlinear systems an excellent hunting ground for the designer who is looking for something more sophisticated and out of the way than he might find in the realm of linear systems. He may, in many instances, find good reasons *intentionally* to introduce non-linearities into the system in order to achieve certain objectives. For example, he may use "maximum-effort" controllers in order to achieve time optimality, or he may introduce nonlinear dampers in order to obtain an amplitude-dependent time response.

In many practical situations, we have to accept nonlinearities of the *incidental* variety. No physical component is linear in the true mathematical sense. We must contend with irregularities like backlash, static friction ("stiction"), hysteresis, saturation, and a score of other generally *undesirable* characteristics that usually are unavoidable. For medium- and low-precision servos, we often can entirely neglect these side effects and with sufficient accuracy work with a linear model. *It should also be noted that the feedback in itself actually linearizes an otherwise nonlinear system.* For example, consider the voltage regulator in Fig. 6-33. Without feedback, i.e., in open-loop operation, the output voltage would vary quite nonlinearly with respect to the reference-voltage setting, as an electrical generator of this type is characterized by a considerable degree of saturation within the normal operating range. The feedback desensitizes against this, just as it desensitizes against speed variations and other disturbances. The situation is not quite this simple in the case of high-precision servos. For example, in designing the control mechanisms for an antenna that must be pointed continuously toward a communication satellite within error limits of less than a minute of arc, it becomes an absolute necessity to understand and to find means for eliminating the effects of all those incidental nonlinearities present in the overall system.

In this chapter, we shall discuss the following aspects of nonlinear control-system theory:

1. The two most useful analysis methods, the state-space and the describing-function methods
2. The concept of stability as it applies to nonlinear feedback systems
3. Some nonlinear phenomena that are of specific importance for the control-system designer
4. Intentional nonlinear design

8-2 THE STATE-SPACE ANALYSIS METHOD

The transfer-function methods, the indispensible tools in linear analysis, are of only limited usefulness in the study of nonlinear systems. Complete information concerning the dynamics of a nonlinear system can *only* be obtained by integration of the differential equations describing it. It is natural, therefore, that we should be able to find considerable use for the state-variable method that we presented in the early chapters.

Consider the control system depicted in Fig. 8-1. We shall assume that both the plant and the controller are nonlinear. The plant is characterized by the

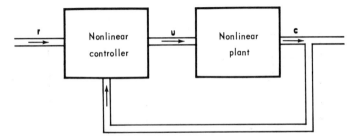

Fig. 8-1   Nonlinear control system.

state vector **x** and the output vector **c**.   For these vectors, we assume the equations

$$\dot{\mathbf{x}} = \mathbf{f}(\mathbf{x},\mathbf{u})$$
$$\mathbf{c} = \mathbf{Cx} \tag{8-1}$$

The controller supplies a control-force vector **u**, which is related to the reference input **r** and the output **c** in the following nonlinear way:

$$\mathbf{u} = \mathbf{g}(\mathbf{c},\mathbf{r}) = \mathbf{g}(\mathbf{Cx},\mathbf{r}) \tag{8-2}$$

By substitution of this expression for **u** in Eq. (8-1), we obtain the *closed-loop* system of differential equations for **x**

$$\dot{\mathbf{x}} = \mathbf{f}_c(\mathbf{x},\mathbf{r}) \tag{8-3}$$

Should the plant be subject to disturbance inputs **z**, we would obtain the modified equation

$$\dot{\mathbf{x}} = \mathbf{f}_c(\mathbf{x},\mathbf{z},\mathbf{r}) \tag{8-4}$$

If the reference input **r** is constant $= \mathbf{r}^0$, then it is possible to write Eq. (8-3) in the *autonomous* form

$$\dot{\mathbf{x}} = \mathbf{f}_c(\mathbf{x},\mathbf{r}^0) \overset{\Delta}{=} \mathbf{F}_c(\mathbf{x}) \tag{8-5}$$

In the above derivation, we tacitly made the important assumption that it is possible to describe the controller action in terms of the *algebraic* equation system **g**.   Should the controller contain energy-storage elements, e.g., integrators, this would not be possible, and it then becomes necessary to introduce *additional* state variables in our mathematical model for the closed-loop system.

Example 8-1

Consider the SISO system shown in Fig. 8-2, characterized by a linear second-order plant and a nonlinear "maximum-effort" or "on-off" type of controller. This block diagram could represent, for example, the attitude-control system for an orbiting space capsule, assuming that the reaction-jet moment u is applied in a

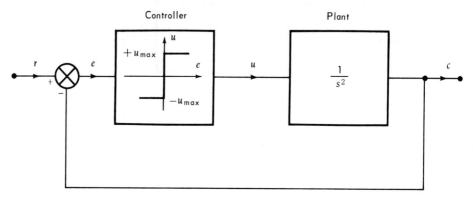

Fig. 8-2 "Bang-bang" control system.

"bang-bang" fashion (which usually is the case). The plant differential equation reads, in this case,

$$\ddot{c} = u$$

and by introduction of the state vector

$$\mathbf{x} = \begin{bmatrix} x_1 \\ x_2 \end{bmatrix} \triangleq \begin{bmatrix} c \\ \dot{c} \end{bmatrix}$$

the plant equations (8-1) take on the normal form

$$\dot{x}_1 = x_2$$
$$\dot{x}_2 = u \qquad \text{with } c \triangleq x_1 \tag{8-6}$$

The controller supplies a maximum control force $\pm u_{\max}$, depending upon the sign of the error $e = r - c$ in accordance with the rule

$$u = \frac{e}{|e|} u_{\max} = \frac{r - c}{|r - c|} u_{\max} = \frac{r - x_1}{|r - x_1|} u_{\max} \tag{8-7}$$

This then is the nonlinear controller equation g (scalar in this case) corresponding to (8-2). By eliminating u between Eqs. (8-6) and (8-7), we finally obtain the closed-loop system [corresponding to (8-3)]

$$\dot{x}_1 = x_2$$
$$\dot{x}_2 = \frac{r - x_1}{|r - x_1|} u_{\max} \tag{8-8}$$

8-2.1 PHASE TRAJECTORIES

Although we rarely are able to obtain *explicit* solutions for $\mathbf{x}$ [the system (8-8) is an exception] from the nonlinear differential equations (8-3) because they seldom integrate into elementary functions, we nevertheless are able to draw very important conclusions regarding the nature of the solution by a study of the so-called *phase trajectories* of the system. The reader was exposed very lightly to the notion of phase trajectory in Chap. 3 in connection with the introduction of state variables (Fig. 3-1). We shall now proceed to discuss these concepts in greater depth.

Consider the vector differential equation (8-3), which expresses the *rate of change* of the state of the closed-loop control system. Assume that we observe the system at the moment t^* and find that the state equals $\mathbf{x}^*$. The reference input at this moment equals $\mathbf{r}^*$. If we repeat the observation δt sec later, we observe that the state has changed with the amount $\delta\mathbf{x}$ to the new state $\mathbf{x}^* + \delta\mathbf{x}$.

If δt is sufficiently small, we obtain from Eq. (8-3)

$$\delta\mathbf{x} \approx \mathbf{f}_c(\mathbf{x}^*,\mathbf{r}^*)\, \delta t \tag{8-9}$$

or, in component form,

$$\delta x_i \approx f_{c_i}(x_1^*, x_2^*, \ldots, x_n^*; r_1^*, r_2^*, \ldots, r_p^*)\, \delta t \qquad \text{for } i = 1, 2, \ldots, n$$

We conclude that the change of the state during the short interval δt is basically dependent upon the state itself, $\mathbf{x}^*$, and, of course, the magnitude of the reference input $\mathbf{r}^*$. If we repeatedly make use of the formula (8-9), we can compute the new states at the end of the time intervals $t^* + \delta t$, $t^* + 2\delta t$, $t^* + 3\delta t$, etc. Differently expressed, we obtain the sequence of states $\mathbf{x}(t^*)$, $\mathbf{x}(t^* + \delta t)$, $\mathbf{x}(t^* + 2\delta t), \ldots$, with time t being reduced to the role of a parameter. This procedure involves, of course, an exorbitant amount of computational effort in view of the fact that δt must be chosen sufficiently small to preserve accuracy. With the aid of a high-speed digital computer, the technique becomes, however, quite practical and indeed represents the standard numerical approach for "non-solvable" differential equations. The sequence of computed states can be plotted in the n-dimensional $\mathbf{x}$ space, and we obtain a continuous curve or *phase trajectory*, exemplified for a two-dimensional case in Fig. 8-3. The vector

$$\dot{\mathbf{x}}(t) = \frac{\delta\mathbf{x}(t)}{\delta t} = \mathbf{f}_c(\mathbf{x},\mathbf{r})$$

represents the rate of change at time t of the state $\mathbf{x}$, and we shall refer to it as the *velocity* vector (although, in general, it may *not* have the physical dimension of velocity). As the vector $\delta\mathbf{x}$ is tangential to the trajectory in each point and as the quantity δt is a scalar, *the velocity vector must be tangential to the phase trajectory*. Physically, the velocity vector indicates the speed with which the motion along the phase trajectory takes place.

8-2.2 SINGULAR POINTS OR EQUILIBRIUM STATES

Equation (8-9) discloses that the state increment $\delta\mathbf{x}$ depends not only on the state but also on the reference input $\mathbf{r}$. If we restrict the class of inputs to *constant* vectors $\mathbf{r}^0$ only, then we can conclude that each point in the n-dimensional space is associated with as many trajectories as there are levels of $\mathbf{r}^0$. For instance, if we are interested in the response of a system to *one* constant input $\mathbf{r}^0$ only, then we know that through each point in $\mathbf{x}$ space, we have one and only one trajectory.

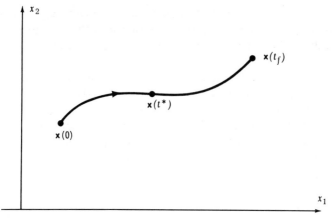

Fig. 8-3   Phase trajectory in two-dimensional state space.

In the case of an on-off controller, each point is associated with two trajectories, and so on.

By imposing the constancy requirement upon **r**, we have, of course, rather severely restricted the choice of inputs.   A constant input or a step is, however, the simplest type of input we can find, and although it does not carry the same significance for test purposes as it did in the linear case, we still find it useful in our following discussion.

A control system subject to a *constant* reference input $\mathbf{r}^0$ ideally should settle down to a constant output $\mathbf{c} = \mathbf{r}^0$.   If it does not, we may conclude either that the system does not have perfect "follow-up" (i.e., zero static error) or that it is "unstable."   The concept of stability is considerably harder to both define and study than in the case of linear systems, and we shall return to it in the next section of this chapter.   If, as a result of a step reference input $\mathbf{r}^0$, the state of the system will settle down to an *equilibrium* state $\mathbf{x}^0$, this can immediately be ascertained from the behavior of the phase trajectories.   A system which is in a state of equilibrium $\mathbf{x}^0$ is characterized by zero motion in the state space; i.e., the velocity vector equals zero.   We therefore conclude from Eq. (8-5) that such an *equilibrium point* $\mathbf{x}^0$ (or *singular point*, or *point of stagnancy*) must satisfy the equations

$$\mathbf{F}_c(\mathbf{x}^0) = \mathbf{0} \tag{8-10}$$

or, in component form,

$$F_{c_i}(x_1{}^0, x_2{}^0, \ldots, x_n{}^0) = 0 \qquad \text{for } i = 1, 2, \ldots, n$$

It should be noted that all systems do not necessarily possess equilibrium points.   For example, consider the servo depicted in Fig. 8-2.   By using Eq. (8-8), we seek a point

$$\mathbf{x}^0 = \begin{bmatrix} x_1{}^0 \\ x_2{}^0 \end{bmatrix}$$

that would be characterized by zero velocity; that is,

$$0 = x_2{}^0$$

$$0 = \frac{r^0 - x_1{}^0}{|r^0 - x_1{}^0|} u_{max}$$

(8-11)

We are able to satisfy the first of these equations, certainly, but *not* the second one, as obviously the right member can only take on one of the two values $\pm u_{max}$. The physical reason for the lack of an equilibrium state in this case is obvious—the plant is undamped, and as the control force can assume only the nonzero values $\pm u_{max}$, the system evidently will be in constant motion. The best we can hope to achieve is that the system will oscillate around an "average" state or perform what, in nonlinear lingo, is referred to as *limit cycles*. The actual shape of the phase trajectories for this system will be investigated in the next section.

8-2.3 CONSTRUCTION OF PHASE TRAJECTORIES—THE PHASE PLANE

It is quite easy to talk about and even conceive of a phase trajectory in *n*-dimensional space. This is, of course, in itself of great importance. Actually, the abstract idea of state space is, at the present time, the most fundamental concept in the theory of ordinary differential equations, linear or nonlinear, time-dependent or time-invariant. When it comes to actually constructing the trajectories for a specific system, it becomes extremely cumbersome to handle any system of order in excess of the second. For obvious reasons, the difficulties of data presentation become excessive. In the two-dimensional case, we refer to the state space as a *phase plane* or *state plane*.

Poincaré used the phase plane for analysis purposes in the nineteenth century.[1] We shall discuss briefly the most effective methods available for constructing the phase trajectories in the two-dimensional case, when Eqs. (8-3) reduce to

$$\dot{x}_1 = f_{c1}(x_1, x_2; r)$$

$$\dot{x}_2 = f_{c2}(x_1, x_2; r)$$

(8-12)

(For simplicity, we have assumed that the reference input r is one-dimensional.)

From (8-12), we get

$$\frac{dx_2}{dx_1} = \frac{f_{c2}(x_1, x_2; r)}{f_{c1}(x_1, x_2; r)}$$

(8-13)

dx_2/dx_1 represents the slope S of the phase trajectories in the phase plane, and Eq. (8-13) therefore tells us that, generally, for a *time-variant input* $r(t)$, the slope will be a function of *both* the phase-plane coordinates and the time t. *Only if we limit attention to constant r inputs will the shape of the trajectories remain fixed in time.* All the construction methods discussed in the following are based upon this assumption.

A great variety of phase-plane plotting methods have been reported in the literature since the days of Poincaré. We shall include here only those methods that have proved most useful in the control area.

The Direct-solution Method

The most obvious method of finding the phase trajectories is by direct solution of the differential equation (8-13). If this is possible, we obtain a solution of the type

$$F[x_1, x_2, r^0, x_1(0), x_2(0)] = 0 \tag{8-14}$$

$x_1(0)$ and $x_2(0)$ are the initial states, and r^0 represents (as before) the *constant* reference input. It is worth noting that a solution of the type (8-14) (giving x_2 as a function of x_1) may be found in spite of the fact that we are unable to find explicit *time solutions* for either x_1 or x_2. We demonstrate† the direct-solution method with the following example:

Example 8-2

Consider the on-off servo shown in Fig. 8-2. From Eqs. (8-8), we get

$$\frac{dx_2}{dx_1} = \frac{r^0 - x_1}{|r^0 - x_1|} \frac{u_{\max}}{x_2} \tag{8-15}$$

We separate the variables and integrate:

$$\int_{x_2(0)}^{x_2} x_2 \, dx_2 = \frac{r^0 - x_1}{|r^0 - x_1|} u_{\max} \int_{x_1(0)}^{x_1} dx_1$$

and obtain the solution

$$\tfrac{1}{2}[x_2{}^2 - x_2{}^2(0)] = \frac{r^0 - x_1}{|r^0 - x_1|} u_{\max}[x_1 - x_1(0)] \tag{8-16}$$

This, then, is our trajectory equation (8-14). The trajectories are plotted in Fig. 8-4. We note that the trajectories actually are represented by two families of parabolas:

$$x_2{}^2 = 2u_{\max}x_1 + \text{const} \qquad \text{for } x_1 < r^0$$

$$x_2{}^2 = -2u_{\max}x_1 + \text{const} \qquad \text{for } x_1 > r^0$$

The two families are marked T' and T'', respectively.

The initial states $x_1(0)$ and $x_2(0)$ determine the constants in the above pair of equations and therefore also the specific trajectory in each family. For example, assume that initially we are located in the initial state marked $\mathbf{x}(0)$ in the figure. As $x_1(0)$ evidently is less than r^0, the state must change along the T' trajectory that passes through the point in question (this trajectory is marked

---

† A perfect demonstration example on the usage of the direct-solution method is the broom balancer discussed in Chap. 2 when a "bang-bang" control strategy is employed. We have so often made reference to this system that we have, instead, used this problem as an end-of-chapter exercise (Exercise 8-8).

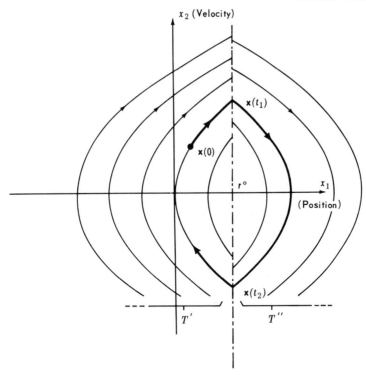

Fig. 8-4 Phase trajectories for the system in Fig. 8-2.

boldface). It is not immediately clear whether we move to the left or to the right. However, we can settle this question easily from the first of Eqs. (8-8), that is,

$$\frac{dx_1}{dt} = x_2$$

As both dt and x_2 are obviously positive, dx_1 must also be positive and the motion along the trajectory must take place to the *right*. The state of the system changes in a manner indicated by the arrows. Eventually, after t_1 sec, we reach the state $\mathbf{x}(t_1)$; and because x_1 now ceases to be less than r^0, the relay switches and we transfer to a T'' trajectory, which we follow until the relay again switches at time t_2. At this moment, we again transfer over to a T' trajectory, which for reasons of symmetry must be identical with the one from which we originally started. After T sec, the system returns to the original state $\mathbf{x}(0)$, and unless we change the reference input r^0, the periodic oscillation will continue indefinitely. The relay system is "limit cycling."

Limit-cycle oscillation is a typical nonlinear phenomenon that is very common in nonlinear control systems, particularly when on-off controllers are present. The phenomenon is not limited, of course, to second-order systems. It is important to note also that the oscillations are, in general, *nonsinusoidal*. The periodicity of a limit-cycling system may be expressed by

$$\mathbf{x}(t + T) = \mathbf{x}(t) \tag{8-17}$$

If the amplitudes of oscillation are sufficiently small, limit cycling may be tolerated—indeed, even desired. It is interesting to note that the concept of "stability," as applied to nonlinear systems, is sufficiently broad (see the next section) to include a limit-cycling control system within the family of "stable" systems.

A graphical state-transfer representation of the type presented in Fig. 8-4 gives, in a very illustrative manner, information about the nature of the system dynamics. As we pointed out earlier, the phase plane does *not* give explicit information about the *time* response. In the example just treated, we can obtain this information by direct time-domain integration of the original equation (8-8). This is left as an exercise for the reader. The result is shown in Fig. 8-5. The graphs in Fig. 8-5 correspond to the boldface trajectory in Fig. 8-4. Note that x_1 is *not sinusoidal*. More often than not, the nonlinear state-transfer equations defy integration, and we are then forced to resort to some numerical and/or graphical technique to obtain $x_1(t)$ and $x_2(t)$. In the present case, we could have proceeded as follows:

From the equation

$$\frac{dx_1}{dt} = x_2$$

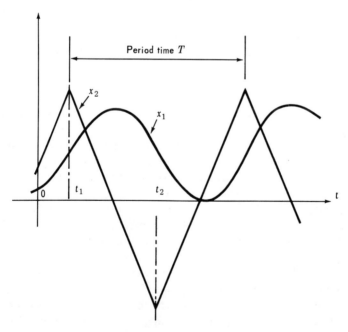

Fig. 8-5 The limit cycles shown in the time domain.

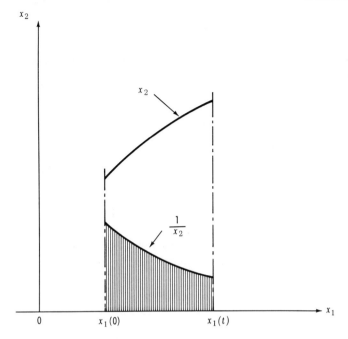

Fig. 8-6   Determining the time response by graphical integration.

we obtain

$$dt = \frac{dx_1}{x_2}$$

Therefore,

$$t = \int_{x_1(0)}^{x_1(t)} \frac{1}{x_2}\, dx_1 \tag{8-18}$$

As x_2 is known from the phase plane, it obviously is possible to obtain the parameter t by integrating graphically the inverse function $1/x_2$, as shown in Fig. 8-6. The shaded surface equals the sought integral (8-18). This approach clearly gives poor accuracy for those parts of the phase trajectory where $x_2 = 0$.

In the example just discussed, the phase plane served as a tool for *analysis*. Its usefulness for system *synthesis* is probably of greater importance to the control engineer. We shall return to this important topic in a later section. Now we shall present another phase-plane construction method.

Phase-plane Construction by Means of the Isocline Method

It was pointed out in connection with Eq. (8-13) that the ratio dx_2/dx_1 represents the slope S of the trajectories in the x_1x_2 plane. We thus have

$$\frac{dx_2}{dx_1} = S = \frac{f_{c2}(x_1,x_2; r^0)}{f_{c1}(x_1,x_2; r^0)} \tag{8-19}$$

(The reference input is assumed constant $= r^0$.)

Assisted by Eq. (8-19), we now may determine those regions of the phase plane that are characterized by the same values of the trajectory slope. By assigning constant values to S, the differential equation (8-19) reduces to an *algebraic* equation

$$H(x_1,x_2,r^0,S) = 0 \qquad (8\text{-}20)$$

that is satisfied for those value pairs (x_1,x_2) for which the trajectories have slope S. Equation (8-20) thus gives the loci for states of equal slope (in Greek, *isos* means "equal" and *klinein*, "to slope").

We demonstrate with an example.

Example 8-3

Consider the feedback system depicted in Fig. 8-7. The linear second-order plant is controlled by an element that is characterized by a dead zone and abrupt saturation. The response characteristics to step inputs r^0 are sought.

We establish first a mathematical model for the system. As the plant transfer function $G_p(s)$ equals

$$G_p(s) = \frac{C(s)}{U(s)} = \frac{1}{s^2 + s}$$

we have

$$\ddot{c} + \dot{c} = u \qquad (8\text{-}21)$$

The nonlinear controller is characterized by

$$u = N(e) = N(r^0 - c) \qquad (8\text{-}22)$$

where the nonlinear function $N(e)$ is defined by

$$N(e) = +1 \qquad \text{for } e > 1$$
$$N(e) = 0 \qquad \text{for } -1 < e < 1$$
$$N(e) = -1 \qquad \text{for } e < -1$$

As in the previous example, we now could choose c and $\dot{c}$ as components in our state vector $\mathbf{x}$. It will prove somewhat more convenient to work with e

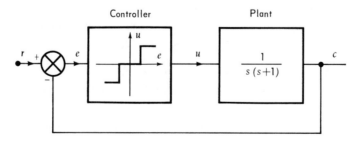

Fig. 8-7   "Bang-bang" system with dead zone.

(error) and $\dot{e}$ (error rate), as the state of the nonlinear element $N(e)$ will be a function of e rather than c.

We therefore define

$$\mathbf{x} = \begin{bmatrix} x_1 \\ x_2 \end{bmatrix} \triangleq \begin{bmatrix} e \\ \dot{e} \end{bmatrix} = \begin{bmatrix} r^0 - c \\ -\dot{c} \end{bmatrix} \tag{8-23}$$

By combining Eqs. (8-21) to (8-23), we obtain the nonlinear system of differential equations

$$\begin{aligned} \dot{x}_1 &= x_2 \\ \dot{x}_2 &= -x_2 - N(x_1) \end{aligned} \tag{8-24}$$

In order to obtain the isoclines, we form the ratio

$$\frac{dx_2}{dx_1} = S = \frac{-[x_2 + N(x_1)]}{x_2} \tag{8-25}$$

We next divide the $x_1 x_2$ plane into the three regions shown in Fig. 8-8, each corresponding to the three different states of the nonlinear element N.

Region I   This region is defined by

$$e = x_1 < -1$$

and therefore $N(e) = N(x_1) = -1$.

From Eq. (8-25), we thus get

$$S = -\frac{x_2 - 1}{x_2} \tag{8-26}$$

The isoclines are thus independent of x_1 and must therefore be horizontal lines.   For example, if we seek the locus for $S = 1$, we obtain

$$1 = -\frac{x_2 - 1}{x_2}$$

Hence,

$$x_2 = \tfrac{1}{2}$$

and so on.

Some representative isoclines are indicated in Fig. 8-8.   The short line segments along the isoclines indicate the slope associated with the isoclines in question.

Region II   This region represents the dead zone of the nonlinear element, that is,

$$-1 < e < 1$$

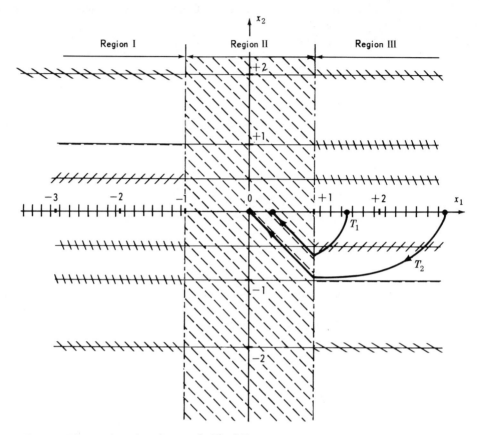

Fig. 8-8   Phase trajectories of system in Fig. 8-7.

Therefore,

$$N(e) = N(x_1) = 0$$

Equation (8-25) gives

$$S = -\frac{x_2 + 0}{x_2} = -1 \qquad (8\text{-}27)$$

This *entire* region is thus characterized by trajectories which all have a slope -1 .

Region III   Here we have

$$e = x_1 > +1$$

and

$$N(e) = N(x_1) = +1$$

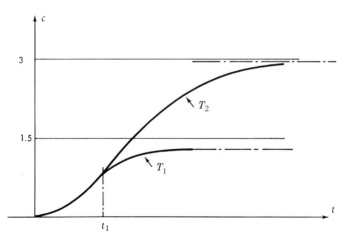

Fig. 8-9 Time responses of system in Fig. 8-7.

Therefore,

$$S = -\frac{x_2 + 1}{x_2} \qquad (8\text{-}28)$$

As in region I, the isoclines are horizontal lines.

Having thus determined the isoclines for the entire $e\dot{e}$ plane, we have no difficulty sketching the phase trajectories. Two different trajectories, T_1 and T_2, are shown. They correspond to step inputs r^0 of magnitudes 1.5 and 3, respectively. Note that in neither case is the final state zero. Due to the dead zone, we shall always have to contend with nonzero FVE. The static error will, however, be less the larger-magnitude step we apply. Figure 8-9 shows the response picture in the time domain. Note that up to time t_1, all step inputs in excess of 1.5 will give identical outputs. The larger the inputs are, the higher will be the velocity $\dot{c}$ imparted to the output member. This is clearly evidenced by the phase trajectories. The reader should convince himself in what manner and why this velocity affects the FVE.

The two phase-plane construction methods presented in this section are by far the most generally useful ones. As in so many other areas of nonlinear theory, there exist *special* methods for solving *special* equations. There would be very little sense in enumerating these here. The reader who wants a more thorough coverage of this (and also other aspects of nonlinear control) is referred to more detailed treatises on nonlinear control (see, for example, Ref. 2).

As already mentioned, the difficulties of data presentation prohibit, in practice, the use of the above methods with systems of third and higher orders. Efforts in this direction have been made, however, and in particular the work by Ku[3] should be mentioned. He used the technique of projecting the actual third-order phase trajectory onto any two of the three possible planes containing the axes x_1, x_2 or x_2, x_3 or x_1, x_3. Flügge-Lotz[5] makes use of the same technique in designing optimal relay controllers for third- and fourth-order plants.

8-3 STABILITY OF NONLINEAR SYSTEMS

In discussing the concept of stability in nonlinear control systems, it is very fruitful to make comparisons with the corresponding situations in their linear time-invariant counterparts. We remember that it was possible to determine the stability of such systems solely on the basis of the location of the eigenvalues in the s plane. If the λ's were located in the left half of the plane, excluding the $j\omega$ axis, we defined the system as stable; otherwise, it was unstable. It is worthwhile to remind the reader of the following features characterizing a stable linear time-invariant system:

1. The stability is entirely independent of whether or not the system is driven.
2. The state of an undriven stable system will always return to the origin of the state space, independent of the magnitude of the finite initial state $\mathbf{x_0}$.

The situation is unfortunately not this clear-cut in the case of nonlinear systems. Bellman (whose work on dynamic programming we shall discuss in Chap. 11) has called "stability" that "much overburdened word with an unstabilized definition." Gibson[2] mentions that there are 28 different classes of stability in current use. Before we make an attempt to clarify some of these concepts—at least to the extent that they are made useful for our immediate purposes—let us consider some of the more important ways in which nonlinear systems differ from linear ones in respect to stability characteristics:

1. The stability of a nonlinear system is dependent upon the input. For example, an unforced system may be stable, but the same system, subject to a step input, may be divergent. Systems can be found where the opposite holds true; i.e., the application of an input stabilizes the otherwise unstable system.
2. The stability of an unforced system can be very dependent upon the initial state $\mathbf{x_0}$.

8-3.I DEFINITIONS

As the stability of a nonlinear system obviously depends to a great measure upon type and magnitude of input and also upon the particular region of the state space in which the state vector ranges, it is only natural that we should take these factors into account when defining what we mean by a "stable" system.

First, we shall restrict ourselves in the following to nonlinear systems subject to *constant* inputs only. The reason for this is quite simple—the stability theory for systems subject to arbitrary inputs is very undeveloped. Therefore, we shall consider only those control systems that, in accordance with Eq. (8-5), can be described by an autonomous vector differential equation of the form

$$\dot{\mathbf{x}} = \mathbf{F}_c(\mathbf{x})$$

Secondly, we shall classify the stability on a regional basis, as follows.†

1. Local stability, or *stability in the small*
2. Finite stability
3. Global stability, or *stability in the large*

Local Stability

Assume that the system (8-5) has a singular point in $\mathbf{x}^0$. The system is said to be *locally stable* if when subject to a sudden *small* perturbation, it tends to remain within a *small specified* region R surrounding $\mathbf{x}^0$.

This definition suffices from our practical point of view. It can be given a stricter mathematical definition.[4] It should be noted that stability in the above sense *does not require the state to return eventually* to $\mathbf{x}^0$. If we add this requirement, then we classify the stability as *asymptotic*. The difference between these two degrees of stability is demonstrated for a two-dimensional case in Fig. 8-10*a* and *b*. Evidently, asymptotic stability excludes the possibility of small limit cycles.

Monotonic stability (shown in Fig. 8-10*c*) is a still stronger condition. We now require that the distance to the equilibrium point decrease monotonically.

Local stability is, in principle, quite simple to study. As we are concerned with the dynamics in the immediate neighborhood of the singular point, we can *linearize* the vector equation (8-5) around the point in question. This linearization technique was discussed in Chap. 3. By introducing the deviation vector $\boldsymbol{\delta}\mathbf{x}$, defined by

$$\boldsymbol{\delta}\mathbf{x} \triangleq \mathbf{x} - \mathbf{x}^0 \tag{8-29}$$

and by defining the Jacobian matrix [see Eq. (3-46)]

$$\mathbf{A} \triangleq \begin{bmatrix} \dfrac{\partial F_{c1}}{\partial x_1} & \cdots & \dfrac{\partial F_{c1}}{\partial x_n} \\ \cdots\cdots\cdots\cdots\cdots \\ \dfrac{\partial F_{cn}}{\partial x_1} & \cdots & \dfrac{\partial F_{cn}}{\partial x_n} \end{bmatrix} \tag{8-30}$$

We can obtain the following *linear* vector differential equation *valid in the immediate neighborhood* of $\mathbf{x}^0$:

$$\boldsymbol{\delta}\dot{\mathbf{x}} \approx \mathbf{A}\,\boldsymbol{\delta}\mathbf{x} \tag{8-31}$$

[Compare Eq. (3-48).]

It was shown in Chap. 4 that the stability of this system depends entirely upon the nature of the eigenvalues obtained from the equation

$$|s\mathbf{I} - \mathbf{A}| = 0 \tag{8-32}$$

---

† There is considerable difference of opinion concerning the names used. The ones chosen here seem to be settling down to common usage.

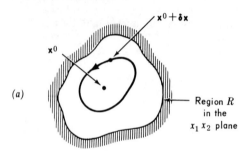

(a)

Region *R*
in the
$x_1 x_2$ plane

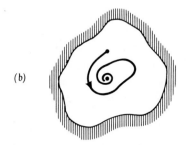

(b)

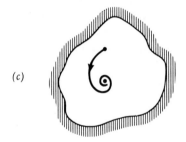

(c)

Fig. 8-10 Phase trajectories depict (*a*) "stable" system, (b) asymptotically stable system, (*c*) monotonically stable system.

It is of particular interest to study somewhat more closely the situation in the two-dimensional case. Figure 8-11 shows the six different eigenvalue combinations that may be encountered and the corresponding trajectory behavior around the singular points.

We shall comment briefly upon how the trajectories in Fig. 8-11 have been obtained. In the two-dimensional case, Eqs. (8-31) reduce to

$$\delta \dot{x}_1 = a_{11}\, \delta x_1 + a_{12}\, \delta x_2$$
$$\delta \dot{x}_2 = a_{21}\, \delta x_1 + a_{22}\, \delta x_2$$

(8-33)

By a canonical transformation,†

$$\boldsymbol{\delta x} = \hat{\mathbf{E}}\, \boldsymbol{\delta x}^{*}$$

(8-34)

† Described in Chap. 5.

these equations can be transformed into the *decoupled* set

$$\delta\dot{x}_1^* = \lambda_1\,\delta x_1^*$$
$$\delta\dot{x}_2^* = \lambda_2\,\delta x_2^*$$

(8-35)

(we have tacitly assumed the eigenvalues to be distinct).

Note that the transformation (8-34) results in a new, generally not rectangular, coordinate system (Fig. 8-12) having the same origin $\mathbf{x}^0$ as the old one. Equations (8-35) can be written

$$\frac{d(\delta x_2^*)}{\delta x_2^*} = \frac{\lambda_2}{\lambda_1}\frac{d(\delta x_1^*)}{\delta x_1^*}$$

which, upon integration, yields

$$\delta x_2^* = C(\delta x_1^*)^{\lambda_2/\lambda_1}$$

(8-36)

(C = integration const.)

For instance, if both λ's are real and of equal sign, then we obtain a trajectory of the node type shown in Fig. 8-12. The question of whether the trajectories approach or depart from the equilibrium point (or, in other words, whether we have a stable or an unstable node) can be answered by a sign study of Eq. (8-35). For example, we have

$$d(\delta x_1^*) = \lambda_1\,\delta x_1^*\,dt$$

and if we thus have all three factors of the right member positive, then $d(\delta x_1^*)$ must also be positive and the node is unstable.

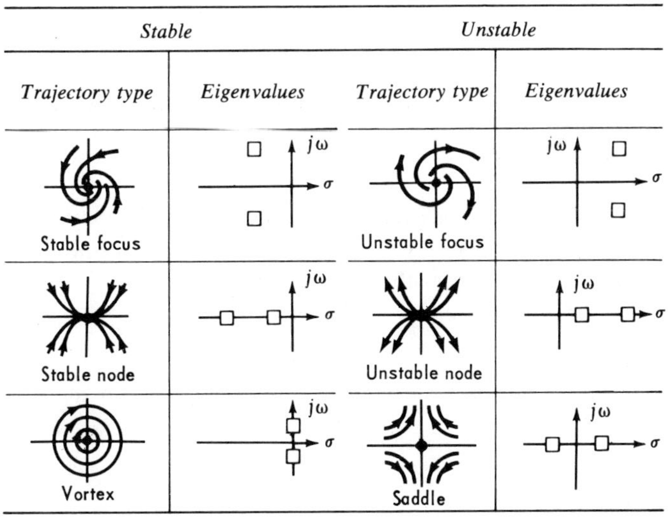

Stable		Unstable	
Trajectory type	*Eigenvalues*	*Trajectory type*	*Eigenvalues*
Stable focus		Unstable focus	
Stable node		Unstable node	
Vortex		Saddle	

Fig. 8-11   Various types of singularities.

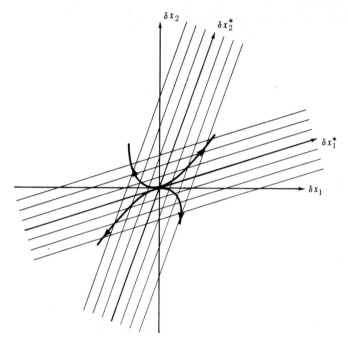

Fig. 8-12 Unstable node.

Example 8-4

We wish to use the previous methods in studying the dynamics of a second-order regulator employing nonlinear damping. The system is depicted in Fig. 8-13 and consists of a linear plant having the transfer function

$$G_p = \frac{1}{s^2}$$

We arrange so that the control force u will be applied in a proportional-plus-derivative manner; that is,

$$u = Ke + f(e)\dot{e} \tag{8-37}$$

where the *amount of derivative control is dependent upon the magnitude of the error expressed by the factor* $f(e)$. We wish to show that certain advantages can be gained by an intelligent choice of the function $f(e)$.

The plant dynamics is defined by the differential equation

$$u = \ddot{c} \tag{8-38}$$

and by using e and $\dot{e}$ as our state variables x_1 and x_2, we obtain the set of state equations

$$\dot{x}_1 = x_2$$
$$\dot{x}_2 = -x_1 - f(x_1)x_2 \tag{8-39}$$

For simplicity, we have put $K = 1$.

(The equations hold, of course, only for constant reference inputs.)

We seek first the equilibrium points of the system. If any such points exist, they obviously must satisfy the steady-state equations

$$0 = x_2{}^0$$
$$0 = -x_1{}^0 - f(x_1{}^0)x_2{}^0 \tag{8-40}$$

We note from these equations that the origin, that is, $x_1{}^0 = x_2{}^0 = 0$, is the only point in the phase plane that qualifies as a singular point.

We next compute the Jacobian matrix. From Eq. (8-30), we get

$$\mathbf{A} = \begin{bmatrix} 0 & 1 \\ -1 & -f(0) \end{bmatrix} \tag{8-41}$$

In the close neighborhood of origin, we thus obtain the *linear* behavior

$$\dot{x}_1 = x_2$$
$$\dot{x}_2 = -x_1 - f(0)x_2 \tag{8-42}$$

(Note that because $\mathbf{x}^0$ equals zero, we find no reason to introduce any new δx coordinates.)

The characteristic equation reads

$$s[s + f(0)] + 1 = 0 \tag{8-43}$$

yielding the eigenvalues

$$\left.\begin{matrix} \lambda_1 \\ \lambda_2 \end{matrix}\right\} = -\tfrac{1}{2}f(0) \pm \sqrt{\tfrac{1}{4}f^2(0) - 1} \tag{8-44}$$

We conclude from the table in Fig. 8-11 that the following possible responses

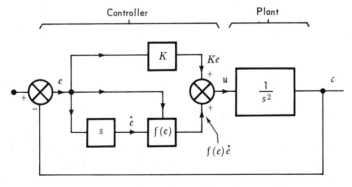

Fig. 8-13   Proportional-plus-nonlinear derivative control.

can be obtained:

1. $f(0) > 2$ stable node
2. $0 < f(0) < 2$ stable focus
3. $f(0) = 0$ vortex
4. $-2 < f(0) < 0$ unstable focus
5. $f(0) < -2$ unstable node

Clearly, the first three cases ensure *local* stability around origin—the first two cases, even asymptotic stability.

Having thus confirmed that the system will settle down if subjected to *small* reference step inputs, we ask the next logical question: What will the response look like if the servo is subjected to *large* input steps? This, of course, ties directly in with the question of the *finite* or possibly *global* stability of the system. We shall discuss these concepts in the next subsection. Before we leave the present example, however, we wish to demonstrate by means of the phase plane that it is possible to "control" and shape to one's specification the behavior of a nonlinear system to a much greater extent than is possible in the case of a linear system. To show this, let us assume that we assign the following different types of derivative control:

case I $f(e) = 3$

case II $f(e) = 1$

case III $f(e) = 0$

case IV $f(e) = \dfrac{0.1}{|e|} = \dfrac{0.1}{|x_1|}$

The first three cases are obviously *linear*, and this means that Eqs. (8-42) hold throughout the entire phaseplane.

Using the isocline method, we obtain the following slope equations for the linear cases:

case I $S = -\dfrac{x_1 + 3x_2}{x_2} = -3 - \dfrac{x_1}{x_2}$

case II $S = -1 - \dfrac{x_1}{x_2}$ (8-45)

case III $S = -\dfrac{x_1}{x_2}$

In all three cases, the slope will be constant for constant ratio x_1/x_2, and we immediately conclude, therefore, that the isoclines must be straight lines through origin. The phase trajectories for a unit-step input are shown for the three cases in Fig. 8-14a. In Fig. 8-14b, we show the corresponding time responses, which actually range from completely undamped to overdamped. *Note that the price we pay for damping is a slowed-down or sluggish response.*

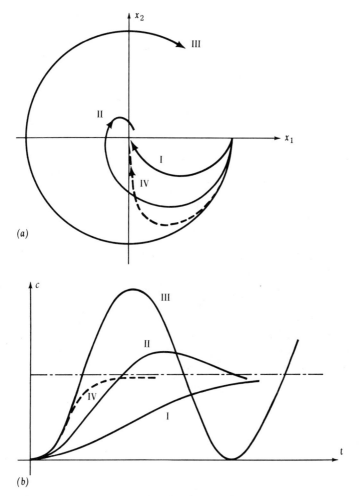

(a)

(b)

Fig. 8-14 Nonlinear damping gives improved response.

We feel intuitively (and intuition is at a premium in nonlinear design) that we should be able to combine the vigor of the undamped system with the settling-down characteristics of the overdamped one by choosing a damping that is low for *large* errors and large for *small* ones. This, then, is the reason for our $f(e)$ choice in case IV.

We obtain for this case the isocline equation

$$\frac{dx_2}{dx_1} = S = -\frac{x_1 + 0.1(x_2/|x_1|)}{x_2} = -\frac{x_1}{x_2} - 0.1\frac{1}{|x_1|} \tag{8-46}$$

The phase trajectory for this nonlinearly damped servo is depicted in Fig. 8-14a, with the corresponding time response in Fig. 8-14*b* (dotted graphs). The results are indeed as expected.

Increased system complexity and very sluggish response for *small* step inputs are the price we have paid for the improvements.

Finite and Global Stability

The concepts of stability, asymptotic stability, and monotonic stability were defined above in a local sense. Since it can be tested by linear analysis, "stability in the small" is, as a rule, relatively simple to ascertain. In many practical situations, however, it is not a sufficiently strong measure.† It may be necessary to know the ability of a control system to recover from *large* disturbances or to respond properly to inputs of considerable amplitude.

Consider a system represented by the closed-loop differential equation

$$\dot{\mathbf{x}} = \mathbf{F}_c(\mathbf{x})$$

We shall assume that the system has one equilibrium point only, an assumption that generally holds true for all properly designed control systems (a control system having several equilibrium points for one step input presumably would not find many buyers). As it is always possible by means of a coordinate translation $\xi = \mathbf{x} - \mathbf{x}^0$ to place this equilibrium point in origin, we shall, without loss of generality in the following, assume $\mathbf{x}^0 = \mathbf{0}$.

Consider now a region R of *finite* dimensions surrounding the origin. For instance, it may be convenient to choose a region R consisting of the interior of the circle

$$x_1^2 + x_2^2 = R_0^2$$

in the two-dimensional state space, a sphere

$$x_1^2 + x_2^2 + x_3^2 = R_0^2$$

in the three-dimensional space, and an n-dimensional "sphere"

$$x_1^2 + x_2^2 + \cdots + x_n^2 = R_0^2$$

in the n-dimensional state space. (As always, it becomes difficult to visualize these things geometrically when $n > 3$.)

If the state of this system will return to origin from *any* point $\mathbf{x}$ within R, then the system is said to be *asymptotically stable within the finite region R*. If the system does not return to the origin but does not go outside R either, then we just call it *stable within R*. The system is said to be *globally stable* if R includes the entire finite state space.

"Stability," as defined above, is usually considered too weak a condition by control engineers, who probably would prefer "asymptotic stability" as a more

---

† Cases also may be encountered on rare occasions where the linearization technique using the Jacobian matrix does not work. This was amply demonstrated in Example 3-5.

practical measure. For example, the space capsule performing the large-amplitude limit cycles shown in the phase plane of Fig. 8-4 is "stable" in a mathematical sense, but an astronaut passenger would quite certainly be willing to argue that point.

The problem of determining large-scale stability by *analytical* means is not an easy one. We stress the word "analytical" because we must not forget that the task of numerical solution of differential equations, linear *or* nonlinear, is no problem for a modern analog or digital computer. The most obvious stability test is to determine by some known method the totality of phase trajectories throughout the region *R* and then study their behavior. If all of them tend to the origin, the system is asymptotically stable in the region in question. This is, of course, the sledgehammer approach. The method works fairly well in the two-dimensional case. We shall refer to this as the "indirect method" for stability determination.

A method considerably more elegant was devised by Liapunov almost a century ago. It has enjoyed great popularity in recent years and has been subject to extensive research by, in particular, Soviet scientists. By means of this method, sometimes referred to as *Liapunov's direct method*, it is possible to obtain information concerning the stability *without actually solving the differential equations or even computing the phase trajectories*. We shall present both methods.

Stability Test by the Indirect Approach

This method is best demonstrated by means of two typical examples.

Example 8-5

Our first example is not related to the field of control at all but is included because of its simplicity. We wish to determine the stability characteristics of the simple pendulum shown in Fig. 8-15. The differential state equations for this system are readily derived and read

$$\dot{x}_1 = x_2$$

$$\dot{x}_2 = -\frac{g}{L} \sin x_1 \qquad \text{with } \mathbf{x} \triangleq \begin{bmatrix} \varphi \\ \dot{\varphi} \end{bmatrix}$$

If for simplicity we set $g/L = 1$, we obtain

$$\dot{x}_1 = x_2$$
$$\dot{x}_2 = -\sin x_1 \qquad (8\text{-}47)$$

We obtain the two equilibrium states (indicated by I and II in Fig. 8-15)

$$\mathbf{x}_I^0 = \begin{bmatrix} 0 \\ 0 \end{bmatrix} \qquad \text{and} \qquad \mathbf{x}_{II}^0 = \begin{bmatrix} \pm\pi \\ 0 \end{bmatrix}$$

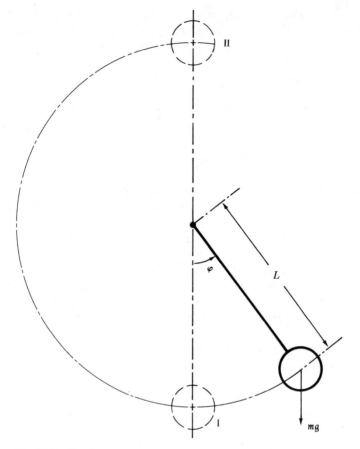

Fig. 8-15 Simple pendulum.

The Jacobian matrix equals

$$\mathbf{A} = \begin{bmatrix} 0 & 1 \\ -\cos x_1 & 0 \end{bmatrix}$$

For the two different equilibrium states, the $\mathbf{A}$ matrix takes on the values

$$\mathbf{A}_\mathrm{I} = \begin{bmatrix} 0 & 1 \\ -1 & 0 \end{bmatrix} \quad \text{and} \quad \mathbf{A}_\mathrm{II} = \begin{bmatrix} 0 & 1 \\ 1 & 0 \end{bmatrix}$$

The small-scale dynamics in the neighborhoods of the two equilibrium points is thus characterized by the eigenvalues

For $\mathbf{x}_\mathrm{I}$ $\left.\begin{array}{c} \lambda_1 \\ \lambda_2 \end{array}\right\} = \pm j$ vortex!

For $\mathbf{x}_\mathrm{II}$ $\left.\begin{array}{c} \lambda_1 \\ \lambda_2 \end{array}\right\} = \pm 1$ saddle!

In order to obtain the stability in the *finite* phase plane, we determine first the phase trajectories. From Eq. (8-47), we get

$$x_2 \, dx_2 = -\sin x_1 \, dx_1$$

which, upon integration, yields

$$x_2{}^2 = 2 \cos x_1 + \text{const} \qquad\qquad\qquad (8\text{-}48)$$

The trajectories are plotted in Fig. 8-16 for different values of the integration constant. Those trajectories (dotted in the figure) that pass through the saddle points at $x_1 = \pm\pi$ are of particular interest. They are obtained by substituting

$$\mathbf{x} = \begin{bmatrix} \pi \\ 0 \end{bmatrix}$$

into Eq. (8-48) and solving for the integration constant. The analysis yields

$$x_2{}^2 = 2 \cos x_1 + 2 \qquad\qquad\qquad (8\text{-}49)$$

As the phase plane shows, these trajectories, referred to as *separatrices*, separate the stable regions (shaded markings) from the unstable ones. If the system is placed in an initial state somewhere outside the separatrices, e.g., in point A, it will proceed on a divergent trajectory, taking it eventually to $x_1 = \infty$. In this example, it proved relatively simple to identify the regions of stability.

Example 8-6

In this example, we return to the PPD servo depicted in Fig. 8-13, the behavior of which we analyzed (Fig. 8-14) for different types of derivative control $f(e)$. We shall do some additional experimenting with this system. First, we recap some of the earlier conclusions that we reached.

By choosing $f(e) = \text{const}$ and positive, we obtained a linear damped system with a speed of response which we could improve by reducing the damping for large errors. The damping, however, must be made positive and large for small

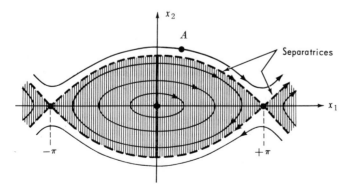

Fig. 8-16 Phase trajectories for pendulum.

errors, as we want the system to settle down without oscillations. We conclude, by the way, that because the chosen damping $f(e) \sim 1/|e|$ is positive for *all* errors, the system must be stable throughout the entire phase plane. Indeed, the system is asymptotically stable globally.

The thought strikes us that we may be able to make this system still faster by not only reducing the damping to low values but *actually making it negative.* From the expression for the control force,

$$u = ke + f(e)\dot{e}$$

it becomes clear that as $\dot{e}$ is negative immediately following a step input (why?), the damping term $f(e)\dot{e}$ can be made *positive* by choosing negative $f(e)$. This term will then actually *increase u* and thereby speed up the system. However, we must return to positive damping as the error decreases or else the system will just overshoot, with increasing amplitudes as a consequence. For instance, we may try out a damping factor of the type shown in Fig. 8-17. For errors in excess of $|e| = 1$, the damping is negative. We may expect that step inputs of the magnitude of, say, about 2 will give very good responses. However, if we apply too large steps, not only do we experience large negative damping, but the system is subject to it for longer periods of time, with the result that the available positive damping is not enough to damp out the oscillations. This is a *qualitative* prediction; we would wish to have some *quantitative* information also.

For this purpose, we first write the state differential equations. In view of the chosen $f(e)$ function, it becomes necessary to divide the $e\dot{e}$ plane into the

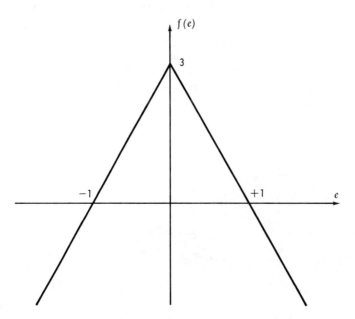

Fig. 8-17 Amplitude-dependent damping.

following two regions:

1. $x_1 > 0$

In this region, we have

$$f(x_1) = 3 - 3x_1$$

The Eqs. (8-39) therefore take on the form

$$\dot{x}_1 = x_2$$
$$\dot{x}_2 = -x_1 - (3 - 3x_1)x_2 \tag{8-50}$$

2. $x_1 < 0$

Now we have

$$f(x_1) = 3 + 3x_1$$

resulting in the corresponding state equations

$$\dot{x}_1 = x_2$$
$$\dot{x}_2 = -x_1 - (3 + 3x_1)x_2 \tag{8-51}$$

In the previous example, it was possible to separate the variables in Eq. (8-47), integrate the equation, and obtain the explicit trajectory equations (8-48).

This method is not applicable here; instead, we shall resort to the isocline method. Equations (8-50) and (8-51) yield directly:

$$\frac{dx_2}{dx_1} = S = -\frac{x_1}{x_2} - 3 + 3x_1 \qquad \text{for } x_1 > 0 \tag{8-52}$$

$$\frac{dx_2}{dx_1} = S = -\frac{x_1}{x_2} - 3 - 3x_1 \qquad \text{for } x_1 < 0 \tag{8-53}$$

It is more convenient to write these equations in the form

$$x_2 = -\frac{x_1}{3 + S - 3x_1} \qquad \text{for } x_1 > 0$$

$$x_2 = -\frac{x_1}{3 + S + 3x_1} \qquad \text{for } x_1 < 0 \tag{8-54}$$

Equations (8-54) were used in constructing the phase plane in Fig. 8-18. Three phase trajectories are indicated in the diagram, corresponding to step inputs of magnitudes 1.5, 2.0, and 3.0. The corresponding time responses are sketched in Fig. 8-19. As we predicted, step inputs that are too large result in instability. A closer trajectory study reveals that the region for stability is contained within the odd-shaped dotted contour. Any trajectories emanating from the interior of this contour tend to the origin—thus indicating asymptotic stability.

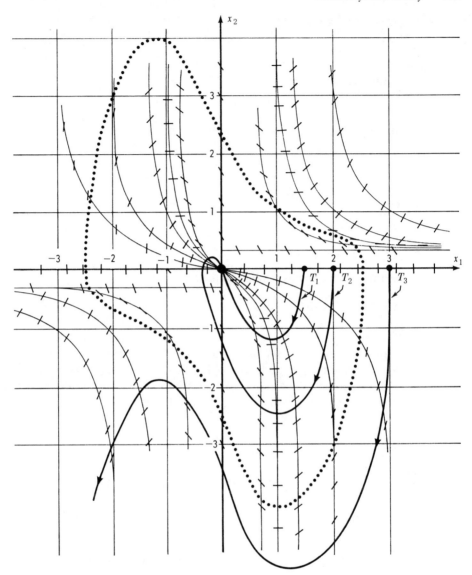

Fig. 8-18   Phase trajectories for system in Fig. 8-13 with damping factor of the type shown in Fig. 8-17.

This example teaches us several important lessons:

1. Nonlinear system design offers opportunities not to be found in linear systems.
2. A specific design grows out of a thorough knowledge of the physics of the system.
3. Intuition is helpful.
4. The specific advantage that may be obtained through introduction of a non-linearity has, as a rule, limited "range."   In the above example, we obtain a

very excellent response for a step input of magnitude around 2. The system is completely useless if the magnitude is 3 or higher.

Stability Test by Liapunov's Direct Method

Liapunov has shown that it is possible to determine the stability characteristics of a differential equation without actually solving it. The method is very interesting from a theoretical viewpoint as it reveals some important relationships between the energy stored in the system and the system dynamics. However, the Liapunov method is beset with some serious practical limitations and has for this reason not found wide acclaim among control engineers as a convenient technique of predicting stability. We shall afford it a brief discussion at this time. For a deeper penetration, the reader is referred to Liapunov's own story[6] or a very lucid discussion in a monograph by LaSalle and Lefschetz.[4]

We shall introduce the reader to the main features of the method by means of a very simple linear problem. (It should be added that Liapunov's method, in principle, can be applied to every type of differential equation, linear as well as nonlinear.) Consider the mechanical system in Fig. 3-2a. The spring-constrained mass m performs horizontal dynamics on a frictionless table. A dashpot has been added (not shown in the figure) to make the motions damped.

This autonomous (undriven) system obeys, as the reader easily can verify, the differential equation

$$m\ddot{y} + k_d\dot{y} + k_s y = 0 \tag{8-55}$$

For simplicity, we shall set $m = k_d = k_s = 1$, and upon introduction of the state vector

$$\mathbf{x} = \begin{bmatrix} x_1 \\ x_2 \end{bmatrix} \triangleq \begin{bmatrix} y \\ \dot{y} \end{bmatrix}$$

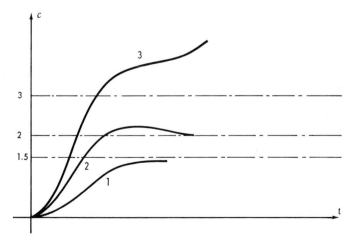

Fig. 8-19   Time responses corresponding to the trajectories in Fig. 8-18.

Eq. (8-55) attains the normal form

$$\dot{x}_1 = x_2$$
$$\dot{x}_2 = -x_1 - x_2$$

(8-56)

This linear system is easily solved, and we obtain the solution

$$x_1 = \frac{2}{\sqrt{3}} e^{-t/2} \sin\left(\frac{\sqrt{3}}{2}t + \frac{\pi}{3}\right)$$

$$x_2 = -\frac{2}{\sqrt{3}} e^{-t/2} \sin\left(\frac{\sqrt{3}}{2}t\right)$$

(8-57)

which is valid for the initial conditions

$$\mathbf{x}(0) = \begin{bmatrix} 1 \\ 0 \end{bmatrix}$$

The solution is plotted in Fig. 8-20 both in phase-trajectory form and versus time. These diagrams completely settle the questions of type of dynamics and stability and tell us everything we may wish to know about the system in question. We note, in particular, that the system is asymptotically stable in a global sense.

With these results in mind, we shall now look at the system from a different viewpoint. We earlier (in Chap. 3) discussed briefly the relationships between system dynamics and the energies stored within them. The kinetic energy stored in the moving mass equals

$$\tfrac{1}{2}m\dot{x}_1^2 = \tfrac{1}{2}mx_2^2$$

The potential energy in the spring has the magnitude

$$\tfrac{1}{2}k_s x_1^2$$

The total stored energy is thus

$$V = \tfrac{1}{2}k_s x_1^2 + \tfrac{1}{2}mx_2^2 \qquad \text{watt-sec}$$

(8-58)

This energy is being dissipated in heat in the dashpot at the rate of (remember the formula: power = force times velocity)

$$\dot{V} = -k_d \dot{x}_1 x_2 = -k_d x_2^2 \qquad \text{watts}$$

(8-59)

Using our simple numerical values, we obtain

$$V = \tfrac{1}{2}x_1^2 + \tfrac{1}{2}x_2^2$$

(8-60)

$$\dot{V} = -x_2^2$$

(8-61)

We note that the loci for constant energy are *circles* in the $x_1 x_2$ phase plane. [They would be ellipses in the more general case (8-58).] We also note from (8-61)

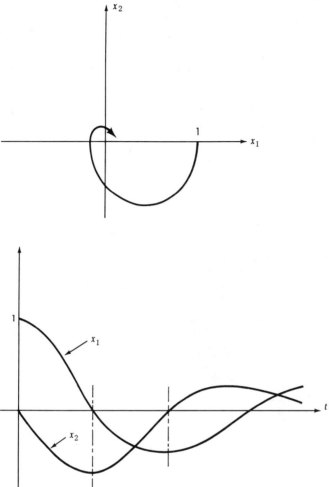

Fig. 8-20   Phase trajectory and time responses of the mechanical system
in Fig. 3-2a.

that the energy rate $\dot{V}$ is *always negative*, and as time passes, these circles must therefore inevitably shrink, as shown in Fig. 8-21a.   Time is implicit, as always in a diagram of this type.   We can show, of course, the explicit energy variation versus *time*.   By substituting Eqs. (8-57) into (8-60) and (8-61), we obtain

$$V = \tfrac{2}{3}e^{-t}\left[\sin^2\left(\frac{\sqrt{3}}{2}t\right) + \sin^2\left(\frac{\sqrt{3}}{2}t + \frac{\pi}{3}\right)\right] \tag{8-62}$$

$$\dot{V} = -\tfrac{4}{3}e^{-t}\sin^2\left(\frac{\sqrt{3}}{2}t\right) \tag{8-63}$$

V and $\dot{V}$ are plotted versus time in Fig. 8-21*b*. The diagrams in Fig. 8-21*a* and *b* tell the same story in different words: *The total stored energy V vanishes with increasing time.*

At this point, we make a very fundamental observation: *The energy*

$$V = \tfrac{1}{2}(x_1{}^2 + x_2{}^2)$$

can take on a zero value only if x_1 and x_2 both equal zero simultaneously. This, combined with the fact that V vanishes with increasing time, obviously can mean only one thing—asymptotic stability! In other words, from the behavior of the V function, we have been able to draw conclusions concerning the stability of the system.

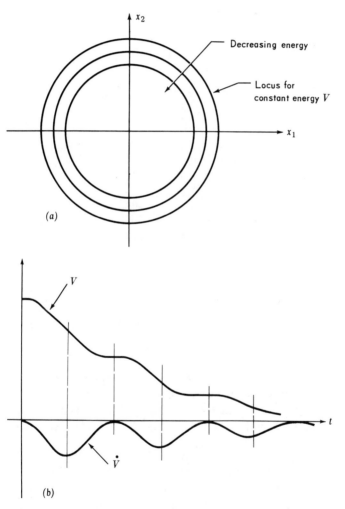

(a)

Decreasing energy

Locus for constant energy V

(b)

Fig. 8-21　The constant-energy loci are circles, and furthermore the energy vanishes with time.

A key factor enabling us to do the above reasoning is the particular nature of the energy function V. For instance, if, instead of

$$V = \tfrac{1}{2}(x_1{}^2 + x_2{}^2)$$

we had used the function

$$V = \tfrac{1}{2}(x_1 + x_2)^2 \tag{8-64}$$

then we could *not* have made the above observation, as V now obviously would have vanished for *any nonzero* combination of x_1 and x_2 that would satisfy the equality

$$x_1 = -x_2$$

Let us see what makes the function

$$V(x_1,x_2) = \tfrac{1}{2}x_1{}^2 + \tfrac{1}{2}x_2{}^2$$

so special!

We conclude:

1. $V(x_1,x_2)$ is positive for *all* nonzero values of x_1 and x_2.
2. $V(0,0) = 0$.

A mathematician names a scalar function possessing these properties *positive definite*. (For good measure, he also adds the requirements that the function be continuous and that it possess first partial derivatives.) A function like the one represented by Eq. (8-64), being positive for all x_1 and x_2 except at certain points (*including origin*, where it may be zero), is referred to as *semidefinite*.

We can introduce a V axis perpendicular to the x_1x_2 plane and can then represent a positive definite function $V(x_1,x_2)$ as a cup-shaped three-dimensional surface. The positive definite function (8-60) is depicted in Fig. 8-22a. For comparison, the semidefinite function (8-64) is shown also. Note that (8-60) is actually a parabolic "mirror" pointing upwards.

We realize now that we could have predicted asymptotic stability by using any one of an infinite number of functions which possess the following two properties:

1. $V(x_1,x_2)$ must be positive definite.
2. $V(x_1,x_2)$ must vanish with increasing time.

The reason for our choice of the function $\tfrac{1}{2}(x_1{}^2 + x_2{}^2)$ is that it makes physical sense and also permits simple analysis.

Note that the second property is guaranteed if $\dot{V} < 0$ for all t. If we have the somewhat weaker condition $\dot{V} \leqslant 0$, then we cannot guarantee "asymptotic stability," but we can certainly guarantee "stability." This is clear from Fig. 8-23. (Note, however, that the condition $\dot{V} \leqslant 0$ actually does not exclude "asymptotic stability," as was demonstrated in Fig. 8-21.)

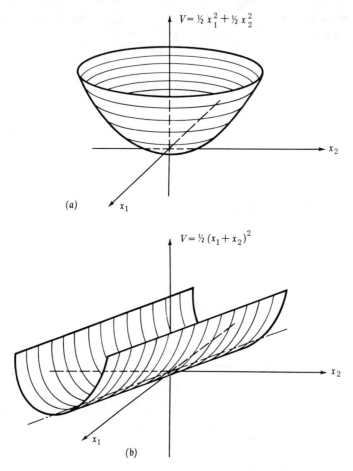

Fig. 8-22 (*a*) Positive definite function; (*b*) semidefinite function.

We now can summarize the *Liapunov stability theorem*. In doing so, we extend the above discussions from two- to *n*-dimensional state space. This should not meet any mental difficulties, except that we lose the ability to visualize things geometrically.

theorem *Consider the autonomous system*

$$\dot{\mathbf{x}} = \mathbf{F}_c(\mathbf{x})$$

If it is possible to find a positive definite function $V(\mathbf{x})$ which will vanish along all the trajectories of the given system originating within a closed region R surrounding the origin, then the system is asymptotically stable within R.

A function $V(\mathbf{x})$ possessing these features is called a *Liapunov function.* As was pointed out above, we can be certain of having secured a Liapunov function only if we know that $\dot{V}(\mathbf{x}) < 0$ along the trajectories. This condition can be given a very interesting and natural geometrical interpretation. To demonstrate this, we write

$$\dot{V}(\mathbf{x}) = \frac{d}{dt} V(x_1, x_2, \ldots, x_n) = \frac{\partial V}{\partial x_1} \dot{x}_1 + \frac{\partial V}{\partial x_2} \dot{x}_2 + \cdots + \frac{\partial V}{\partial x_n} \dot{x}_n \qquad (8\text{-}65)$$

Now we introduce the *gradient vector*

$$\text{grad } V \triangleq \begin{bmatrix} \dfrac{\partial V}{\partial x_1} \\ \cdot \\ \cdot \\ \cdot \\ \dfrac{\partial V}{\partial x_n} \end{bmatrix} \qquad (8\text{-}66)$$

The student is reminded that grad V is a vector with a direction which is *normal* to the V surfaces (defined positive in increasing V direction) and a magnitude which is a measure of the rate of increase of V with respect to the space coordinates.

We now, in accordance with formula (A-5) in Appendix A, can write (8-65) as the inner product of velocity vector $\dot{\mathbf{x}}$ and grad V:

$$\dot{V}(\mathbf{x}) = \dot{\mathbf{x}}^T \text{ grad } V \qquad (8\text{-}67)$$

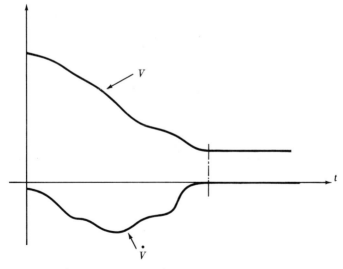

Fig. 8-23 Graphs show that $\dot{V} \leqslant 0$ does not necessarily guarantee asymptotic stability.

In accordance with the stability theorem, we now must require

$$\dot{\mathbf{x}}^T \text{ grad } V < 0 \tag{8-68}$$

But from formula (A-6) in Appendix A, we conclude that this means

$$\cos \theta < 0 \tag{8-69}$$

In words: *The velocity vector $\dot{\mathbf{x}}$ must always have a negative projection on the gradient vector.*

The situation can be visualized easily in the two-dimensional case by combining the two phase diagrams of Figs. 8-20 and 8-21. This has been done in Fig. 8-24. The requirement expressed by Eq. (8-69) simply means that the motion along the phase trajectory takes place in the direction of decreasing V loci.

One may say that the Liapunov functions are simply an extension of the energy concept. In trying to apply the method to a specific system, we encounter, as we might expect, severe difficulties associated with the choice of a suitable V function. It is not hard to find a function that is positive definite but very hard to secure the additional condition $\dot{V} < 0$. In those cases where we are successful, the theorem results in regions of stability that are very conservative as a rule. We shall demonstrate with an example.

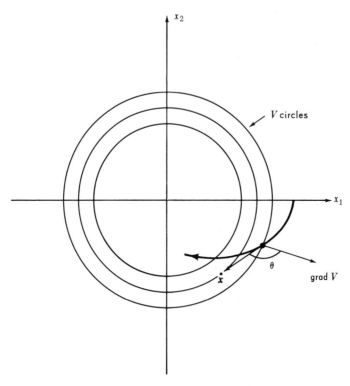

Fig. 8-24 Constant V loci and phase trajectories depicted in the same phase plane.

Example 8-7

Let us use the Liapunov method to find the region of stability for the control system studied in Examples 8-4 and 8-6. We shall try the same type of V function as we used above, that is,

$$V = x_1^2 + x_2^2 \tag{8-70}$$

By differentiating this expression with respect to t, we get

$$\dot{V} = 2x_1\dot{x}_1 + 2x_2\dot{x}_2 \tag{8-71}$$

By substituting from Eq. (8-39) the values for $\dot{x}_1$ and $\dot{x}_2$ characterizing this particular system, we obtain the following expression for the rate of change of the Liapunov function:

$$\dot{V} = -2f(x_1)x_2^2 \tag{8-72}$$

As x_2^2 is always positive, we realize that the requirement $\dot{V} < 0$ is fulfilled if

$$f(x_1) > 0 \tag{8-73}$$

In view of the chosen $f(x_1)$ function (see Fig. 8-17), the $\dot{V}$ requirement is satisfied throughout the lightly shaded strip-shaped region in Fig. 8-25. However, we can guarantee stability only for that part of this region containing the largest of the V circles. This obviously is within the heavily shaded circular region of radius 1. Any trajectory starting within this circle must by necessity be a stable trajectory, as exemplified by T_2 in Fig. 8-25. A trajectory starting outside the unit circle but within the strip will move in the direction of decreasing V circles as long as it stays inside the strip. However, when it leaves the strip region, $\dot{V}$ turns positive, and the trajectory now moves outward from the origin. If the exit from the strip takes place at a considerable distance from the x_1 axis, then the factor x_2^2 in (8-72) will be large, resulting in a large growth rate $\dot{V}$. As a consequence, the trajectory turns sharply outward and the system is clearly unstable, as depicted by trajectory T_1. If the exit takes place close to the x_1 axis, then we may obtain a stable behavior, shown by trajectory T_3.

It is of interest to compare the size of the stability region obtained by this method with the one we already obtained by other means in Fig. 8-18. As we mentioned before, the Liapunov method always brings us on the safe side. There is a possibility that by a better choice of V function, we could have widened the region R. The search for a best possible V function is a trial-and-error proposition, and herein lies the weakness of the method.

The literature abounds with suggested V functions to fit specific types of systems. The Russians have been particularly active in this field. Letov[7] gives a good survey (and also an extensive reference list) of the activities in this area in the U.S.S.R. There would be little sense in cluttering up our presentation

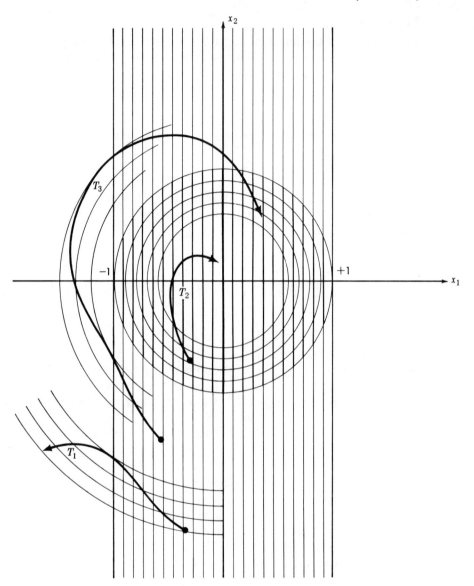

Fig. 8-25   Stability can be guaranteed only within the unit circle.

with a list of all of these. However, we wish to make mention of a particularly simple and often useful type of Liapunov function, the so-called *quadratic form*

$$Q(x_1, x_2, \ldots, x_n) = Q(\mathbf{x}) = \sum_{i,j=1}^{n} a_{ij} x_i x_j \tag{8-74}$$

It is possible to express Q as a vector-matrix-vector product of the form

$$Q = \mathbf{x}^T \mathbf{A} \mathbf{x} \tag{8-75}$$

where $\mathbf{A}$ is an $n \times n$ *symmetric* matrix.

For example, if $n = 2$, we get

$$Q(x_1, x_2) = [x_1 \quad x_2] \begin{bmatrix} a_{11} & a_{12} \\ a_{21} & a_{22} \end{bmatrix} \begin{bmatrix} x_1 \\ x_2 \end{bmatrix}$$

$$= a_{11} x_1^2 + (a_{12} + a_{21}) x_1 x_2 + a_{22} x_2^2$$

Assume, for example, that we wish to generate the quadratic form

$$Q = 2x_1^2 - 3x_1 x_2 + 4x_2^2$$

By inspection, we realize that this can be accomplished with the symmetric matrix

$$\mathbf{A} = \begin{bmatrix} 2 & -1.5 \\ -1.5 & 4 \end{bmatrix}$$

Not all quadratic forms, of course, are positive definite (PD). If we wish to use a quadratic form as a V function, we must make sure that it is PD. The $\mathbf{A}$ matrix gives the clue as to positive definiteness. We summarize without proof a few helpful rules for selection of an acceptable $\mathbf{A}$ matrix:[†]

rule 1 Q will be PD if $\mathbf{A}$ is *diagonal* and if all the diagonal elements $a_{ii} > 0$. (This rule is obvious, and we already made use of this type of a V function in Example 8-7.)

rule 2 Q will be PD if all the n eigenvalues λ of $\mathbf{A}$ are positive.

rule 3 Consider *any* real, nonsingular matrix $\mathbf{D}$. The matrix $\mathbf{A} \triangleq \mathbf{D}^T\mathbf{D}$ will generate a PD quadratic form.

The last rule is particularly useful. For example, take at random

$$\mathbf{D} = \begin{bmatrix} 1 & 2 \\ 3 & -4 \end{bmatrix}$$

We note by inspection that the matrix is nonsingular. We now compute the $\mathbf{A}$ matrix:

$$\mathbf{A} = \mathbf{D}^T\mathbf{D} = \begin{bmatrix} 1 & 3 \\ 2 & -4 \end{bmatrix} \begin{bmatrix} 1 & 2 \\ 3 & -4 \end{bmatrix} = \begin{bmatrix} 10 & -10 \\ -10 & 20 \end{bmatrix}$$

[†] Proofs may be obtained in Ref. 8.

Thus, the quadratic form

$$Q = 10x_1{}^2 - 20x_1x_2 + 20x_2{}^2$$

is positive definite and will qualify as a candidate for a V function.

Example 8-8
We shall work one additional example before we leave this topic, and we choose to study the famous *van der Pol equation*

$$\ddot{y} + \epsilon(y^2 - 1)\dot{y} + y = 0 \qquad \epsilon = \text{const} \tag{8-76}$$

This equation is encountered on many occasions in different areas of engineering. Let us see how it may occur in the area of control. For that purpose, let us introduce the state vector

$$\mathbf{x} = \begin{bmatrix} x_1 \\ x_2 \end{bmatrix} \triangleq \begin{bmatrix} y \\ \dot{y} \end{bmatrix} \tag{8-77}$$

The given equation then can be written in the form

$$\begin{aligned} \dot{x}_1 &= x_2 \\ \dot{x}_2 &= -x_1 - \epsilon(x_1{}^2 - 1)x_2 \end{aligned} \tag{8-78}$$

and we recognize immediately the identity with Eqs. (8-39) if we choose (see Fig. 8-26)

$$f(x_1) = \epsilon(x_1{}^2 - 1)$$

In other words, the servo in Fig. 8-13 will be describable with a van der Pol equation if we choose the damping term $f(e)$ parabolically depending upon the error. Note that the constant ϵ must be chosen *negative* in order to make the origin in the $e\dot{e}$ plane a stable equilibrium point [compare also Eq. (8-44)]. Just as in Example 8-7, we could now choose

$$V = x_1{}^2 + x_2{}^2$$

This would lead to Eq. (8-72) for $\dot{V}$, and just as in Fig. 8-25, we again could have concluded that the interior of the unit circle is stable.

We shall approach the problem somewhat differently. Instead of choosing the state vector $\mathbf{x}$ as defined by Eq. (8-77), let us try instead

$$\mathbf{x} = \begin{bmatrix} x_1 \\ x_2 \end{bmatrix} \triangleq \begin{bmatrix} y \\ \int_0^t y \, dt \end{bmatrix} \tag{8-79}$$

Note that the x_1 component is the same as before.

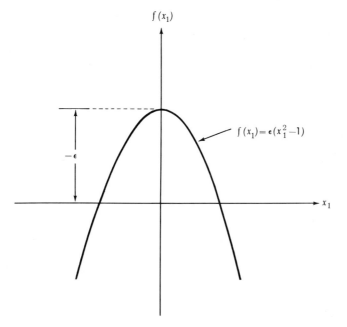

Fig. 8-26 Parabolic velocity damping.

In terms of these new state variables, Eq. (8-76) can be written in the normal form

$$\dot{x}_1 = -x_2 - \epsilon\left(\frac{x_1^2}{3} - 1\right)x_1$$

$$\dot{x}_2 = x_1 \tag{8-80}$$

Let us now, as in the previous case, use the Liapunov function

$$V(x_1,x_2) = x_1^2 + x_2^2$$

Thus,

$$\dot{V} = 2x_1\dot{x}_1 + 2x_2\dot{x}_2 = 2x_1\left[-x_2 - \epsilon\left(\frac{x_1^2}{3} - 1\right)x_1\right] + 2x_2x_1$$

and therefore,

$$\dot{V} = -2\epsilon x_1^2\left(\frac{x_1^2}{3} - 1\right) \tag{8-81}$$

We remember that $\epsilon < 0$, and in order to keep $\dot{V} < 0$, we therefore must require

$$\frac{x_1^2}{3} < 1$$

or

$$|x_1| < \sqrt{3} \tag{8-82}$$

We conclude that we have been able to increase the circular region of convergence from radius 1 to $\sqrt{3}$ by the trick of using a different set of state variables.

The last example is representative of the trickiness that usually is associated with the usage of the Liapunov method. The greatest value of the method probably lies in the approach itself. It provides a different and clearer view of the concept of stability.

8-4 THE METHOD OF HARMONIC LINEARIZATION (MHL)

The methods that we have presented so far have all used the exact state differential equations as their point of departure. From the days of Poincaré comes a different approach that has been very widely accepted in the last two decades by control engineers who, frustrated by the limitations of the *exact* methods of handling nonlinear systems, have looked for some *approximate* techniques capable of predicting the behavior of a wider class of systems than the phase-plane technique can accommodate. In particular, they would like to be able analytically to command systems of order in excess of the second.

The methods we are referring to and which we wish to discuss in this section can all be classified under the heading of "harmonic linearization." The basic feature characterizing all these methods is the assumption that we can find an *associated linear system* that, in some chosen sense, approximates the actual nonlinear system under investigation. We are *not* limiting ourselves to small-scale dynamics but are actually seeking a linear model that is powerful enough to give a decent *large-scale* approximation. It would be rather naïve to expect that we should be able to find a linear model that could handle all situations faithfully, albeit within reasonable approximate limits. Indeed, it is important to point out right at the outset that the techniques we are about to present have rather severe limitations. Instead of enumerating all the things that we *cannot* master, we shall stress the following strong points of these methods:

1. They are capable of predicting, within excellent accuracy limits, the frequency and amplitude of limit cycles.
2. They permit us to compute the "frequency response" of a nonlinear system.
3. They extend, with remarkable accuracy, Nyquist stability theorem to nonlinear systems.
4. They permit, to limited extent, usage of the root-locus technique to predict transient response of nonlinear systems.

Much of what will be said in this section lacks complete mathematical justification. We are looking for *plausible* solutions, and *heuristic* approaches are used freely. Intuition is at a premium. It is no wonder, then, in view of this "disrespect" for mathematical strictness, that the harmonic linearization methods sometimes fail and fail badly. Engineers who have acquired skill in these techniques usually employ them in the preliminary design stage. In the final analysis, they are checked out by means of computer simulation.

8-4.I HARMONIC BALANCE

We shall introduce the reader to the basic features of the MHL by investigating the nature of the limit cycles of the van der Pol equation

$$\ddot{y} - (1 - y^2)\dot{y} + y = 0 \tag{8-83}$$

It is appropriate to start the discussion with a *plausible* proof that limit cycles may, indeed, be expected for this system. We do so by comparing the given system with the following *linear* one:

$$\ddot{y} + 2\alpha\dot{y} + y = 0 \tag{8-84}$$

The reader is reminded that for this system, the factor 2α determines the nature of the damping. Different damping factors α result in the following types of response:

$$\infty > \alpha > 1 \qquad \text{system stable, nonoscillatory}$$
$$1 > \alpha > 0 \qquad \text{system stable, oscillatory}$$
$$0 > \alpha > -1 \qquad \text{system unstable, oscillatory}$$
$$-1 > \alpha > -\infty \qquad \text{system unstable, nonoscillatory}$$

The van der Pol equation has a damping factor $-(1 - y^2)$ *that depends upon the amplitude y*. We conclude also that the only point of equilibrium is for $y = \dot{y} = 0$. Let us place the system in this point, i.e., the origin of the $y\dot{y}$ phase plane (see Fig. 8-27). As the damping factor for zero y equals -1, we *intuitively* feel that the system response should correspond to what we would anticipate for the *linear* case with $\alpha = -\frac{1}{2}$, that is, an oscillatory buildup of amplitudes. When the amplitudes increase, the damping factor $-(1 - y^2)$ will increase, the rate of buildup should decrease and cease entirely when the damping factor equals zero, and the system should remain in a state of limit cycling.

If instead we had started the system from an initial state characterized by considerable amplitude y, then the total damping factor $-(1 - y^2)$ would be positive and large, and the system state therefore would decay rapidly. The rate of decay would decrease with the amplitude y, and eventually we would again end up in a limit cycle, quite obviously the same one as before. The situation is depicted in Fig. 8-27. We conclude that we can expect not only a limit cycle but actually a *stable* one; i.e., whatever the initial state, we end up in the same oscillation, which in the time domain might look something like the one shown in Fig. 8-28.

At this point, we invoke the principle of *harmonic balance*. In steady state, according to Fourier, we can express the limit-cycle oscillation in the form

$$y(t) = A \sin \omega t + \text{higher-order harmonics} \tag{8-85}$$

This value, substituted back into the given equation, must satisfy it. The principle of harmonic balance implies that we consider only the first term in the above solution, and by substitution we thus get

$$-A\omega^2 \sin \omega t - (1 - A^2 \sin^2 \omega t)A\omega \cos \omega t + A \sin \omega t = 0$$

The fundamental component of the term

$$\sin^2 \omega t \cos \omega t$$

equals $\frac{1}{4} \cos \omega t$; and by focusing attention only on terms of frequency ω, we thus get

$$A(1 - \omega^2) \sin \omega t + \left(\frac{A^2}{4} - 1\right)A\omega \cos \omega t + \cdots = 0$$

This equation can be satisfied only if

$$1 - \omega^2 = 0 \quad \text{and} \quad \frac{A^2}{4} - 1 = 0 \tag{8-86}$$

Hence,

$$\omega = 1 \quad A = 2 \tag{8-87}$$

This then determines approximately the amplitude and frequency of the

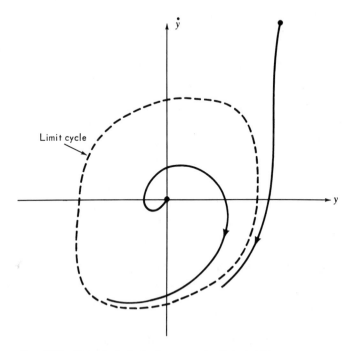

Fig. 8-27   Phase trajectories for a van der Pol equation.

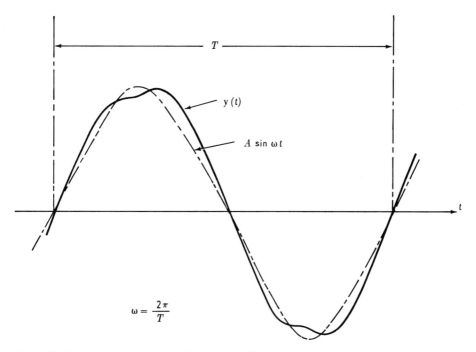

Fig. 8-28   Time response of van der Pol equation (in steady state).

fundamental component.   How accurate the information is must be determined from case to case, *but experience confirms that for most systems encountered in the control field, the errors usually lie within a few percent.*   The method fails in those cases where the system, for some reason, accentuates some of the higher harmonics.   Usually, the frequency characteristics of a control system are those of a "low-pass" filter; i.e., for frequencies above what in Chap. 6 was termed the "bandwidth," the damping is quite pronounced.   This is one fundamental reason why the above approximate method works very well.

8-4.2 DESCRIBING FUNCTIONS

The most useful concept that these harmonic approximation methods have produced is that of the *describing function.*

We shall introduce the reader to this concept by reference to the relatively simple on-off servo depicted in Fig. 8-2.   The double-integrator plant in this system represented, as the reader will remember, a space body being attitude-controlled by means of a maximum-effort type of reaction jet.   We had concluded in the phase plane of Fig. 8-4 that this system would perform limit cycling.   We divide the double integrator into two single integrators, as shown in Fig. 8-29, and then we plot versus time the signals as they appear at the points P_1, P_2, and P_3.   In this order, these signals represent acceleration, velocity, and position. They are all periodic and nonsinusoidal, with period time T.

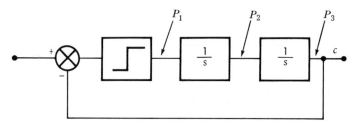

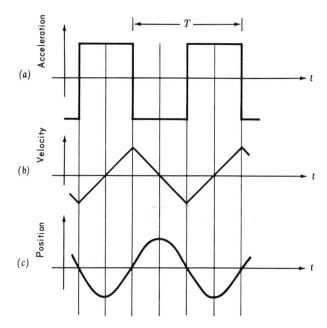

Fig. 8-29   A second-order bang-bang system.   The signals depicted
in graphs *a*, *b*, and *c* appear at points P_1, P_2, and P_3, respectively.

The acceleration signal is obviously a square wave and therefore contains
spectral components of frequencies $1/T, 3/T, 5/T, \ldots$ cps.   Fourier tells us that the
relative magnitudes of these spectral components are $1, \frac{1}{3}, \frac{1}{5}, \ldots$.

As each integrator has an FTF of $1/j\omega$, it becomes clear that the relative
magnitudes of each of these components as they appear in the velocity and
position signals are:

Velocity: $1, (\frac{1}{3})^2, (\frac{1}{5})^2, \ldots$

Position: $1, (\frac{1}{3})^3, (\frac{1}{5})^3, \ldots$

This means that in the output *c*, the third harmonic is represented by a
magnitude of only 3.7 percent of the fundamental component, the fifth harmonic
by only 0.8 percent, etc.   This is the low-pass characteristic that we referred to

$$i(t) = A \sin \omega t$$
$$o(t) = C_1 \sin(\omega t + \varphi_1) + \text{terms of higher}$$
$$\text{frequencies}$$

Fig. 8-30   Nonlinear element.

above.   We conclude, therefore, that we commit an error of only about 4 percent by suggesting that the error signal, *i.e.*, *the signal that enters the nonlinear element, is purely sinusoidal.*   (This signal, depicted in graph *c* of Fig. 8-29, actually consists of *parabolic* segments.)

It is thus clear that although the output signal from the nonlinear element contains higher-frequency components to a nonnegligible degree, we may neglect these completely if we are concerned only with the output *c*.

Therefore, as far as the nonlinear element is concerned, we are, in effect, interested only in the relationship between the sine waves of *equal* frequency. The reader is reminded that for linear time-invariant systems, we could express this relationship by means of the frequency transfer function FTF.   It is therefore only natural that we now extend this concept to nonlinear elements as well, and we do this by means of the so-called *describing function* (DF), defined in full analogy with the FTF as the complex ratio between the output and input amplitudes of the fundamental frequency components; that is,

$$\text{DF} \triangleq \frac{C_1}{A} e^{j\varphi_1} \tag{8-88}$$

All symbols are defined in Fig. 8-30.

Calculation of DF

Example 8-9

Find the DF for the on-off controller in Fig. 8-29.   If a sinusoidal signal of amplitude A enters the nonlinear element, the output signal will be a square wave of amplitude u_{max}, as depicted in the first graph of Fig. 8-29.   The fundamental component of this wave will be *in phase* with the input and will have an amplitude of $(4/\pi)u_{max}$ (see Appendix B).

Therefore,

$$C_1 = \frac{4}{\pi} u_{max}$$

$$\varphi_1 = 0$$

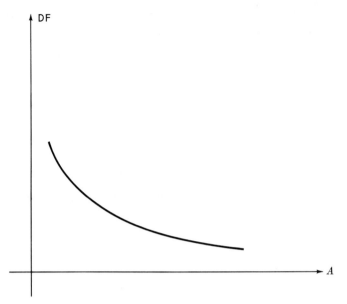

Fig. 8-31   DF for an on-off controller.

and the DF will thus be

$$DF = \frac{4u_{max}}{\pi A} \tag{8-89}$$

It is important to note that the DF or the "equivalent harmonic gain" is strongly dependent upon the signal level A. This, of course, must be expected since, in the present case, the output will be the same whatever the magnitude of the input. Actually, the equivalent gain will vary throughout the range $0 \cdots \infty$, as shown in Fig. 8-31.

The concept of DF was independently introduced by Goldfarb,[10] Oppelt,[11] and, in this country, Kochenburger[9] and has proved to be of great value in estimating the stability of nonlinear systems. Before we discuss in greater detail its application possibilities, we shall demonstrate with two additional examples how the DF can be computed. (It should be added that the DF has been found for all nonlinearities that conceivably could be encountered in engineering applications. For example, the reader will find a very complete tabulation in Ref. 2.)

Example 8-10

Find the DF for a relay with dead zone. The relay (see Fig. 8-32) has a dead zone of width $2D$ and a saturated output of $\pm S$.

Due to the discontinuity, it is necessary to consider separately the following two input levels:

1. $A < D$
2. $A > D$

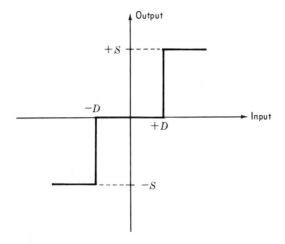

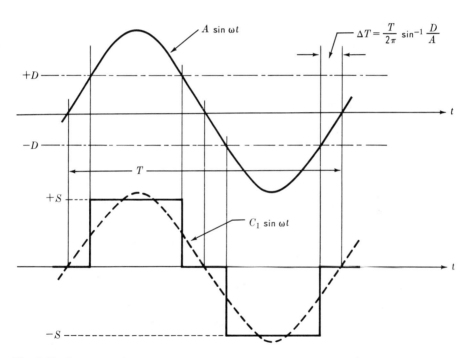

Fig. 8-32 Response of a dead-zone element to a sinusoidal input. Upper graph represents the input to and the lower graph the output from the nonlinear element.

In the first case, there is obviously no output, and consequently DF = 0. In the second case, the output will consist of pulses, as shown in Fig. 8-32.

By making use of formulas (B-3) in Appendix B, we obtain

$$C_1 = 4 \frac{2}{T} \int_{\Delta T}^{T/4} S \sin \left(\frac{2\pi}{T} t \right) dt$$

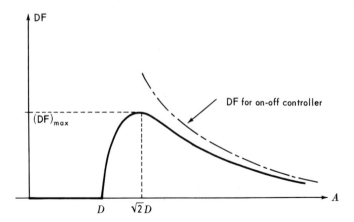

Fig. 8-33   DF for dead-zone element.

By integration, we obtain

$$C_1 = \frac{4S}{\pi} \frac{\sqrt{A^2 - D^2}}{A} \tag{8-90}$$

We thus conclude that the DF for this nonlinearity equals

$$DF = 0 \qquad \text{for } A < D$$

$$DF = \frac{4S}{\pi} \frac{\sqrt{A^2 - D^2}}{A^2} \qquad \text{for } A > D \tag{8-91}$$

The DF is plotted versus A in Fig. 8-33.   It is easy to prove that the DF has a maximum value of $(DF)_{\max} = 2S/\pi D$ that occurs for $A = \sqrt{2}D$.

Note also that the DF in this case approaches asymptotically the DF for the on-off controller shown in Fig. 8-31.   Why?

Example 8-11

The two nonlinearities for which we have computed the DF above had one thing in common—their DF's were *real*; i.e., the input and output waves had equal phase.

This is not generally true.   In this last example, we shall compute the DF for a *backlash* element depicted in Fig. 8-34.   Backlash occurs to a certain extent in all mechanical gear trains, and its severity is characterized by the "play" $2P$. In Fig. 8-35, we show the actual output wave form resulting from a sinusoidal input.   (The figure is valid only under the assumption that the input amplitude A exceeds P.)   It is quite clear that the fundamental component of the output is *not* in phase with the input.   By using the formulas (B-3) in Appendix B, we compute the cosine and sine components of the fundamental harmonic component of the output:

$$A_1 = \frac{4}{T}\left[\int_0^{T_1} (A - P) \cos \omega t \, dt + \int_{T_1}^{T/2} (A \cos \omega t + P) \cos \omega t \, dt \right]$$

$$B_1 = \frac{4}{T}\left[\int_0^{T_1} (A - P) \sin \omega t \, dt + \int_{T_1}^{T/2} (A \cos \omega t + P) \sin \omega t \, dt \right]$$

where $\omega \overset{\Delta}{=} 2\pi/T.$

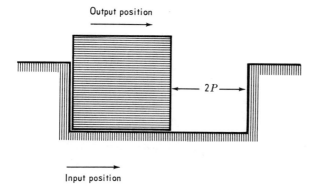

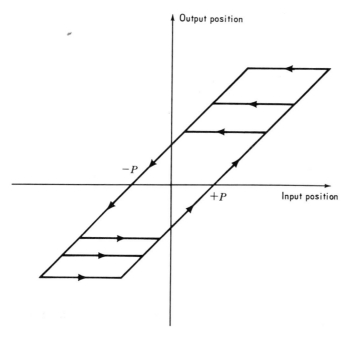

Fig. 8-34 Element with hysteresis.

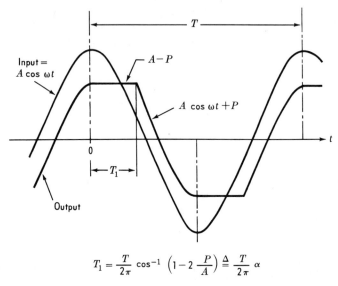

$$T_1 = \frac{T}{2\pi} \cos^{-1}\left(1 - 2\frac{P}{A}\right) \overset{\Delta}{=} \frac{T}{2\pi}\, \alpha$$

Fig. 8-35 Response of element in Fig. 8-34 to a sinusoidal input.

Upon integration, we obtain the following rather cumbersome expressions for A_1 and B_1:

$$A_1 = A\left[1 - \frac{\alpha}{\pi} + \frac{2}{\pi}\left(1 - 2\frac{P}{A}\right)\sin\alpha - \frac{1}{2\pi}\sin 2\alpha\right]$$

$$B_1 = A\left[\frac{1}{\pi} - \frac{2}{\pi}\left(1 - 2\frac{P}{A}\right)\cos\alpha + \frac{1}{\pi}\cos 2\alpha\right]$$

(8-92)

where $\alpha \overset{\Delta}{=} \cos^{-1}[1 - 2(P/A)]$.

We then obtain the DF

$$DF = \begin{cases} 0 & \text{for } A < P \\ \dfrac{C_1}{A}\, e^{j\varphi_1} & \text{for } A > P \end{cases}$$

(8-93)

where

$$C_1 \overset{\Delta}{=} \sqrt{A_1^2 + B_1^2}$$

$$\varphi_1 \overset{\Delta}{=} -\tan^{-1}\frac{B_1}{A_1}$$

The DF (gain $|DF|$ and phase $\angle DF$) have been plotted versus input amplitude A in Fig. 8-36. We note that the backlash element will introduce a phase lag of as much as 90°. For this reason, a worn gear train quite often may be the culprit in an unstable servo.

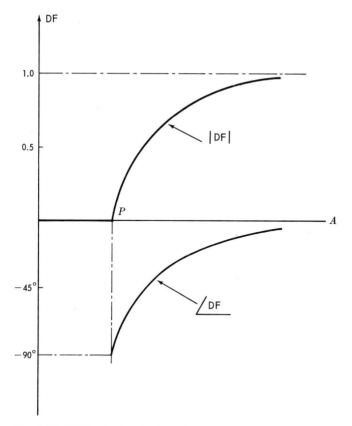

Fig. 8-36   DF for hysteresis element.

In the above examples, the DF's were found to be extremely dependent on the input-signal level.   If the nonlinearity contains energy storages, the DF also will be a function of frequency.   The reader will meet an example of this type in Exercise 8-2 at the end of this chapter.

It also should be emphasized that on many occasions, the DF really is not computed but is measured experimentally.   The actual nonlinearities encountered in practical cases usually are not of the simple straight-line variety we have used as examples in this section.

Uses of DF

The describing function finds its widest use in stability investigations and studies of limit cycles in closed-loop systems.   It is important to remind the reader that before the DF is brought to work, one must very carefully make sure that those conditions are at hand on the basis of which the DF was computed in the first place.   The most important point on the checklist is the requirement for a nearly sinusoidal input to the nonlinear element.   This last point usually complicates

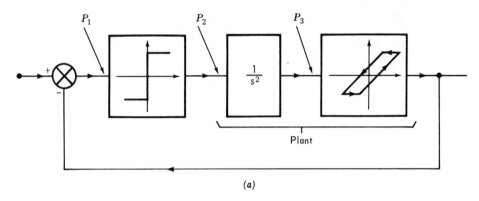

(*a*)

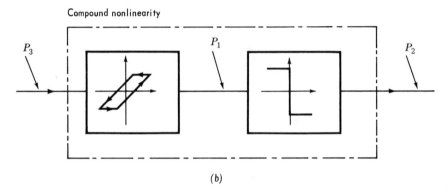

(*b*)

Fig. 8-37   Compound nonlinearity.

the situation when several nonlinearities are present in the loop.   Consider, for example, the system in Fig. 8-37*a*.   Due to the filtering effect of the linear part of the plant, we can assume that the signal at point P_3 is nearly sinusoidal.   But this is *not* the case for the signal at point P_1.   We therefore *cannot* make use directly of the describing functions that we computed earlier for each element separately.   However, we can *combine* the two nonlinearities into *one*, as shown in Fig. 8-37*b*, and then we can develop a *new* DF for this *compound* nonlinearity. As a matter of curiosity, this is (*in this case*) a considerably simpler task than finding the DF for the backlash element *alone*.   (This statement may sound paradoxical, but the reader is challenged to prove its correctness.)

Example 8-12

We shall apply the DF concept to a very typical problem.   Consider the servo shown in Fig. 8-38, consisting of a third-order plant controlled by an on-off controller.   We first shall give a *plausible* proof that limit cycles will occur in this system, and later we shall determine the character of these oscillations by means of the DF method. Assume that the system is initially in zero state, that the reference is also zero, and that we close the loop by closing the switch S. The relay output can take on only one of the two possible outputs $\pm u_{max}$. Assume it puts out $+u_{max}$. The output c thus will tend to increase, but this results in the error e going negative, and the relay switches to $-u_{max}$. As a result, c will "turn around"; and when it again passes through zero, so does e, and the relay switches, etc. Thus there is, on plausible grounds, reason to anticipate oscillations. The question is: Do these oscillations grow, decrease, or take on a stable finite amplitude and frequency? We can give an answer to this question by a daring extension of either the Nyquist stability theorem or the root-locus method. We shall present both methods, and the student may then choose whatever method he finds least unpalatable. Both are utterly heuristic, lack all mathematical basis, and have really only one *raison d'être*—they work!

Consider first the "Nyquist approach." We plot in polar form the FTF for the plant (plot I in the diagram of Fig. 8-39). Note that it passes through the real axis at $-\frac{1}{2}$ for the angular frequency $\omega = 1$. We next let the relay enter the picture. Upon the closing of S, the initial oscillations must be of small amplitude and the equivalent gain (see Fig. 8-31) therefore very high. This means that the open-loop Nyquist FTF

$$\frac{DF}{j\omega(1 + j\omega)^2}$$

must be located far to the left in the diagram (plot II). This, of course, is indicative of a very unstable loop. The small oscillations thus will experience a fast buildup, resulting in a constantly decreasing DF and a Nyquist plot that "shifts to the right," a process that will go on for as long as there is a tendency for amplitude buildup. As this tendency will persist as long as the Nyquist plot lies to the left of the point $G(s) = -1$, we conclude that a steady state will be reached only when the Nyquist plot reaches the dotted position.

Although the above explanation sounds plausible enough, it violates, of course, several mathematical rules. For one thing, there is no "shifting" Nyquist plot. We remember that in deriving the FTF in Chap. 6, we assumed *linearity*

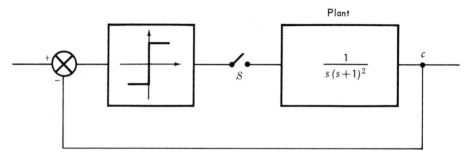

Fig. 8-38 System exhibiting limit cycles.

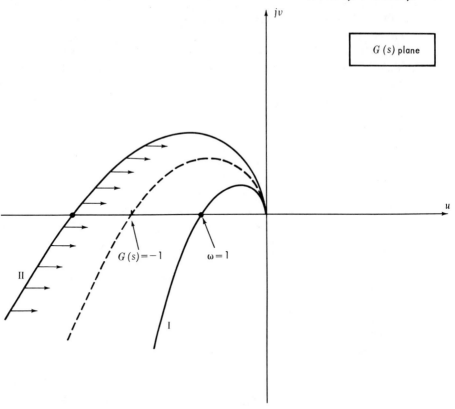

Fig. 8-39 Nyquist plots for system in Fig. 8-38.

and *time-invariant* parameters. In a strict sense, therefore, we are unable even to talk about an FTF, *because it does not exist.*

The example typifies a situation that an engineer often will encounter. It may be possible and also necessary to tamper in a careful fashion with some of the strict mathematical concepts he is using.

We should also say something about the *quantitative* data we can obtain from the Nyquist plot in Fig. 8-39. The dotted Nyquist plot corresponds to a gain of 2, and it furthermore indicates that the frequency of oscillation should be $\omega = 1$, or 0.160 cps.

Using formula (8-89), we find that the above gain corresponds to an amplitude (in the output) of

$$A = \frac{4u_{max}}{2\pi} = 0.638u_{max}$$

The system actually was put on a simulator, and we obtained the following experimental data:

$f = 0.163$ cps

$A = 0.680u_{max}$

The frequency and amplitude errors are thus 2 and 7 percent, respectively.

Truxal[12] has suggested extending the use of root-locus methods to problems of this nature. We demonstrate this technique in the present example. For this purpose, we construct first the root loci for the open-loop transfer function

$$G(s) = \frac{K}{s(s+1)^2}$$

This has been done in Fig. 8-40.

If we earlier could swallow the concept of "shifting Nyquist plots," we now should be willing to accept "shifting closed-loop poles." For small amplitudes and thus high equivalent gain, our closed-loop poles (or eigenvalues) λ_1, λ_2, and λ_3 will be found far out on the loci, as indicated in the figure. The system is obviously unstable, resulting in increasing amplitudes, reduced gain, and as a consequence, a "shifting" of the eigenvalues toward the center. Eventually, the two unstable poles λ_1 and λ_2 will reach the $j\omega$ axis, and the oscillation will now continue at a constant amplitude and frequency.

With the eigenvalues in this final position, we find directly from the plots, as before,

Equivalent gain: DF $= 2$

Limit-cycle frequency: $\omega = 1$ rad/sec

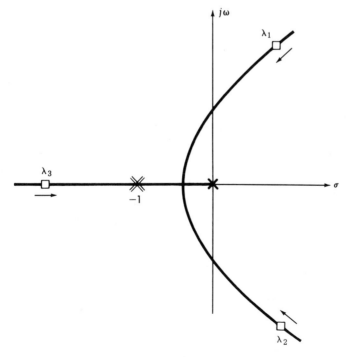

Fig. 8-40   Root loci for system in Fig. 8-38.

The above example is representative of the type of situation where the DF provides remarkably accurate information simply by helping us to extend linear analysis into the area of nonlinear systems.

It has been proposed to extend the use of DF to:

1. Finding the transient response of nonlinear systems
2. Studying the closed-loop so-called "frequency response" of nonlinear systems

As a general statement, it is fair to say that neither of these uses results in reliable information. There is obviously a limit to how far a nonlinear system can be approximated with a linear model. In our opinion and experience, the first suggestion is quite useless.

The second suggestion, i.e., to study the closed-loop frequency response, at least is based upon proper assumptions. We now would apply a sinusoidal reference input *r* and study the resulting output *c*. (Truxal[12] has demonstrated this approach, and Gibson[2] gives additional examples.) Apart from finding some rather interesting nonlinear phenomena (so-called "jump phenomena"), one is tempted, of course, to ask what use one can make of such computed (or experimentally obtained) data. It certainly cannot be correlated with transient response (as could be done in linear systems). And whenever is a servo excited by a sinusoidal input under normal operation?

8-4.3 EFFECTS OF HIGH-FREQUENCY BIAS SIGNAL

Dual-input Describing Function (DIDF)

It has been known for a considerable time that injection into a nonlinear control system of a high-frequency dither signal will in certain instances upgrade the performance of the system. The frequency of this signal usually is chosen considerably above the cutoff of the system so that its presence cannot be detected in the output. For instance, it is quite common to diminish the effect of static friction (stiction) by use of a superimposed high-frequency signal. The "dynamic lubrication" provided by such a signal was first (in 1945) pointed out by Mac-Coll, who analyzed its effect on an on-off type of servo. He also showed that if the servo possessed a dead zone, the nonsensitivity for small signals could be removed by adding a high-frequency signal.

The phenomenon has been studied in great detail in recent years by Oldenburger,[13,14] Boyer,[14] Elgerd,[15,16] and others. For an introduction to this phenomenon, let us consider the dead-zone element in Fig. 8-41. The output from the element is shown in two cases.

In the first case, the input consists of a low-frequency sine wave, $A \sin \omega t$, the amplitude of which does not exceed the width a of the insensitivity region. Under the circumstances, the output clearly will be zero.

Without changing the amplitude of the low-frequency signal, we then add a high-frequency bias $A_0 \sin \omega_0 t$ to the input. The output now will be nonzero. It is quite apparent that the output signal will contain a component of the same

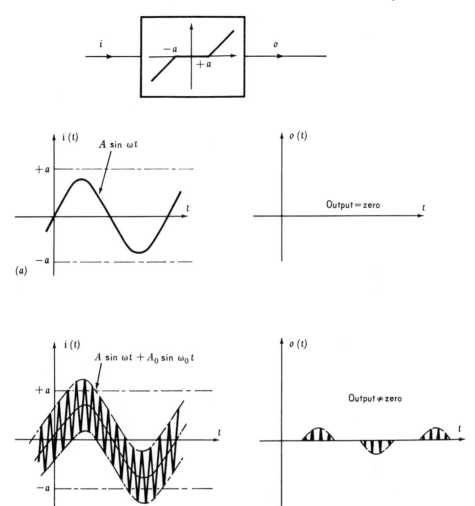

Fig. 8-41   Dither signal affects low-frequency gain of nonlinear element.

frequency ω and phase as the low-frequency input signal.   By focusing attention on this component and disregarding the high-frequency components (we note, for instance, that the bias frequency ω_0 is well represented in the output), we now can introduce a *dual-input describing function* (DIDF), defined as the complex ratio between the output and input components of angular frequency ω.

As in the case of the (single-input) DF, we make the assumption that all frequency components in excess of frequency ω will be filtered out by the low-pass characteristics of the controlled plant.   *We make the important observation that the presence of the high-frequency bias signal has affected the value of the low-frequency gain.*

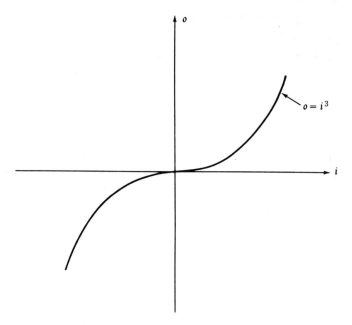

Fig. 8-42   Cubic nonlinearity.

Take, as a second example, the cubic nonlinearity in Fig. 8-42. Let us investigate the spectral composition of the output in the case where the input contains only one component of frequency ω and amplitude A and also in the case of a dual input containing two components of amplitudes A and A_0 and frequencies ω and ω_0. The result is given in Table 8-1. For the single-input

Table 8-1   Spectral composition in the output from a cubic nonlinearity with single and dual inputs

Input $i(t)$	Output $o(t)$
Single: $\quad i(t) = A \cos \omega t$	$\begin{aligned} o(t) &= (A \cos \omega t)^3 \\ &= \tfrac{3}{4}A^3 \cos \omega t + \tfrac{1}{4}A^3 \cos 3\omega t \end{aligned}$
Dual: $\quad i(t) = A \cos \omega t + A_0 \cos \omega_0 t$	$\begin{aligned} o(t) &= (A \cos \omega t + A_0 \cos \omega_0 t)^3 \\ &= \tfrac{3}{4}A(A^2 + 2A_0{}^2) \cos \omega t \\ &\quad + \tfrac{3}{4}A_0(2A^2 + A_0{}^2) \cos \omega_0 t \\ &\quad + \tfrac{1}{4}A^3 \cos 3\omega t \\ &\quad + \tfrac{1}{4}A_0{}^3 \cos 3\omega_0 t \\ &\quad + \tfrac{3}{4}A^2 A_0 \cos (\omega_0 + 2\omega)t \\ &\quad + \tfrac{3}{4}A^2 A_0 \cos (\omega_0 - 2\omega)t \\ &\quad + \tfrac{3}{4}A A_0{}^2 \cos (2\omega_0 + \omega)t \\ &\quad + \tfrac{3}{4}A A_0{}^2 \cos (2\omega_0 - \omega)t \end{aligned}$

case, the output will consist of two spectral lines of frequencies ω and 3ω. The describing function is

$$\text{DF} = \tfrac{3}{4}A^2 \tag{8-94}$$

For the dual-input case, the output will contain eight spectral lines, and if we focus attention on the low-frequency component ω, we find that the dual-input describing function equals

$$\text{DIDF} = \tfrac{3}{4}(A^2 + 2A_0{}^2) \tag{8-95}$$

Again we note the strong effect of the bias amplitude on the low-frequency gain. For example, if we choose $A_0 = A$, then we have

$$\text{DIDF} = 3\text{DF}$$

that is, an increase of the gain by 200 percent.

Basing our findings on the two previous examples, we summarize the following effects of the dither signal injected at the input of a nonlinearity:

1. It creates a considerable spectrum of new frequency components in the output.
2. The dither *amplitude* strongly affects the value of the low-frequency gain (the DIDF).
3. The dither *frequency* ω_0 has no measurable effect on the DIDF.

Spectral Composition of the Output

It is of interest to look at the dual-input phenomenon in a somewhat more general fashion. Specifically, we wish to investigate the nature of the output signal from a more "general" type of nonlinearity than that in the two cases we have looked at so far. Nonlinearities can be classified as either single-valued or multivalued, sometimes referred to as *nonmemory* and *memory*, respectively. Hysteresis is a typical multivalued nonlinearity; the output is here a function not only of the present value of the input but also of the input history. If attention is limited to a single-valued nonlinearity, it can be said to be of "general type" if the output-input relationship can be expressed as an infinite power series

$$o(t) = \sum_{\nu=0}^{\infty} a_\nu i^\nu(t) \tag{8-96}$$

where the a_ν's are real constants.

Expressed in words: An arbitrarily defined functional input-output relationship of a nonlinear element can be approximated to any degree of accuracy by a polynomial. This is sometimes referred to as *curve fitting*. Usually, only a few terms are sufficient (in the case of a "cubic," only one) to describe accurately the nonlinearity.

Should a dual input now be applied to such a nonlinearity, then the output will be determined from

$$o(t) = \sum_{\nu=0}^{\infty} a_\nu (A \cos \omega t + A_0 \cos \omega_0 t)^\nu \tag{8-97}$$

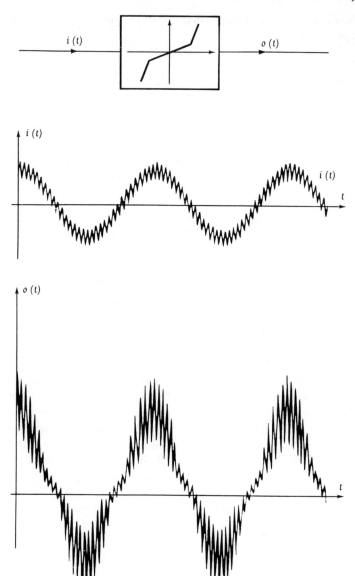

Fig. 8-43   Example of dither modulation.

For increasing v values, the following terms will be obtained in addition to a constant, or "d-c," term:

$\cos \omega t, \cos \omega_0 t, \cos^2 \omega t, \cos^2 \omega_0 t, \cos \omega t \cos \omega_0 t,$

$\cos^3 \omega t, \cos^3 \omega_0 t, \cos^2 \omega t \cos \omega_0 t, \cos^2 \omega_0 t \cos \omega t,$ etc.

In other words, the output contains (in addition to a constant) the frequencies

$\omega, \omega_0, 2\omega, 2\omega_0, \omega \pm \omega_0, 3\omega, 3\omega_0, \omega \pm 2\omega_0, \omega_0 \pm 2\omega,$ etc.

The output thus is made up of spectral components having the frequencies

$m\omega_0 + n\omega$

where m can take on all *positive* integer values including zero and n *every* integer value.

In compact form, we thus can write

$$o(t) = \sum_{m=0}^{+\infty} \sum_{n=-\infty}^{+\infty} C_{m,n} \cos \left[(m\omega_0 + n\omega)t + \varphi_{m,n} \right] \tag{8-98}$$

If we put $m = 0$ and $n = 1$, then we get the particular output component that we are concerned with in our definition of DIDF, that is,

$$\text{DIDF} \triangleq \frac{C_{0,1}}{A} e^{j\varphi_{0,1}} \tag{8-99}$$

It is of interest to note that the output spectrum is very *dense*. By assigning different values to m and n, we can create practically any frequency we want. Indeed, this is a standard method of creating new frequencies in the communication field. (The communication man refers to them as "modulation products.") Note, by the way, that it is possible to assign values to m and n that result in frequencies *lower than* ω. We talk about *subharmonics*. One can prove that if $\omega_0 \gg \omega$, these subharmonics have such low amplitudes that they are completely negligible beside the ω component. This is amply demonstrated in Fig. 8-43, depicting the situation in a case where

$\omega_0 \approx 30\omega$

Computation of DIDF: The Concept of Equivalent Nonlinearity

Computation of the DIDF for a specific nonlinear element generally is more difficult than finding the DF for the same element. One reason is that the DIDF is very much dependent upon the wave shape of the bias signal.

It is possible to find an exact expression for the amplitude coefficients $C_{m,n}$ in formula (8-98). However, this expression will contain double integrals and is exceedingly cumbersome to handle. If $\omega_0 \gg \omega$, it is possible to find the particular coefficient $C_{0,1}$ by means of approximate methods. Two approaches can be taken, both of which will be discussed briefly.

The first approach is based upon the reasonable assumption that the output $o(t)$ is approximately periodic with the period time $T = 2\pi/\omega$. (In a mathematical

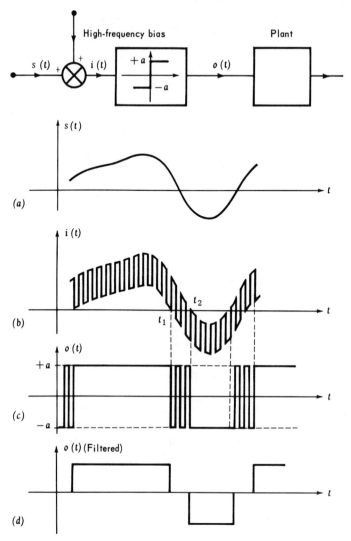

Fig. 8-44 Finding the equivalent nonlinearity for on-off element.

sense, this would be exactly true only if ω_0 were an integer multiple of ω.) As is demonstrated in Fig. 8-43, the approximation is very good indeed, and we thus get, in accordance with Fourier,

$$C_{0,1} = \frac{2}{T} \int_0^T o(t) \cos \omega t \, dt \tag{8-100}$$

Generally, of course, this integral will not integrate into a simple elementary function, and it is therefore necessary to use numerical integration methods.

In preparing the integral for a computer program, the integral is first written as a sum

$$C_{0,1} = \frac{2}{q} \sum_{v=1}^{q} o\left(v\frac{T}{q}\right) \cos\left(\omega v\frac{T}{q}\right) \tag{8-101}$$

q is the number of subdivisions of the interval 0 to T and v is the summation variable. The choice of q is largely dependent on the ratio ω_0/ω, because one must make the intervals sufficiently small to account accurately for the change in the most rapidly varying term, i.e., the one due to $\cos \omega_0 t$.

The second method for computation of the DIDF is based upon the concept of *equivalent nonlinearity*. This concept is presented most conveniently by means of a simple example. Consider the on-off controller in Fig. 8-44. The graphs *a* and *b* depict the input signal with and without a high-frequency *square*-wave bias signal. The low-frequency signal $s(t)$ could represent, for example, the error signal in a servo. The graph *c* in the figure represents the *actual* output $o(t)$ from the nonlinear element. Now, as usual, we shall assume that the nonlinearity is followed by a low-pass plant that effectively filters out all high-frequency components. For those time periods during which the relay "chatters" (for instance, between t_1 and t_2), the *effective* output, i.e., the average of $o(t)$, is zero, and the plant therefore *effectively* feels the output of graph *d*. We realize that this "filtered" output would have been obtained if the low-frequency signal $s(t)$, *without the bias added, had been passed through the nonlinearity of Fig. 8-45*. This

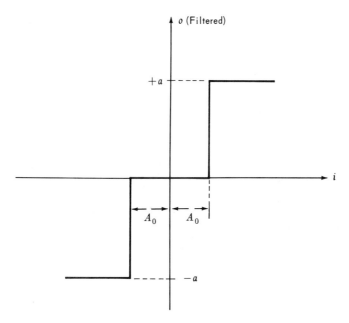

Fig. 8-45   Equivalent nonlinearity for element in Fig. 8-44—rectangular bias signal.

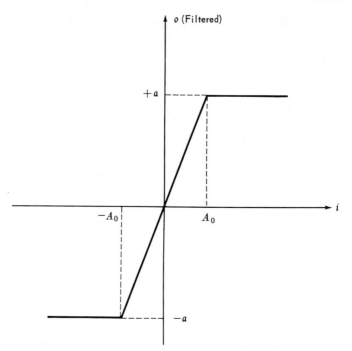

Fig. 8-46   Equivalent nonlinearity for element in Fig. 8-44—triangular bias signal.

nonlinearity is referred to as the *equivalent nonlinearity* of the one in Fig. 8-44. We now can compute the DIDF for the on-off controller simply by computing the DF for the equivalent nonlinearity in Fig. 8-45.   This we already have done [see Fig. 8-33 and Eq. (8-91)].

It is obvious that the equivalent nonlinearity will be a function of the wave shape of the bias signal.   For instance, if the bias wave in Fig. 8-44 were triangular rather than rectangular, then the equivalent nonlinearity would be the one shown in Fig. 8-46.   (Compare also Exercise 8-3.)   *Note that once the equivalent nonlinearity has been found for a specific nonlinear element, then the DIDF can be computed by computing the DF for the equivalent nonlinearity.*

It must be emphasized that the concept of "equivalent nonlinearity" has validity only when the bias frequency is well above the cutoff frequency of the remainder control system but well below the cutoff frequency of the nonlinear element.   In comparison with a fixed nonlinear controller, the method possesses the following advantages:

1. A great variety of different "equivalent nonlinearities" can be selected by properly choosing amplitude and wave shape of the dither signal.
2. The "equivalent nonlinearity" (and thereby the transient response) can be controlled continuously and speedily by changing the bias amplitude.

Once the "equivalent nonlinearity" has been determined, the transient response can be predicted by the conventional analysis methods discussed earlier in this chapter.

We shall conclude this discussion by demonstrating with an example the stability improvement obtained by dither injection. The system in question contains a saturation nonlinearity. The three graphs in Fig. 8-47 are recorded responses for a step input. Without bias (graph *a*), we note a substantial limit-cycle oscillation that would render the system useless. Added dither effectively quenches these oscillations. Two types of dither are used, sinusoidal and random noise, and corresponding responses are shown in graphs *b* and *c*, respectively.

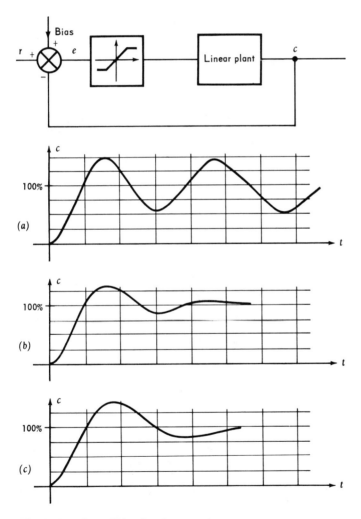

Fig. 8-47 Effect of bias signal on transient response.

8-5 SUMMARY

A chapter on the topic of nonlinear control theory can at best be a collection of loosely connected special analysis techniques. In all probability, an all-encompassing general theory can never be found. Although this is a distressing situation from the analyst's point of view, the control engineer can take solace from the fact that nonlinear design offers many interesting and useful solutions unobtainable by linear methods. *Intentional* introduction of nonlinear control elements can result in superior system characteristics, as was exemplified in this chapter. It is necessary, however, if we want to share in the blessings of nonlinear design, that we learn more about nonlinear phenomena. The average engineer has an inborn aversion toward leaving the calm water of the linear sea for the more unpredictable waves of the nonlinear ocean.

As exact analysis methods probably never will be developed to a point of universal usefulness, we had better increase our arsenal of *heuristic* approaches, which in combination with computer methods are the best hope for the future.

Exercises

8-1 It was shown in the text that the on-off servo in Fig. 8-2 is characterized by limit cycling, which, although rendering the system "stable," makes it unsuitable from a practical point of view. Add a proportional-plus-derivative controller to the system, as shown in Fig. 8-48, and show by means of phase trajectories that by proper choice of the ratio K_1/K_2, one can improve the response considerably.

Hint: Note that the equation

$$K_1 e + K_2 \dot{e} = 0$$

represents a straight line in the $e\dot{e}$ phase plane.

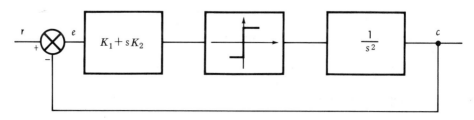

Fig. 8-48 System discussed in Exercise 8-1.

8-2 Consider the three cascaded elements depicted in Fig. 8-49. They constitute part of a control system. Two of the elements are nonlinear, one is linear (an integrator).

Why is it *not* recommendable to obtain the *overall* frequency response of this system by multiplication of the FTF of the integrator by the individual DF's of each nonlinear element?

Suggest a better method and then use it to obtain the overall DF of the three elements. Note that because we have an energy-storage element in the system, the overall DF must be a function of ω. Plot the DF versus ω!

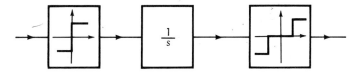

Fig. 8-49   System discussed in Exercise 8-2.

8-3 Find the "equivalent nonlinearity" for the on-off element in Fig. 8-44 if sinusoidal dither is used.

8-4 Study the effect of dither injected at the input of a backlash element.   Will the wave shape of the dither appreciably affect the equivalent nonlinearity?

8-5 The relay in the system depicted in Fig. 8-38 is replaced by the dead-zone nonlinearity shown in Fig. 8-32.

a Can this system go into limit-cycle oscillation by itself?

b If the system is "helped" into oscillation by a proper *r* input (what type of input would do it?), prove that these oscillations will be sustained if the nonlinear element is characterized by a sufficiently high S/D ratio.

c Could the oscillations in problem *b* be quenched by dither injection?

(This problem makes for an interesting simulation experiment on an analog computer.)

8-6 Consider the following system of differential equations:

$$\dot{x}_1 = -x_1 + x_1 x_2$$

$$\dot{x}_2 = -2x_2 + x_1 x_2$$

x_1 and x_2 may represent biological populations—bacteria, for instance.

The nonlinear terms $x_1 x_2$ express the interaction between the populations.   For *small* populations, the linear terms will dominate, $\dot{x}_1$ and $\dot{x}_2$ both will be negative, and the populations will die out.   For *large* populations, the nonlinear terms will dominate, the rates $\dot{x}_1$ and $\dot{x}_2$ will be positive, and the populations will experience unlimited growth.

a Show that the system possesses two points of equilibrium, and study by linearization the local stability of each.

b You will find in problem *a* that origin is a stable point.   Employ now Liapunov's method to determine a *finite* region around origin within which you can guarantee stability.

c Sketch the phase trajectories by using one of the methods outlined in the text.   In particular, find the separatrices and then compare the actual stability regions with the ones that you found in problem *b*.

8-7 The system in Fig. 8-50 demonstrates a very interesting nonlinear phenomenon referred to as *slip-stick* motion.   A spring-constrained mass rests on an endless band, which runs at constant speed *v*.   Under certain conditions (to be determined by the student), the mass will experience sustained horizontal oscillations.   The phenomenon is due to the fact that the *static* friction ("stiction") between the mass and the band is larger than the *dynamic* friction.   The situation is clarified by the graph in Fig. 8-50, which shows the friction force between mass and band as a function of the *relative velocity* between them.

Describe the motion of *m* in a phase plane.

The violinist makes use of this phenomenon when exciting the strings into limit cycles by means of a well-rosined bow.   Can you think of any other uses of this phenomenon?

Explain what would happen to the oscillations if the support *S* (see Fig. 8-50) were being moved *rapidly* back and forth at a frequency far in excess of the undamped resonance frequency

$$\omega = \sqrt{\frac{k_s}{m}}$$

of the spring-mass system.

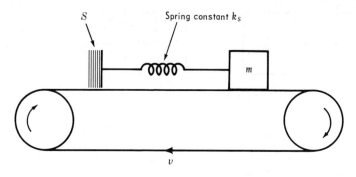

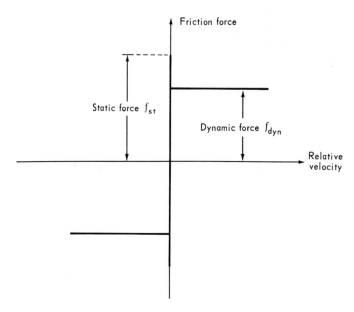

Fig. 8-50   System exhibiting "slip-stick" motion.

8-8 Study the φ dynamics of the broom-balancing system described in Chap. 2 assuming that we use the nonlinear maximum-effort control strategy depicted in Fig. 2-10.   Study separately the two cases:

1. $u = \dfrac{\varphi}{|\varphi|} u_{max}$

2. $u = \dfrac{\varphi}{|\varphi|} u_{max} + k_2 \dot{\varphi}$

In the latter case, we obviously have assumed a mixed linear-nonlinear control strategy.   *Hint:* Use a $\varphi\dot{\varphi}$ phase plane.   For simplicity use the following simple numerical values:

$m = M = 1$ kg

$L = 1$ m

$g = 10$ m/sec²

References

1. H. Poincaré, "Les Méthodes nouvelles de la mécanique céleste," vols. I and II, Gauthier-Villars, Paris, 1892. (Reprinted by Dover Publications, Inc., New York, 1957.)

2. J. Gibson, "Nonlinear Automatic Control," McGraw-Hill Book Company, New York, 1963.

3. Y. H. Ku, "Analysis and Control of Nonlinear Systems," The Ronald Press Company, New York, 1958.

4. J. LaSalle and S. Lefschetz, "Stability by Liapunov's Direct Method," Academic Press Inc., New York, 1961.

5. I. Flügge-Lotz, Synthesis of Third-order Contactor Control Systems, *Proc. Congr. IFAC*, 1st, Moscow (1960).

6. A. A. Liapunov, "Problème général de la stabilité du mouvement," Ph.D. thesis, 1892. (Reprinted in "Annals of Mathematics Studies #17," Princeton University Press, Princeton, N.J., 1949.)

7. A. M. Letov, Liapunov's Theory of Stability of Motion, chap. 6 in J. Peschon (ed.), "Disciplines and Techniques of Systems Control," Blaisdell Publishing Co., New York, 1964.

8. R. Bellman, "Introduction to Matrix Analysis," McGraw-Hill Book Company, New York, 1960.

9. R. Kochenburger, Frequency Response Method for Analysis of a Relay Servo, *Trans. AIEE*, **69** (1950).

10. L. C. Goldfarb, On Some Nonlinear Phenomena in Regulatory Systems, *Automatika i Telemekhanika*, **8**(5) (September–October, 1947).

11. W. Oppelt, Locus Curve Method for Regulators with Friction, *J. Inst. Elec. Engrs. (London)*, **94**, pt. IIA (1 and 2) (May, 1947).

12. John G. Truxal, "Control System Synthesis," McGraw-Hill Book Company, New York, 1955.

13. R. Oldenburger and T. Nakada, Signal Stabilization of Self-oscillating Systems, *Proc. Congr. IFAC*, 1st, Moscow, 664–670 (1960).

14. R. Oldenburger and R. C. Boyer, Effects of Extra Sinusoidal Inputs to Nonlinear Systems, presented at ASME Winter Annual Meeting in New York, 1961.

15. Olle I. Elgerd, Asynchronously Excited Oscillations in Non-linear Control Systems, *IRE Trans. Auto. Control*, **AC-5**(3): 179–192 (August, 1960).

16. Olle I. Elgerd, Continuous Control by High Frequency Signal Injection, *Instr. Control Systems*, **37**(12) (December, 1964).

chapter 9

SIGNAL-MODULATED SYSTEMS

9-1 INTRODUCTION

In all our previous discussions, we tacitly made the assumption that the signals which appear throughout the control system are available in *continuous* form. The output voltage from a d-c tachometer generator, the power from a heater coil, or the thrust force emanating from a rocket engine are but a few examples of such *continuous-data* or *analog-type* signals. As these signals usually are of low-frequency character, containing energy in the frequency spectrum extending from zero up to a few cps (seldom above 100 cps), we often refer to them as "d-c signals," even when they are not electrical in nature.

In a great many control systems, it becomes necessary for a variety of practical reasons to work with *modulated* signals. In Fig. 9-1 are shown the most common forms of modulation schemes employed in control engineering. In this order, the figure depicts:

1. (Suppressed-carrier) amplitude modulation (AM).†
2. Pulse-amplitude modulation (PAM). The term *sampled data* is preferred by control people.
3. Pulse-width modulation (PWM).

In this chapter we shall be concerned exclusively with the first two methods as they are by far the most popular and important modulation schemes presently in use.

9-2 WHY MODULATION?

Transforming a continuous signal $e(t)$ into any one of the modulated signal trains shown in Fig. 9-1 seemingly would represent a considerable increase in system complexity, and it is important therefore that we motivate the need for their employment.‡

† The term "a-c carrier" is also widely used.

‡ We shall use the symbol e for unmodulated (or d-c) signals, even if they do not represent "error."

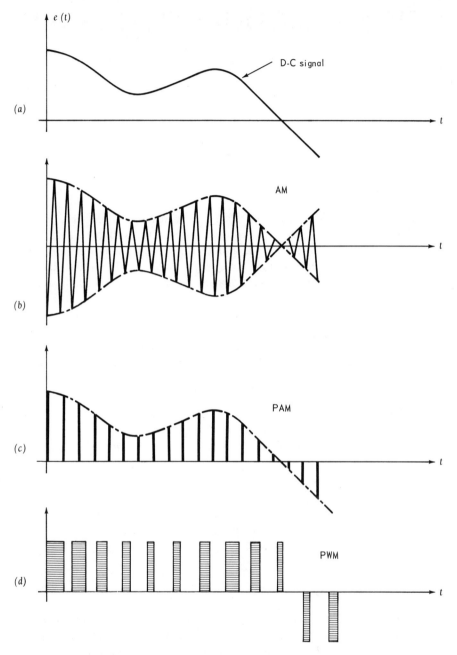

Fig. 9-1   Various modulation schemes.

Here are some of the most outstanding reasons:

1. AM systems are often characterized by higher accuracy.
2. AM signals can be amplified more conveniently than unmodulated signals, and usually one gains considerable hardware cost and weight advantages.
3. An array of very special and, for control purposes, very suitable electrical components are available that inherently work only on AM signals.
4. If the control signals must be transmitted over considerable distances, modulation becomes a necessity since, as a rule, better accuracy and noise insensitivity can be obtained with modulation than without modulation.
5. Time sharing of components necessitates data sampling.
6. Many control components (radar, for instance) deliver their outputs in discrete, or sampled-data, form.
7. Whenever a digital computer constitutes part of a control system, the continuous signals must be "discretized" in order to be digestible by the computer.

We wish to illustrate some of these points by means of a few typical control problems with solutions which incorporate modulation techniques for reasons of necessity or convenience.

Example 9-1

Consider the problem of sensing the angular position $e(t)$ of a mechanical member, as depicted in Fig. 9-2. The angular position $e(t)$ is assumed to be *very minute*. Two different sensor arrangements are shown in Fig. 9-2. Both output a pick-off voltage which is proportional to $e(t)$. The solution in Fig. 9-2a would be very impractical, if not impossible, as it is not feasible to obtain potentiometers with the necessary resolution within the small linear range Δ. In addition, as actual contact must be maintained between the pot and the gliding contact, we also introduce an undesired friction moment. The solution in Fig. 9-2b by means of a so-called "E transformer" is much more attractive. The middle coil is excited from an a-c source (usually 400 cps). The output voltage is evidently a 400-cps a-c voltage with amplitude proportional to the difference between the two fluxes φ_1 and φ_2. As most of the magnetic reluctance is concentrated to the air gaps, this difference will vary *strongly* (and, by the way, quite *linearly*) with the armature position, and the result is a *high-resolution* sensor. [Note that it is also *sign sensitive*, as the *phase* of the 400-cps output voltage changes with 180° between positive and negative errors $e(t)$.]

Example 9-2

Consider next the problem of *amplification* of electrical signals. In earlier chapters, we concluded that the loop gain is an important design factor the value of which affects sensitivity, stability, and response. It is therefore of importance to have a convenient means of amplifying electrical signals. Any electrical junior knows that it is much easier to amplify an a-c signal of type b in Fig. 9-1 than a d-c signal of type a. A d-c amplifier requires resistor rather than capacitor coupling between the stages, resulting in problems of drift and reduced accuracy.

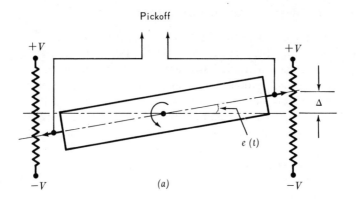

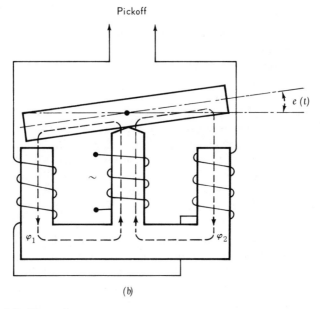

Fig. 9-2   E transformer.

Example 9-3

Synchro devices† commonly are used for position sensing when considerable physical distance is involved between the point of reference setting and the position of the output member, e.g., between cockpit and stabilizer on an aircraft.   Without going into a detailed description of the physics of these devices, we inform the reader that the error position, as obtained from a synchro pair (Fig. 9-3), appears in the form of an AM signal.   The device is relatively linear for small angular errors.

† For further details on synchros and a-c motors, see Refs. 1 and 2.

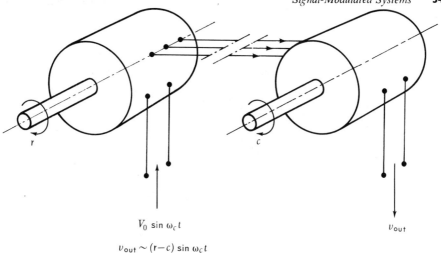

$$V_0 \sin \omega_c t$$

$$v_{\text{out}}$$

$$v_{\text{out}} \sim (r - c) \sin \omega_c t$$

Fig. 9-3 Synchro pair.

In conjunction with synchros, we often find employed so-called *a-c servo motors* (Fig. 9-4). This device accepts an AM signal as input and delivers a d-c type of output in the form of a torque. The device is nonlinear; i.e., the torque is not linearly dependent upon the input $e(t)$. The torque is also a function of the speed.† It does, however, have sign sensitivity. A typical servo arrangement incorporating all the above-mentioned devices is shown in Fig. 9-5. We give a brief account of its operation.

† For further details, see Fig. 9-19.

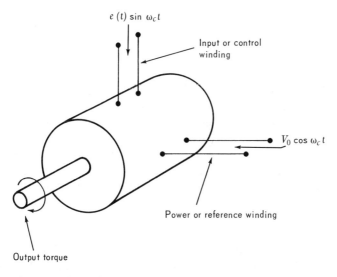

$e(t) \sin \omega_c t$

Input or control winding

$V_0 \cos \omega_c t$

Power or reference winding

Output torque

Fig. 9-4 Alternating-current servomotor.

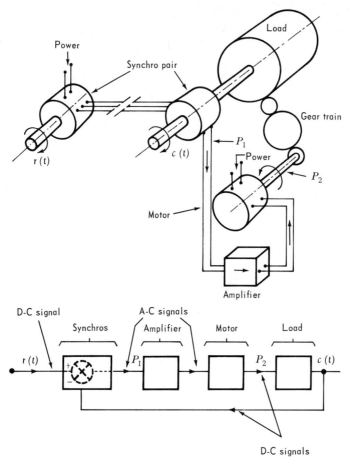

Fig. 9-5   Typical a-c servo configuration.

Upon a reference setting $r(t)$, an AM error signal appears at P_1. This signal is amplified (in an a-c amplifier) and fed into the a-c servomotor, which responds with a continuous (or d-c) torque. The motor continues to run until the error is eliminated. A block diagram of the system is provided in Fig. 9-5. The synchro pair acts here as a combined *comparator-modulator*. The motor is a combined *actuator-demodulator*. Because of the particular characteristics of these devices, we need no separate demodulators or modulators in this system. This, of course, is not generally true in a-c systems.

Example 9-4

Consider finally an example of time sharing of facilities. This is often the case when the control loop simultaneously incorporates both an airborne vehicle and a ground-based computing facility. The telemetering (TM) system must carry

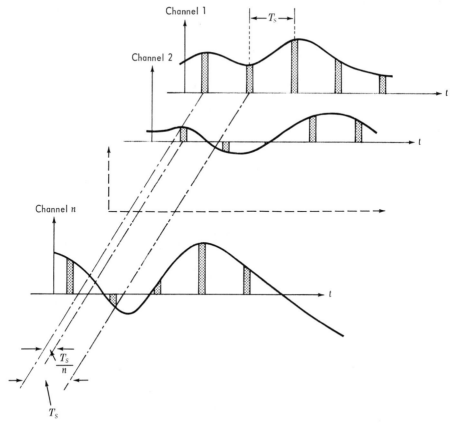

Fig. 9-6 Time-division multiplexing.

a number *n* of signal channels, and this can be done by means of *time-division multiplexing*, the principle of which is illustrated in Fig. 9-6. This method necessitates the "chopping" up of each d-c signal into pieces or samples at a regular rate of $1/T_s$ cps. On the average, each signal thus uses only one-*n*th of the channel capacity.

These, then, are some typical examples of situations where it becomes necessary to employ signal-modulation techniques in one form or the other. We shall proceed with a presentation of the AM and PAM methods.

9-3 THEORY OF AMPLITUDE-MODULATED CONTROL SYSTEMS

9-3.1 SPECTRAL-ENERGY DISTRIBUTION

A proper understanding of some of the characteristics of AM signals can be achieved by analyzing their spectral character. Consider, for that purpose, the unmodulated d-c signal $e(t)$. Its spectrum can be obtained from its Fourier transform [see Appendix B, Eq. (B-11)]

$$E(j\omega) = \mathscr{F}[e(t)] = \int_{-\infty}^{+\infty} e(\tau)e^{-j\omega\tau}\,d\tau \tag{9-1}$$

As outlined in Appendix B, the spectrum $E(j\omega)$ of the *aperiodic* function $e(t)$ is *continuous*.

$E(j\omega)$ is generally a complex frequency function, which we may write

$$E(j\omega) = |E(j\omega)|\,e^{j/E(j\omega)} \tag{9-2}$$

The *spectral intensity* $|E(j\omega)|$ is an *even* function of frequency [Eq. (B-13)], and plotted versus ω, it typically may look something like the plot in Fig. 9-7, which informs us where in the frequency range we may find the signal *energy*.

As has already been pointed out, a typical unmodulated control signal contains most of its energy in a *low-frequency* band, from zero upward. The bandwidth (BW) very seldom exceeds 100 rad/sec.

We now modulate this signal with a harmonic *carrier* of frequency

$$f_c = \frac{\omega_c}{2\pi}$$

where

$$\omega_c \gg \text{BW}$$

We obtain

$$e_m(t) = e(t)\cos\omega_c t = e(t)\frac{e^{j\omega_c t} + e^{-j\omega_c t}}{2} \tag{9-3}$$

This AM signal has a spectrum that equals

$$
\begin{aligned}
E_m(j\omega) = \mathscr{F}[e_m(t)] &= \int_{-\infty}^{+\infty} e_m(\tau)e^{-j\omega\tau}\,d\tau \\
&= \int_{-\infty}^{+\infty} e(\tau)\frac{e^{j\omega_c\tau} + e^{-j\omega_c\tau}}{2}e^{-j\omega\tau}\,d\tau \\
&= \tfrac{1}{2}\int_{-\infty}^{+\infty} e(\tau)e^{-j(\omega-\omega_c)\tau}\,d\tau + \tfrac{1}{2}\int_{-\infty}^{+\infty} e(\tau)e^{-j(\omega+\omega_c)\tau}\,d\tau
\end{aligned}
\tag{9-4}
$$

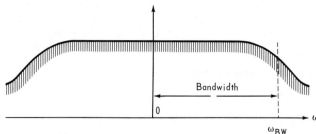

Fig. 9-7 Typical Fourier spectrum of d-c control signal.

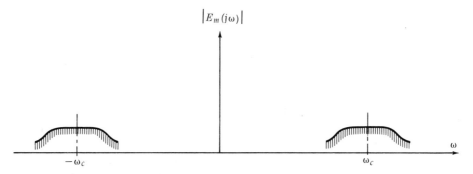

Fig. 9-8   Fourier spectrum of AM-modulated signal.

By comparison with Eq. (9-1), we thus have

$$E_m(j\omega) = \tfrac{1}{2}E[j(\omega - \omega_c)] + \tfrac{1}{2}E[j(\omega + \omega_c)] \tag{9-5}$$

We conclude that the spectrum of the modulated signal $e_m(t)$ can be related *directly* to that of the unmodulated signal $e(t)$.   The spectral terms $\tfrac{1}{2}E[j(\omega \pm \omega_c)]$ look identical (with respect to *both* amplitude and phase) to the term $E(j\omega)$ with two exceptions:

1. The amplitude is reduced to one-half.
2. Whereas $E(j\omega)$, which also can be written $E[j(\omega + 0)]$, is centered symmetrically around $\omega = 0$, the terms $\tfrac{1}{2}E[j(\omega \pm \omega_c)]$ must be centered symmetrically around the frequencies $\mp\omega_c$, that is, the carrier frequency.

We summarize our findings in Fig. 9-8.
Upon modulation with the harmonic carrier, the energy in the signal has been shifted upward in the frequency band and now is centered around the carrier frequency.   This fact will have significant bearing upon our efforts to change or modify the signal by means of compensation networks.

9-3.2 AM-SIGNAL COMPENSATION

Derivation of Transfer Function for Compensation Network

Design of control systems in which some signals may be AM-modulated follows generally the same procedures as outlined for unmodulated-signal systems in earlier chapters.   Thus, we will find it necessary in most cases to introduce compensation networks in order to meet stipulated stability and performance specifications.   In principle, we have a choice as to where we want to place such networks.   Either we can attempt to compensate the unmodulated signals, or we can insert the networks in the modulated sections.   For example, consider the "hybrid" system in Fig. 9-5.   Should we find upon closing the loop that compensation is needed, we have the following choices:

1. Compensate the d-c signals. All d-c signals are *mechanical* in nature, e.g., the torque delivered by the motor or the output signal $c(t)$ itself. Therefore, we conceivably could use a *mechanical* compensation network. This type of compensation usually takes the form of an *oscillation damper* connected to the load shaft, and its effect is simply to change the dynamics of the load as felt by the rest of the system. (See Ref. 2.) This type of compensation is often referred to as *load compensation*.
2. Compensate in the forward branch in the modulated signal either before or after the amplifier. As these signals are electrical, this type of compensation must be performed with electrical networks. We shall refer to this as *series compensation*. (It is also possible to apply a minor feedback loop around the motor to affect its apparent dynamics. This loop usually then takes the form of tachometer feedback, and the signals in this loop are of the AM type.†)

Electrical compensation is usually preferred because of the many advantages associated with electrical networks as compared with mechanical networks. This, therefore, motivates us to investigate the particular problems that crop up due to the fact that the network usually must work on AM signals.

In all types of compensation, we basically are interested in the effect of the network on the *d-c signal* or, in the case of AM compensation, in the effect on the *envelope* of the AM signal. Compare the two situations in Fig. 9-9. In the d-c case, we want to find a d-c network that affects the d-c input $i(t)$ in a certain prescribed fashion. If the network is *linear*, we may specify its characteristics by means of its transfer function $G(s) = O(s)/I(s)$.

Let us now turn our attention to the AM case. Our goal is to find a network, characterized by a transfer function

$$G_m(s) = \frac{O_m(s)}{I_m(s)}$$

which will affect the envelope of $i_m(t)$ *in exactly the same manner as* $G(s)$ *is affecting* $i(t)$. The situation is illustrated in the figure.

Mathematically, we can express this requirement as follows:
If the input to G_m equals $i_m(t) = i(t) \cos \omega_c t$, we require the output to be of the form

$$o_m(t) = o(t) \cos \omega_c t$$

† If an a-c servomotor is run with the control winding (see Fig. 9-4) open-circuited but excited with a carrier frequency in the "reference winding," then there will appear an a-c voltage across the control winding, which has an amplitude proportional to the speed of the motor.[2] In effect, then the a-c motor is serving as a tachometer generator.

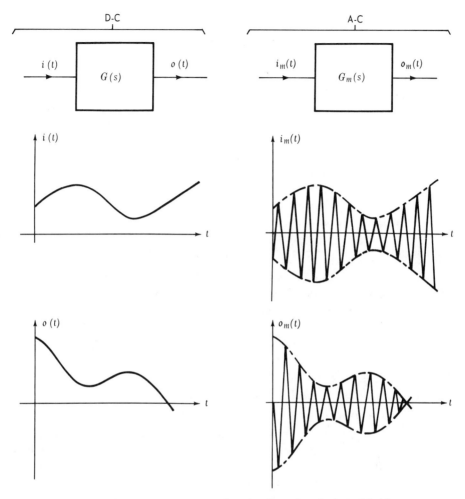

Fig. 9-9   Compensation of a-c signal must affect signal envelope in desired fashion.

Thus, if the situation depicted in Fig. 9-9 is to prevail, we must require that the transfer function $G_m(s)$ be

$$G_m(s) = \frac{\mathscr{L}[o(t) \cos \omega_c t]}{\mathscr{L}[i(t) \cos \omega_c t]} \tag{9-6}$$

By actually performing the required Laplace transformations, the expression (9-6) yields

$$G_m(s) = \frac{G(s - j\omega_c)I(s - j\omega_c) + G(s + j\omega_c)I(s + j\omega_c)}{I(s - j\omega_c) + I(s + j\omega_c)} \tag{9-7}$$

[We have made use of the formula

$$\mathscr{L}[f(t)\cos \omega t] = \mathscr{L}\left[f(t)\frac{e^{j\omega t} + e^{-j\omega t}}{2} \right]$$

$$= \tfrac{1}{2}F(s - j\omega) + \tfrac{1}{2}F(s + j\omega)$$

See Eq. (B-22) in Appendix B.]

The transfer function specified by Eq. (9-7) cannot be realized *exactly*. As $G_m(s)$ is a function of $I(s + j\omega_c)$ and $I(s - j\omega_c)$, we draw the conclusion that Eq. (9-7) requires that $G_m(s)$ *be a function of the input signal*.

However, under certain conditions (which, as a rule, are present in many practical situations), we can realize $G_m(s)$ *approximately*. Such an approximate design is possible only because of the very special spectral characteristics of the unmodulated $i(t)$ signal. The situation will be clearer if we look for a moment at the frequency characteristics of $G_m(s)$; that is, we turn our attention to the FTF

$$G_m(j\omega) = \frac{G[j(\omega - \omega_c)]I[j(\omega - \omega_c)] + G[j(\omega + \omega_c)]I[j(\omega + \omega_c)]}{I[j(\omega - \omega_c)] + I[j(\omega + \omega_c)]} \tag{9-8}$$

Consider the terms $I[j(\omega \pm \omega_c)]$. We encountered similar terms in Eq. (9-5) and concluded at that time that they represented the Fourier transform of the unmodulated signals translated from $\omega = 0$ to $\omega = \mp\omega_c$. If the bandwidth of the $i(t)$ spectrum is considerably less† than ω_c, then, as is revealed immediately by Fig. 9-8, we can assume the terms $I[j(\omega \pm \omega_c)]$ to be zero everywhere except *at* and *around* the frequencies $\mp\omega_c$.

Under this assumption, Eq. (9-8) reduces to

$$\begin{aligned} G_m(j\omega) &\approx G[j(\omega - \omega_c)] &&\text{for } \omega \text{ at and } \textit{around } \omega_c \\ G_m(j\omega) &\approx G[j(\omega + \omega_c)] &&\text{for } \omega \text{ at and } \textit{around } -\omega_c \end{aligned} \tag{9-9}$$

These equations tell us what characteristics we must build into G_m to obtain an envelope compensation for the signal $i_m(t)$ that equals the d-c compensation of $i(t)$ by the G network.

We can formulate the rule in words as follows:

The AM compensation network G_m must have the same frequency characteristics (gain and phase) at and around the frequencies $\omega = \pm\omega_c$ as the d-c compensation network G has at and around $\omega = 0$.

What happens at other frequencies is of no real interest because the signal contains energy only in narrow bands around $\omega = \pm\omega_c$.

Example 9-5

Consider the lag network‡ depicted in Fig. 9-10a. With the parameter values given in the figure, its transfer function equals

$$G(s) = \frac{1 + s}{1 + 10s}$$

---

† If the bandwidth typically is 20 cps and the carrier frequency is 400 cps, this assumption certainly is realistic.

‡ Its name refers to the fact that the output-voltage wave lags the input wave in phase.

Therefore,

$$G(j\omega) = \frac{1 + j\omega}{1 + j10\omega}$$

This transfer function is plotted in Fig. 9-10b. We note that all its important features lie within an approximate frequency range of $-0.5 < \omega < +0.5$ rad/sec.

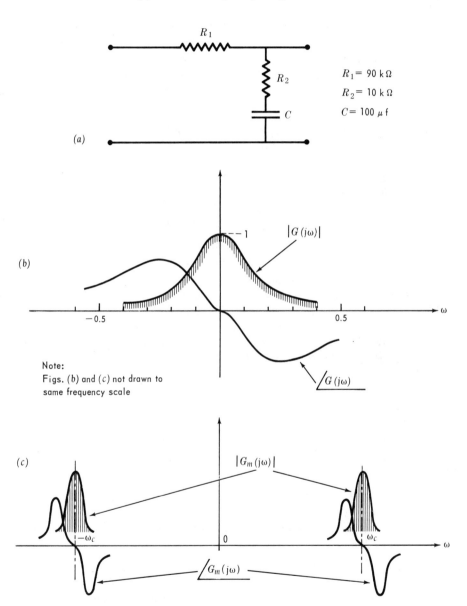

Fig. 9-10 Lag compensation for a-c signals.

If we now wish to design a compensation network that will transform the envelope of an AM signal the way this lag network transforms a d-c signal, then we must find a network with the characteristics in Fig. 9-10c. We shall attend to this problem now.

Design of AM Compensation Networks

The problem of synthesizing a network having the frequency characteristics specified by Eq. (9-9) has a number of solutions. The most straightforward and also mathematically most attractive approach is by means of the *method of frequency transformation.*

This method is basically very simple and ingenious. As the equations

$$G_m(j\omega) \approx G[j(\omega \pm \omega_c)]$$

must be approximately satisfied at and around the frequencies $\omega = \mp\omega_c$, we need only find a frequency function

$$W = W(\omega)$$

satisfying the requirement

$$G(jW) \approx G[j(\omega \pm \omega_c)] \qquad \text{for } \omega \text{ at and around } \mp\omega_c \qquad (9\text{-}10)$$

If such a function can be found, then it follows directly from (9-9) that $G(jW)$ must indeed qualify as a candidate for $G_m(j\omega)$.

It is clear that we can find an infinite number of W functions that would satisfy this rather easy-to-meet requirement. *If, however, we impose the added restriction that the resulting frequency-transfer function $G(jW)$ must be physically realizable by means of passive RLC elements, then our choice will be considerably thinned out.* Even so, we have a wide choice, and we shall settle here for the following specific W function, which not only meets the above two requirements but also results in very simple network configurations. We choose

$$W(\omega) \triangleq \frac{\omega}{2}\left(1 - \frac{\omega_c^2}{\omega^2}\right) \qquad (9\text{-}11)$$

The behavior of this function versus ω is sketched in Fig. 9-11. In particular, we note the linearity at and around the frequencies $\pm\omega_c$. We have

$$W(\omega) = \frac{\omega}{2}\left(1 - \frac{\omega_c^2}{\omega^2}\right) = \frac{\omega}{2}\left(1 - \frac{\omega_c}{\omega}\right)\left(1 + \frac{\omega_c}{\omega}\right)$$

For *narrow* bands around $\omega = \pm\omega_c$, the factors $(1 \pm \omega_c/\omega)$ are approximately equal to 2, and we thus get

$$W(\omega) \approx \omega \mp \omega_c \qquad \text{for } \omega \text{ at and around } \pm\omega_c \qquad (9\text{-}12)$$

This certainly proves that Eq. (9-10) is satisfied. Let us illustrate with the lag network in Fig. 9-10.

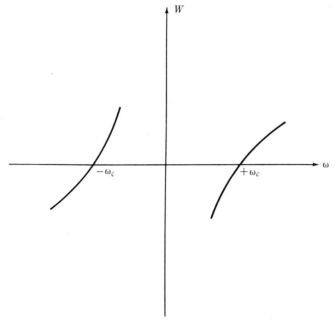

Fig. 9-11   Behavior of function (9-11) around the carrier frequency.

We had the FTF for this network

$$G(j\omega) = \frac{1 + j\omega}{1 + 10j\omega}$$ (9-13)

Therefore,

$$G(jW) = \frac{1 + j(\omega/2)(1 - \omega_c^2/\omega^2)}{1 + j10(\omega/2)(1 - \omega_c^2/\omega^2)}$$ (9-14)

Equation (9-12) guarantees that this expression reduces to

$$G(jW) \approx \frac{1 + j(\omega \mp \omega_c)}{1 + j10(\omega \mp \omega_c)} \qquad \text{for } \omega \text{ at and around } \pm\omega_c$$

We thus conclude: *The transfer function $G(jW)$ behaves at and around $\omega = \pm\omega_c$ exactly as $G(j\omega)$ behaves at and around $\omega = 0$.*

In accordance with Eq. (9-9), $G(jW)$ therefore qualifies as a candidate for $G_m(j\omega)$, *provided we can build the corresponding network.*

We thus are forced to provide an answer to the following question:
Does the frequency transformation

$$W(\omega) \triangleq \frac{\omega}{2}\left(1 - \frac{\omega_c^2}{\omega^2}\right)$$

define a physically realizable network?

To find out, let us return to the example with the lag network. The only
impedance element that will change as a result of the frequency transformation is
the capacitor. Its impedance will change from

$$Z(j\omega) = \frac{1}{j\omega C}$$

in Eq. (9-13) to

$$Z(jW) = \frac{1}{jWC} = \frac{1}{j(\omega/2)(1 - \omega_c^2/\omega^2)C}$$

in Eq. (9-14).

The last expression can be slightly rewritten to

$$Z(jW) = \frac{1}{j\omega\dfrac{C}{2} + \dfrac{1}{j\omega(2/C\omega_c^2)}} \tag{9-15}$$

We immediately recognize this to be the impedance of a *parallel* combination
of a capacitor and an inductor having, respectively, the capacitance and inductance
values

$$C_1 \triangleq \frac{C}{2}$$

$$L_1 \triangleq \frac{2}{C\omega_c^2} \tag{9-16}$$

We conclude therefore that the network shown in Fig. 9-12 has approximately
the same frequency characteristics around $\omega = \pm\omega_c$ as the network in Fig. 9-10
has around $\omega = 0$.

Note that the inductance L_1 will vary with the carrier frequency. For
example, let us assume that we work with a 400-cps carrier. Then we have

$$L_1 = \frac{2}{100 \times 10^{-6}(2\pi400)^2}$$

$$= 0.003171 = 3.171 \text{ millihenrys}$$

It is of great practical significance to realize that networks of the type just designed
must be *exactly* tuned. In the given example, the inductance must be 3.171
millihenrys, *not* 3.181. This would mean an approximate error of 0.3 percent,
resulting in a circuit tuned for a frequency of $400 - 0.15$ percent $= 399.4$ cps.

An error of 0.6 cps does not seem to warrant a lot of fuss. But realize that
0.6 cps corresponds to about 4 rad/sec, and this is *eight times* the low-frequency

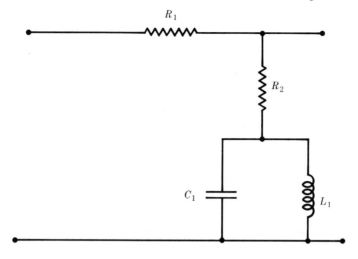

$R_1 = 90 \ k\Omega$

$R_2 = 10 \ k\Omega$

$C_1 = \dfrac{C}{2} = 50 \ \mu f$

$L_1 = \dfrac{2}{C\omega_c^2} = 3.171 \ mh$

Fig. 9-12   Notch filter for example in text.

band of 0.5 rad/sec shown in Fig. 9-10*b*.   It may be a worthwhile exercise for the reader to determine to what accuracy this circuit must be tuned and what component accuracy this would entail.

We tabulated in Chap. 7 (Fig. 7-19) a number of simple *RC* networks which proved useful for compensation of unmodulated control systems.   Using the technique just outlined, they can all be transformed for use as AM compensation networks simply by replacing the capacitors with the L_1C_1 parallel combination. Such networks are sometimes referred to as *notch filters*.

9-3.3   A DESIGN EXAMPLE

Description of System

We shall conclude our discussion of AM systems by working in some detail the following example.

The example is somewhat lengthy, but we believe it will be a worthwhile exercise for the following reasons:

1. The system is exceedingly important in today's space-oriented technology.
2. It incorporates components that work on AM signals.
3. It is basically nonlinear.
4. It is of the MIMO type, with cross coupling (interaction) between the channels.

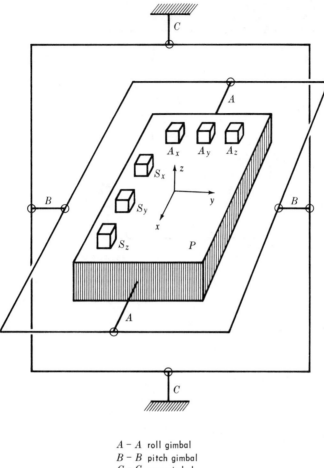

$A - A$ roll gimbal
$B - B$ pitch gimbal
$C - C$ yaw gimbal

Fig. 9-13   Inertial platform.

The control system, which evidently incorporates many of the things we have been discussing in this and previous chapters, is depicted in Fig. 9-13 and contains as its basic element a *stable inertial* platform P.   The platform is to be kept fixed in *inertial space*—which, in the strictest sense, means a coordinate system *xyz* fixed relative to the stars.   Such a platform is a basic requirement in all our present-day so-called *inertial navigational systems,* which find use in submarines, ships, aircraft, and space vehicles.   The objective of the platform, which is isolated from the vehicle structure by a three-axis gimbal system, is to carry three *orthogonally oriented* accelerometers A_x, A_y, and A_z, which measure the three components of the vehicle acceleration in inertial space.   If we know these three acceleration components (plus the initial position and velocity), it is possible to integrate the accelerations twice and obtain the vehicle position in the *inertial coordinate system* as a function of time. Corrections must be made for the gravitational acceleration, which the accelerometers cannot distinguish from the true vehicle acceleration, but this is a fine point that we shall avoid getting involved in here. Our basic concern will be to design a control system that will keep the platform fixed, independent of the vehicle movements, in relationship to the inertial reference system *xyz*.

The basic components in this control system are the three platform-based *sensors* S_x, S_y, and S_z and the three *torquers* T_A, T_B, and T_C. The sensors (to be described later) are orthogonally oriented and sense, respectively, any angular rotations around the inertial axes *x*, *y*, and *z*. The torquers are connected via gear trains to each gimbal axis and upon command, can exert torques on each gimbal.

We rather arbitrarily have named the three gimbal axes "roll," "pitch," and "yaw." Figure 9-14 depicts how the roll torquer is mounted. The pitch and yaw torquers are mounted in a similar manner in relation to their respective gimbals.

After an initial alignment of the platform with the *xyz* system, the control system must be capable of keeping the platform in this position. Using our earlier-defined terminology (see Chap. 6), the system thus can be classified as a three-input, three-output *regulator*. It would be nice if we could consider each channel separately by assuming *noninteraction*. This would mean that the roll torquer T_A would respond only to commands from the *x* sensor S_x, the pitch torquer T_B to commands from S_y, etc. In effect, this *is* actually the case when the gimbals are oriented as shown in Fig. 9-13. Note that all three gimbal axes in this figure are lined up with the *x*, *y*, and *z* axes, respectively; i.e., the gimbal axes are *orthogonal*.

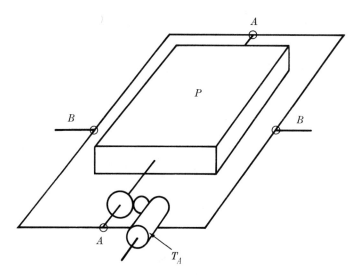

Fig. 9-14 Torquer arrangement.

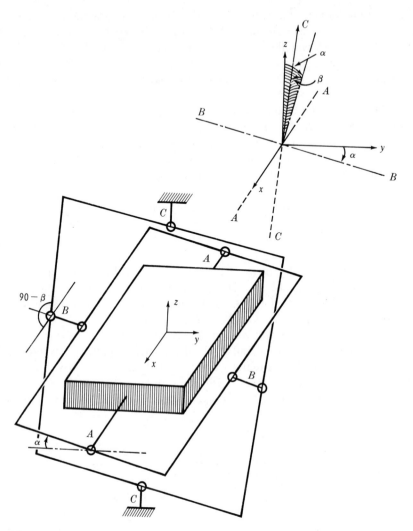

Fig. 9-15   Gimbal geometry.

Quite clearly, this can *only* happen for *one* particular orientation of the vehicle structure.   When the vehicle maneuvers, the gimbal axes generally will *not* remain orthogonal.   Figure 9-15 illustrates the gimbal geometry for a more general vehicle position.   The platform is still aligned with the *xyz* inertial systems, *but the three gimbal axes are no longer orthogonal.*   We can consider the new gimbal position to be a result of two independent rotations in the following sequence:

The system rotates first through the angle α around the *AA* axis, followed by a rotation through the angle β around the *BB* axis.

We note that in the new position, only the roll axis still keeps the initial alignment with respect to the inertial coordinate system xyz.

This resulting "misalignment" will have significant bearing, of course, upon the ability of each individual torquer to control the angular position of the platform with respect to the *xyz* system. For example, in the original alignment, the *A*, *B*, and *C* torquers could independently control the rotations around the *x*, *y*, and *z* axes, respectively. Assume, for instance, that the vehicle maneuvers into a new position, characterized by

$$\alpha = 90°$$

$$\beta = 0°$$

In this position, the "pitch" and "yaw" channels obviously change roles. Or consider the case when $\beta = 90°$. This means that the "roll" and "yaw" axes are *colinear*. How should the control system know how to "untangle" this situation? We can unravel this rather complex situation quite simply by making use of some well-known facts concerning motions of a rigid body, i.e., the platform.

In our following discussion, let us make the reasonable assumption that the platform turning rates are considerably faster than the turning rates of the vehicle; i.e., we shall consider the angles α and β as *constants*. For instance, the vehicle turning rates may be of the order of 1 cps, at the most, whereas the platform control loops are so stiff (for accuracy reasons) that the platform speeds may be as high as 50 cps.

In the short time interval dt, it is assumed that the platform turns through the angles $d\varphi_x$, $d\varphi_y$, and $d\varphi_z$, as measured around the *x*, *y*, and *z* axes (and sensed by the sensors S_x, S_y, and S_z).

The angular rates $\dot\varphi_x = d\varphi_x/dt$, $\dot\varphi_y = d\varphi_y/dt$, and $\dot\varphi_z = d\varphi_z/dt$, constitute the components of the rotation vector

$$\dot{\boldsymbol{\varphi}}_{\text{iner}} \triangleq \begin{bmatrix} \dot\varphi_x \\ \dot\varphi_y \\ \dot\varphi_z \end{bmatrix}$$

Each component in this vector represents the angular rotation rate along the inertial axes *x*, *y*, and *z*, respectively.

As viewed from the nonorthogonal coordinate system formed by the *A*, *B*, and *C* axes, the platform-rotation vector has the value

$$\dot{\boldsymbol{\varphi}}_{\text{gim}} \triangleq \begin{bmatrix} \dot\varphi_A \\ \dot\varphi_B \\ \dot\varphi_C \end{bmatrix}$$

In analogy to the previous case, the components represent the rotations around the axes *A*, *B*, and *C*.

If, as assumed, the two coordinate systems do not move relative to each other, *the two rotation vectors must have the same magnitudes.* We thus can obtain the relations between the two sets of components in each coordinate system by direct projection. For example, consider the component $\dot{\varphi}_A$. As seen from Fig. 9-15, the only component of the vector $\dot{\boldsymbol{\varphi}}_{\text{iner}}$ that has a projection along the A axis is $\dot{\varphi}_x$. We thus get

$$\dot{\varphi}_A = \dot{\varphi}_x$$

By projection along the B and C axes, we similarly obtain

$$\dot{\varphi}_B = \dot{\varphi}_y \cos \alpha - \dot{\varphi}_z \sin \alpha$$

$$\dot{\varphi}_C = \dot{\varphi}_x \sin \beta + \dot{\varphi}_y \sin \alpha \cos \beta + \dot{\varphi}_z \cos \alpha \cos \beta$$

We can summarize these equations in vector form:

$$\dot{\boldsymbol{\varphi}}_{\text{gim}} = \mathbf{T}\dot{\boldsymbol{\varphi}}_{\text{iner}} \tag{9-17}$$

where

$$\mathbf{T} \triangleq \begin{bmatrix} 1 & 0 & 0 \\ 0 & \cos \alpha & -\sin \alpha \\ \sin \beta & \sin \alpha \cos \beta & \cos \alpha \cos \beta \end{bmatrix} \tag{9-18}$$

Note that for $\alpha = \beta = 0$, $\mathbf{T}$ equals $\mathbf{I}$. This corresponds to the initial vehicle position when the two coordinate systems are perfectly aligned with each other.

As the sensors sense the rotations with respect to the xyz coordinate system and as the torquers actually are providing control action in the ABC system, it becomes necessary to "mix" the command signals between sensors and torquers in the manner indicated by the $\mathbf{T}$ matrix. This signal mixing is accomplished by means of so-called *resolvers*, to be discussed later.

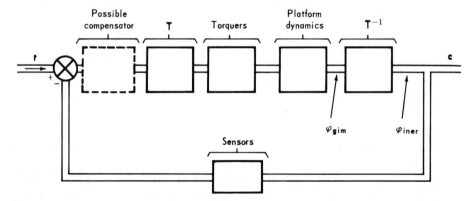

Fig. 9-16 The platform system can be considered a MIMO regulator (three inputs, three outputs).

We are now in a position to sketch the overall control loop. This has been done in Fig. 9-16. The following comments can be made about this diagram:

1. The reference input vector $\mathbf{r} = \mathbf{0}$.

2. The matrix $\mathbf{T}^{-1}$ must be included as the output vector $\mathbf{c}$ is defined as the three-vector

$$\mathbf{c} = \boldsymbol{\varphi}_{\text{iner}} \triangleq \begin{bmatrix} \varphi_x \\ \varphi_y \\ \varphi_z \end{bmatrix}$$

but the torquer output is the vector

$$\boldsymbol{\varphi}_{\text{gim}} \triangleq \begin{bmatrix} \varphi_A \\ \varphi_B \\ \varphi_C \end{bmatrix}$$

3. As the angles α and β are functions of time, the overall system will be describable in terms of differential equations with *time-variant* parameters. At a first glance, this would seem to prohibit our using Laplace-transform techniques in analyzing the system. Fortunately, things do not get that bad. The reason is that, although α and β both are time-variant, they vary, as has already been pointed out, relatively slowly in comparison with the platform rates. In view of this situation, it is perfectly permissible to consider α and β as *constants* when studying the platform dynamics—thus enabling us to make use of transform calculus.

It is necessary at this juncture to take a more detailed look at the fundamental components of the system.

The Sensors

The inertial sensors constitute the most critical components of the overall platform control loops. They should be able to sense, *in a completely closed environment*, accurately, and for sustained periods of time, specified directions in space and to provide recognizable output signals telling of possible deviations.

The gyroscope,† or gyro for short, constitutes the heart of all inertial sensors. An exact and exhaustive study of gyro dynamics is extremely complex. Volumes have been written on the topic. The complexity of the problem derives from the fact that the differential equations describing the gyro are nonlinear. When gyros are operated as platform sensors, their motions are very amplitude-restricted and it is possible to describe their dynamics with linear equations, which greatly simplifies the analysis.

† "Turn watcher," freely translated from Greek.

From classical mechanics, we borrow the basic law of motion of a rigid body

$$\boldsymbol{\tau} = \dot{\mathbf{h}} \tag{9-19}$$

The vector $\mathbf{h}$ is the angular-*momentum* vector, and the vector $\boldsymbol{\tau}$ is the moment (resulting from external forces) acting on the body. The law is basic, and it is important to add that both $\boldsymbol{\tau}$ and $\mathbf{h}$ *are measured in relation to an inertial fix.*

If the resulting external moment is zero, then we have

$$\dot{\mathbf{h}} = \mathbf{0}$$

Thus

$$\mathbf{h} = \mathbf{h}(0) = \text{const} \tag{9-20}$$

This is the law of "conservation of angular momentum." A symmetrical wheel, characterized by a moment of inertia I_s about the spin axis and spinning around its symmetry axis with an angular speed of ω_s rad/sec, has an angular-momentum vector of magnitude

$$|\mathbf{h}| = I_s \omega_s \tag{9-21}$$

directed along the axis of rotation as shown in Fig. 9-17. If no external torque is acting on the wheel, then Eq. (9-20) tells us that the axis of the wheel will retain its spatial orientation *in an inertial coordinate system.* For example, the axis of our spinning earth always points toward Polaris.

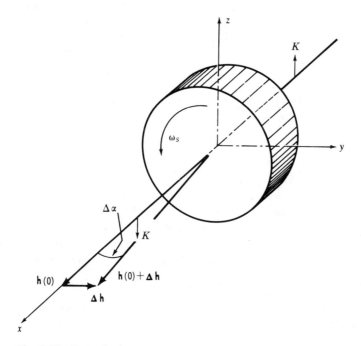

Fig. 9-17   Gyro wheel.

If the wheel is subject to a torque $\boldsymbol{\tau}$ during the short interval Δt, then in accordance with Eq. (9-19), it will experience a change $\boldsymbol{\Delta h}$ in its angular-momentum vector:

$$\boldsymbol{\Delta h} = \boldsymbol{\tau} \, \Delta t \tag{9-22}$$

Consider the torque to be applied under two different conditions:

1. With $\omega_s = 0$, that is, wheel *not* spinning
2. With $\omega_s = $ very large

Assume in both cases that the torque vector is directed along the positive y axis; i.e., we may consider it to be caused by the couple K indicated in Fig. 9-17. As $\boldsymbol{\tau}$ is directed along the y axis, so must $\boldsymbol{\Delta h}$ be.

In the first case, the $\mathbf{h}$ vector changes from $\mathbf{0}$ to $\boldsymbol{\Delta h}$, and the new momentum vector is thus aligned along the y axis, meaning that the wheel now must have a rotation vector along this axis. *Conclusion: The wheel is spinning in the zx plane.*

Consider then the second case. Everything now will be the same as in the first case, with the following exception: The $\mathbf{h}$ vector now will change from $\mathbf{h}(0)$ to $\mathbf{h}(0) + \boldsymbol{\Delta h}$. The latter vector is contained in the xy plane. The new state is reached by the wheel axis turning *in the xy plane* from the original orientation by an angle $\Delta\alpha$:

$$\Delta\alpha = \frac{|\boldsymbol{\Delta h}|}{|\mathbf{h}|} = \frac{\tau \, \Delta t}{I_s \omega_s} = \frac{\tau}{I_s \omega_s} \, \Delta t \tag{9-23}$$

We note that the wheel axis turns in the xy plane†—*precesses*—at a constant precession rate

$$\omega_p = \frac{\Delta\alpha}{\Delta t} = \frac{\tau}{I_s \omega_s} \tag{9-24}$$

If the couple is removed, then the precession ceases, with the gyro axis remaining in the new position.

Whereas the average person will accept the response in the first case as being quite "natural," he will usually not anticipate the second one. This is what makes a gyro such an intriguing toy.

The precession rate ω_p can be made arbitrarily small by choosing a high product $I_s \omega_s$; that is, the "unwillingness" of the gyro to move under the influence of a torque is greater the higher the angular momentum it possesses.

If we could mount a gyro in a manner such that the resulting torque acting on it were exactly zero, then it would retain its orientation indefinitely and we would truly have an excellent inertial "pointer." However, in a practical case, we cannot balance out all torques perfectly; the gyro, as a result, will experience a slight precession rate; i.e., it "drifts."

---

† The statement is not *exactly* accurate. The gyro axis will dip a little. Figure 9-18b illustrates the actual situation.

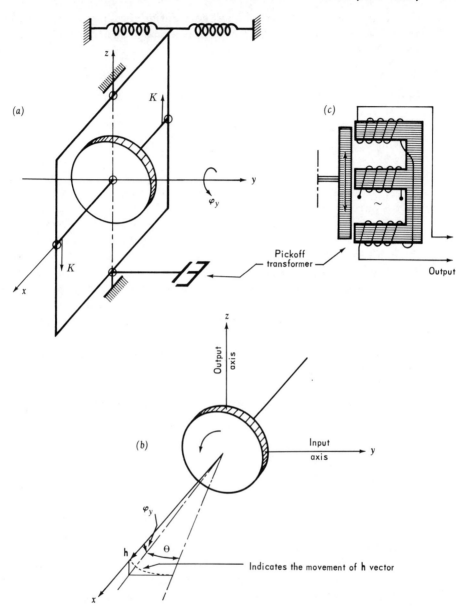

Fig. 9-18   Constrained gyro.

As a sensor, the gyro can be used in a number of different configurations, depending upon the specific job it is intended to do. In general, its axis of sensitivity, or *input axis*, is perpendicular to its spin axis. The *output axis* will then be the third axis in the orthogonal set consisting of the spin axis and the input axis. Figure 9-18a shows a typical arrangement. The *xyz* system is the inertial coordinate system of Fig. 9-13. In this configuration, for instance, it could be used as the sensor S_y in Fig. 9-13.

Used in this manner, it is referred to as a *restrained gyro*. As we shall see, an output signal is obtained as a result of a *displacement of the gyro axis itself*. A *free gyro* is a gyro suspended in a full-freedom gimbal system, and an output here will be obtained as a result of the movement of *the instrument cage* around the inertially fixed gyro.

The restrained gyro works in the following manner: Assume that the platform performs a minute rotation (angle φ_y) around the *y* axis, clockwise as viewed in positive *y* direction. As a result the spin axis is acted upon by the couple *K*, and the resulting torque forces the gyro to precess through the angle θ. We can measure this precession from the pick-off (usually a variant of the E transformer, depicted in Fig. 9-18c), and we thus can sense the initial rotation.

A quantitative treatment follows. We first need to introduce the following symbols:

m_y = moment (torque) of the couple K
$h = \omega_s I_s$ = gyro momentum (as before)
I_y = moment of inertia of gyro + gimbal about y axis (the *input* axis)
I_z = moment of inertia of gyro + gimbal about z axis (the *output* axis)
k_d, k_s = damping and spring coefficients acting on the system around the output axis, measured in newton-meters/radians per second and newton-meters/radians, respectively.

We then have (assuming *small* angles) total angular momentum in y direction

$$h_y = h\theta + I_y \dot{\varphi}_y \tag{9-25}$$

and total angular momentum in z direction

$$h_z = -h\varphi_y + I_z \dot{\theta} \tag{9-26}$$

By application of formula (9-19), we then get

$$m_y = h\dot{\theta} + I_y \ddot{\varphi}_y$$
$$-k_s \theta - k_d \dot{\theta} = -h\dot{\varphi}_y + I_z \ddot{\theta} \tag{9-27}$$

We have obtained a *linear* set of differential equations. This has come about as a consequence of the the assumption of *small* angular deviations.

We Laplace-transform these equations and obtain the transfer functions

$$\frac{\Theta}{\Phi_y} = \frac{sh}{s^2 I_z + s k_d + k_s} \tag{9-28}$$

$$\frac{\Theta}{M_y} = \frac{h}{s I_y (s^2 I_z + s k_d + k_s + h^2/I_y)} \tag{9-29}$$

We have used the symbols

$$\Theta \triangleq \mathscr{L}(\theta)$$
$$\Phi_y \triangleq \mathscr{L}(\varphi_y)$$
$$M_y \triangleq \mathscr{L}(m_y) \quad .$$

The transfer functions (9-28) and (9-29) tell us the full story about the small-angle gyro dynamics. It is of interest to study a few special cases:

case 1 In Eq. (9-28), set $k_d = 0$ and assume also that

$$s^2 I_z \ll k_s$$

This inequality is satisfied for *low*-frequency signals, i.e., when

$$\omega^2 I_z \ll k_s$$

If these conditions are met, then Eq. (9-28) yields

$$\frac{\Theta}{\Phi_y} \approx s \frac{h}{k_s} \tag{9-30}$$

Therefore,

$$\theta \approx \frac{h}{k_s} \dot{\varphi}_y$$

that is, the output angle is proportional to the derivative of the input angle. We refer to this as a *rate gyro*, and we use the signal obtained from the pick-off coil for stabilizing purposes. (Remember how we stabilized the broom!)

case 2 Set $k_s = k_d = 0$. Equation (9-28) now yields

$$\frac{\Theta}{\Phi_y} \approx \frac{h}{sI_z}$$

Hence,

$$\theta \approx \frac{h}{I_z} \int \varphi_y \, dt \tag{9-31}$$

We refer to this as an *integrating gyro*.

case 3 Design the gyro with very high damping k_d. Equation (9-28) then yields

$$\frac{\Theta}{\Phi_y} \approx \frac{h}{k_d}$$

Hence,

$$\theta \approx \frac{h}{k_d} \varphi_y \tag{9-32}$$

The gyro in this case is an *angle indicator*.

A more realistic approximation in this case is to keep the term $s^2 I_z$ but discard the k_s term. We then obtain

$$\frac{\Theta}{\Phi_y} \approx \frac{sh}{s^2 I_z + sk_d} = \frac{h}{k_d} \frac{1}{1 + sT_g} \qquad \text{where } T_g \triangleq \frac{I_z}{k_d} \tag{9-33}$$

In other words: We must figure with a time constant T_g between the φ_y and θ signals.

Gyro dynamics is a very interesting topic, but as we are pressed for time and space, it is necessary for us to move on. For the reader who wants to obtain a deeper insight into inertial sensors the recent treatise by Broxmeyer[3] is recommended.

The Torquer

Before we take a look at the overall control loop, it is necessary to investigate to some depth the dynamics of the torquer. Since the signal as obtained from the gyro sensor is AM-modulated, we shall prefer to make use of an a-c servomotor connected to the platform via a high-ratio gear train. The characteristics of this motor are shown in the torque-speed diagram of Fig. 9-19. The torque-versus-speed curves usually are slightly bent, but it is customary to approximate the curves

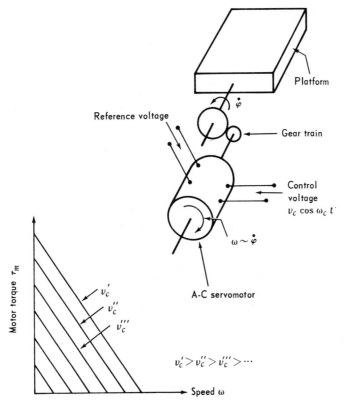

Fig. 9-19   Torque-versus-speed characteristics of servomotor.

with the straight lines

$$\tau_m \approx -k_1\omega + k_2 v_c \tag{9-34}$$

The motor speed ω is proportional to the turning rate of the platform, $\dot{\varphi}$; that is,†

$$\omega \sim \dot{\varphi} \tag{9-35}$$

and if we consider the platform a pure "inertia load," then we also have proportionality between the motor torque τ_m and angular platform acceleration $\ddot{\varphi}$; that is,

$$\tau_m \sim \ddot{\varphi} \tag{9-36}$$

By combining Eqs. (9-34) to (9-36), we obtain the differential equation

$$\ddot{\varphi} + k_3\dot{\varphi} = k_4 v_c \tag{9-37}$$

k_3 and k_4 are constants that are functions of the motor parameters k_1 and k_2, platform inertia and gear ratio.

Upon Laplace transformation, we thus obtain the motor-load transfer function

$$\frac{\Phi}{V_c} = \frac{k_4}{s(s + k_3)} = \frac{K_m}{s(1 + sT_m)} \tag{9-38}$$

It is worthwhile to remember that this transfer function was derived on the basis of following assumptions:

1. Linearized torque-speed curves
2. Inertia-type load

We should add, in passing, that the model has further discrepancies. In the first place, the motor curves in Fig. 9-19 are obtained experimentally by *static* measurement. The voltage is applied to the control winding, and the torque is then measured at various speeds. In reality, a short time interval will elapse between the application of the voltage and the presence of the torque (a torque in any electrical machine is created by the *currents*, not by the voltages), and in many applications, we must take this electrical time delay into account by adding a delay T_e to the transfer function (9-38):

$$\frac{\Phi}{V_c} = \frac{K_m}{s(1 + sT_m)(1 + sT_e)} \tag{9-39}$$

† We have removed the subscript for φ as this theory applies equally well to any one of the A, B, and C axes.

The assumption that the platform behaves like an inertia load does not stand up either under a closer scrutiny. For one thing, we have neglected completely the *reaction torque* set up by the sensor. We remember (see Fig. 9-18) that when the platform is being tilted through the angle φ_y, the gyro experiences the moment m_y. The *negative* value of this same moment is felt of course by the torquer. In general, we cannot neglect this reaction torque, and in principle, it would not meet any difficulties to include it in our analysis. We have left it out in order to obtain simple transfer functions.

The Signal Mixers (Resolvers)

A few paragraphs will be devoted to the device that does the "signal mixing" in Fig. 9-16. What we need† is a component that accepts an input voltage of AM type

$e(t) \cos \omega_c t$

and delivers as an output the voltage

$e(t) \cos \alpha(t) \cos \omega_c t$

or

$e(t) \sin \alpha(t) \cos \omega_c t$

This can be achieved very conveniently in a so-called *resolver*, which basically is a transformer having the secondary winding or windings placed on a *rotational core*.

Consider the arrangement in Fig. 9-20, depicting a transformer having the primary winding P on the stator and the two secondary windings A and B on the rotor. For simplicity, let us assume that all windings have an equal number of turns, and furthermore let us neglect all leakage fluxes. If φ is the total flux created by the primary winding P, only the fractions $\varphi \cos \alpha$ and $\varphi \sin \alpha$ are linked with the A and B windings, respectively. The output voltages from these two windings are thus, respectively,

$e(t) \cos \alpha(t) \cos \omega_c t$

$e(t) \sin \alpha(t) \cos \omega_c t$

The resolver is physically located at the gimbal bearing so that it rotates through the required angle α.

It is necessary, as evidenced from Eq. (9-17), that we also be in a position to generate signals of the type

$e(t) \cos \alpha(t) \sin \beta(t) \cos \omega_c t$

This, of course, is accomplished by using the output voltage from the α resolver as the input voltage to the β resolver.

---

† Compare Eq. (9-17).

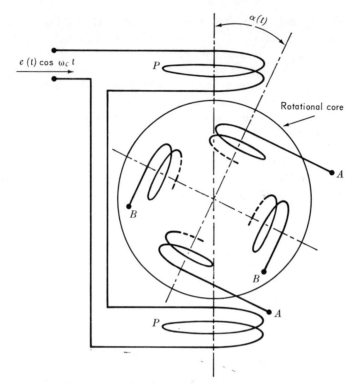

Fig. 9-20   Resolver.

The Complete System

We are now in a position to give the block diagram for the overall platform system. We have indicated in this diagram (Fig. 9-21) the nature of the signals throughout the system.

A system of this complexity is a typical candidate for analysis by simulation or some other computer method, to be discussed in later chapters.   We also must add that, in addition to those simplifications that we already have admitted, there are other important features that are not included in the diagram in Fig. 9-21. The most important one is a nonnegligible *cross coupling* between the channels that is due to the fact that the gyro in Fig. 9-18 *will deliver an output for input rotations other than those along the input axis*.   It is obvious that the restrained gyro in Fig. 9-18 will provide an output for rotations around the z axis as such a rotation will move the platform in relation to the *fixed* gyro and thus cause a false output. The fact that this gyro obviously will provide an output for rotations around *both* the y and the z axes brings up an interesting question: Why do we designate the y axis, and not the z axis, as the "input axis"?   We shall leave this question for the student to ponder.

These cross couplings will introduce additional loops the stability of which one

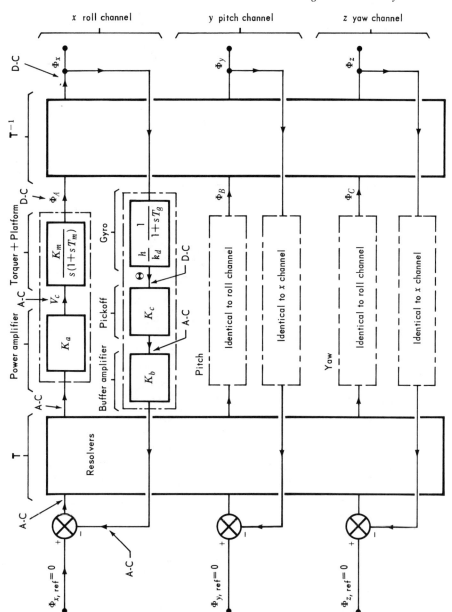

Fig. 9-21 Complete platform-control system.

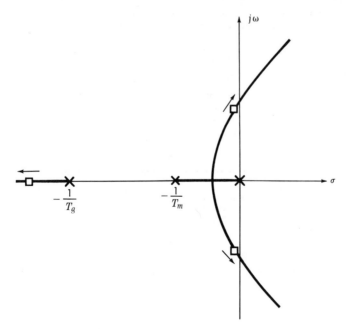

Fig. 9-22 Root loci for the *x* roll channel.

must check, and they also bring into still clearer focus the need for computer-assisted analysis methods. Generally speaking, one should try to exhaust all conventional means for analysis before one resorts to computers. We shall not attempt a complete analysis of the system at this time. However, before we leave it, we make a few comments as to possible compensation.

We note that if all interactions between channels are neglected (and this is exactly true† for the *x* channel), we can write the open-loop transfer function in the form

$$H(s)G(s) = \frac{K}{s(1 + sT_m)(1 + sT_g)}$$

Figure 9-22 depicts the root-locus picture for this system. We note that the two time constants tend to make the system unstable. There is a definite need for *lead* compensation. Using the lead network 4 in Fig. 7-19, we may try to place the compensation zero on top of the pole at $-1/T_m$. Physically, it would be convenient to place the network between the resolver and the power amplifier. It thus is necessary to design the network as a notch filter, which would mean that the capacitor would be replaced with the L_1C_1 combination along rules outlined in the previous section. The reader is urged to work out the details of this suggested compensation procedure and, in particular, to note its effect on the root loci.

† See also Exercise 9-1.

9-4 SAMPLED-DATA SYSTEMS

In the introductory part of the present chapter, reasons were given for the fact that data sampling or pulse-amplitude modulation sometimes must be employed in control-system design. Time sharing of transmission facilities and/or incorporation of digital computers as part of the control loop were mentioned as the main reasons.

These are examples of control systems with *inherent* sampling. There are many control systems where the job conceivably could be done by using analog-type methods but where it can be done so much better if sampling or discretizing of certain signals is employed. As a typical example, consider the problem of automatic positioning of a precision tool over a large output range. Assume that we would like to be able to control the position of a drill table to within an accuracy of 0.001 in. throughout a total range of maybe 100 in.† The necessary resolution in this example is thus 1:100,000 *over the total range of operation*. To detect the output position by means of an analog device, e.g., a potentiometer, would be a practical impossibility. There is, however, no difficulty in solving this problem by using digitally encoded output sensors.

9-4.i THE SAMPLING PROCESS—SPECTRUM ANALYSIS

In this presentation, we shall limit attention to sampling processes with constant sampling rate $f_s = 1/T_s$ cps. (In certain rare cases, there are advantages to using a variable sampling rate or multiple sampling frequencies.) Figure 9-23 depicts a signal $e(t)$ which is subject to periodic sampling, resulting in the spiky signal $e_s(t)$. This signal may be thought of as being generated by the modulation function $p(t)$ shown in Fig. 9-23c operating on the unmodulated signal $e(t)$ in the product fashion

$$e_s(t) = e(t)p(t) \tag{9-40}$$

Physically, we can obtain the sampled signal quite easily by switching the unsampled signal using the *sampling switch* shown in Fig. 9-23d. The switch operates periodically and is closed for Δ sec during each cycle.

In the case of AM signals, we found it exceedingly helpful to study the spectral composition of the modulated signal. That will apply here also. The spikiness of the sampled signal implies that we should find signal energy at high frequencies. We proceed with a quantitative analysis of the spectrum.

First, we consider the spectrum of the *unmodulated* signal $e(t)$. For reasons earlier discussed, we shall assume that all energy is concentrated in a low-frequency band of bandwidth BW (Fig. 9-7).

As the modulation function $p(t)$ is a *periodic* function, we know (see Appendix B) that it has a *discrete* spectrum; and using Eq. (B-6) in Appendix B, we thus write

$$p(t) = \sum_{\nu=-\infty}^{+\infty} P(j\omega_\nu)e^{j\omega_\nu t} \tag{9-41}$$

† Similar accuracy requirements are not uncommon in the machine-tool industry.

(a)

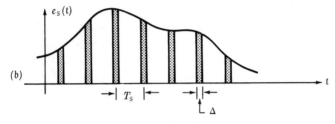

(b)

T_s Δ

(c)

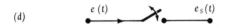

(d)

Fig. 9-23   Sampled-data signals.

where the discrete frequencies ω_ν are obtained from

$$\omega_\nu = \nu\omega_s = \nu\frac{2\pi}{T_s} \qquad \text{for } \nu = 0, \pm 1, \pm 2, \ldots$$

The pulse-modulated signal $e_s(t)$ thus can be written

$$e_s(t) = e(t) \sum_{\nu=-\infty}^{+\infty} P(j\omega_\nu)e^{j\omega_\nu t} \qquad (9\text{-}42)$$

The Fourier coefficients $P(j\omega_\nu)$ have been derived in Appendix B [formula (B-10)] for this special type of periodic function.
We obtained

$$P(j\omega_\nu) = \frac{1}{\pi\nu}\sin\nu\alpha\pi \qquad \text{for } \nu = 0, \pm 1, \pm 2, \ldots \text{ and } \alpha \triangleq \frac{\Delta}{T_s} \qquad (9\text{-}43)$$

We are concerned mostly with situations that are characterized by

$$\Delta \ll T_s$$

that is,

$$\alpha \ll 1$$

and in Appendix B (Fig. B-2) is shown how, in this case, the spectral coefficients diminish very slowly with increasing ν.

Note that if $\alpha \ll 1$, we can write Eq. (9-43)

$$P(j\omega_\nu) \approx \frac{1}{\pi\nu}\, \nu\alpha\pi = \alpha \qquad\qquad (9\text{-}44)$$

This approximate equation is valid at least for those ν values that make the angle $\nu\alpha\pi \ll 1$, that is, for ν values satisfying

$$\nu \ll \frac{1}{\alpha\pi}$$

In the limit $\alpha \to 0$, the formula therefore applies to all *finite* ν.

Equation (9-44) implies that the spectral components are *independent of* ν, that is, the spectrum is *flat*.

We are now in a position to determine the spectrum for $e_s(t)$. By Fourier-transforming (9-42), we get directly

$$E_s(j\omega) \stackrel{\Delta}{=} \mathscr{F}\left[e(t)\sum_{\nu=-\infty}^{+\infty} P(j\omega_\nu)e^{j\omega_\nu t}\right]$$

$$= \mathscr{F}\sum_{\nu=-\infty}^{+\infty} P(j\omega_\nu)e(t)e^{j\omega_\nu t} = \sum_{\nu=-\infty}^{+\infty} \mathscr{F}[P(j\omega_\nu)e(t)e^{j\omega_\nu t}]$$

$$= \sum_{\nu=-\infty}^{+\infty} P(j\omega_\nu)\mathscr{F}[e(t)e^{j\omega_\nu t}] = \sum_{\nu=-\infty}^{+\infty} P(j\omega_\nu)E[j(\omega - \omega_\nu)] \qquad (9\text{-}45)$$

We already have pointed out in connection with Eq. (9-5) that the terms $E[j(\omega - \omega_\nu)]$ represent the low-frequency, or d-c, spectrum translated up to frequency ω_ν, and Eq. (9-45) therefore signifies that the sampled signal $e_s(t)$ contains energy in bands *around every multiple* (including zero) *of the sampling frequency* ω_s, *in proportion to the factors* $P(j\omega_\nu)$. The situation is illustrated in Fig. 9-24. As we predicted, we find the energy of the sampled signal spread out over a very wide frequency band.

In the specific limit case $\alpha \to 0$, we concluded that all $P(j\omega_\nu)$ are equal, and therefore all energy "bumps" in Fig. 9-24 are of equal size. However, as $P(j\omega_\nu)$ equals α (Eq. 9-44) and as α vanishes, each bump has a vanishing amplitude.

The practical significance of our findings is very important:

1. The tremendous bandwidth of the sampled signal will seriously limit our ability to transmit it.
2. The energy content of a sampled signal is very minute. This, of course, can be

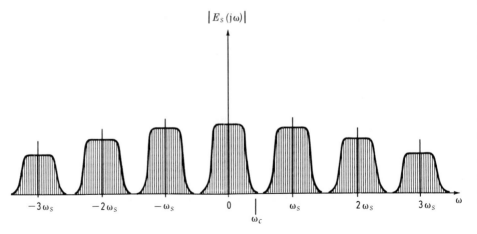

Fig. 9-24   Fourier spectrum of sampled-data signal.

realized immediately, as we have sliced up a signal of finite energy into a sequence of infinitesimal "time slices." (Take an infinitesimal sample slice of a finite number of loaves and you have hardly got a mouthful.)

9-4.2 DEMODULATION OF SAMPLED-DATA SIGNAL

It is obvious that the sampled signal $e_s(t)$ cannot be used directly, as it is in the control loop. For one thing, we have just concluded that it contains too little energy to be directly useful. For instance, when a stream of data is received via a multiplexer, the signal in each channel will appear in the form $e_s(t)$. Before making use of these data, it is necessary to *reconstruct* the analog signal from which they were obtained in the first place. This process is referred to as *demodulation*. An interesting question now presents itself: Under what conditions can a perfect reconstruction be accomplished? In other words, is it possible on the basis of $e_s(t)$ to reconstruct an exact replica of $e(t)$?

We feel intuitively that the *sampling rate* must have great bearing upon this question. We realize from purely physical reasoning that there must be some *lower* limit to ω_s. If we sample at too low a rate, we quite obviously are bound to lose some information. There should not, however, be any *upper* limit, for the simple reason that the higher the sampling rate we use, the closer the pulse train $e_s(t)$ will resemble $e(t)$.

The spectral diagram in Fig. 9-24 gives us an immediate clue as to the lowest possible ω_s we can use. Each "bump" in this spectrum has a shape identical to that of the unmodulated signal $e(t)$. It is possible (at least theoretically) to send the signal $e_s(t)$ through a *low-pass* filter and filter out all the energy maxima except the one around zero frequency—*if and only if there is a free spacing between the energy bands in the $e_s(t)$ spectrum.* If it were not a free spacing, the different bands would overlap and mix and, in the process, get their initial shape distorted, and we would lose information about $e(t)$.

If ω_c is the highest frequency† at which $e(t)$ contains any energy, we conclude that the lowest theoretical limit for ω_s is $2\omega_c$. This is sometimes referred to as *Shannon's sampling theorem.*

In a practical case, there is no sense in "pushing the limit" unless we are absolutely forced to by circumstances, and as a rule, one should choose as high a sampling rate as is practically possible with all considerations taken into account.

In accordance with the above discussion, the perfect demodulator should remove all upper side bands from the sampled signal and leave the lowest one unaffected. There exists a number of solutions to this problem, all more or less approximate, and we want to mention at this time the so-called *data extrapolators*, or *data holds*, since they are by far the most commonly used. Figure 9-25 demonstrates the principle of these devices. In the simplest one, the so-called *zero-order*

† Defined in Fig. 9-24.

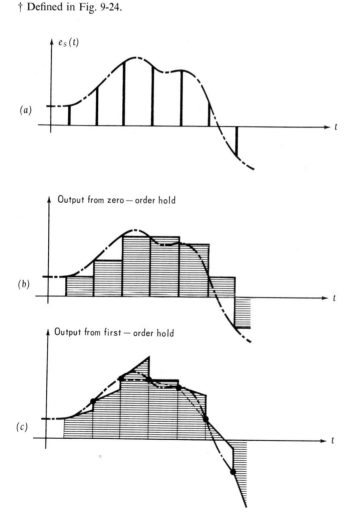

Fig. 9-25 Zero- and first-order data reconstruction.

hold depicted in Fig. 9-25*b*, we simply let the demodulated signal at any moment of time take on the value of the last-received sample. In the *first-order hold*, we let the *last two* samples determine the signal. The graphs should be self-explanatory. Generally, in an *n*th-order hold, we base our extrapolation on the last $n + 1$ samples. The actual instrumentation of the data hold increases rapidly in complexity with the order, and there are few applications that go beyond the zero order. Combining this simple demodulator with a high sampling rate usually provides satisfactory performance.

9-4.3 DIFFERENCE EQUATIONS AND THE SAMPLING PROCESS

Difference equations play as important a role in the analysis of sampled-data systems as do differential equations in the analysis of continuous-data systems. For this reason, we now offer a brief discussion of difference equations, which also will serve as an incentive for the introduction of *z* transforms in the next section. It is possible that the student is unfamiliar with such equations, and we therefore shall illustrate their usage by working a sampled-data system in some detail. We shall study, in parallel, a continuous-data system to illustrate the similarities and dissimilarities between the continuous and the discrete cases. The two systems are depicted in Fig. 9-26. The controlled plant in both cases is represented by a simple integrator. Except for the fact that in one system the error signal is sampled (and reconstructed in a zero-order data hold), the two systems are identical. Note, by the way, that the continuous-data system can be obtained from the sampled one by letting the sampling frequency approach infinity. Let us first turn

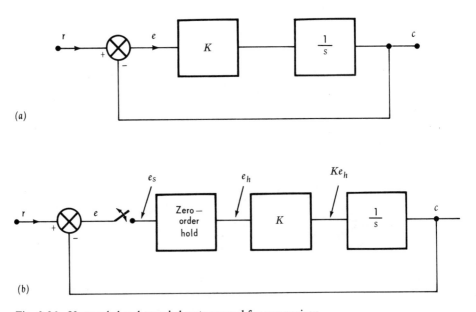

Fig. 9-26   Unsampled and sampled systems used for comparison.

our attention to the unsampled system, which is characterized by the set of equations

$$r - c = e$$
$$\dot{c} = Ke \tag{9-46}$$

resulting in the following first-order differential equation for the output c:

$$\dot{c} + Kc = Kr \tag{9-47}$$

We know that this equation has the solution

$$c(t) = c(0)e^{-Kt} + \int_0^t e^{-K(t-\tau)}Kr(\tau)\,d\tau \tag{9-48}$$

We remind the reader that the first term represents the *transient* part and the second term the *driven* part of the total solution. For example, if we assume zero initial conditions, that is, $c(0) = 0$, and a unit-step input, that is, $r(\tau) = 1$, then we get

$$c(t) = \int_0^t e^{-K(t-\tau)}K\,d\tau = e^{-Kt}\int_0^t Ke^{K\tau}\,d\tau = 1 - e^{-Kt} \tag{9-49}$$

that is, a regular exponential buildup. Consider next the sampled system. The signal Ke_h entering the plant is *piecewise constant*, as illustrated in Fig. 9-27a, and the output from the integrator plant therefore must be *piecewise linear*. The "corners" of the c signal must occur at the sampling moments. It is clear that in this case the output is completely known if we know the signal samples $c_\nu \triangleq c(\nu T_s)$ at these corner points. (We caution the reader *not* to consider this to be generally true for any type of plant. It happens to be the case here because the signal is piecewise *linear*.) We proceed to compute these c_ν values, which in the following discussion we shall refer to as a *discrete-data sequence*. As the signal in Fig. 9-27b is the integral of the one in Fig. 9-27a, we obtain directly

$$c_{\nu+1} = c_\nu + KT_s e_\nu \tag{9-50}$$

This is a *difference equation* relating the signal values at a particular discrete sampling instant $(\nu + 1)T_s$, with the signal values at the preceding one νT_s. We can eliminate the error e_ν by making use of the relation

$$e_\nu = r_\nu - c_\nu$$

and obtain as a result the difference equation

$$c_{\nu+1} = (1 - KT_s)c_\nu + KT_s r_\nu \tag{9-51}$$

The equation is:

1. Linear in c_ν and r_ν
2. Index-invariant; that is, the coefficients for $c_{\nu+1}$, c_ν, and r_ν are independent of ν
3. First-order; that is, $c_{\nu+1}$ depends only on c_ν (not on $c_{\nu-1}$, $c_{\nu-2}$, etc.)

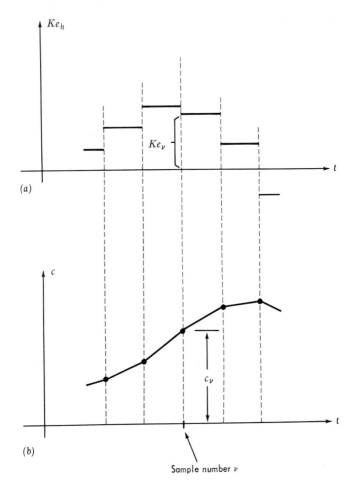

Fig. 9-27   Signals as they appear before and after the plant in Fig. 9-26b.

We can write Eq. (9-51) in the form

$$\frac{c_{\nu+1} - c_{\nu}}{T_s} + Kc_{\nu} = Kr_{\nu} \tag{9-52}$$

The first term in this difference equation is the discrete-case equivalent of the derivative $\dot{c}$ in the continuous-case differential equation, and we note the obvious similarities between Eqs. (9-47) and (9-52).

The solution of a difference equation of the type (9-51) is obtained simply by repeated use of the equation for $\nu = 0, 1, 2, \ldots$. Let us assume that the initial condition c_0 is known, and also the input-data sequence $r_0, r_1, \ldots, r_\nu$. The equation then yields, in repeated sequence,

$$c_1 = (1 - KT_s)c_0 + KT_s r_0$$

$$c_2 = (1 - KT_s)c_1 + KT_s r_1 = (1 - KT_s)^2 c_0 + (1 - KT_s)KT_s r_0 + KT_s r_1$$

$$\cdots\cdots\cdots\cdots\cdots\cdots\cdots\cdots\cdots\cdots\cdots\cdots\cdots\cdots\cdots\cdots\cdots\cdots\cdots$$

$$c_\nu = (1 - KT_s)^\nu c_0 + KT_s \sum_{i=0}^{\nu-1} (1 - KT_s)^{\nu-1-i} r_i \tag{9-53}$$

Again we note the great similarity with the situation in the continuous case, i.e., the solution (9-48). The first term of (9-53) depends only on c_0 and represents the *transient* solution; the second term is a function of the input in the interval $0 < t < \nu T_s$ and therefore gives us the *driven* part of the solution.

[We note, as a matter of interest, that the continuous-data solution (9-48) can be obtained readily from the discrete-data solution (9-53) by letting the sampling rate approach infinity. By letting

$$\nu T_s \to t = \text{the continuous-time parameter}$$

$$\nu \to \infty \qquad \text{and} \qquad c_0 \to c(0)$$

the first term in (9-53) takes on the value

$$\lim_{\nu \to \infty} [c_0(1 - KT_s)^\nu] = \lim_{\nu \to \infty} \left[c(0)\left(1 - \frac{Kt}{\nu}\right)^\nu \right]$$

$$= c(0) \lim_{\nu \to \infty} \left(1 - \frac{Kt}{\nu}\right)^\nu = c(0)e^{-Kt}$$

which obviously is identical with the first term in solution (9-48). The student is asked to verify similarly the identity of the second terms.]

Just as the solution (9-48) in the continuous-data case informs us about response type, static accuracy, stability, etc., the corresponding sampled-data solution helps us to gain insight in regard to the same features in the sampled-data system. As a rule, the necessary computations become more involved numerically. Let us illustrate!

Stability

The stability of the system is determined by the ability of the system to recover from an initial disturbance c_0, and therefore, as in the continuous-data case, we must turn our attention to the *transient* part of the solution. In the continuous case, the stability is ensured since the eigenvalue $\lambda = -K$ is located in the left-hand s plane for all positive K values. Things are not that clear-cut in the discrete case, and here we now encounter the first basic difference between the two systems.

For stability, we must require that the term

$$\lim_{\nu \to \infty} [(1 - KT_s)^\nu c_0]$$

tends to zero *for any finite* c_0, which, of course, can happen if and only if

$$\lim_{v \to \infty} [(1 - KT_s)^v] \to 0$$

Obviously, stability is ensured if $|1 - KT_s| < 1$; that is, we must require

$$0 < KT_s < 2 \tag{9-54}$$

We thus conclude that stability is guaranteed if

$$T_s < \frac{2}{K} \tag{9-55}$$

This example teaches us an important (and general) characteristic of sampled-data control systems—they become unstable if the sampling rate is too low. This, of course, is quite understandable from a physical point of view, as a low sampling rate basically deprives the system of up-to-date feedback during the long intervals between samples.

Response Type

Other interesting differences between the sampled and unsampled systems come into focus as we study the effect of the sampling rates on the response in general. To illustrate, let us compute the output of the above system for a unit-step input, which we shall apply just before the zero sampling instant. We shall assume zero initial conditions for c; that is, $c_0 = 0$. As all $r_i = 1$ for $i = 0, 1, 2, \ldots, v - 1$, Eq. (9-53) yields

$$c_v = KT_s \sum_{i=0}^{v-1} (1 - KT_s)^{v-1-i} = KT_s[(1 - KT_s)^{v-1} + (1 - KT_s)^{v-2} + \cdots + 1]$$

Hence,

$$c_v = 1 - (1 - KT_s)^v \tag{9-56}$$

In Fig. 9-28, we have plotted the output versus time for a few different cases characterized by decreasing sampling rate. Note the following features:

1. For high sampling rate, the response, as expected, approaches the exponential response of an unsampled system (graph *a*).
2. For a specific sampling frequency $T_s = 1/K$, the final value $= 1$ is reached after a *finite* time $1/K$. We refer to this as *deadbeat* response (graph *b*).
3. For sampling rates lower than the one resulting in deadbeat response, the system becomes *oscillatory* of frequency $f = 1/2T_s$ (graph *c*).
4. For sampling rates below the critical value $f_s = K/2$, the oscillations grow indefinitely (graph *d*). This, of course, is the stability limit which we already had found in Eq. (9-54).
5. The system possesses *zero static error*; that is, $c_\infty \to 1$ (or $e_\infty \to 0$) for the stable cases.

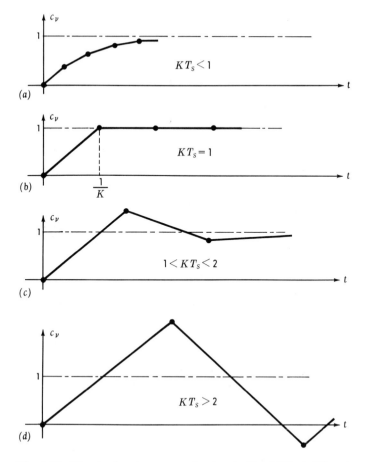

Fig. 9-28 The step-input response of system in Fig. 9-26b at different sampling rates.

Although all the above findings referred to a specific system, we wish to point out that the four first ones apply in general to any sampled system. Very specifically, we can always expect instability for a sufficiently low sampling rate, and we can always achieve deadbeat response. Note that a system may be deadbeat for one type of input (a step, for instance) but not necessarily for another.

Before we leave the topic of difference equations, we wish to point out some additional interesting features that will serve to illuminate the characteristics of the sampling process. We found above that the first-order system which we chose as an example could be described by the first-order difference equation (9-51) which we can write in shorter form:

$$a_1 c_{v+1} + a_0 c_v = b_0 r_v \tag{9-57}$$

If we have an *n*th-order plant, then we obtain an *n*th order linear difference equation

$$a_n c_{v+n} + a_{n-1} c_{v+n-1} + \cdots + a_0 c_v = b_0 r_v + b_1 r_{v+1} + \cdots + b_{n-1} r_{v+n-1} \qquad (9\text{-}58)$$

(The student is encouraged to exemplify this by writing the difference equation for the above system with the simple integrator replaced by a second-order plant. See also Exercise 9-4 at the end of the chapter.)

If the input sequence $r_v, r_{v+1}, \ldots, r_{v+n-1}$ equals zero, then we refer to the difference equation as *homogeneous*, in full analogy with the situation in the case of differential equations.

If the coefficients $a_0, \ldots, a_n$ in the above difference equation are *constants*, it is possible to find an explicit solution for c_v. Before we do this, let us again take advantage of our knowledge of linear differential equations with constant coefficients; i.e., let us consider the equation

$$a_n \frac{d^n c}{dt^n} + \cdots + a_0 c = br(t) \qquad (9\text{-}59)$$

In order to preserve the formal likeness with Eq. (9-58), we have chosen this form rather than the *normal* form on which most of our work in Chap. 4 was based.

The solution of the *homogeneous* part of Eq. (9-59) is of the form

$$c(t) = \rho_1 e^{\lambda_1 t} + \cdots + \rho_n e^{\lambda_n t} \qquad (9\text{-}60)$$

where the λ's are the eigenvalues (assumed *distinct*) and the ρ coefficients are functions of the initial conditions. The eigenvalues λ are obtained if we substitute this solution back into Eq. (9-59). This substitution yields

$$\begin{aligned}
&\rho_1 e^{\lambda_1 t}(a_n \lambda_1{}^n + a_{n-1}\lambda_1{}^{n-1} + \cdots + a_0) \\
&+ \rho_2 e^{\lambda_2 t}(a_n \lambda_2{}^n + a_{n-1}\lambda_2{}^{n-1} + \cdots + a_0) + \cdots \\
&+ \rho_n e^{\lambda_n t}(a_n \lambda_n{}^n + a_{n-1}\lambda_n{}^{n-1} + \cdots + a_0) = 0
\end{aligned} \qquad (9\text{-}61)$$

We note that this equation can be satisfied *for any t* if and only if we require that the expressions within $(\cdot)$ are forced to zero; i.e., we must assign those *n* values to λ which we obtain from the *characteristic* equation

$$a_n \lambda^n + a_{n-1}\lambda^{n-1} + \cdots + a_0 = 0 \qquad (9\text{-}62)$$

(The student should convince himself that these λ values are identical to those that he would obtain from the equation

$$|s\mathbf{I} - \mathbf{A}| = 0$$

discussed in Chap. 4.)

We now return to the *homogeneous* part of the *difference* equation. We shall show that this equation has a general solution of the form

$$c_v = \rho_1 \lambda_1{}^v + \rho_2 \lambda_2{}^v + \cdots + \rho_n \lambda_n{}^v \qquad (9\text{-}63)$$

Note: The λ's and ρ's do *not* have the same meaning as they did in Eq. (9-60).

Substitution of (9-63) into the homogeneous part of Eq. (9-58) gives

$$\rho_1 \lambda_1{}^\nu (a_n \lambda_1{}^n + a_{n-1} \lambda_1{}^{n-1} + \cdots + a_0)$$
$$+ \rho_2 \lambda_2{}^\nu (a_n \lambda_2{}^n + a_{n-1} \lambda_2{}^{n-1} + \cdots + a_0) + \cdots$$
$$+ \rho_n \lambda_n{}^\nu (a_n \lambda_n{}^n + a_{n-1} \lambda_n{}^{n-1} + \cdots + a_0) = 0 \tag{9-64}$$

We note the similarity between this equation and Eq. (9-61). It can be satisfied for *any* ν if we require that the n factors within the $(\cdot)$ are forced to zero; i.e., we must require that the n λ values be derived from the characteristic equation

$$a_n \lambda^n + a_{n-1} \lambda^{n-1} + \cdots + a_0 = 0 \tag{9-65}$$

Compare with Eq. (9-62)!

This completely determines the solution (9-63) since the ρ values, as before, can be assigned only after specification of n independent initial values. By "initial values," we understand in this discrete case n specified values for c_ν, $c_{\nu+1}, \ldots, c_{\nu+n-1}$.

We stress that the above discussion concerns the *homogeneous* solution only. It is possible now, just as in the case of solution of differential equations, to find a *particular* solution, or *driven* solution, depending upon the input sequence r_ν, $r_{\nu+1}, \ldots, r_{\nu+n-1}$ [see Eq. (9-58)], which together with the above homogeneous solution will constitute the *total* solution. We shall forego this and instead draw an important conclusion concerning the stability of the sampled system by direct investigation of the λ values.

We first remind the reader that the solution (9-60), pertaining to the continuous case, is stable if *all* terms $e^{\lambda t}$ tend to zero with increasing t. This leads to the well-known requirement that all eigenvalues λ must be located in the left-hand s plane.

The solution (9-63) is likewise stable if, for increasing ν, all terms tend to zero. We therefore immediately recognize that we must require that all λ's in the discrete case be characterized by

$$|\lambda_i| < 1 \qquad \text{for } i = 1, 2, \ldots, n \tag{9-66}$$

that is, *all the characteristic roots λ must lie within a unit circle in the λ plane.*

Example 9-6

Let us use the method just outlined to compute the response of the sampled system in Fig. 9-26. We had obtained the difference equation (9-51), the homogeneous part of which equals

$$c_{\nu+1} - (1 - KT_s)c_\nu = 0 \tag{9-67}$$

By comparing with (9-57), we thus have

$$a_0 = -(1 - KT_s)$$
$$a_1 = 1$$

From Eq. (9-65), we now get

$$1\lambda - (1 - KT_s) = 0$$

Since we are solving a first-order difference equation, we have only *one* λ value:

$$\lambda = 1 - KT_s \tag{9-68}$$

Using Eq. (9-63), we now can write the homogeneous solution directly:

$$c_v = \rho\lambda^v = \rho(1 - KT_s)^v \tag{9-69}$$

which agrees with Eq. (9-53)!

We shall end this section with the following observation. The reader may have wondered, and will find additional reasons to do so in the next section, why it is that in view of the constant similarities between the continuous-data and discrete-data theories, there is one apparent dissimilarity.

In the continuous-data case, we always run into the *continuous* time function $e^{\lambda t}$, whereas in the discrete-data case, we encounter the *discrete* function λ^v. However, these two functions are not too distant relatives. Due to the equality

$$\lambda = e^{\ln \lambda}$$

we can actually write

$$\lambda^v = e^{v \ln \lambda}$$

and this then should restore our feeling for symmetry.

9-4.4 *z*-TRANSFORM THEORY

Definition of the Direct Transform

The *z*-transform method extends the power and convenience of transform calculus to the realm of discrete-data systems. Before we enter into the details of this method, let us make one important observation concerning the sampling process. We do this in connection with the simple first-order system treated in the previous section and shown in Fig. 9-26. Because of the action of the sampler, the system feels the effects of the input signal $r(t)$ *as it appears at the sampling instants only. This means, in effect that we can get the same response for different input signals.* The situation is depicted in Fig. 9-29, showing two different input signals which would cause equal responses. *We conclude that it is not the continuous input signal $r(t)$ that counts, but the discrete-input-data sequence $r_0, r_1, r_2, \ldots, r_v$.* We shall find it convenient to use a special symbol for this sequence and adopt herewith the notation $\{r_v\}$. [We could, of course, have used the vector notation **r**, but we then would have collided with the notation already used for MIMO systems in previous chapters. Note that it would not be wise to use the notation $r_s(t)$ in analogy with $e_s(t)$ in Fig. 9-23*b*, as this latter notation applies to signals with small but *finite* duration Δ and we wish now to talk about the case where $\Delta = 0$.]

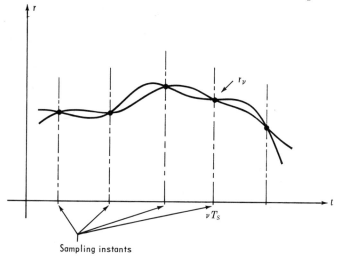

Fig. 9-29 Two different reference input signals that would give identical responses.

Figure 9-29 implies that there is not a *unique* response situation in sampled systems as we knew it from continuous-data systems—the only thing we can say with certainty is that *one* particular data sequence $\{r_v\}$ must give rise to *one* and only one output-data sequence $\{c_v\}$. The z-transform theory emphasizes this by concerning itself exclusively with the relationship between data sequences, rather than with continuous signals, as does the Laplace transform. With this background, let us now *define* the following function $F(z)$ of the complex variable z:

$$F(z) \triangleq \mathscr{Z}\{f_v\} \triangleq \sum_{v=0}^{\infty} f_v z^{-v} \tag{9-70}$$

It is of importance to realize that with this definition, we tacitly have made the assumption that the data sequence $\{f_v\}$ starts out with f_0; that is, any data points f_v for *negative* v do not exist. Compare this with the assumption we make when arbitrarily setting the lower integration limit $= 0$ for the Laplace-transform integral.

$F(z)$ is said to be the direct z transform of the discrete-data sequence $\{f_v\}$. One should observe the striking similarity between the z transform $F(z)$ of a discrete-data sequence $\{f_v\}$ and the Laplace transform $F(s)$ of a *continuous* function $f(t)$:

$$F(s) \triangleq \mathscr{L}[f(t)] \triangleq \int_0^{\infty} f(t)e^{-st}\, dt$$

$$= \int_0^{\infty} f(t)(e^s)^{-t}\, dt \tag{9-71}$$

Because of the similarities between Eqs. (9-70) and (9-71), striking resemblances between Laplace and z-transform theory will result. Indeed, the reader should pause at this juncture to contemplate the similarities (but *not* identities) between continuous-time functions, differential equations, infinite integrals, and Laplace transforms on one side and discrete-data sequences, difference equations, infinite sums, and z transforms on the other.

The defining series (9-70) does not necessarily converge, and in such a case the corresponding data sequence $\{f_v\}$ is said to be non-z-transformable. [Remember that a time function $f(t)$ is non-Laplace-transformable if the infinite integral (9-71) fails to converge.]

The tremendous usefulness of the Laplace transform when applied to *linear* differential equations with *constant* coefficients is due basically to a handful of well-known properties, which are summarized in Appendix B. If we would single out one particularly useful concept associated with Laplace-transform theory, this no doubt would be the concept of a *transfer function*, which permits us to describe in an extremely convenient fashion the relationships between the continuous-data inputs to and outputs from a particular linear element.

When the z transform is operated on a *linear* difference equation with *constant* coefficients, we find a number of similar properties which permit us to determine rather conveniently the transfer characteristics of sampled systems. Before we go into details, we wish to illustrate with an example how the z transform is computed.

Example 9-7

Compute the z transform of the data sequence

$$\{f_v\} = 1, a, a^2, \ldots = \{a^v\} \qquad a = \text{real const}$$

From (9-70), we get

$$\mathscr{Z}\{a^v\} = F(z) \triangleq \sum_{v=0}^{\infty} a^v z^{-v} = \sum_{v=0}^{\infty} \left(\frac{a}{z}\right)^v = \frac{1}{1 - a/z} = \frac{z}{z - a} \tag{9-72}$$

The convergence of the above series is guaranteed for $|z| > a$, that is, for all z in the z plane outside a circle of radius a.

By differentiating Eq. (9-72) with respect to z, we obtain

$$\frac{d}{dz}\left(\sum_{v=0}^{\infty} a^v z^{-v}\right) = \frac{d}{dz}\frac{z}{z - a}$$

Upon differentiating term by term in the series we obtain

$$-\frac{a}{z^2} - \frac{2a^2}{z^3} - \cdots = -\frac{a}{(z - a)^2}$$

Hence

$$\sum_{v=0}^{\infty}(v + 1)a^{v+1}z^{-v} = \frac{az^2}{(z - a)^2}$$

Table 9-1 *z*-transform pairs

No.	Data sequence $\{f_\nu\}$	$F(z)$
1	$f_\nu = 1$	$\dfrac{z}{z-1}$
2	$f_\nu = \nu$	$\dfrac{z}{(z-1)^2}$
3	$f_\nu = \nu^2$	$\dfrac{z(z+1)}{(z-1)^3}$
4	$f_\nu = a^\nu$	$\dfrac{z}{z-a}$
5	$f_\nu = e^{\nu a}$	$\dfrac{z}{z-e^a}$
6	$f_\nu = \nu a^\nu$	$\dfrac{za}{(z-a)^2}$
7	$f_\nu = \sin \omega\nu$	$\dfrac{z \sin \omega}{z^2 - 2z \cos \omega + 1}$
8	$f_\nu = \cos \omega\nu$	$\dfrac{z(z - \cos \omega)}{z^2 - 2z \cos \omega + 1}$
9	$f_\nu = e^{-a\nu} \sin \omega\nu$	$\dfrac{ze^{-a} \sin \omega}{z^2 - 2ze^{-a} \cos \omega + e^{-2a}}$

From Eq. (9-70), we then get directly

$$\mathscr{Z}[(\nu + 1)a^{\nu+1}] = \frac{az^2}{(z - a)^2} \tag{9-73}$$

Again the transformation makes sense only for $|z| > a$.

As in the case of Laplace transforms, we can compute and accumulate tables of z transforms. A brief table of this kind is given as Table 9-1. The reader should check the items in it to appreciate how it is obtained.

Some Useful Properties of the z Transform

The reader is familiar with the fact that manipulation of Laplace transforms is greatly facilitated by a handful of special properties. This applies also to the z transform. We shall now present the more useful theorems.

theorem 1 (*Linearity*) *Assume that we have two (or more) data sequences $\{f_\nu\}$ and $\{g_\nu\}$ and two (or more) constants a and b. The linearity property is expressed as*

$$\mathscr{Z}(a\{f_\nu\} + b\{g_\nu\}) = aF(z) + bG(z) \tag{9-74}$$

The theorem follows directly from the defining equation (9-70). *Compare*:

$$\mathscr{L}[af(t) + bg(t)] = aF(s) + bG(s).$$

Example 9-8

Find

$$\mathscr{L}[(v + 1)a^{v+1}]$$

We have

$$(v + 1)a^{v+1} = ava^v + aa^v$$

From Table 9-1, we get

$$\mathscr{L}\{va^v\} = \frac{za}{(z - a)^2}$$

and

$$\mathscr{L}\{a^v\} = \frac{z}{z - a}$$

Hence,

$$\mathscr{L}[(v + 1)a^{v+1}] = a\frac{za}{(z - a)^2} + a\frac{z}{z - a} = \frac{az^2}{(z - a)^2}$$

in full agreement with (9-73).

theorem 2   (*Real Translation*)   *This theorem states*

$$\mathscr{L}\{f_{v-n}\} = z^{-n}F(z) \qquad n = integer > 0 \tag{9-75}$$

proof

$$\mathscr{L}\{f_{v-n}\} \triangleq \sum_{v=0}^{\infty} f_{v-n}z^{-v} = f_0 z^{-n} + f_1 z^{-(n+1)} + \cdots$$

$$= z^{-n}\sum_{i=0}^{\infty} f_i z^{-i} = z^{-n}F(z)$$

(The third step in this derivation follows from the fact that we have assumed that no data points f_{v-n} exist for negative index $v - n$.)   *Compare*:

$$\mathscr{L}[f(t - t_0)] = e^{-st_0}F(s)$$

Example 9-9

Consider the two data sequences $\{f_v\}$ and $\{g_v\}$ depicted in Fig. 9-30. The first one is an exponential sequence $\{f_v\} = 1, e^{-1}, e^{-2}, \ldots$, and the second one is the same sequence delayed two samples, that is,

$$\{g_v\} = 0, 0, 1, e^{-1}, e^{-2}, \ldots$$

(Note that the first two samples in the $\{g_v\}$ sequence must be zeros since there are no corresponding f samples to delay.)

Using the translation theorem, we thus conclude

$$G(z) = z^{-2}F(z) = z^{-2}\frac{z}{z - e^{-1}} = \frac{1}{z(z - e^{-1})}$$

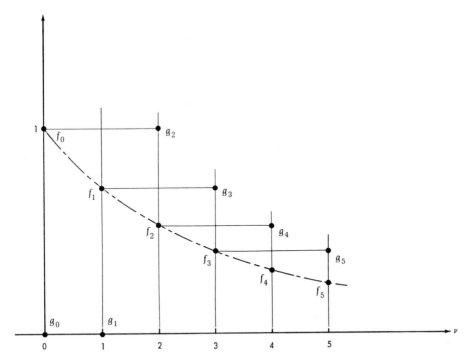

Fig. 9-30   Delayed data sequence.

theorem 3   *This theorem states that*

$$\mathscr{L}\{f_{\nu+1}\} = z\mathscr{L}\{f_\nu\} - zf_0 \qquad (9\text{-}76)$$

proof:

$$\mathscr{L}\{f_{\nu+1}\} \overset{\Delta}{=} \sum_{\nu=0}^{\infty} f_{\nu+1} z^{-\nu} = f_1 + f_2 z^{-1} + f_3 z^{-2} + \cdots$$

$$= z(f_0 + f_1 z^{-1} + f_2 z^{-2} + \cdots) - zf_0 = z\mathscr{L}\{f_\nu\} - zf_0$$

This theorem corresponds to the well-known property

$$\mathscr{L}[\dot{f}(t)] = s\mathscr{L}[f(t)] - f(0)$$

and plays the same role in the solution of difference equations that the above Laplace theorem does in the solution of differential equations.

We can generalize formula (9-76) to embrace the case $\{f_{\nu+n}\}$ just as we can find a formula for

$$\mathscr{L}\left[\frac{d^n f}{dt^n}\right]$$

The general formula reads

$$\mathscr{L}\{f_{\nu+n}\} = z^n F(z) - (z^n f_0 + z^{n-1} f_1 + \cdots + z f_{n-1}) \qquad (9\text{-}77)$$

and can be derived in a manner similar to that used for (9-76).

Example 9-10

Consider Eq. (9-51), which we solved earlier by other means. Since the equation holds for any integer $v > 0$, we obtain

$$\{c_{v+1}\} = (1 - KT_s)\{c_v\} + KT_s\{r_v\}$$

We z-transform the above data sequences and, upon using the linearity rule, obtain

$$\mathscr{L}\{c_{v+1}\} = (1 - KT_s)\mathscr{L}\{c_v\} + KT_s\mathscr{L}\{r_v\}$$

By using Theorem 3 and at the same time introducing $C(z)$ and $R(z)$, we get

$$zC(z) - zc_0 = (1 - KT_s)C(z) + KT_s R(z)$$

We solve now for $C(z)$:

$$C(z) = \frac{z}{z - (1 - KT_s)} c_0 + \frac{KT_s}{z - (1 - KT_s)} R(z) \tag{9-78}$$

We obtain now, just as for Laplace transforms, the data sequence $\{c_v\}$ by an *inverse* transformation of $C(z)$. The easiest way to inverse-transform is to look up a table. We get

$$\{c_v\} = \mathscr{L}^{-1}[C(z)] = \mathscr{L}^{-1}\left[\frac{z}{z - (1 - KT_s)} c_0\right] + \mathscr{L}^{-1}\left[\frac{KT_s}{z - (1 - KT_s)} R(z)\right]$$

Our brief Table 9-1 will give us only the first one (the *transient*) of the above two sequences (item 4 in the table):

$$\mathscr{L}^{-1}\left[\frac{z}{z - (1 - KT_s)} c_0\right] = \{c_0(1 - KT_s)^v\}$$

and this agrees very nicely with the solution (9-53) obtained earlier. We shall postpone the solution of the second term (the driven solution) until we have discussed the topic of inverse transformation in the next section.

theorems 4 and 5 (*Initial- and Final-value Theorems*) *We have*

$$f_0 = \lim_{z \to \infty} F(z) \tag{9-79}$$

$$f_\infty = \lim_{z \to 1} [(1 - z^{-1})F(z)] \tag{9-80}$$

Compare the corresponding theorems in the Laplace-transform domain.

As both theorems can be proved quite simply and directly from the defining equation, we leave this as an exercise for the reader.

It should be noted that the final-value theorem can only provide an answer where an answer exists, i.e., for a data sequence that *has* a final value.

Example 9-11

Let us seek the final value c_∞ for the data sequence $\{c_v\}$ in the previous example [Eq. (9-78)].

We have

$$c_\infty = \lim_{z \to 1} \left[(1 - z^{-1}) \frac{z}{z - (1 - KT_s)} c_0 + (1 - z^{-1}) \frac{KT_s}{z - (1 - KT_s)} R(z) \right] \quad (9\text{-}81)$$

The first term within the [·] clearly will approach zero, indicating that the transient term will die out. [Note, however, that this also will happen should $|1 - KT_s| > 1$ and the system thus be unstable, proving to us that the final-value theorem (just as is the case with Laplace transforms) does not "work" if a final value does not exist.]

The second term can be evaluated only after we have decided on an input. Let us assume that we apply a unit step, that is, $\{r_v\} = 1, 1, \ldots$. From our table, we thus find

$$R(z) = \frac{z}{z - 1}$$

We now can complete our analysis. The second term in (9-81) reads

$$c_\infty = \lim_{z \to 1} \left[(1 - z^{-1}) \frac{KT_s}{z - (1 - KT_s)} \frac{z}{z - 1} \right] = \lim_{z \to 1} \left[\frac{KT_s}{z - (1 - KT_s)} \right] = 1$$

in full agreement with the stable graphs in Fig. 9-28.

This example thus proves that we actually can determine the final value *without having to solve explicitly for* $\{c_v\}$.

There are some additional theorems that would prove useful on occasion, but as our space is limited, we must stop here and instead devote some pages to the topic of inverse z transformation.

The Inverse z Transform

The previous example convinced us of the need for methods for inverse z transformation. The three most popular techniques are:

1. Table look-up
2. The partial-fraction method
3. The power-series method

The first method needs no comment, so we shall concentrate our efforts on the other two.

Inverse transformation through partial fraction expansion We remember that in performing an inverse Laplace transformation

$$\mathcal{L}^{-1}[F(s)]$$

we could proceed as follows:

First, we expand the function $F(s)$ as a partial fraction, which in most cases takes on the form

$$F(s) = \frac{A_1}{s - s_1} + \frac{A_2}{s - s_2} + \cdots + \frac{A_n}{s - s_n}$$

Each term in this expansion can be inverse-transformed directly, and we obtain

$$f(t) = A_1 e^{s_1 t} + A_2 e^{s_2 t} + \cdots + A_n e^{s_n t}$$

In the case of the z transform, we expand the function $F(z)$ in the following way:

$$F(z) = A_1 \frac{z}{z - z_1} + A_2 \frac{z}{z - z_2} + \cdots + A_n \frac{z}{z - z_n} \tag{9-82}$$

From Table 9-1 (item 4), we then get

$$\{f_v\} = A_1\{z_1{}^v\} + A_2\{z_2{}^v\} + \cdots + A_n\{z_n{}^v\} \tag{9-83}$$

Example 9-12

Let us compute the inverse transform of the second term in Eq. (9-78), which earlier we had postponed. For a unit-step input and thus $R(z) = z/(z - 1)$, we are faced with the problem of finding

$$\mathscr{L}^{-1} \left[\frac{KT_s}{z - (1 - KT_s)} \frac{z}{z - 1} \right]$$

First, we note that

$$\frac{KT_s z}{[z - (1 - KT_s)](z - 1)} = \frac{z}{z - 1} - \frac{z}{z - (1 - KT_s)}$$

Therefore,

$$\mathscr{L}^{-1}[\,\cdot\,] = \{1^v\} - \{(1 - KT_s)^v\}$$

or

$$c_v = 1 - (1 - KT_s)^v$$

which agrees with Eq. (9-56).

We should note that an expansion of the form (9-82) is possible only if the z_i's are *distinct*. If we have double roots, for instance, then the expansion will contain terms of the type

$$\frac{z}{(z - z_i)^2}$$

and making use of item 6 in Table 9-1, we conclude that the solution sequence will contain a term

$$\{v z_i{}^v\}$$

Compare the situation in the continuous case, where a double root results in a solution of the form

$$te^{s_i t}$$

Inverse transformation by means of power series   This method is based upon the technique of expanding $F(z)$ in powers of z^{-1}, that is,

$$F(z) = f_0 + f_1 z^{-1} + f_2 z^{-2} + \cdots + f_\nu z^{-\nu} + \cdots \tag{9-84}$$

As this expansion obviously is identical with the defining series for a z transform [see Eq. (9-71)], we conclude that the coefficients $f_0, f_1, \ldots, f_\nu$ actually represent the sought solution.

Example 9-13

Let us apply the method to the previous example.   We obtain by long division

$$\frac{KT_s z}{[z - (1 - KT_s)](z - 1)} = 0z^0 + KT_s z^{-1} + (2KT_s - K^2 T_s^2)z^{-2} + \cdots$$

Therefore,

$$f_0 = 0$$
$$f_1 = KT_s$$
$$f_2 = 2KT_s - K^2 T_s^2 = KT_s(2 - KT_s)$$

. . . .

These, then, are the first three data points in the solution pictured in Fig. 9-28.

The Pulse Transfer Function (PTF)

In transmitting signal data through a network, one can distinguish, as far as the nature of input and output signals are concerned, between four different types of situations, all of them illustrated in Fig. 9-31.   Depending upon whether these signals are of discrete or continuous character, we differentiate between:

1. Analog-to-analog $(A \to A)$ conversion
2. Digital-to-digital $(D \to D)$ conversion
3. Digital-to-analog $(D \to A)$ conversion
4. Analog-to-digital $(A \to D)$ conversion

If the network is *linear*, with *time-independent* parameters, we have seen how it is possible in the $A \to A$ case to describe the network by means of a *transfer function*.   We shall now concern ourselves with linear and time-invariant networks where at least one of the signals appears in discrete form.   We shall find that it is still possible to describe the networks by means of transfer functions, but because of the fact that several cases may occur (2 to 4 above), we have to exercise some care in their usage.

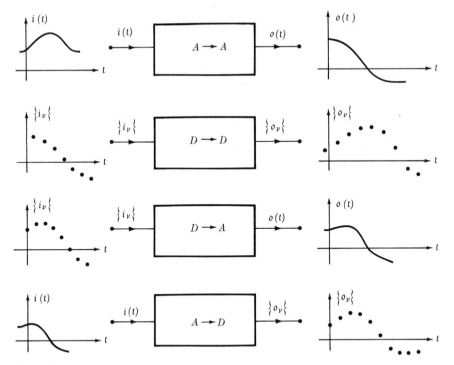

Fig. 9-31   Networks can be classified on the basis of signal type.

The reader has encountered $A \to D$ and $D \to A$ converters in previous sections.   Modulators and demodulators are simple examples of networks falling in these categories. $D \to D$ conversion takes place in digital computers where both the input and the output signals are of discrete nature.   So-called "digital controllers" (which basically are simple special-purpose digital computers) are also networks of the $D \to D$ type.

The $D \to D$ case   In defining the PTF for a network, it is most convenient to start with the $D \to D$ case.   We shall find that if such a network operates on the input-data sequence $\{i_\nu\}$ in a linear and time-invariant fashion, then we can show that this network can be described completely by means of a PTF defined by

$$G(z) \triangleq \frac{\mathscr{L}\{o_\nu\}}{\mathscr{L}\{i_\nu\}} = \frac{O(z)}{I(z)} \tag{9-85}$$

Consider the first two networks illustrated in Fig. 9-31.   In the first one, an $A \to A$ network, we shall assume that the network operates on the input signal $i(t)$ in a manner describable in terms of the linear constant-coefficient differential equation

$$a_n \frac{d^n o(t)}{dt^n} + a_{n-1} \frac{d^{n-1} o(t)}{dt^{n-1}} + \cdots + a_0 o(t) = b i(t) \tag{9-86}$$

We Laplace-transform this equation, and by *disregarding any initial values of $o(t)$, $\dot{o}(t)$, etc.*, we obtain

$$(a_n s^n + a_{n-1} s^{n-1} + \cdots + a_0) O(s) = b I(s)$$

We now can define the transfer function $G(s)$ as

$$\frac{O(s)}{I(s)} \triangleq G(s) = \frac{b}{a_n s^n + a_{n-1} s^{n-1} + \cdots + a_0} \tag{9-87}$$

We next turn our attention to the $D \to D$ network. We shall assume that it operates on the input-data sequence $\{i_\nu\}$ in a manner describable in terms of the linear constant-coefficient *difference* equation

$$a_n o_{\nu+n} + a_{n-1} o_{\nu+n-1} + \cdots + a_0 o_\nu = b i_\nu \tag{9-88}$$

Using formula (9-77), we z-transform this equation, and by *disregarding any initial values of o_ν, $o_{\nu+1}$, etc.*, we obtain

$$(a_n z^n + a_{n-1} z^{n-1} + \cdots + a_0) O(z) = b I(z)$$

We now can define a PTF as

$$\frac{O(z)}{I(z)} \triangleq G(z) = \frac{b}{a_n z^n + a_{n-1} z^{n-1} + \cdots + a_0} \tag{9-89}$$

It is to be noted that neither of the transfer functions $G(s)$ and $G(z)$ contains any s or z terms in the numerator. This would have been the case if we had assumed that the defining equations (9-86) and (9-88) had contained terms of the types di/dt, $d^2 i/dt^2$, ..., $d^m i/dt^m$ and $i_{\nu+1}$, $i_{\nu+2}$, ..., $i_{\nu+m}$, respectively. A more general expression for the PTF would then be

$$G(z) = \frac{b_m z^m + \cdots + b_0}{a_n z_n + \cdots + a_0} \tag{9-90}$$

PTF's obey the same "cascading" rules as ordinary (Laplace) transfer functions. That is, if we have several $D \to D$ networks in series, each having the PTF $G_1(z)$, $G_2(z)$, etc., then the *overall* PTF can be computed from the formula

$$G(z) = G_1(z) \cdot G_2(z) \cdots \tag{9-91}$$

Note: The formula is valid only if the data sequences between the networks all are *synchronous*; i.e., all data points of equal index must appear simultaneously. It is also worth stressing that the formula *only* applies to cascaded networks of the $D \to D$ type.

The mixed $(D \to A \quad A \to D)$ case—concept of mathematical sampler The PTF concept can be used even when one of the signals is of the analog or continuous type. Consider, for instance, the $D \to A$ network depicted in Fig. 9-31, which accepts as an input the discrete-data sequence $\{i_\nu\}$ and outputs the continuous-time signal $o(t)$. In accordance with our earlier discussions, any physical $D \to A$ system must contain some sort of demodulator or data hold, and in what follows, we shall assume for simplicity that this data hold is of zero order.

   In principle, it seems simple enough to treat the signal transfer through the $D \to A$ network. As we know the input $\{i_\nu\}$ and supposedly also the characteristics of the $D \to A$ network, we should be in a position to :

1. Find the Laplace transform $\mathscr{L}\{i_\nu\}$ of the input-data sequence.
2. Characterize the $D \to A$ network (which is assumed linear) with a transfer function $G_{DA}(s)$. This transfer function should consist of two parts: one part $G_{DH}(s)$ emanating from the data hold and one part $G_{AA}(s)$ due to the $A \to A$ part of the network.
3. Finally, compute $o(t) = \mathscr{L}^{-1}[G_{DA}(s)\mathscr{L}\{i_\nu\}]$.

   If we attempt to follow this procedure, we encounter some serious difficulties. Let us demonstrate by considering the situation shown in Fig. 9-32.

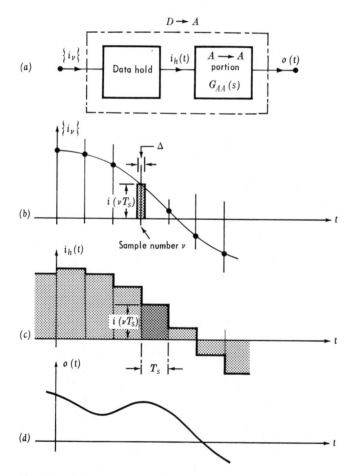

Fig. 9-32 Typical $D \to A$ configuration.

We first seek the Laplace transform for the discrete-data sequence by computing the transform for each data point. As each data point is the limit case of the *finite pulse* shown in Fig. 9-32b having the amplitude $i(\nu T_s)$ and duration Δ and as the Laplace transform of this finite pulse equals

$$\mathscr{L}(\text{⊓}) = i(\nu T_s) \frac{1 - e^{-s\Delta}}{s}$$

we can derive the Laplace transform of the data point i_ν by the limit process

$$\mathscr{L}(i_\nu) = \lim_{\Delta \to 0} [\mathscr{L}(\text{⊓})] = \lim_{\Delta \to 0} \left[i(\nu T_s) \frac{1 - e^{-s\Delta}}{s} \right] \tag{9-92}$$

Before we perform this limit process, let us look at the transfer function $G_{DH}(s)$ for the data hold. The output from the data hold resulting from the input-data point i_ν is the heavily shaded pulse in Fig. 9-32c, and the Laplace transform for this pulse equals

$$\mathscr{L}(\text{⊐}) = i(\nu T_s) \frac{1 - e^{-sT_s}}{s} \tag{9-93}$$

By definition, we therefore have

$$G_{DH}(s) = \lim_{\Delta \to 0} \left[\frac{\mathscr{L}(\text{⊐})}{\mathscr{L}(\text{⊓})} \right] \tag{9-94}$$

Let us now perform the limit process called for in (9-92) and (9-94). We have

$$\lim_{\Delta \to 0} \left[i(\nu T_s) \frac{1 - e^{-s\Delta}}{s} \right] = i(\nu T_s)0 = 0$$

We conclude therefore that the input transform approaches zero and $G_{DH}(s)$ approaches ∞, and in computing the output from the data hold, we therefore obtain an *indeterminate* expression of the type 0∞.

We can circumvent this difficulty by making use of some simple mathematical trickery. We can write the transform $I_h(s)$ of the signal $i_h(t)$ as the product

$$I_h(s) = \mathscr{L}(\text{⊓})G_{DH}(s) = \mathscr{L}(\text{⊓}) \frac{\mathscr{L}(\text{⊐})}{\mathscr{L}(\text{⊓})}$$

$$= \mathscr{L}(\text{⊐}) = i(\nu T_s) \frac{1 - e^{-sT_s}}{s}$$

The third step in this operation evidently eliminates the troublemaker $\mathscr{L}(\text{⊓})$ completely, and we now have a perfectly good and valid expression for $I_h(s)$ that is *mathematically well behaved*. We can write it as

$$I_h(s) = \underbrace{i(\nu T_s)}_{I^*(\nu T_s)} \underbrace{\frac{1 - e^{-sT_s}}{s}}_{G^*_H(s)} \tag{9-95}$$

We have defined two new quantities, $I^*(\nu T_s)$ and $G^*_{DH}(s)$, which must both be considered *purely as mathematical artifices.* *They both have meaning only when appearing together, and they give then, when multiplied, the right expression for* $I_h(s)$. Let us take a closer look at the first of these artifices, $I^*(\nu T_s)$. We note first that it does not vanish with decreasing Δ, as $\mathscr{L}(\_\!\!\!\sqcap\!\!\!\_)$ had the habit of doing. As we can write

$$I^*(\nu T_s) = i(\nu T_s)1$$

and as 1 is the Laplace transform for an *impulse*† of unit intensity, we conclude that the *quantity* $I^*(\nu T_s)$ *is the Laplace transform of an impulse of intensity* $i(\nu T_s)$.

Our discussion has been concerned so far with a single data point. We clearly can apply it to a sequence of data points. In so doing, we shall define the concept of *mathematical sampler* S_m, shown in Fig. 9-33b. This device is another mathematical artifice. It accepts the actual physical signal $i(t)$ and outputs a sequence of *impulses*, each having an intensity equalling the actual value $i(\nu T_s)$ of the physical signal $i(t)$ at the sampling moments in question. Upon passing through the transfer block G^*_{DH}, this sequence of nonexisting impulses $\{i^*_\nu\}$ gives rise, in accordance with our previous discussion, to the actual physical signal

† An impulse of unit intensity, or *unit impulse*, is the limit value of a *pulse* of duration Δ and amplitude $1/\Delta$ when Δ approaches 0. The area of an impulse is the intensity of the impulse.

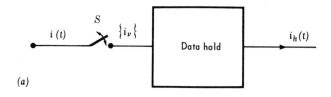

(a)

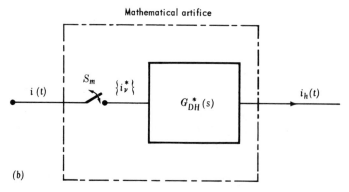

(b)

Fig. 9-33 Mathematical sampler. The *physical* system in *a* is properly described by the *mathematical* model in *b*.

$i_h(t)$. *The combination of S_m and $G^*_{DH}(s)$, although neither exists in a physical sense, has the same effect upon the input signal $i(t)$ as the actual physical system has.*

We shall avoid much mental anguish in the following discussion if we realize right from the outset that the impulses do not appear anywhere in the system but only serve the purpose of mathematical expediency.

Summarizing our results, we conclude that we now can obtain the output signal from the data hold from the formula

$$i_h(t) = \mathscr{L}^{-1}[I_h(s)] = \mathscr{L}^{-1}[G^*_{DH}(s)\mathscr{L}\{i^*_v\}] \tag{9-96}$$

For brevity in writing, we adopt the symbol

$$I^*(s) \triangleq \mathscr{L}\{i^*_v\} \tag{9-97}$$

and we then have

$$i_h(t) = \mathscr{L}^{-1}[G^*_{DH}(s)I^*(s)] \tag{9-98}$$

and for the output from the $D \to A$ network in Fig. 9-32,

$$o(t) = \mathscr{L}^{-1}[G^*_{DH}(s)I^*(s)G_{AA}(s)] \tag{9-99}$$

In the above formulas, all transfer functions are well defined, nonzero, and finite, and this then is the great advantage of the mathematical sampler. The reader should consider carefully which quantities in the above formulas are starred (and thus nonexistent, in a physical sense) and which are not.

It is of great importance to realize that the quantities $I^*(s)$ and $G^*_{DH}(s)$ make *sense only when they appear together.* This should be clear immediately from the way they were introduced. Ridiculous results may be obtained if we violate this rule.

Two different expressions can be derived for $I^*(s)$, each finding a different use in analysis of sampled-data systems. The first expression can be obtained by direct Laplace transformation of the sum of impulses

$$\{i^*_v\} = \sum_{v=0}^{\infty} i(vT_s)\, \delta(t - vT_s) \tag{9-100}$$

$\delta(t - vT_s)$ is the adopted symbol for a unit impulse occurring at $t = vT_s$.

Using Eq. (B-21) in Appendix B, we therefore get

$$\mathscr{L}\{i^*_v\} = I^*(s) = \sum_{v=0}^{\infty} i(vT_s)e^{-svT_s} \tag{9-101}$$

A second expression can be obtained if, in analogy with (9-40), we write

$$\{i^*_v\} = i(t)p^*(t) \tag{9-102}$$

$p^*(t)$ is a periodic modulation factor consisting of a sequence of unit impulses, and in accordance with Eq. (B-6) in Appendix B, it therefore has a discrete spectrum

$$p^*(t) = \sum_{\omega_v=-\infty}^{+\infty} P^*(j\omega_v)e^{j\omega_v t} \tag{9-103}$$

As the amplitude of each impulse of $p^*(t)$ is larger by a factor of $1/\Delta$ than each pulse of $p(t)$ in (9-40), we clearly can obtain the spectrum $P^*(j\omega_\nu)$ most conveniently directly from (9-44) as follows:

$$P^*(j\omega_\nu) = \frac{1}{\Delta} P(j\omega_\nu) = \frac{1}{\Delta} \alpha = \frac{1}{T_s} \tag{9-104}$$

We therefore have

$$p^*(t) = \frac{1}{T_s} \sum_{\omega_\nu = -\infty}^{+\infty} e^{j\omega \nu}$$

and upon substitution, (9-102) yields

$$\{i_\nu^*\} = i(t) \frac{1}{T_s} \sum_{\omega_\nu = -\infty}^{+\infty} e^{j\omega_\nu t}$$

By Laplace-transforming this expression term by term, we get

$$\mathscr{L}\{i_\nu^*\} \triangleq I^*(s) = \frac{1}{T_s} \sum_{\omega_\nu = -\infty}^{+\infty} \mathscr{L}[i(t)e^{j\omega_\nu t}]$$

Hence,

$$I^*(s) = \frac{1}{T_s} \sum_{\omega_\nu = -\infty}^{+\infty} I(s - j\omega_\nu) \tag{9-105}$$

Although quite different in appearance, the two expressions (9-101) and (9-105) are, of course, identical. At this time we make two interesting observations concerning $I^*(s)$:

observation 1 From the expression (9-101), we find that if we replace e^{sT_s} by z or let $s \to (\ln z)/T_s$, the expression $I^*(s)$ will be identical with $I(z)$, that is,

$$I^*(s) = \sum_{\nu=0}^{\infty} i(\nu T_s)e^{-s\nu T_s}$$
$$= \sum_{\nu=0}^{\infty} i(\nu T_s)(e^{sT_s})^{-\nu} \to \sum_{\nu=0}^{\infty} i(\nu T_s)z^{-\nu}$$
$$\triangleq I(z)$$

observation 2 The expression (9-105) obviously will not change if we replace s by $s + jm\omega_\nu$, where m is any finite integer. Differently expressed: $I^*(s)$ is a periodic function with period $j\omega_\nu$, that is,

$$I^*(s) = I^*(s + j\omega_\nu) \tag{9-106}$$

Example 9-14

Let us compute the output signal from the $D \to A$ system in Fig. 9-34. Using formula (9-99), we get

$$O(s) = I^*(s) \frac{1 - e^{-sT_s}}{s} \frac{1}{s^2} = \frac{1 - e^{-sT_s}}{s^3} \sum_{\nu=0}^{\infty} i(\nu T_s)e^{-s\nu T_s}$$
$$= \frac{1}{s^3} \sum_{\nu=0}^{\infty} \{i(\nu T_s) - i[(\nu - 1)T_s]\}e^{-s\nu T_s}$$

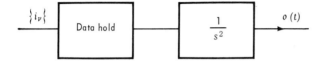

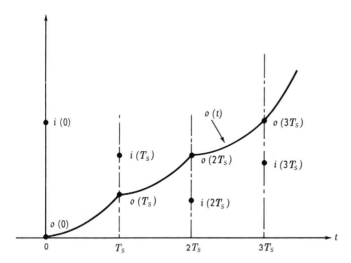

Fig. 9-34 System discussed in Example 9-14.

By inverse-transforming term by term, we thus obtain

$$o(t) = \mathcal{L}^{-1}[O(s)] = \sum_{v=0}^{\infty} \{i(vT_s) - i[(v-1)T_s]\} \frac{(t - vT_s)^2 u(t - vT_s)}{2}$$

where $u(t - vT_s)$ is a unit-step function starting at $t = vT_s$.

In Fig. 9-34 are shown the first three terms in the above series.

This example shows the feasibility of obtaining the complete response picture for a $D \rightarrow A$ system. It demonstrates, however, that considerable numerical difficulties may be encountered.

A problem like the one just studied can be solved considerably more simply if we are willing to pay a slight price. Consider the response picture in Fig. 9-34. The previous analysis gave us information about the total continuous output $o(t)$. Assume now that we decide that it would be perfectly sufficient to know the *corner points only*; i.e., we would be content to know the discrete-output-data sequence $\{o_v\}$ consisting of the data points

$$\{o_v\} = o(0), o(T_s), \ldots, o(vT_s)$$

Under these circumstances, we can use the full power of the z transform since we have, in effect, reduced the system to a type $D \rightarrow D$, albeit an *hypothetical* one. The only question that we must answer before we can make use of this

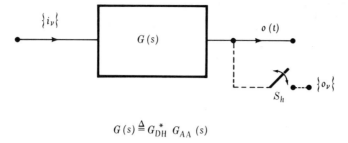

$$G(s) \triangleq G_{DH}^* \, G_{AA}(s)$$

Fig. 9-35   Hypothetical sampler

technique is how to compute the PTF of this hypothetical system.   For this purpose, consider the system in Fig. 9-35.   We lumped the data hold plus the $A \rightarrow A$ parts of Fig. 9-32 into one transfer function $G(s)$.   Then we also added the *hypothetical sampler*† S_h, which samples the continuous signal $o(t)$ synchronously with the input-data sequence $\{i_\nu\}$.   Let us now find a relationship between the input- and output-data sequences.   Specifically, let us derive an expression for the output-data point $o(\nu T_s)$.   As the system is assumed linear, we know that $o(\nu T_s)$ can be considered as the *sum* of the individual responses caused by the $\nu + 1$ input-data points that already have arrived at the input side.   Consider the effect of *one* of these data points, for instance, the first one, $i(0)$, occurring at $t = 0$. The output due to this single data point, according to our previous findings, can be considered as caused by an impulse of intensity $i(0)$; that is,

$$\mathscr{L}^{-1}[i(0)G(s)] = i(0)\mathscr{L}^{-1}[G(s)] \triangleq i(0)g(t) \tag{9-107}$$

$g(t)$ is referred to as the *impulse response* of the network $G(s)$, as caused by a *unit* impulse $\delta(t)$.

We are now in a position to find the total output $o(\nu T_s)$.   Clearly, it must be the sum of the responses of the $\nu + 1$ impulses arriving before $t = \nu T_s$; that is,

$$o(\nu T_s) = i(0)g(\nu T_s) + i(T_s)g[(\nu - 1)T_s] + i(2T_s)g[(\nu - 2)T_s] + \cdots + i(\nu T_s)g(0)$$

We now multiply this expression by $z^{-\nu}$ and perform at the same time a summation from $\nu = 0$ to $\nu = \infty$; that is,

$$\sum_{\nu=0}^{\infty} o(\nu T_s)z^{-\nu} = \sum_{\nu=0}^{\infty} i(0)g(\nu T_s)z^{-\nu} + \sum_{\nu=0}^{\infty} i(T_s)g[(\nu - 1)T_s]z^{-\nu}$$

$$+ \sum_{\nu=0}^{\infty} i(2T_s)g[(\nu - 2)T_s]z^{-\nu} + \cdots$$

We can write this equation as

$$\sum_{\nu=0}^{\infty} o(\nu T_s)z^{-\nu} = i(0)z^0 \sum_{\nu=0}^{\infty} g(\nu T_s)z^{-\nu} + i(T_s)z^{-1} \sum_{\nu=0}^{\infty} g[(\nu - 1)T_s]z^{-(\nu-1)}$$

$$+ i(2T_s)z^{-2} \sum_{\nu=0}^{\infty} g[(\nu - 2)T_s]z^{-(\nu-2)} + \cdots \tag{9-108}$$

† Do not confuse this sampler with the mathematical sampler S_m.

In each of the summations on the right side, no contribution is obtained for negative index, and we thus conclude that

$$\sum_{\nu=0}^{\infty} g[(\nu-1)T_s]z^{-(\nu-1)} = \sum_{\nu=0}^{\infty} g[(\nu-2)T_s]z^{-(\nu-2)} = \cdots$$

$$= \sum_{\nu=0}^{\infty} g(\nu T_s)z^{-\nu}$$

As a consequence, (9-108) yields

$$\sum_{\nu=0}^{\infty} o(\nu T_s)z^{-\nu} = [i(0)z^0 + i(T_s)z^{-1} + \cdots]\sum_{\nu=0}^{\infty} g(\nu T_s)z^{-\nu}$$

$$= \sum_{\nu=0}^{\infty} i(\nu T_s)z^{-\nu} \sum_{\nu=0}^{\infty} g(\nu T_s)z^{-\nu} \tag{9-109}$$

We now define, in usual manner,

$$O(z) \stackrel{\Delta}{=} \sum_{\nu=0}^{\infty} o(\nu T_s)z^{-\nu}$$

$$I(z) \stackrel{\Delta}{=} \sum_{\nu=0}^{\infty} i(\nu T_s)z^{-\nu} \tag{9-110}$$

$$G(z) \stackrel{\Delta}{=} \sum_{\nu=0}^{\infty} g(\nu T_s)z^{-\nu}$$

In terms of these z transforms, we then, in accordance with Eq. (9-109), can express the response of the hypothetical $D \rightarrow D$ network of Fig. 9-35 in the form

$$O(z) = G(z)I(z) \tag{9-111}$$

The z transform $G(z)$, which sometimes is symbolized $\mathscr{L}[G(s)]$ or $G^*(s)$, obviously is obtained by deriving the impulse response of the network. Let us demonstrate by an example.

Example 9-15

Consider a case where the $A \rightarrow A$ portion of the system in Fig. 9-32 can be characterized by a simple time constant, that is,

$$G_{AA}(s) = \frac{1}{s+1}$$

We then have

$$G(s) = G_{DH}^*(s)G_{AA}(s) = \frac{1 - e^{-sT_s}}{s} \frac{1}{s+1}$$

We wish to derive the PTF for the overall $D \rightarrow D$ system; i.e., we wish to compute $G(z)$, or in different symbolism, we shall set out to find the z transform

$$\mathscr{L}\left(\frac{1 - e^{-sT_s}}{s} \frac{1}{s+1}\right)$$

We proceed by first computing the impulse response of $G(s)$, that is,

$$g(t) = \mathscr{L}^{-1}[G(s)] = \mathscr{L}^{-1}\left[\frac{1}{s(s+1)} - \frac{e^{-sT_s}}{s(s+1)}\right]$$

$$= \mathscr{L}^{-1}\left[\frac{1}{s(s+1)}\right] - \mathscr{L}^{-1}\left[\frac{e^{-sT_s}}{s(s+1)}\right] \qquad (9\text{-}112)$$

The first term in (9-112) can be written

$$\mathscr{L}^{-1}\left[\frac{1}{s(s+1)}\right] = \mathscr{L}^{-1}\left(\frac{1}{s} - \frac{1}{s+1}\right) = \mathscr{L}^{-1}\left(\frac{1}{s}\right) - \mathscr{L}^{-1}\left(\frac{1}{s+1}\right)$$

$$= 1 - e^{-t} \qquad \text{valid for } t > 0$$

This corresponds therefore to a data sequence

$$1 - 1, 1 - e^{-T_s}, 1 - e^{-2T_s}, \ldots$$

or

$$\{1 - e^{-vT_s}\}$$

or

$$\{1\} - \{e^{-vT_s}\}$$

From Table 9-1, we find

$$\mathscr{L}\{1\} = \frac{z}{z-1}$$

$$\mathscr{L}\{e^{-vT_s}\} = \frac{z}{z - e^{-T_s}}$$

Hence,

$$\mathscr{L}\left[\frac{1}{s(s+1)}\right] = \frac{z}{z-1} - \frac{z}{z - e^{-T_s}}$$

The second term in (9-112) is disposed of quite easily. As the factor e^{-sT_s} implies a time delay of exactly one sample period T_s, we get directly by using (9-75)

$$\mathscr{L}\left[\frac{e^{-sT_s}}{s(s+1)}\right] = z^{-1}\mathscr{L}\left[\frac{1}{s(s+1)}\right] = \frac{1}{z-1} - \frac{1}{z - e^{-T_s}}$$

We finally summarize

$$\mathscr{L}\left(\frac{1 - e^{-sT_s}}{s} \cdot \frac{1}{s+1}\right) = \frac{z}{z-1} - \frac{z}{z - e^{-T_s}} - \left(\frac{1}{z-1} - \frac{1}{z - e^{-T_s}}\right)$$

$$= \frac{1 - e^{-T_s}}{z - e^{-T_s}} \qquad (9\text{-}113)$$

Caution: It is very tempting to try an approach as follows:

$$\mathscr{L}\left[\frac{1}{s(s+1)}\right] = \mathscr{L}\left(\frac{1}{s}\right)\mathscr{L}\left(\frac{1}{s+1}\right)$$

The impulse responses of the networks $1/s$ and $1/(s+1)$ are, respectively,

$$\mathscr{L}^{-1}\left(\frac{1}{s}\right) = u(t)$$

$$\mathscr{L}^{-1}\left(\frac{1}{s+1}\right) = e^{-t}$$

and, as above, we then would get

$$\mathscr{L}\left(\frac{1}{s+1}\right) = \frac{z}{z-e^{-T_s}} \qquad \text{and} \qquad \mathscr{L}\left(\frac{1}{s}\right) = \frac{z}{z-1}$$

and, finally,

$$\mathscr{L}\left[\frac{1}{s(s+1)}\right] = \frac{z}{z-1}\frac{z}{z-e^{-T_s}}$$

This is WRONG! The student is encouraged to decide why!

Note the difference between the correct and the incorrect solutions. We clearly have the inequality

$$\mathscr{L}[G_1(s)G_2(s)] \neq G_1(z)G_2(z)$$

and this gives us reason to introduce a special symbol for the z transform of a product. We define

$$\mathscr{L}[G_1(s)G_2(s)] \stackrel{\Delta}{=} G_1G_2(z)$$

The symbol $\overline{G_1G_2}(z)$ also is found in the literature. Note, however, that if both networks G_1 and G_2 are of the $D \to D$ type, then, as we pointed out in Eq. (9-91), we have

$$\mathscr{L}[G_1(s)G_2(s)] = G_1(z)G_2(z)$$

The z transform as applied to the $D \to A$ type of system neglects completely the response *between* samples. There is a remote possibility, as illustrated by Fig. 9-36, that in this way we may miss essential information in the form of "hidden" oscillations. By using the so-called *modified z-transform technique* (see Ref. 4) the response between the data points can be obtained.

Control-systems Analysis by Means of the z Transform

In the previous section, we learned that care must be exercised in the analysis of sampled-data systems by means of the z transform. In particular it is necessary to differentiate carefully between $D \to D$ and $D \to A$ types of system components. If all these rules are properly adhered to, the z transform proves as useful a tool

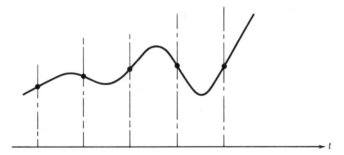

Fig. 9-36 Hidden instability.

in analysis of sampled-data systems as the Laplace transform does in the study of continuous-data systems. When applying the *z*-transform theory to control processes, the matter is complicated by the fact that the sampling can take place at various parts of the loop.

Example 9-16

We shall illustrate *z*-transform analysis of control systems by treating in some detail a rather typical system, depicted in Fig. 9-37*a*. The system consists of a first-order plant, with the sampler being placed in the error channel. The data reconstruction is being done by means of a zero-order data hold. All signals except the one entering the data hold are of the continuous type. In order to make the system amenable to *z*-transform analysis, we must, according to our previous discussions, disregard the continuous nature of the output signal and turn our attention to the data sequence

$$\{c_v\} = c(0),\ c(T_s),\ c(2T_s),\ \ldots,\ c(vT_s)$$

Instead of analyzing the actual system of Fig. 9-37*a*, we therefore concentrate our efforts on the *hypothetical* discrete system of Fig. 9-37*b*, in which the input and output signals appear as discrete-data sequences.

It is important to realize that the output data sequence in Fig. 9-37b is identical to the actual output in Fig. 9-37a as measured at the discrete instants $t = 0$, T_s, $2T_s$, ...

We next establish the mathematical model for this system. First, we borrow the results from the previous section and relate the output-data sequence $\{c_v\}$ to the error sequence $\{e_v\}$:

$$C(z) = G_0(z)E(z) \tag{9-114}$$

$G_0(z)$ is the "open-loop" PTF, defined as

$$G_0(z) \overset{\Delta}{=} \mathscr{L}[G^*_{DH}(s)G_p(s)] = G^*_{DH}G_p(z) = \mathscr{L}\left(\frac{1 - e^{-sT_s}}{s}\ \frac{K}{s+1}\right) \tag{9-115}$$

Secondly, we know that the comparator action ensures the relation

$$\{r_v\} - \{c_v\} = \{e_v\}$$

Therefore,

$$R(z) - C(z) = E(z) \tag{9-116}$$

By elimination of $E(z)$ between (9-114) and (9-116), we obtain the following relationship between $R(z)$ and $C(z)$:

$$C(z) = R(z) \frac{G_0(z)}{1 + G_0(z)} \triangleq R(z)G_c(z) \tag{9-117}$$

We thus obtain a formula quite similar to the one we were encountering in the continuous-data case. The *closed-loop* PTF $G_c(z)$ completely determines the nature of the response, just as the closed-loop transfer function $G_c(s)$ did in the continuous-data case. Since we shall proceed to study the system in more detail, we shall need to compute the actual values for the transfer functions.

We first need the open-loop PTF $G_0(z)$. Except for a gain factor K, Eq. (9-115) is identical to the z transform we computed in Example 9-15; and by borrowing the result from (9-113), we therefore have

$$G_0(z) = K \frac{1 - e^{-T_s}}{z - e^{-T_s}} \tag{9-118}$$

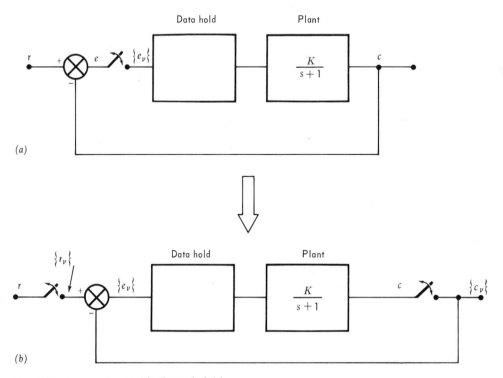

Fig. 9-37 System discussed in Example 9-16.

Hence,

$$G_c(z) = \frac{G_0(z)}{1 + G_0(z)} = \frac{K_c}{z - \lambda} \tag{9-119}$$

where $K_c \overset{\Delta}{=} K(1 - e^{-T_s})$ and $\lambda \overset{\Delta}{=} e^{-T_s}(1 + K) - K$.

λ is the single pole of $G_c(z)$ or, expressed differently, the eigenvalue obtained from the characteristic equation

$$1 + G_0(z) = 0 \tag{9-120}$$

Let us, for instance, study the response due to a step input-data sequence, that is,

$$\{r_v\} = 1, 1, 1, \dots$$

From Table 9-1, we get

$$R(z) = \frac{z}{z - 1}$$

and Eq. (9-117) then yields

$$C(z) = \frac{z}{z - 1} \frac{K_c}{z - \lambda} = \frac{K_c}{\lambda - 1} \frac{z}{z - \lambda} - \frac{K_c}{\lambda - 1} \frac{z}{z - 1} \tag{9-121}$$

It is worth noting that the first term emanates from the pole λ of the closed-loop PTF and thus represents the *transient* response. The second term is due to the input and thus will give rise to the *driven* response.

By inverse transformation (from Table 9-1), we get

$$\{c_v\} = \frac{K_c}{\lambda - 1} \{\lambda^v\} - \frac{K_c}{\lambda - 1} \{1\} \tag{9-122}$$

or

$$c_v = \frac{K_c}{\lambda - 1} (\lambda^v - 1) \tag{9-123}$$

Clearly, the transient part of this solution will vanish with increasing v only if $|\lambda| < 1$. We conclude therefore the following simple *stability rule*:

For stability, the root of the closed-loop transfer function, or the eigenvalue, must be located inside the unit circle in the z-plane.

It is obvious that we can extend this rule directly to higher-order systems. For an nth-order system, we can expand the closed loop PTF as follows:

$$G_c(z) = A_1 \frac{z}{z - \lambda_1} + \cdots + A_i \frac{z}{z - \lambda_i} + \cdots + A_n \frac{z}{z - \lambda_n}$$

where $\lambda_1, \lambda_2, \dots, \lambda_n$ are the eigenvalues or the roots of the characteristic equation (9-120). We consider them for the moment *distinct*.

The *transient* solution will consist of terms of the type

$$A_i \lambda_i^\nu$$

all of which will vanish with increasing ν if and only if

$$|\lambda_i| < 1$$

Note that the presence of *multiple* roots will not change the picture essentially. For example, if λ_i were a double root, the above expansion would contain a term

$$\frac{z}{(z - \lambda_i)^2}$$

which, upon inverse transformation, would yield

$$\nu \lambda_i^\nu$$

This term would also vanish with increasing ν if $|\lambda_i| < 1$.

The unit circle takes on the same role in the z plane as the $j\omega$ axis did in the s plane; i.e., it represents the dividing line between stable and unstable regions. The situation is illustrated in Fig. 9-38.

We note another similarity between the continuous-data and discrete-data control systems. As the characteristic equations are of identical form in the two cases, we *can use the root-locus techniques we developed for the s plane in unmodified form for the z plane.* This, of course, is of tremendous help, and we wish to demonstrate with the system just discussed.

The open-loop pole of the system (9-118) is located at $z = e^{-T_s}$. The root locus (only *one*, in this case) now will look as depicted in Fig. 9-39. The locus will penetrate the unit circle for a gain K, obtainable from the equation

$$G_0(-1) + 1 = 0$$

that is, for K values satisfying the equation

$$K \frac{1 - e^{-T_s}}{-1 - e^{-T_s}} + 1 = 0 \tag{9-124}$$

Equation (9-124) yields

$$K = \frac{1 + e^{-T_s}}{1 - e^{-T_s}} \tag{9-125}$$

For stability, we thus must require

$$K < \frac{1 + e^{-T_s}}{1 - e^{-T_s}} \tag{9-126}$$

We also can write this equation in the form

$$T_s < \ln\left(\frac{K + 1}{K - 1}\right) \tag{9-127}$$

informing us about the largest possible sampling period (i.e., the lowest sampling frequency) that we can tolerate for a specific gain setting in order to preserve stability.

Synthesis of sampled-data control systems is beyond the scope of this book. The reader will find a lucid treatment of this topic in Ref. 4. Basically, the difference in synthesis between continuous-data and sampled-data systems is not too great, particularly since we may employ root-locus techniques in both cases. In

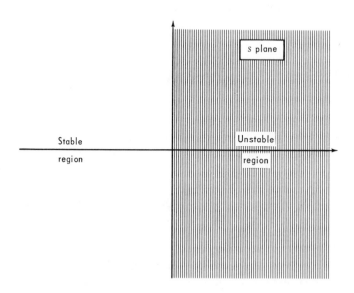

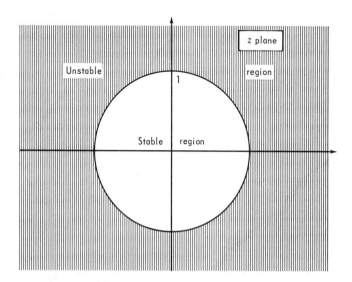

Fig. 9-38 A comparison of stability regions in s and z planes.

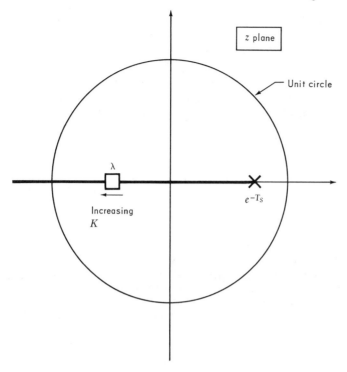

Fig. 9-39   Root locus for system in Fig. 9-37.

detail, however, there are considerably more variations to the latter. For one thing, we obviously have a choice of designing the compensation networks either $A \rightarrow A$ or $D \rightarrow D$. As the cascading rule [Eq. (9-91)] applies in the latter but not in the former case, it is easier to predict the effect of the $D \rightarrow D$ type of compensation.

9-5 SUMMARY

For a variety of practical reasons, a large number of control systems incorporate components which operate on modulated signals. In this chapter, we developed the theory for a-c carrier and sampled-data systems. We concluded that, in both cases, the modulation results in a shift of the low-frequency signal energy to the high-frequency region. In the case of AM modulation, we find the signal energy at and around the carrier frequency; in the sampled-data case, the energy is bunched around every multiple of the sampling frequency.

We found it convenient to analyze the a-c carrier servos from a frequency point of view—leading us in particular to the design via the method of "frequency transformation." The important difference between a-c servos and conventional d-c systems lies in the necessity for designing a-c compensation networks which operate on the envelope of the modulated signal.

In developing the theory for sampled-data systems, we found it natural to introduce the reader to the concept of discrete-data sequences and difference equations. A comparison was made between continuous systems and differential equations on one hand and sampled data systems and difference equations on the other. This approach also permitted us to introduce in a natural way the *z* transform and relate it to the more familiar Laplace transform. Finally, we presented the concept of "pulse transfer function" and used it in analysis of a simple feedback system.

Exercises

9-1 The resolver matrix **T** was defined by Eq. (9-18). Compute the inverse, $\mathbf{T}^{-1}$, and from the result prove the statement made in the text that the *x* roll channel is decoupled completely from the other two channels in Fig. 9-21.

9-2 It is easy to prove that

$$|\mathbf{T}| = \cos \beta$$

For $\beta = 90°$, we get $|\mathbf{T}| = 0$, and thus the **T** matrix is *singular*. We have a situation referred to as *gimbal lock*. What is the physical significance of the singularity of **T** and what actually do you think happens in this situation? *Hint:* Note what happens with the command signals to the roll and yaw torquers.

9-3 Consider the case when the spectrum of the unmodulated signal $e(t)$ consists of one single discrete line, that is,

$$e(t) = e_{max} \sin \omega_0 t$$

Shannon's sampling theorem states that $\omega_s > 2\omega_0$.

Give a physical reason why no lower sampling rates can be accepted.

9-4 *a* Write the difference equation for the second-order sampled-data control system obtained if the plant in Fig. 9-37 is of the double-integrator type, that is,

$$G_p(s) = \frac{K}{s^2}$$

b Find a solution in the form expressed by Eq. (9-63). Assume the system is undriven ($r_v = 0$) and set $c_0 = 1$.

c Find the open-loop PTF for the system and show by means of root loci that the system is unstable for all K and all T_s.

d Give a physical interpretation of the results in problem *c*.

9-5 Consider the system depicted in Fig. 9-37, which was analyzed in detail in the text. Put the sampler plus data hold in the feedback branch. Will this essentially change the response features as developed in the text? If you conclude that this is a different system from that in Fig. 9-37, analyze it. In particular, find the response to a step input and compare with Eq. (9-123).

9-6 Replace the first-order plant in Fig. 9-37 with the second-order plant

$$G_p(s) = \frac{1}{s(s + 1)}$$

Compute the closed-loop PTF for this system and obtain the roots of the characteristic equation. In particular, find the lowest sampling frequency that can be used with preserved stability.

References

1. A. E. Fitzgerald and C. Kingsley, "Electric Machinery," McGraw-Hill Book Company, New York, 1961.
2. John C. Truxal (ed.), "Control Engineers' Handbook," McGraw-Hill Book Company, New York, 1958.
3. C. Broxmeyer, "Inertial Navigation Systems," McGraw-Hill Book Company, New York, 1964.
4. B. C. Kuo, "Analysis and Synthesis of Sampled-data Control Systems," Prentice-Hall, Inc., Englewood Cliffs, N.J., 1963.

chapter 10

OPTIMUM CONTROL–
THE STATIC CASE

10-1 INTRODUCTION

During the past decade, optimization methods have taken on an extremely important role in all areas of engineering. Increased competition plus man's desire to perform in an optimum fashion, combined with the fact that he faces an ever-shrinking supply of natural resources, represent some of the reasons. In modern technology, one encounters with increasing frequency situations where, for various technological reasons, one can accept only those engineering solutions which are optimal in some defined sense.

A specific engineering problem does not have a unique solution; indeed, it has in most cases an infinite number of possible solutions. If we judge the various solutions on the basis of a specific *payoff function* (*cost index, value function, index of performance, figure of merit*, etc.), each possible solution is characterized, as a rule, by a different value of this function. The one solution associated with the optimum value is referred to as the *optimum solution*. It is appropriate to point out that the word "optimum" may refer to either a maximum or a minimum, depending upon the situation at hand. The most obvious method of optimization is an outright search process—all possible solutions in the total set of possible ones are compared and the best one is selected. Unless the search process is particularly attractive (as in the case of selecting Miss America out of 50 entries), this is not a recommended procedure, but it is one that nevertheless must be employed when no other road is open.

In this and the next chapter, we shall concern ourselves with the methods and procedures of *optimum control*, a term which we defined in Chap. 7 (Sec. 7-2.3). Some authors[1] include under this broad term any control system that optimizes some selected index of performance, subject to given design constraints. This then would include in the "optimal" family even the so-called "analytical" design methods briefly discussed in Chap. 7. As analytical design utilizes some a priori assumptions concerning system structure, most proponents of optimum control would exclude this group on the basis that these assumptions place undue constraint on the design. This viewpoint has been adopted in this book. The types of control problems that we shall attend to will all contain the following basic elements:

1. The plant dynamics

   $$\dot{\mathbf{x}} = \mathbf{f}(\mathbf{x},\mathbf{u})$$

   are known and also, in most of our examples, assumed to be *linear*.
2. Attention will be limited to the *deterministic* case; i.e., we shall not include stochastic disturbance inputs $\mathbf{z}$, and furthermore, we tacitly assume that our measurements of the state vector are not contaminated with noise.
3. The state vector $\mathbf{x}$ and/or the control-force vector $\mathbf{u}$ are *constrained*. The constraints may be of various types. For instance, we may specify that the components of $\mathbf{u}$ must range only within certain limits (*inequality constraints*), or we may specify certain "initial" and "final" values for the state vector $\mathbf{x}$ (*equality constraints*). In certain applications, it even may be necessary to impose restrictions on the *control interval* t_f.
4. A performance index I is decided upon, and as in most practical cases the payoff is a function of both state $\mathbf{x}$ and control effort $\mathbf{u}$ and as it generally grows cumulatively with time, we shall be concerned as a rule with indices of the form

$$I = \int_0^{t_f} F(\mathbf{x},\mathbf{u})\, dt \tag{10-1}$$

In the so-called *static-optimization case*, we shall be more concerned with the *rate of change* of I than with I itself. From (10-1), we get directly

$$\frac{dI}{dt} = F(\mathbf{x},\mathbf{u}) \tag{10-2}$$

We wish to emphasize the fact that the constraints in point 3 are the *only* ones we work with. We thus make no assumptions concerning the *structure* or *form* of the optimal controller. In this respect, optimum control is radically different from the classical approach, where we always worked with a priori chosen structures.

Concisely stated, the optimal-control problem reduces to the problem of finding the optimal-control force $\mathbf{u} = \mathbf{u}_{\text{opt}}$ that optimizes I subject to the various imposed constraints. We shall refer to $\mathbf{u}_{\text{opt}}$ as the *optimal-control strategy*.

This fairly simply stated problem is, in general, very difficult to solve. Only in very rare cases is it possible to obtain analytically the optimum-control strategy. Indeed, even if we lower our goal and ask only for a numerical solution valid for a specific set of parameters, we find that we often must tax the modern computer to the limit. In a great many instances, we simply are faced with a nonsolvable problem. The difficulties are due to the inherent problem of optimizing an integral of type (10-1). The mathematical nature of the problem complex has attracted the attention of a very large number of applied and pure mathematicians, who, in fact, are responsible for much of the progress that has been made in recent years. The literature on optimum control, mostly due to researchers from the United States and the U.S.S.R., has been prolific. Unfortunately for the engineer, however, most of it has been inaccessible due to the comparatively high mathematical level, uncommon symbolic language, and formal presentation. We shall make an attempt in these two chapters to take an engineer's view of the topic of optimum control, even if it necessitates our taking on occasion some mathematical shortcuts.

10-2 STATIC-VERSUS-DYNAMIC OPTIMUM CONTROL

The optimum-control problem can be divided conveniently into the following two classes:

1. The static-optimization problem
2. The dynamic-optimization problem

In this section, we shall define these terms and also exemplify them with some representative engineering examples.

The *static*-optimization problem is encountered whenever we are asked to control optimally a plant *the normal state of which is a steady state.*

Consider a plant described by the dynamic vector equation

$$\dot{\mathbf{x}} = \mathbf{f}(\mathbf{x},\mathbf{u})$$

Assume now that we wish to control the plant so as to keep the state at the *constant, steady* value

$$\mathbf{x} = \mathbf{x}^0 \tag{10-3}$$

In this steady state, the *dynamic* vector *differential* equation reduces to the *static algebraic* vector equation

$$\mathbf{f}(\mathbf{x}^0,\mathbf{u}^0) = \mathbf{0} \tag{10-4}$$

from which we may solve for the *constant, steady* control force $\mathbf{u}^0$ that will keep us in the state in question.

With both $\mathbf{x}$ and $\mathbf{u}$ reduced to constants, we conclude that the rate of change of the payoff function (10-2) also turns to the constant value

$$\left(\frac{dI}{dt}\right)^0 = F(\mathbf{x}^0,\mathbf{u}^0) \tag{10-5}$$

We conclude that the cost index grows at a constant rate, and we therefore can optimize the process by optimizing this rate. Let us demonstrate with the following very typical example of static optimum control.

Example 10-1

Consider the operation of an electric-utility company depicted in Fig. 10-1. Its system consists of n generators $G_1, G_2, \ldots, G_n$ feeding electric energy at the rates

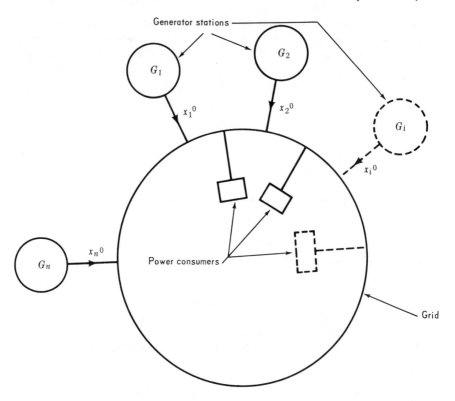

Fig. 10-1 Electric-utility system.

$x_1^0, x_2^0, \ldots, x_n^0$ kw into the system. Electric power is a commodity that cannot be stored, and we therefore must require that the total production at every moment of time equals the customer demand P, over which we have no control. The power state of the system therefore (neglecting all losses) must satisfy the equality constraint

$$x_1^0 + x_2^0 + \cdots + x_n^0 = \sum_{i=1}^{n} x_i^0 = P \tag{10-6}$$

This relation is kept satisfied automatically by continuously controlling the frequency to 60 cps on the dot. For instance, a frequency increase to 60.1 cps would be an indication that we momentarily had overproduced, i.e., the sum

$$\sum_{i=1}^{n} x_i^0$$

is in excess of P, and the surplus energy is used to increase the kinetic energy of the system, i.e., the speed of the generators and thus the frequency.

The power company is faced with the problem of *how to divide the production between its various generators.* It should be pointed out that the customer need

P is a fairly *slowly* changing variable in comparison with the rates at which the generator outputs x_i^0 can be changed, *and we can thus consider Eq. (10-6) a static equation.*

In selecting the proper load division between the generators, the power company must base its decision on a reasonable figure of merit, and in the majority of cases, it settles on the *overall production cost.* Due to differences in such factors as geographical location, fuel, and generator size, the cost of energy production will vary for the different generator stations. Let $u_i^0(x_i^0)$ denote the cost rate, expressed, for instance, in dollars per hour, to produce x_i^0 kw in station i. Then we obtain the *overall* steady-state cost rate as

$$\left(\frac{dI}{dt}\right)^0 = \sum_{i=1}^{n} u_i^0(x_i^0) \qquad \text{dollars/hr} \tag{10-7}$$

With a little imagination, we can here consider the cost rate u_i^0 as playing the role of a "control force." The generator station accepts u_i^0 as the input and supplies x_i^0 as the output (Fig. 10-2). The problem now is to minimize the overall cost (10-7) *under proper observance of the equality constraint* (10-6). How this actually should be accomplished will be shown in the next section.

This is a rather typical example of static optimization, which is quite prevalent in the general area of industrial process control. Continuous productions of sheet steel, gasoline, paper, electricity, and even passenger or freight miles in a jetliner are basically steady-state "processes" which can be optimized on the basis of a figure of merit that most often is dollars and/or "quality of product." Granted that it is not generally so easy to settle for an I figure as in the example cited. After all, a kilowatt is a kilowatt, be it produced in a 60-year-old hydro plant or in a hypermodern nuclear-power station. This then brings into focus the problem which was hinted at in Chap. 7—the difficulty of settling on an index of performance. The choice is often purely subjective. Even in the above "clear-cut" example, there is some doubt about the propriety of choosing dollars as our criterion. Certainly, the stockholders would agree, but if we were to ask the customers of the utility company, they probably would wish to include "continuity of service" as equally important.

We proceed with the presentation of a control problem that clearly must be placed in the category of *dynamic optimum control.*

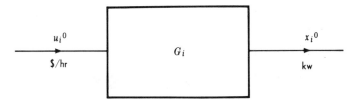

Fig. 10-2 The power outputs of generators may be chosen as state variables.

Example 10-2

This problem concerns the optimal thrusting during the final phase of a soft lunar-landing maneuver. The lunar-excursion module (LEM) has been lowered from a lunar orbit, and at $t = 0$, which we define as the starting time for the landing phase, we find it hovering at an altitude $y(0)$ (Fig. 10-3). As fuel is at a premium at this distance from earth, we wish to perform a controlled landing *with minimum fuel consumption*. There is no atmosphere on the moon, so we cannot "fly" the LEM. Our only means is to control it by controlling properly the thrust force u. Let us look at the quantitative aspects of this problem. It is obvious that we must keep the LEM on "right keel," so we certainly must have additional thrusters to perform attitude control. The main fuel consumption, however, takes place at the bottom engine, so we shall consider only the vertical motion. Newton's law of acceleration gives

$$m\ddot{y} = -mg + u(t)$$

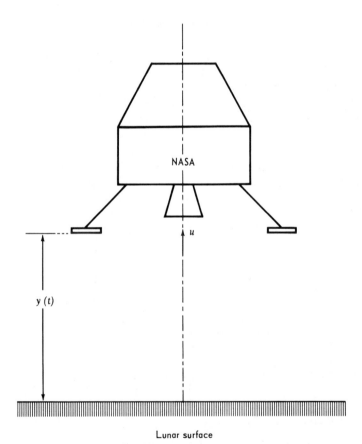

Fig. 10-3 Moon-landing vehicle.

where

g = surface gravity of moon

By introducing the *range y* and *range rate ẏ* as our state variables, we have

$$\mathbf{x} = \begin{bmatrix} x_1 \\ x_2 \end{bmatrix} \triangleq \begin{bmatrix} y \\ \dot{y} \end{bmatrix}$$

Therefore,

$$\dot{x}_1 = x_2$$
$$\dot{x}_2 = -g + \frac{1}{m} u(t) \tag{10-8}$$

The thrust $u(t)$ is proportional to the velocity k of exhaust gases relative to the vehicle and burning rate $dm/dt = \dot{m}$, in accordance with the formula

$$u = -k\dot{m} \tag{10-9}$$

Note that as $\dot{m}$ is negative by necessity, and as we wish to define $u(t)$ positive, we need a minus sign in formula (10-9). Note also that as k is a constant depending upon the fuel used, our only way to vary u is to vary the burning rate $\dot{m}$. We assume that this can be done "inertia-less."

Our index of performance is the total fuel consumed during the landing phase, i.e., the sum (= integral) of the burning rate

$$I = -\int_0^{t_f} \dot{m}\, dt = \int_{t_f}^0 dm = m(0) - m(t_f) \tag{10-10}$$

(Note that we again needed a minus sign to make $I > 0$.)

From the relationship (10-9), we obtain

$$I = \frac{1}{k} \int_0^{t_f} u\, dt \tag{10-11}$$

The function F in Eq. (10-1) in this case obviously equals

$$F = \frac{1}{k} u$$

Our optimum-control problem consists now of selecting a thrusting strategy $u(t)$ that will minimize the integral (10-11) *and simultaneously meet any constraints that, from a physical point of view, we must impose.*

What are these constraints? Clearly, we must meet the following *state* constraints

$$\mathbf{x}(0) = \begin{bmatrix} y(0) \\ 0 \end{bmatrix} \tag{10-12}$$

and

$$\mathbf{x}(t_f) = \begin{bmatrix} 0 \\ 0 \end{bmatrix}$$

Note that no explicit constraints need to be put on the time interval t_f.

We make the important observation that our problem is of the so-called *split-boundary* type; i.e., we must transfer the system state between values specified at two different instants of time. As we specify *both* components of the state vector and as we have only *one* control force, it is very appropriate to ask the important question of whether the proposed control maneuver is physically possible in the first place. We realize immediately that this question can be answered in the affirmative only if we conclude that the plant is *controllable*. A simple check reveals that it indeed is.

In addition to the *state* constraints, we may note that there are *u* constraints also. We cannot apply negative thrust,† and as the engine is of limited size, we therefore must execute the above maneuver with a *u* force in the range

$$0 < u < u_{max}$$

It probably has occurred to the reader that the above problem is not an easy one to attack. The situation is complicated further by the fact that the two astronauts have only *one* chance, *and they must have the on-board capability of deciding upon the optimum strategy in real time.*

There is certainly nothing static about the given problem. Control force and state are changing throughout the maneuver. The problem is a good example of a *dynamic*-optimization process. As its solution goes somewhat beyond our scope, we shall not attempt a solution, which the interested reader may obtain from Ref. 2.

In the next chapter, however, we shall consider in detail the solution of the following problem, also of the *dynamic* variety:

Example 10-3

In Chaps. 3 and 5, we considered the temperature dynamics of an electrically heated oven, depicted in Fig. 3-4. We found that the temperature state **x** obeyed the linear vector differential equation

$$\dot{\mathbf{x}} = \mathbf{A}\mathbf{x} + \mathbf{b}u$$

We now pose the following problem: What control strategy should we use if we wish to heat the oven from the initial temperature state $\mathbf{x}(0)$ to the final state $\mathbf{x}(t_f)$ *in minimum time* t_f? This is an example of a *time-optimal control* problem, and we can include it under our integral criterion (10-1) if we set $F(\mathbf{x},\mathbf{u}) \triangleq 1$, that is,

$$I = \int_0^{t_f} 1 \, dt = t_f$$

First, we conclude that the problem statement makes physical sense only if the system is controllable, which we confirmed to be the case in Chap. 5. We also remember that controllability implies that we can transfer the system between

---

† Assuming one engine only.

any finite states in *any* finite time; the above problem statement therefore would seem rather meaningless as we obviously can heat the oven in as short a time as we please. The crux of the matter is that in discussing controllability, we *always* tacitly assumed *unlimited* control force *u*. Clearly, we can heat the oven in as short time as we please if we permit any magnitude for the heat input *u*. We therefore make the following important conclusion:

A *time-optimal control problem exists only in those cases where amplitude constraints are imposed upon the* **u** *vector*. We shall solve this problem in detail in the next chapter.

The above three examples have served to demonstrate some typical varieties of optimal-control problems. Additional examples will be given as we proceed. We shall concentrate now on the static-optimization problem, which is by far the simplest one to handle.

10-3 STATIC OPTIMIZATION

We shall devote the remaining part of this chapter to the static-optimum-control problem.

Static optimization of controlled processes can be achieved in either of the two following ways:

1. By *open-loop* optimization, where complete reliance is put on an a priori known model of the controlled process. This method, referred to in the following as the *mathematical-model approach*, can be used only when the process is well defined, its parameters generally known, and the effects of disturbances negligible.
2. By *closed-loop* optimization, used in processes where the parameters are ill-defined and/or possibly changing with time and where random disturbances may have considerable influence on the plant state. We shall refer to this method as *optimization through experimentation*.

10-3.1 THE MATHEMATICAL-MODEL APPROACH

We shall concern ourselves now with control processes which are characterized by fairly "clean" mathematical models.

We remember that the static-optimum-control problem basically reduced to one of optimizing the rate function (10-5):

$$\left(\frac{dI}{dt}\right)^0 = F(\mathbf{x}^0, \mathbf{u}^0) \tag{10-13}$$

As $\mathbf{u}^0$ and $\mathbf{x}^0$ are related [Eq. (10-4)] through the equation

$$\mathbf{f}(\mathbf{x}^0, \mathbf{u}^0) = \mathbf{0}$$

it is possible, at least in principle, to solve for $\mathbf{u}^0$, and after substitution of this $\mathbf{u}^0$ value into (10-13), the rate function can be expressed as a function of the steady state $\mathbf{x}^0$ alone,

$$\left(\frac{dI}{dt}\right)^0 = F(\mathbf{x}^0, \mathbf{u}^0) = H(\mathbf{x}^0) = H(x_1^0, x_2^0, \ldots, x_n^0) \tag{10-14}$$

This H function will assume different values, depending upon the particular $\mathbf{x}^0$ vector that we select. Our success in finding the value which renders H an optimum depends basically upon the following three factors:

1. The specific nature of the H function
2. Dimensionality of $\mathbf{x}^0$
3. Constraints

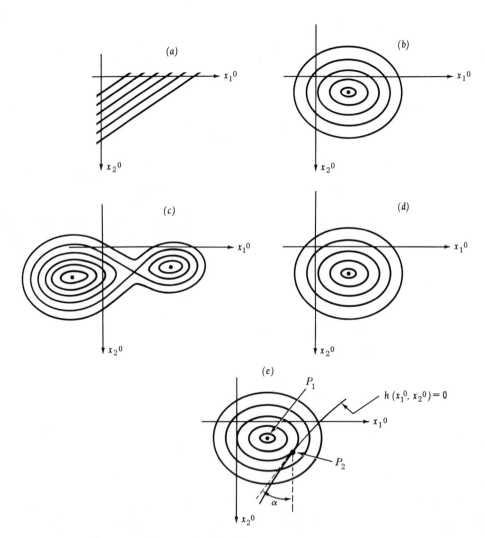

Fig. 10-4 Various types of H contours.

If H is plotted versus x_1^0, x_2^0, ..., x_n^0 in n-dimensional state space, we obtain a multidimensional *performance surface*. The situation is not visualized easily in the general case, but we may give it a simple graphical representation for the case $n = 2$. In this case, the function (10-14) reduces to

$$H(x_1^0, x_2^0)$$

and if we assign different constant values H^0 to H in accordance with

$$H(x_1^0, x_2^0) = H^0 \tag{10-15}$$

then we obtain a sequence of curves, or *contours*, in the $x_1^0 x_2^0$ plane, one for each assigned H^0 value, as shown in Fig. 10-4. The shape of these contours is a function of the particular type of H function. For instance, the *quadratic* function

$$H(x_1^0, x_2^0) = x_1^{0^2} + x_2^{0^2} = H^0 \tag{10-16}$$

results in a family of concentric circles centered in origin. A still better visual picture is obtained if we introduce an H axis perpendicular to the $x_1^0 x_2^0$ plane. In the cartesian coordinate system thus obtained, Eq. (10-15) is represented by a three-dimensional surface according to Fig. 10-5. The student should clarify to his own satisfaction the correspondence between the graphs in Figs. 10-4 and 10-5.

It is obvious that if the coordinates x_1^0 and x_2^0 are *unconstrained*, some types of surfaces may *not* have an optimum at all. This is particularly true for the *linear* H function

$$H(x_1^0, x_2^0) = \alpha_1 x_1^0 + \alpha_2 x_2^0 \tag{10-17}$$

where α_1 and α_2 are constants.

This type of surface, a plane, is shown in Figs. 10-4a and 10-5a. Other types of surfaces may have optima of the "smooth" or "calculus" type (Figs. 10-4b and 10-5b) or of the "peaky" type (Figs. 10-4d and 10-5d). A confusing situation is represented by the surface in Fig. 10-4c or 10-5c, which has two optima with different relative magnitudes.

The situation changes radically if, as usually is the case, certain constraints on the state variables must be observed. These constraints may take the form of equality constraints

$$h_v(x_1^0, x_2^0, \ldots, x_n^0) = 0 \qquad \text{for } v = 1, 2, \ldots, p; \quad p < n \tag{10-18}$$

or, in the vector form,

$$\mathbf{h}(\mathbf{x}^0) = \mathbf{0}$$

or they may be inequality constraints of the type

$$g_\mu(x_1^0, x_2^0, \ldots, x_n^0) < 0 \qquad \text{for } \mu = 1, 2, \ldots, q \tag{10-19}$$

Consider, for example, the H surface depicted in Fig. 10-5b. Its *unconstrained* maximum point obviously is located "on top" of the surface in point P_1. Let us

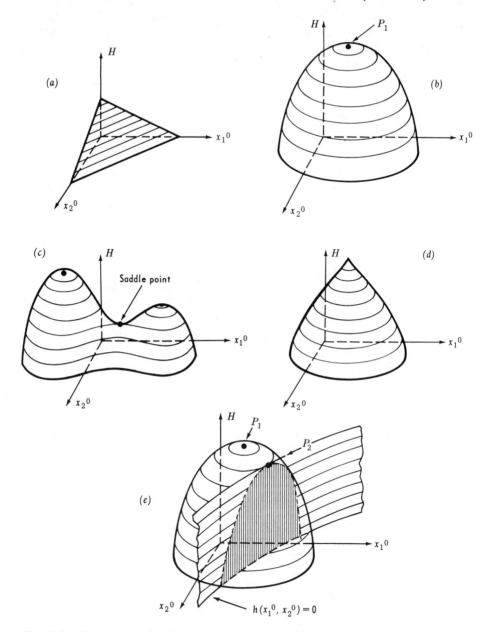

Fig. 10-5 Alternate way of depicting the contours in Fig. 10-4.

now assume that we apply the equality constraint

$$h(x_1^0, x_2^0) = 0 \tag{10-20}$$

that is, we require that the state variables x_1^0 and x_2^0 can take on values only in the vertical surface defined by Eq. (10-20). This surface intersects the H surface along the dotted lines in Fig. 10-5e, and the maximum value therefore must be sought along this line. The resulting *constrained maximum* occurs at P_2. *Note that P_2 is the tangency point between the constant H contour and the curve $h(x_1^0, x_2^0) = 0$ in the point in question.*

The above presentation has been entirely qualitative. Let us now look at the problem of determining the optima from a quantitative point of view. We shall discuss only those cases of greatest practical significance.

Linear Performance Function with Linear Constraints

This problem is usually referred to as "linear programming." We shall here be concerned with an H function of the linear type

$$H(\mathbf{x}^0) = \alpha_1 x_1^0 + \alpha_2 x_2^0 + \cdots + \alpha_n x_n^0 \tag{10-21}$$

The constraints, equality as well as inequality, are also linear.

This type of problem is encountered in various areas of control, particularly in the areas of logistics and business. Let us look at a very typical example.

Example 10-4

An industry produces two different products, A and B, on which it makes $50 profit per unit. How should it divide its production in order to optimize the profit when it is known that the manufacturing process is subject to the following limitations:

The products must go through two different processes; the first requires 10 hr for A and 5 hr for B, and the second 5 hr for A and 6 hr for B. Each process has a yearly total run of 3,500 hr.

On the basis of this information, the profit function H assumes the form

$$H = 50x_1^0 + 50x_2^0 \tag{10-22}$$

where x_1^0 and x_2^0 represent the number of units of A and B, respectively.

The production constraints can be expressed as the set of linear inequalities

$$10x_1^0 + 5x_2^0 < 3,500$$
$$5x_1^0 + 6x_2^0 < 3,500$$

Also, of course,

$$x_1^0 > 0$$
$$x_2^0 > 0$$

These constraints have been indicated in the $x_1^0 x_2^0$ diagram in Fig. 10-6. They actually box in the permissible x_1^0 and x_2^0 values within a four-corner

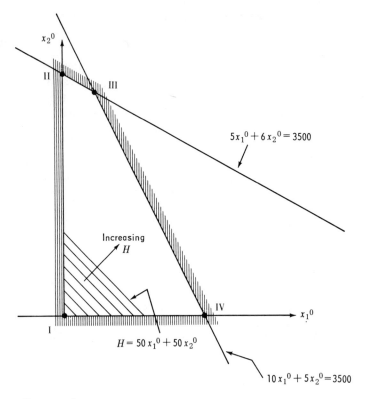

Corner coordinates:

  I $x_1^0 = x_2^0 = 0$

  II $x_1^0 = 0;\ x_2^0 = 583$

  III $x_1^0 = 100;\ x_2^0 = 500$

  IV $x_1^0 = 350;\ x_2^0 = 0$

Fig. 10-6 Example of linear programming.

polygonal area. As the profit function H represents a plane, it is obvious that the optimum value must be located on the periphery of this area, quite probably in the corner points. Linear programming implies a straightforward search process aimed at finding the optimum. In the present case, only corners II to IV are of interest, and using the coordinate values indicated in the figure, we compute the H values in those corners:

$H = 50 \times 0 + 50 \times 583 = \$29{,}150$ corner II

$H = 50 \times 100 + 50 \times 500 = \$30{,}000$ corner III

$H = 50 \times 350 + 50 \times 0 = \$17{,}500$ corner IV

result: Optimum profit is obtained by producing 100 units of A and 500 units of B.

In a high-dimensional case, one proceeds in a similar manner. The basic problem is to find all the corner points. Both digital- and analog-computer programs have been developed for this search process.[3]

H Function Exhibiting Calculus Optima—
The Method of Lagrange Multipliers

A very important case from a practical point of view is the one where the *H* function is characterized by "smooth" optima of the so-called "calculus" type (see, for instance, Fig. 10-5*b*). The classical techniques of extremum search can now be employed. The optimum point in the *unconstrained* case is identified by the fact that no change in *H* should take place when a small arbitrary deviation from the optimum occurs; that is, *H* is *stationary*.

From (10-14), we have

$$dH = \frac{\partial H}{\partial x_1{}^0} dx_1{}^0 + \frac{\partial H}{\partial x_2{}^0} dx_2{}^0 + \cdots + \frac{\partial H}{\partial x_n{}^0} dx_n{}^0 \tag{10-23}$$

As the $dx_i{}^0$'s are completely free, the only possible way to ensure that dH remains zero is to require that all partial derivatives vanish. For *unconstrained* *H* extremum, we thus must have

$$\frac{\partial H}{\partial x_i{}^0} = 0 \qquad \text{for } i = 1, 2, \ldots, n \tag{10-24}$$

Note that we say "extremum." Equations (10-24) guarantee only stationary *H*, but we must employ other means to determine whether we have a maximum, a minimum, or a saddle point. Usually, the physical situation tells us what type of extremum we have.

As usual, the two-dimensional case provides us with good visual confirmation. In Fig. 10-5*b*, we realize immediately that only on the "top of the hill" do we indeed have

$$\frac{\partial H}{\partial x_1{}^0} = \frac{\partial H}{\partial x_2{}^0} = 0$$

It is considerably harder to determine a *constrained* optimum. We shall demonstrate with the two-dimensional case

$$H(x_1{}^0, x_2{}^0) \tag{10-25}$$

subject to the constraint

$$h(x_1{}^0, x_2{}^0) = 0 \tag{10-26}$$

In other words, we are seeking the point P_2 in Fig. 10-5*e*. We observed earlier that P_2 is the tangency point between the curve $h(x_1{}^0, x_2{}^0) = 0$ and the constant *H* contour through the point in question, and we shall make use of this fact for its identification.

By differentiation of

$$H(x_1^0, x_2^0) = \text{const}$$

we obtain

$$\frac{\partial H}{\partial x_1^0} dx_1^0 + \frac{\partial H}{\partial x_2^0} dx_2^0 = 0$$

Therefore,

$$\frac{dx_2^0}{dx_1^0} = -\frac{\partial H/\partial x_1^0}{\partial H/\partial x_2^0}$$

Differentiation of (10-26) similarly yields

$$\frac{dx_2^0}{dx_1^0} = -\frac{\partial h/\partial x_1^0}{\partial h/\partial x_2^0}$$

The tangency requirement thus results in the equation

$$\frac{\partial H/\partial x_2^0}{\partial H/\partial x_1^0} = \frac{\partial h/\partial x_2^0}{\partial h/\partial x_1^0} = -\tan \alpha \qquad (10\text{-}27)$$

(See Fig. 10-4*e* for definition of α.)

We may also write Eqs. (10-27) in the form

$$\frac{\partial H/\partial x_1^0}{\partial h/\partial x_1^0} = \frac{\partial H/\partial x_2^0}{\partial h/\partial x_2^0} = -\lambda = \text{const}$$

The constant λ is referred to as the *Lagrange multiplier*. We write the last equations as

$$\frac{\partial H}{\partial x_1^0} + \lambda \frac{\partial h}{\partial x_1^0} = 0$$

$$\frac{\partial H}{\partial x_2^0} + \lambda \frac{\partial h}{\partial x_2^0} = 0 \qquad (10\text{-}28)$$

and if we therefore define the *augmented* function

$$H^* \triangleq H + \lambda h \qquad (10\text{-}29)$$

we thus have concluded that the constrained optimum is characterized by

$$\frac{\partial H^*}{\partial x_1^0} = 0$$

$$\frac{\partial H^*}{\partial x_2^0} = 0 \qquad (10\text{-}30)$$

The result can be extended readily to the *n*-dimensional case with *p* constraints of the type (10-18). We now need *p* "multipliers" $\lambda_1, \lambda_2, \ldots, \lambda_p$, and the augmented function will be defined as

$$H^* = H + \sum_{v=1}^{p} \lambda_v h_v \tag{10-31}$$

The constrained optimum is characterized by

$$\frac{\partial H^*}{\partial x_i^0} = 0 \qquad i = 1, 2, \ldots, n \tag{10-32}$$

(Note that the n equations (10-32) and the p equations (10-18) suffice to render exactly the $p + n$ unknowns $x_1^0, x_2^0, \ldots, x_n^0; \lambda_1, \lambda_2, \ldots, \lambda_p$.)

Example 10-5

We are now properly equipped to complete our earlier problem (Example 10-1) of optimum operation of an interconnected power system. We restate the H function and the constraint equation for easy reference:

$$H = u_1^0(x_1^0) + u_2^0(x_2^0) + \cdots + u_n^0(x_n^0)$$

and

$$x_1^0 + x_2^0 + \cdots + x_n^0 - P = 0$$

The individual generator production-cost rates u_i^0 are, in practice, obtained empirically on the basis of generator data, fuel costs, etc. Figure 10-7a shows a typical graph of cost per hour versus kilowatt output. For a two-generator system, the H surface evidently will take on a "cup-shaped" form, as depicted in Fig. 10-7b, and there is therefore no doubt that the constrained minimum is characterized by the smoothness necessary to permit the use of the "calculus techniques."

In accordance with (10-29), we thus form the augmented cost function

$$H^* \overset{\Delta}{=} u_1^0(x_1^0) + \cdots + u_n^0(x_n^0) + \lambda(x_1^0 + \cdots + x_n^0 - P)$$

By application of Eq. (10-32), we then have

$$\frac{\partial H^*}{\partial x_1^0} = \frac{\partial u_1^0}{\partial x_1^0} + \lambda = 0$$

$$\cdots \cdots \cdots \cdots \cdots$$

$$\frac{\partial H^*}{\partial x_n^0} = \frac{\partial u_n^0}{\partial x_n^0} + \lambda = 0$$

Therefore,

$$-\lambda = \frac{\partial u_1^0}{\partial x_1^0} = \frac{\partial u_2^0}{\partial x_2^0} = \cdots = \frac{\partial u_i^0}{\partial x_i^0} = \cdots = \frac{\partial u_n^0}{\partial x_n^0} \tag{10-33}$$

The partial derivatives $\partial u_i^0 / \partial x_i^0$ represent the so-called *incremental production costs* for the generators (defined in Fig. 10-7), and our analysis thus informs us

(a)

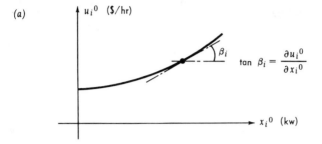

(b)

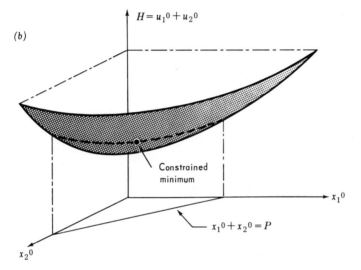

Fig. 10-7   Typical cost-versus-power curves for steam–turbine-driven generators.   Note that the "incremental production cost" $\partial u_i^0/\partial x_i^0$ has dimension dollars per kilowatt hour.

that for optimum profit we should operate the system in such a manner that the incremental costs are equal for all n generators.   In addition, of course, the sum of the outputs must equal the power need P.†

Figure 10-8 shows the basic principles of a control system which *automatically* satisfies the above incremental-cost requirement and thus keeps the power system operating "on top of the profit hill."   The overall system is closed-loop, and as the system frequency is the most sensitive indicator of the power balance within the system (as earlier pointed out), we use the *frequency error* as the basic command signal.   Each of the n generator stations is controlled in parallel from the frequency error signal via a gadget that we have called the

† The fact that the *incremental* production costs are equal throughout the system does *not* imply that the individual *total* generating costs, expressed in dollars per kilowatt-hour, are equal for the various generator units.

"nonlinear optimum controller" (NOC). The NOC is simply a function generator different for each of the n generators, producing an output proportional to the power output x_i^0 for an input proportional to the incremental cost $\partial u_i^0/\partial x_i^0$. This function is obtained empirically from the curve shown in Fig. 10-7a. In its simplest design, the NOC can be made up of simple circuit elements like resistors and diodes, but the common technique is to use a preprogrammed analog or digital computer.[4,5]

The operation of the control system is quite simple: Assume that the customer power demand P increases. The system, as a consequence, is running "heavier," and the frequency starts to drop and the frequency error to increase. As each of the NOC's receives the same input, we glide upward on the x_i^0-versus-$\partial u_i^0/\partial x_i^0$ curves—*always so that Eqs. (10-33) are satisfied.* When the combined power output has increased by an amount equal to the increase in demand, the frequency again will be stable, and we end up in a new steady state, characterized by a larger frequency error.

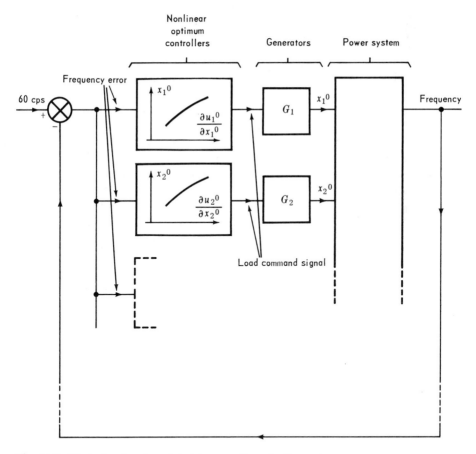

Fig. 10-8 Control system for minimizing overall production cost.

We wish to make the following observations:

1. As $-\lambda = \partial u_i^0 / \partial x_i^0$ [Eq. (10-33)], it is obvious that in this case the λ value is simply proportional to the frequency error. (As a rule, the Lagrange multiplier can be given a physical interpretation.)
2. The above workings of the control system are all *steady state,* and *we tacitly have assumed that the loop is stable.* It is possible that when the dynamics of the loop is studied (and this usually can be done by *linear* analysis around a reference setting), it will turn out that we must provide stability compensation.

At this point, it probably will have occurred to the reader why we refer to an optimization scheme like the one just described as "open-loop." The optimum is as good as the mathematical model is, and this model is entirely precomputed and fixed and takes no account of dynamic disturbances. Indeed, the NOC's in the previous example must be kept up to date continuously with changes in the fuel costs, etc., to be sufficiently accurate to warrant their use. (See also the comments in Sec. 10-3.3.)

10-3.2 OPTIMIZATION BY EXPERIMENTATION

When a sufficiently accurate mathematical model is unobtainable, it is still possible under certain conditions to keep a control process at its static optimum by "experimenting" with the system in real time. The principles involved are very similar to those in the old game of finding out the lowest gasoline-per-mile consumption for a new car. By driving the car at high, low, and medium speeds, one is able, after a while, to pinpoint the exact speed for most economical driving. Quite a few experimenting search schemes have been proposed,[6-8] all of which could be referred to as "hill-climbing techniques," inasmuch as they all have some means or another of first seeking the direction to the "top of the H hill" (see Fig. 10-5) and then proceeding to move in that direction. If the methods are highly sophisticated, they seek not only the general direction but actually the *best* direction in order to reach the optimum as *fast as possible.* We then refer to them as *gradient* methods or *methods of steepest ascent* (or *descent,* in the case of a minimum).

Consider for a moment Eq. (10-23). Divide each term by dt, and we obtain

$$\frac{dH}{dt} = \frac{\partial H}{\partial x_1^0} \frac{dx_1^0}{dt} + \cdots + \frac{\partial H}{\partial x_n^0} \frac{dx_n^0}{dt} \tag{10-34}$$

By making use of the *velocity* and *gradient* vectors introduced in Chap. 8, we can write this equation as the scalar product

$$\dot{H} = \dot{\mathbf{x}}^{0T} \operatorname{grad} H \tag{10-35}$$

For given velocity, *the rate of change of H obviously will be greatest when* $\dot{\mathbf{x}}^0$ and grad H are parallel, i.e., *when we move in the direction of the gradient.* [Note, by the way, that in view of Eq. (10-24), the rate vanishes when we reach the top.] An optimum-seeking control system of the experimenting kind generally must make use of special test inputs (= perturbations) injected into the system. Consider the following analogy: A blindfolded person standing on a hillside does not know in what direction to proceed unless he tries a few steps and finds out in what direction the hill slopes. It should be pointed out, however, that if the system contains "normal" noise of sufficiently high magnitude, one sometimes may be able to dispose of test perturbations altogether.

The block diagram in Fig. 10-9 depicts the general structure of an optimum-seeking control system. Test perturbations are added to each of the m steady-state inputs u_j^0. It is assumed that all those state variables that affect the H function are available for measurement. The "H generator" is a device that, on the basis of the actual state, generates the H value.

Due to the *slow* perturbations, the state variables, and thus H, will change. These changes are interpreted by the *static optimum controller* (SOC), which initiates proper changes in the control forces to move H closer to the optimum. The control loop is closed, and if the SOC is properly designed, the system will slowly move toward the peak. Let us illustrate the detailed workings of a system first proposed by Draper and Li,[6] depicted in Fig. 10-10. The plant is controlled by a single control force, and it is assumed that, in steady state, the process has an

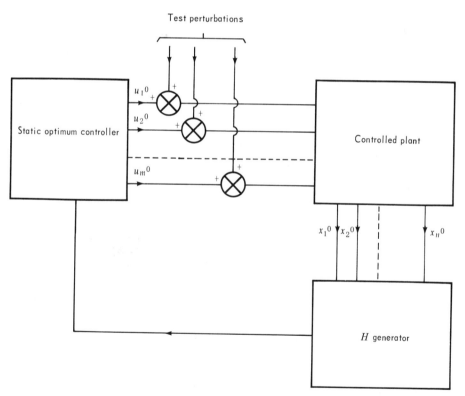

Fig. 10-9 Static optimization utilizing test perturbations.

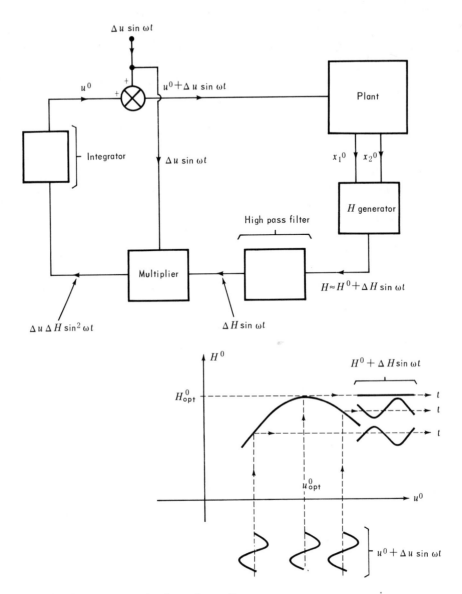

Fig. 10-10 Instrumentation for optimum H.

optimum H value (H^0_{opt}) for a specific u^0 value (u^0_{opt}). The system utilizes small sinusoidal perturbations of amplitude Δu and angular frequency ω, and we thus may write the input to the plant

$$u = u^0 + \Delta u \sin \omega t \qquad (10\text{-}36)$$

If ω is sufficiently lower than the BW of the process, the H value will vary *almost* sinusoidally and in phase with u:

$$H \approx H^0 + \Delta H \sin \omega t \qquad (10\text{-}37)$$

The graph in Fig. 10-10 explains why, and it also shows that the amplitude ΔH of the sinusoidal component of H depends upon u^0, in accordance with the following rules

If $u^0 < u^0_{opt}$, then $\Delta H > 0$

If $u^0 > u^0_{opt}$, then $\Delta H < 0$ $\qquad (10\text{-}38)$

If $u^0 = u^0_{opt}$, then $\Delta H = 0$

This sinusoidal H component is filtered out and *multiplied* by the u perturbation. The output from the multiplier consists of a constant plus a double-frequency part

$$\Delta u \, \Delta H \sin^2 \omega t = \frac{\Delta u \, \Delta H}{2} - \frac{\Delta u \, \Delta H}{2} \cos 2\omega t$$

and this signal is fed into the plant via an integrator as the static input u^0.

If the integrator gain is relatively low, we may disregard the double-frequency term in the output, but the constant term will result in a slowly increasing output. Let us assume that we start in a position characterized by $u^0 < u^0_{opt}$. In accordance with Eq. (10-38), ΔH then will be positive and the term ($\Delta u \, \Delta H$)/2 also will be positive. The integrator output thus will increase in a positive sense, resulting in increasing u^0, and we consequently move toward the maximum. As we do, the slope will decrease, and thus also ΔH and the rate of the integrator output. Eventually, we reach the maximum; the slope and therefore ΔH will be zero, and the output from the integrator u^0 will settle down to the constant value u^0_{opt}.

The chosen example was particularly simple as there was a need to manipulate one input, u, only. Furthermore, it is extremely simple to seek the gradient direction in one-dimensional space. When several control forces must be manipulated, we still can work with sinusoidal perturbations, but in order to make identification possible between them, we must use different frequencies, which will each appear in the variation of the H value; it is thus possible, by filtering, to detect the effects of each of the individual perturbations. In Ref. 9, some of the problems of design of multidimensional optimum-seeking controllers are discussed.

It is unfortunately beyond the scope of this book to go into a detailed study of the very important and interesting family of control systems referred to as *adaptive*. Adaptive control systems are a special variety of systems with *time-variant* parameters, which, due to space constraints, cannot be included to any depth in our discussions.

However, adaptive systems are related so closely to static-optimum-control systems that we would miss an excellent opportunity if at this point we did not at least introduce the reader to the concept of adaptive control.

It becomes necessary in a number of important fields of engineering to devise controllers for plants which exhibit very substantial changes in their dynamic characteristics—changes due, in most instances, to changing environments. The word "adaptive" is borrowed from biology, which abounds with examples of adaptive systems. For instance, when a person makes a fairly rapid move from sea level to 10,000 ft altitude, he experiences some discomfort the first day, due to the rather substantial decrease in oxygen. However, the adaptive controllers of his body go into automatic operation, and in a matter of a few days, the oxygen-carrying capacity of the blood is raised by production of red blood cells to a new level that suits the body under the new circumstances. The period of discomfort would have been avoided if the altitude change had occurred so slowly that the adaptive processes had kept pace with the changes. At sea level, the body processes were in a steady state and the person experienced a sense of well-being, putting him "on top of the H hill." The sudden altitude change moves this hill to a new steady state, and the person drops down into an "H valley." If the move had taken place slowly, the H hill would have moved away slowly also, and it would have been possible for the body to "stay on top."

The adaptive controllers devised for engineering applications are much simpler, but their basic purpose is analogous to that of the cited example—to keep the system on top of the performance "hill" in spite of changing plant dynamics. In most instances, it is imperative that the system not experience a case of "altitude sickness"; i.e., the speed of adaptation must match the speed of parameter changes. It is quite important to note that in those applications where a control system must be made self-adaptive, the changes in plant parameters take place so slowly that the system with very good accuracy can be considered to move from one steady state to another in a continuous fashion. It is also true, as a rule, that the changes to which the plant is subject are in various degrees *predictable*, which quite obviously makes the job of the adaptive controller easier. Let us consider three examples.

Example 10-6

In the earlier example of optimum control of the energy production of a utility company, we pointed out the fundamental importance of the so-called "incremental-cost data" for each generator. These data formed the basis for the nonlinear optimal controller in the proposed system in Fig. 10-8. Such incremental-cost curves are by no means constant. Due to variations in fuel prices, they will change with time over periods of weeks and months. The NOC's must be corrected correspondingly if we wish to remain at peak optimization. We know of no case where such an updating procedure has been attempted on an *automatic* basis. In this case, the most practical engineering approach is to subject the system to regular revisions, and we can talk here about an adaptive process of the typical open-loop variety and with human intervention.

Example 10-7

Consider the problem of properly controlling a space booster. The total flight from lift-off to orbit injection takes about 5 min, and during this period, the dynamics of the vehicle will undergo far-ranging changes. At takeoff, the velocity is zero (resulting in zero aerodynamic forces), the fuel tanks are full, and the dynamics is almost identical to that of the "inverted pendulum" that we studied in great detail in Chap. 2 in connection with the broom balancer. As the flight proceeds, the vehicle mass will decrease, its center of gravity will move aftward, the velocity and thus the aerodynamic forces will build up, and slowly but surely the dynamic model of the vehicle will change character completely (see Exercise 7-2). After the booster leaves the atmosphere, the aerodynamic forces will disappear, but now engine staging will occur which will cause abrupt changes in the dynamic model. It would be practically impossible to design a *fixed-parameter* controller to handle the booster adequately throughout the entire flight envelope. Due to the *very predictable* changes in the booster dynamics along the nominal *precomputed* trajectory, it is possible in this case successfully to use *open-loop* or *preprogrammed* adaptation, which simply takes the form of clock-commanded step changes of one or two controller parameters (usually gain settings) throughout the flight. Unfortunately, this simple scheme is not sufficiently sophisticated to handle the huge, multimillion-pound-thrust boosters of the future. In this application area and in other equally important future engineering systems, it becomes necessary to utilize more fully the hitherto far from adequately understood principles of *closed-loop* adaptation usually found in biological systems. We shall illustrate this type of adaptive system with our third, and final, example.

Example 10-8

A supersonic airliner flies at altitudes ranging from 0 to 70,000 ft and at speeds in the range 0 to Mach 3. If, in addition, the aircraft is designed with retractable wings, we have a system that during a normal flight will indeed change its dynamics between extremes. In principle, we could consider open-loop adaptation along the principles discussed in Example 2. The pilot could be given the job of flipping a set of switches at different altitudes, speeds, and wing configurations, and precomputed changes in the controllers could be initiated which would keep the aircraft responses reasonably constant. It is felt, however, that the crew of this type of craft will be flooded with other duties, and it is proposed to design an adaptive controller which is *automatic* or *closed-loop*.

It is of interest to see what the general requirements for a closed-loop adaptive control system are. We distinguish clearly the following three functions that must be performed by such a system:

Identification of the Plant Dynamics

This is the sensor part of the loop. In order to take any action whatsoever, it is necessary, of course, to know how the system is doing at present. The identification process (see Fig. 10-11) must result in information of some sort or other that, as precisely as possible, identifies the plant dynamics. In many cases, the identification is performed on the basis of test inputs superimposed on the normal signals.

Deciding on Proper Control Strategy

Due to the changing environments, the performance-index optimum is slowly changing position in the state space. The adaptive controller must contain some logic that evaluates the present position in relation to the optimum and then takes action to drive the system toward the optimum.

Modification of the Controller Parameters

The third element of the adaptive process is the *modification of the controller parameters* so that the system actually improves its performance. In most systems that actually have been designed, this modification has been performed by physically changing the parameter values of the controller networks. A popular method employs servo-driven potentiometers which are driven on commands from the decision logic.

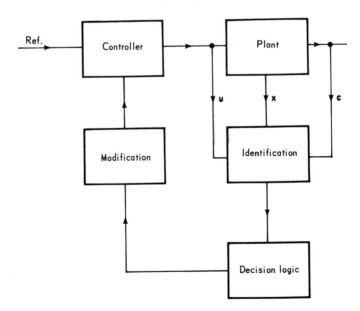

Fig. 10-11   Adaptive control system.

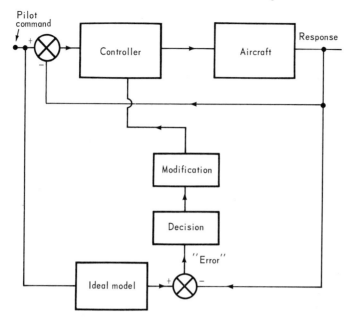

Fig. 10-12 Model-reference adaptive system.

A number of schemes for closed-loop adaptation have been suggested, of which the so-called *model-reference* method seems to have the greatest potential for success. The principal feature of this method (see Fig. 10-12) is a model, usually made up of passive electrical components and incorporating the essential features of the controlled plant plus controller. The output from this ideal model and the actual output from the plant are compared on a continuous basis—as long as the error signal is zero or thereabouts, the indication is that the controller parameters are properly adjusted. Assume now that, as a consequence of changed environments, the plant dynamics slowly changes. As a result, the system response will deviate from the "ideal" response, an error signal will be detected, and the decision and modification functions of the adaptive loop will go into operation, resulting in a change of the controller parameters so that the system response again is approaching that of the model. Those model-reference systems that actually have been designed[10,11] utilize as a performance criterion the ISE measure of the error. The model plus comparator constitute, in this scheme, the identifier part of the adapter.

A closed-loop adaptive control system thus contains the normal *fast* inner feedback loop and, in addition, the *slow* outer adaptive loop.

Exercises

10-1 Consider the static-optimization scheme depicted in Fig. 10-10. Make a study of the "speed of optimization" for this system under the following assumptions:

The H optimum can be considered a parabola around its peak:

$$H^0 = H^0_{opt} - \alpha(u^0 - u^0_{opt})^2$$

where α is a constant expressing the peakiness of the maximum.

The gain of the integrator is k_I.   Define for yourself a meaningful measure for "speed of optimization."

10-2 A two-dimensional process is characterized by the open-loop dynamics

$$\begin{bmatrix} \dot{x}_1 \\ \dot{x}_2 \end{bmatrix} = \begin{bmatrix} 1 & 2 \\ -2 & 1 \end{bmatrix} \begin{bmatrix} x_1 \\ x_2 \end{bmatrix} + \begin{bmatrix} 2 & 1 \\ 0 & 1 \end{bmatrix} \begin{bmatrix} u_1 \\ u_2 \end{bmatrix}$$

The process is by nature a steady-state one, and an analysis of the process has revealed that it will be desirable to operate at a steady state for which the quadratic rate function

$$\left(\frac{dI}{dt}\right)^0 = x_1^{0^2} + x_2^{0^2} + u_2^{0^2}$$

is minimized.   It is also necessary to observe the linear equality constraint
$x_1^0 + x_2^0 = 5$

    a Determine the vectors $\mathbf{x}_{opt}^0$ and $\mathbf{u}_{opt}^0$ that correspond to best operation.

    b Determine the optimum rate $(dI/dt)_{opt}^0$ corresponding to the setting in problem *a* above.

    c What would the proper settings be if, in *addition* to the above equality constraint, we had to satisfy the nonequality constraint

$x_1^0 \leqslant 0$

Compute the optimum rate $(dI/dt)_{opt}^0$ in this case and compare with problem *b* above.

    d Design a controller for this system (see Fig. 10-13) that makes it possible to set the above state values directly at the reference level **r**.   You should try to develop a design that ensures:

1. Stability
2. Static accuracy
3. Noninteraction

For simplicity assume $\mathbf{c} = \mathbf{x}$.

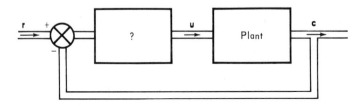

Fig. 10-13   System referred to in Exercise 10-2.

References

1. C. W. Merriam, "Optimization Theory and the Design of Feedback Control Systems," McGraw-Hill Book Company, New York, 1964.
2. J. S. Meditch, On the Problem of Optimal Thrust Programming for a Soft Lunar Landing, *Proc. JACC*, Stanford University (1964).
3. G. A. Korn and T. M. Korn, "Electronic Analog and Hybrid Computers," McGraw-Hill Book Company, New York, 1964.
4. L. K. Kirchmayer, Optimalizing Computer Control in the Electric Utility Industry, *Proc. Congr. IFAC*, 1st, Moscow (1960).
5. E. J. Kompass, The Early Bird Goes Automatic, *Control Eng.* (December, 1956).

6. C. S. Draper and J. T. Li, Principles of Optimalizing Control and an Application to Internal Combustion Engines, *ASME Publ.* (1951).

7. G. Vasu, Experiments with Optimalizing Controls Applied to Rapid Control of Engine Pressures with High-amplitude Noise Signals, *Trans. ASME*, **79** (1957).

8. H. Chestnut, R. R. Duersch, and W. M. Gaines, Automatic Optimizing of a Poorly Defined Process, *Proc. JACC*, New York University (1962).

9. J. G. Balchen, Dynamic Optimization of Continuous Processes, Rept., Institutt for Regulerings teknikk, Trondheim, Norway (1961).

10. H. P. Whitaker, Model Reference Adaptive Control Systems for Large Flexible Booster, Rept. E-1036 *MIT, Instr. Lab.* (1960).

11. A. Kezer, Adaptive Control of Aerospace Vehicles, paper presented at 3d Winter Institute on Advanced Control, University of Florida, February, 1965.

chapter 11

OPTIMUM CONTROL–
THE DYNAMIC CASE

11-1   INTRODUCTORY REMARKS

We shall turn our attention now to those optimum-control problems which are characterized by nonconstant state and control vectors.

Whereas in the static case it was enough to optimize a *function* (10-14), in the dynamic case we must seek the necessary conditions that extremize a *functional* (10-1).

The solution of the dynamic-optimum-control (DOC) problem, *as far as it exists*, yields an optimum-control vector $\mathbf{u}_{opt}(t)$, or $\mathbf{u}_{opt}$ for short, in the interval $0 < t < t_f$.

We may gain a feel for the difference between the static and the dynamic cases by considering the following limping analogy:

In the static maximum problem, we try to stand still on top of a hill, whereas in a dynamic case, we try to walk along the highest crest of a mountain ridge (or along a valley, in the case of a minimum).

It is important to realize that, as we attempt to extremize an integral, there is a need to be able to *predict into the future*. If the lower limit of integration, that is, $t = 0$, is taken to mean the present time, we must by necessity know the future values of $\mathbf{u}$ and $\mathbf{x}$ in order to be able to say something about this integral. As $\mathbf{x}$ certainly will be influenced by future disturbances, an *exact* solution requires our being able to predict these. This is a sobering thought and one that we are wise always to contemplate when we judge the relative value of an optimization scheme. Right at the outset, we wish to stress another important point that very seldom is given the attention it truly deserves. We shall find that the computational requirements are very severe in most practical DOC applications. If, therefore, we ask for strict adherence to the stipulated I criterion, thus requiring great accuracy, we shall have to pay a high price for hardware plus computational equipment. Figure 11-1 shows a typical cost curve that very clearly points out that the "law of diminishing returns" applies. Although it may be an interesting mathematical pastime to hunt for the theoretical limit, an engineer always must consider the gains in a wider perspective.

The types of optima encountered in dynamic studies are as varying as we

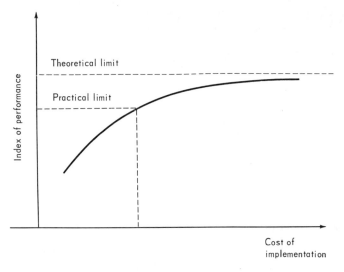

Fig. 11.1   Cost of implementing an optimum solution.

found them in the static case. We find constrained and unconstrained optima and optima that are "smooth" or "peaky" (corresponding to a smooth valley and a canyon, respectively). It is natural, therefore, that we should expect to find that a particular optimization technique which works in one case may fail in another. We shall begin our story with a presentation of the "classical" approach.

11-2 OPTIMIZATION BY MEANS OF CALCULUS OF VARIATIONS

In finding the optimum for a smooth H function in the previous chapter, we studied those conditions under which H is stationary, i.e., those conditions that make dH zero for small variations of the independent differentials dx_i^0. Equations (10-24) resulted, and we observed that they were necessary but not sufficient; i.e., they could not tell us whether we had a maximum, a minimum, or a saddle.

Calculus of variations similarly provides us with the means of determining necessary but not sufficient conditions for the optimum of an integral which is characterized by a smooth optimum. In presenting this tool, we shall limit our derivations for the sake of simplicity to the scalar case. The vector case offers no principal difficulties, but we shall forego this more general case in the interest of space conservation.

We first state the problem:

Find the value of $u(t)$, or u, for short, that renders

$$I = \int_0^{t_f} F(x,u)\, dt \tag{11-1}$$

stationary.

The control interval t_f is assumed fixed, and furthermore we must obey the state differential equation

$$\dot{x} = f(x,u) \tag{11-2}$$

and the equality constraints

$$x(0) = x_0$$
$$x(t_f) = x_f \tag{11-3}$$

No inequality constraints are assumed at the present. We approach the problem by assuming that an optimum does indeed exist and is represented by the boldface curves in Fig. 11-2. These curves, appropriately referred to as x_{opt} and u_{opt}, thus have the property that if they are substituted back into the integral (11-1), they will, after integration, render I an optimum (max or min, whatever the case may be).

If I is indeed stationary, then we can say with certainty that dI must be zero if we deviate *slightly* from the optimum trajectories in Fig. 11-2 (by amounts that we have called δu and δx). It is important to realize that these deviations, or *variations*, are:

1. Small (first-order, in a mathematical sense)
2. Functions of t
3. Arbitrary

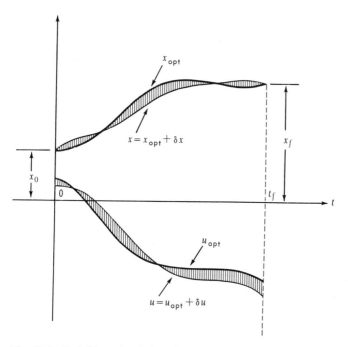

Fig. 11-2 Definition of variations δx and δu. Shaded areas represent the variations δx and δu.

The last point needs some clarification.   Assume that we chose δx arbitrarily [except at the ends, where we must have $\delta x(0) = \delta x(t_f) = 0$ to meet the constraints (11-3)].   Then δu is *not* arbitrary, as it now must assume such values as will satisfy Eq. (11-2).

We see this best by substituting $x = x_{opt} + \delta x$ and $u = u_{opt} + \delta u$ into (11-2), which then yields

$$\frac{d}{dt}(x_{opt} + \delta x) = f(x_{opt} + \delta x, u_{opt} + \delta u)$$

By using a Taylor expansion around the optimum trajectory, we thus get

$$\dot{x}_{opt} + \delta\dot{x} = f(x_{opt}, u_{opt}) + \left(\frac{\partial f}{\partial x}\right)_0 \delta x + \left(\frac{\partial f}{\partial u}\right)_0 \delta u$$

As

$$\dot{x}_{opt} = f(x_{opt}, u_{opt})$$

we conclude therefore that

$$\delta\dot{x} = \left(\frac{\partial f}{\partial x}\right)_0 \delta x + \left(\frac{\partial f}{\partial u}\right)_0 \delta u \tag{11-4}$$

The symbol $(\cdot)_0$ indicates that the partials are computed along the optimum trajectory.   We conclude that if we arbitrarily choose δx, then δu is restricted to values that satisfy (11-4).

We now form the following expression for dI:

$$dI = I(x_{opt} + \delta x, u_{opt} + \delta u) - I(x_{opt}, u_{opt})$$

$$= \int_0^{t_f} F(x_{opt} + \delta x, u_{opt} + \delta u)\, dt - \int_0^{t_f} F(x_{opt}, u_{opt})\, dt$$

Hence,

$$dI = \int_0^{t_f} [F(x_{opt} + \delta x, u_{opt} + \delta u) - F(x_{opt}, u_{opt})]\, dt$$

By again making use of the Taylor expansion, we get

$$dI = \int_0^{t_f} \left[\left(\frac{\partial F}{\partial x}\right)_0 \delta x + \left(\frac{\partial F}{\partial u}\right)_0 \delta u\right] dt \tag{11-5}$$

We next eliminate δu by making use of (11-4):

$$dI = \int_0^{t_f} \left\{ \frac{(\partial F/\partial u)_0}{(\partial f/\partial u)_0} \delta\dot{x} + \left[\left(\frac{\partial F}{\partial x}\right)_0 - \left(\frac{\partial F}{\partial u}\right)_0 \frac{(\partial f/\partial x)_0}{(\partial f/\partial u)_0}\right] \delta x \right\} dt$$

The first term in the integrand can be integrated by parts:

$$\int_0^{t_f} \frac{(\partial F/\partial u)_0}{(\partial f/\partial u)_0} \delta\dot{x}\, dt = \left.\frac{(\partial F/\partial u)_0}{(\partial f/\partial u)_0} \delta x\right]_{t=0}^{t=t_f} - \int_0^{t_f} \delta x \frac{d}{dt}\left[\frac{(\partial F/\partial u)_0}{(\partial f/\partial u)_0}\right] dt$$

The first term on the right side vanishes because $\delta x(0) = \delta x(t_f) = 0$, and we therefore obtain

$$dI = \int_0^{t_f} \left\{ \left(\frac{\partial F}{\partial x} \right)_0 - \left(\frac{\partial F}{\partial u} \right)_0 \frac{(\partial f/\partial x)_0}{(\partial f/\partial u)_0} - \frac{d}{dt} \left[\frac{(\partial F/\partial u)_0}{(\partial f/\partial u)_0} \right] \right\} \delta x \, dt \qquad (11\text{-}6)$$

If indeed x_{opt} and u_{opt} render I an optimum as assumed, then we must require that dI vanish for any *arbitrary* variation δx, and the only way we can be sure this will happen is to require that the expression within $\{\cdot\}$ be identically zero throughout the interval $0 < t < t_f$, that is,

$$\frac{\partial F}{\partial x} - \frac{\partial F}{\partial u} \frac{\partial f/\partial x}{\partial f/\partial u} - \frac{d}{dt} \left(\frac{\partial F/\partial u}{\partial f/\partial u} \right) = 0 \qquad (11\text{-}7)$$

This is one form of the famed Euler-Lagrange (E-L) equations. We have dropped the symbol $(\cdot)_0$ as we shall always tacitly assume *optimum* solutions when we work with the E-L equations. Other forms of the E-L equations are sometimes more convenient to work with, and the reader is referred to Exercise 11-1 at the end of this chapter.

We would have liked the results of the analysis to be an *explicit* solution u_{opt}. Instead, we are told that the solution can be ours only if we can solve a differential equation—the E-L equation. To add to our woes, the E-L equations *in general* cannot be integrated into any analytical solutions. Numerical integration methods are, of course, always available. The functions F and f determine the type of differential equation that we encounter in a specific case.

If f is linear in x and u and if F is quadratic in the same variables, then the E-L equations turn out to be linear differential equations. The fact that the equations are subject to two-point boundary conditions adds further difficulty to our problem of solution. Let us demonstrate with a couple of examples.

Example 11-1

In Chap. 5, we used the simple RC circuit (Fig. 5-1) to demonstrate the concept of controllability. We found that in charging the capacitor from the initial voltage x_0 to the final value x_f, we dissipated energy in the resistor in the amount [Eq. (5-4)]

$$W = RC^2 \int_0^{t_f} \dot{x}^2 \, dt \qquad (11\text{-}8)$$

The dynamic state equation for this circuit [Eq. (5-3)] is

$$\dot{x} = -\frac{1}{RC} x + \frac{1}{RC} u \qquad (11\text{-}9)$$

Let us now ask what control strategy (in controlling the capacitor-voltage state x) we should use if we wish to minimize this dissipated energy. (The student should ask himself why we would not try to *maximize* it.)   *W* thus takes on the role of performance index, and we have

$$W \triangleq I = RC^2 \int_0^{t_f} \dot{x}^2 \, dt = \frac{1}{R} \int_0^{t_f} (u - x)^2 \, dt \tag{11-10}$$

By comparing Eqs. (11-9) and (11-10) with Eqs. (11-1) and (11-2), we conclude that, in this case, we have

$$F(x,u) = \frac{1}{R} (u - x)^2$$

$$f(x,u) = \frac{1}{RC} (u - x) \tag{11-11}$$

Preparatory to making use of the E-L equation, we must compute the partials

$$\frac{\partial F}{\partial x} = -\frac{2}{R}(u - x) \qquad \frac{\partial F}{\partial u} = \frac{2}{R}(u - x)$$

$$\frac{\partial f}{\partial x} = -\frac{1}{RC} \qquad \frac{\partial f}{\partial u} = \frac{1}{RC}$$

Substitution into (11-7) results in the very simple E-L equation

$$\frac{d}{dt}(u - x) = 0 \tag{11-12}$$

Integration yields

$$u - x = \text{const} \tag{11-13}$$

The physical meaning of this result (see Fig. 5-1) is that optimality requires that we shall vary *u* so that the voltage across the resistor is always *constant, which in effect means that the charging current is constant and the capacitor voltage x increases at a constant rate.*

As x_{opt} thus varies linearly with time and as we know that it must start in x_0 and end in x_f, we get directly from Fig. 11-3

$$x_{\text{opt}} = x_0 + \frac{x_f - x_0}{t_f} t \tag{11-14}$$

As the charging current *i* equals $C\dot{x}$, we get

$$i_{\text{opt}} = C \frac{x_f - x_0}{t_f}$$

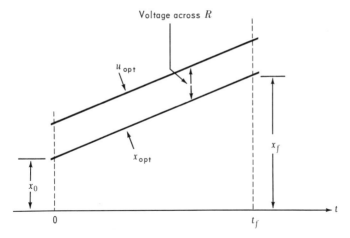

Fig. 11-3   Optimum capacitor-charging strategy.

We summarize the results:

$$x_{\text{opt}} = x_0 + \frac{x_f - x_0}{t_f} t$$

$$u_{\text{opt}} = x_{\text{opt}} + R i_{\text{opt}}$$

$$W_{\text{min}} = RC^2 \frac{(x_f - x_0)^2}{t_f}$$

(The expression for W_{min} is obtained, of course, by substituting the optimal value $\dot{x}_{\text{opt}}$ into (11-8) and then integrating.)

It is of interest to compare this energy, W_{min}, with the energy W_{cap} that we store in the capacitor

$$W_{\text{cap}} = \tfrac{1}{2} C(x_f^2 - x_0^2)$$

The ratio

$$\frac{W_{\text{min}}}{W_{\text{cap}}} \sim \frac{1}{t_f}$$

is a measure of the *efficiency* of the charging process, and we learn therefore that we can charge a capacitor with as small accompanying losses as we please by doing it slowly.

Example 11-2

Consider the following additional example, depicted in Fig. 11-4a. A controlled plant consists of a simple integrator. We wish to control the state of this plant between specified values x_0 and x_f in such a fashion that we minimize the performance criterion

$$I = \int_0^{t_f} (\alpha^2 x^2 + u^2)\, dt \tag{11-15}$$

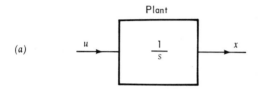

(a)

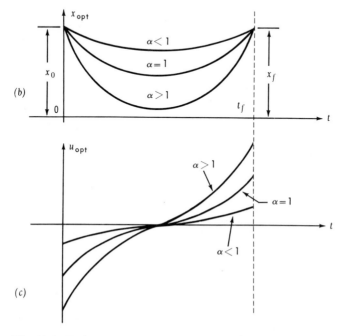

Fig. 11-4   Optimum dynamic control of one-dimensional process.

Note that this criterion penalizes (in ISE sense) both the control effort u and the deviation (= error) from the reference state $x = 0$. The real constant α^2 is an indicator of how we weigh the importance of error versus the control effort.

As the dynamic state equation is

$$\dot{x} = u \tag{11-16}$$

we get, in this case,

$$\frac{\partial F}{\partial x} = 2\alpha^2 x \qquad \frac{\partial F}{\partial u} = 2u$$

$$\frac{\partial f}{\partial x} = 0 \qquad \frac{\partial f}{\partial u} = 1$$

The E-L equation thus takes on the form

$$\alpha^2 x - \dot{u} = 0 \tag{11-17}$$

This equation must now be solved under simultaneous observance of the constraints. As both (11-16) and (11-17) are linear, we use Laplace transforms and obtain

$$sX(s) - x(0) = U(s)$$
$$\alpha^2 X(s) - [sU(s) - u(0)] = 0 \tag{11-18}$$

As we could expect, solution of the two first-order equations necessitates introduction of the two initial conditions $x(0)$ and $u(0)$. We remember, however, that the problem is stated *split-boundary fashion;* i.e., we know $x(0)$ and $x(t_f)$ but *not* $u(0)$. The only way we can proceed is to use the one initial condition that we know, x_0, and to eliminate $u(0)$ later by trying to meet the end condition x_f.

We therefore solve for $X(s)$ in terms of x_0 and $u(0)$:

$$X(s) = \frac{u(0) + sx_0}{s^2 - \alpha^2} = \frac{u(0)}{s^2 - \alpha^2} + \frac{sx_0}{s^2 - \alpha^2}$$

From tables, we then get

$$x(t) = x_{\text{opt}} = \frac{u(0)}{\alpha} \sinh \alpha t + x_0 \cosh \alpha t \tag{11-19}$$

We now seek $u(0)$ so that the state condition x_f is met for $t = t_f$, that is,

$$x_f = x(t_f) = \frac{u(0)}{\alpha} \sinh \alpha t_f + x_0 \cosh \alpha t_f$$

Therefore,

$$u(0) = \alpha \frac{x_f - x_0 \cosh \alpha t_f}{\sinh \alpha t_f}$$

By substituting this value into Eq. (11-19), we obtain the final expression for x_{opt}:

$$x_{\text{opt}} = x_0 \cosh \alpha t + \frac{x_f - x_0 \cosh \alpha t_f}{\sinh \alpha t_f} \sinh \alpha t \tag{11-20}$$

The corresponding optimal-control force is obtained most simply from Eq. (11-16):

$$u_{\text{opt}} = \dot{x}_{\text{opt}} = \alpha x_0 \sinh \alpha t + \alpha \frac{x_f - x_0 \cosh \alpha t_f}{\sinh \alpha t_f} \cosh \alpha t \tag{11-21}$$

This concludes our formal solution of the stated problem. We have sketched the appearance of x_{opt} and u_{opt} in the graphs of Fig. 11-4 for the simple case $x_0 = x_f$. We note how, for increasing α, the trajectories are "pushed downward"—a consequence of the fact that increasing penalty is now put on the first term in the integral criterion. Corresponding control forces will be of high magnitude since it is, of course, the control force that does the "pushing." The student should consider the appearance of the limit cases $\alpha = \infty$ and $\alpha = 0$.

Although the chosen examples were artificially simple, we are able to make some important observations. At the same time, we shall extrapolate the results to more general cases.

observation 1   Because the dynamic state equations were linear with constant coefficients, and as a result of the *quadratic F* functions, the E-L equations turned out to be *linear* and *time-invariant* and therefore amenable to Laplace-transform analysis. This is a *general* characteristic. As a quadratic cost function in many cases makes considerable physical sense, this is therefore an important class of problems.

observation 2   The calculus-of-variation approach worked in the above two cases because a "smooth" optimum really existed. The type of *F* function determines whether or not this is the case. For example, assume that in the second example we had proposed to optimize the process on the basis of the index

$$I = \int_0^{t_f} (|x| + |u|) \, dt$$

The student should investigate how the E-L equation now fails to give any clues and then contemplate *why* it fails. It is important to realize that it is perfectly legitimate to propose a performance index of this type—there certainly must exist a particular optimum strategy that will minimize it. It is only that calculus of variation does not have the power to give it to us.

observation 3   No inequality constraints were considered in the cited examples. The reason is very simple—the calculus of variation is a very clumsy tool in such cases. It *can* be used, but only with the greatest of efforts. Assume, for instance, that we impose saturation constraints on the control force in accordance with Fig. 11-5. We intuitively feel that the optimum strategy now changes from what was shown in Fig. 11-4c to what is depicted in Fig. 11-5. There are two variational approaches we can take to solve a problem of this type:

1. Use the so-called "transversality conditions" to determine at what times t' and t'' the u force saturates.[1]
2. Add a term to the integral criterion that *severely* punishes any excursions of u beyond the saturation level. For example, the term $(u/u_{max})^{100}$ is very small for $u < u_{max}$ but very large for $u > u_{max}$ and would thus nicely do the job. The I criterion would now take on the form

$$I = \int_0^{t_f} \left[\alpha^2 x^2 + u^2 + \left(\frac{u}{u_{max}} \right)^{100} \right] dt$$

and it is obvious that the resulting E-L equation would certainly *not* have analytical solutions. The numerical road still lies open, and in this age of computers, it is not excessively hard to walk. The general procedure here is to *guess* a reasonable solution and then let the computer check it out, improve

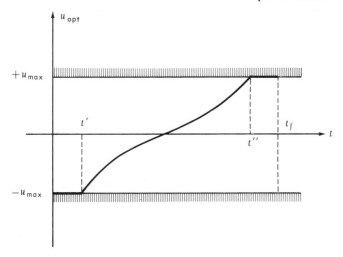

Fig. 11-5 Amplitude-limited control force.

the guess, etc., until finally we converge on a sufficiently accurate solution. The details of these techniques fall beyond our present scope, but the reader is referred to Refs. 2 to 4.

observation 4 The optimum solution is basically of the *unstable* variety as it contains increasing exponential terms. This is a *general* feature.
observation 5 Both u_{opt} and x_{opt} will turn out to be well-behaved *continuous* time functions. This rule will apply also to multidimensional linear plants optimized on the basis of a quadratic criterion.
observation 6 The E-L equation supplies us with an optimum-control strategy which typically is *open-loop*. Note that the equation for u_{opt} (11-21) can be written

$$u_{opt} = u_{opt}(x_0, x_f, t_f, t) \tag{11-22}$$

It is important to realize that this strategy is a function of the a priori known values of the *final state and the control interval*. Of course, an open-loop, or preprogrammed, system works fine if our model is perfect and if no disturbances force us off the optimum trajectory.

Of course, it would be highly desirable to incorporate the advantages of *closed-loop* control. Under certain conditions this can be done. To demonstrate this, let us write Eqs. (11-20) and (11-21) as

$$x_{opt} = x_0(\cosh \alpha t - \coth \alpha t_f \sinh \alpha t) + \frac{x_f}{\sinh \alpha t_f} \sinh \alpha t$$

and

$$u_{opt} = \alpha x_0(\sinh \alpha t - \coth \alpha t_f \cosh \alpha t) + \alpha \frac{x_f}{\sinh \alpha t_f} \cosh \alpha t$$

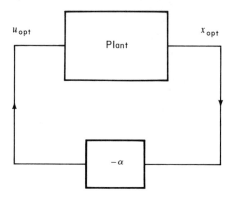

Fig. 11-6   Closed-loop optimum control.

Let us now study the behavior of these expressions for the *case of long control interval* t_f. For large t_f values, we have coth $\alpha t_f \to 1$ and sinh $\alpha t_f \to \infty$, and we thus obtain

$$x_{\text{opt}} \approx x_0(\cosh \alpha t - \sinh \alpha t) = x_0 e^{-\alpha t}$$
$$u_{\text{opt}} \approx \alpha x_0(\sinh \alpha t - \cosh \alpha t) = -\alpha x_0 e^{-\alpha t} = -\alpha x_{\text{opt}}$$

(11-23)

These *approximate* equations become *exact* in the limit $t_f \to \infty$.

We note that in the case of long control intervals, the optimum solutions are very insensitive to the value of the final state and also of the magnitude of t_f itself. In the limit, the optimum strategy actually is independent of what happens at the remote other end. This, of course, makes physical sense.

Of still greater interest is the fact, obviated by the second of Eqs. (11-23), that the *present* value of u_{opt} is directly proportional to the *present* value of the state. This is exactly the assurance we need to construct the *closed-loop* optimum controller shown in Fig. 11-6. Should this system be subject to disturbances resulting in changes in the state, automatic, immediate, and appropriate corrections are propagated to the input and the system proceeds to control itself so that the chosen I integral is minimized. This is also a *general* characteristic for *multidimensional* linear plants optimized on the basis of a quadratic criterion. The feedback will now be made proportional in a matrix sense.

Note, by the way, that the closed-loop system is *stable*, as the limit process eliminated the growing exponentials. The student will find Ref. 5 a highly readable account of optimization of multidimensional linear systems with quadratic integral criteria.

11-3 DYNAMIC PROGRAMMING

From a practical point of view, the methods of calculus of variation are limited basically to control processes that are:

1. Linear
2. Characterized by quadratic cost criteria

3. Unconstrained in both x and u

4. Characterized by low dimensionality

There is clearly a need here for methods that would overcome some of these limitations. Bellman's so-called "dynamic programming"[6,7] has gained considerable popularity in recent years as a complement to the classical methods. Dynamic programming attains its greatest practical significance in conjunction with the modern digital computer. As its name implies, it is basically an ingenious method of computer programming. As the digital computer accepts only *discrete* data or "data sequences" (see Chaps. 9 and 12), it becomes necessary when using Bellman's method to *discretize* the otherwise continuous control processes that we wish to study. When a continuous control process is viewed in this way, it takes on the characteristics of what is referred to as a *multistage decision process.* As it is necessary to have a clear understanding of this concept, we shall demonstrate with a simple example, and we choose for the purpose the simple one-dimensional control process discussed in detail in the previous section (Example 11-2).

In transferring the state of this system from x_0 to x_f in t_f sec, we may use an infinite number of trajectories (Fig. 11-7*a*), but only *one* of these corresponds to a minimum value of the I integral. The E-L equation presented us with the right one. Let us now look at the discretized version of the same process shown in Fig. 11-7*b*. We have divided the control period into N equal *stages*, and we now can let the process unfold in the following manner:

From stage 0 we go to stage 1, from there on to stage 2, etc., until we finally arrive at our destination. At each of the stages 0, 1, ..., $N - 2$, a decision must be made about which of the r possible roads should be chosen. Let us label these decisions $q_0, q_1, \ldots, q_{N-2}$ and arrange them in the *decision vector* **q**:

$$\mathbf{q} = \begin{bmatrix} q_0 \\ q_1 \\ \cdot \\ \cdot \\ \cdot \\ q_{N-2} \end{bmatrix}$$

Note that when, after $N - 1$ decisions, we have arrived in the stage $N - 1$, no further choice is open as a consequence of our specification of the end state. (If we had left x_f *open*, this would not be the case.)

The range of possible states (marked "x range" in the figure) must be determined from the physics of the problem. The more we can narrow this range from the outset, the better.

The **q** vector uniquely determines the overall path taken. The choice of the coarseness of the grid, i.e., the magnitudes of the numbers N and r, will determine the eventual accuracy of our analysis, i.e., how closely the discretized version approximates the continuous one. Clearly, from this point of view, we

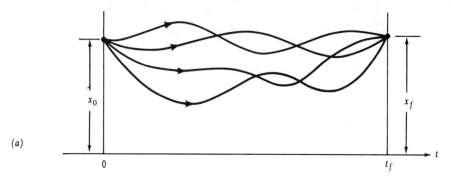

(a)

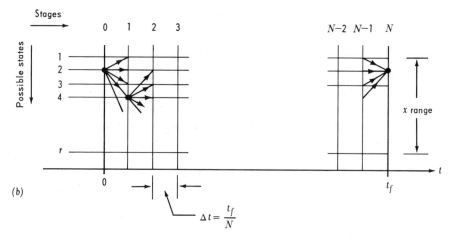

(b)

Fig. 11-7   Multistage decision process.

should like N and r to be as large as possible.   But let us look at the other side of the coin.   We have already indicated that in going from $0 \to 1$, we have r choices or possibilities.   The "two-stage process" of going from $0 \to 1 \to 2$ involves r^2 possibilities, and it is easy to see that the total N-stage process involves r^{N-1} possibilities.   And this is only a one-dimensional process!   Assume that we have a two-dimensional process involving the two state components x_1 and x_2, and let us assume that *each* may assume r different discrete values at each stage.   A simple reasoning tells us that we now have

$$(r^2)^{N-1} = r^{2(N-1)}$$

possible decision sequences to choose between.   For an n-dimensional process we have $r^{n(N-1)}$ choices!

The "decisions" we are talking about must be made, of course, on some logical basis, and this is where our index of performance comes in.   In the continuous process, this index was expressed as the integral

$$I = \int_0^{t_f} dI = \int_0^{t_f} F(x,u)\, dt$$

Of course, we must discretize this index to match it to our discretized process model

$$I = \sum_{v=0}^{N-1} \Delta I_v = \sum_{v=0}^{N-1} F(x_v, u_v)\, \Delta t \qquad (11\text{-}24)$$

The cost increment $\Delta I_v = F(x_v, u_v)\, \Delta t$ is the added cost of transferring the state from stage v to $v + 1$. In computing this increment, we should use some proper average values of x_v and u_v in the interval in question. The total cost will be different, depending upon what path is chosen, and the best path possible is the one resulting in optimum I, corresponding to the optimum-decision sequence $\mathbf{q}_{\text{opt}}$, also referred to as the *optimum policy*.

In selecting the optimum policy, the obvious approach would be to compute the total cost index I along all possible path combinations and then choose the best one. Let us study the practical consequences of this approach by considering the following example:

Compare the computational requirements for two 10-stage processes, each characterized by $r = 10$. One process is one-dimensional, and the other is two-dimensional. The reader will agree that our assumed discretizing is relatively coarse. We shall assume that we have a digital computer available that can perform 1 million "elementary" operations per second. By "elementary," we shall mean the operation of computing I for one possible trajectory path, which thus consists of computing ten ΔI's and then adding them up [see Eq. (11-24)]. For the computers that are presently (1966) on the drawing board, this is a conceivable feat.

In the one-dimensional case, $r^{N-1} = 10^9$, such operations are necessary, corresponding to a total computing time of 10^3 sec, or $\frac{1}{3}$ hr. In the two-dimensional case, we require 10^{18} operations, or 10^{12} sec, that is, 100,000 years!

We have run headlong into the so-called "dimensionality barrier." The dynamic programming in effect penetrates this barrier by presenting a more elegant way of selecting the optimum trajectory from the myriad of possibilities.

11-3.1 THE PRINCIPLE OF OPTIMALITY (PO)

The essential feature of dynamic programming is that it reduces the N-stage-decision process to a sequence of N *single-stage* decision processes, enabling us to solve the problem in a simple iterative manner on a computer.

This reduction is made possible by use of the fundamental *principle of optimality:*

A policy which is optimal over the interval $0 \to N - 1$ is necessarily optimal over any subinterval $v \to N - 1$, where $0 \leqslant v < N - 1$.

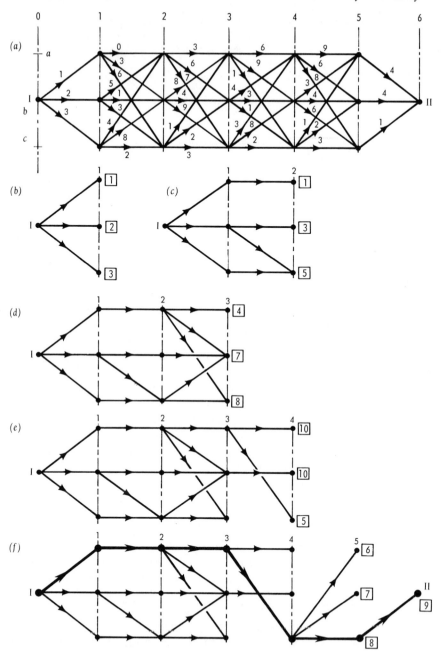

Fig. 11-8   Example of dynamic programming.

A very simple example† will demonstrate the basic idea of dynamic programming and also reveal some of its drawbacks. Consider the one-dimensional decision process shown in Fig. 11-8a. The increments in criterion function between different stages are shown in the graph. [These numbers are the ΔI_v's of formula (11-24).] We desire to find the path that minimizes the total criterion function between I and II. Because we have

$N = 6$

$r = 3$

$n = 1$

we have a total of $3^5 = 243$ different combinations to compare. Instead of doing this, we proceed as follows:

step 1 Go from stage 0 to stage 1, and memorize all the $r = 3$ increments (framed numbers in Fig. 11-8b). Note that we do not know at this time if the optimum policy will take us through the states 1a, b, or c, so we *memorize all possible cost functions* ("invariant embedding").

step 2 Proceed from stage 1 to stage 2. Memorize again the total cost function. Again we check all possible states 2a, b, and c. But in addition we invoke the PO: If it later turns out that the optimum policy will take us through state 2a, then we *certainly* must get there from state 1a. (This conclusion was reached after a comparison of r numbers.) The principle is then applied to *each* of the states in stage 2. A total of 9 ($= r^2$) comparisons must be performed. The result is shown in Fig. 11-8c. Note that the PO in effect has permitted us at this point to *discard* two-thirds of all possible path combinations leading from stage 1 onward, as they cannot possibly be future candidates for the optimum path.

steps 3 to 6 By successive comparisons and application of the principle of optimality, we obtain the results shown in Fig. 11-8d to f. At each step, we discard two-thirds of all remaining possibilities.

The optimum policy from I → II can be determined only in the last step. The result is indicated boldface in Fig. 11-8f.

We make some general observations on the basis of this example.

observation 1 In the earlier-suggested "sledgehammer" approach of comparing *all possible* path combinations, the stress on the computer was due to the enormity of the number $r^{n(N-1)}$. The computational requirements in the above approach stem from the necessity of making comparisons of numbers at each step in the iterative process. Let us see how many such comparisons we must make. In the first and the last steps, we obviously must make r comparisons each, and in each step in between, we must make r^2 comparisons, for a total of

$2r + (N - 2)r^2$

If we had considered an n-dimensional **x** vector, then we would have obtained the total number

$2r^n + (N - 2)r^{2n}$

---

† This example is borrowed from an article by Olle I. Elgerd titled "Optimum Control" in the *Proceedings* from the First Winter Institute on Adaptive Control, University of Florida, February, 1962.

The *order of magnitude* of this number is

$$Nr^{2n}$$

The important thing that has happened is that we have removed N from the exponent! To see what this in effect means, let us again consider the example that we concluded earlier would require 100,000 years of computing time. As we have

$$N = 10$$

$$n = 2$$

$$r = 10$$

we obviously are required to make about

$$10 \times 10^4 = 10^5$$

comparisons of numbers. The assumed speed of the particular computer will permit us to do this now in a *fraction of a second.* Quite a saving!

The reason for this enormous reduction is simply that in invoking the PO at each stage, we in effect have discarded the *vast* majority of path combinations and only saved those *comparatively few* that are possible candidates for the overall optimum path.

observation 2   Although we have made a fantastic reduction in the computational need for the search process, we still must accept the fact that the number

$$Nr^{2n}$$

is of respectable dimensions. Consider, for example, a four-dimensional process discretized to the level

$$r = 10$$

$$N = 100$$

We now need to perform

$$100 \times 10^8 = 10^{10}$$

comparisons. This is not a negligible undertaking, even for the fastest machines available today.

observation 3   Probably the most important fact that the example taught us concerns the need for *fast-memory capacity.* In proceeding from one stage to the next, *we had to remember the r framed numbers* so that they were available for comparison in the next stage. For an *n*-dimensional process, we would need to be able to memorize r^n numbers. We must also consider the fact that as we are going to make the comparisons at the highest speed available, we must be able at each stage to pull them out of and insert them into the memory at the highest

Table 11-1 An approximate comparison of grid coarseness (r) and process dimensionality (n) in present and future computers

Dimension n	Present-day computer permits r =	Future computer permits r =
1	30,000	300,000
2	173	550
3	31	67
4	13	23
5	8	12
6	5	7

rate possible.† The slow tape memories are therefore out of the question, and we must use the high-speed, random-access core-memory banks. This imposes a severe limitation, as the core-memory banks are limited in size. A typical present-day fast-memory capacity is $\approx 30,000$ "words." In the foreseeable future, we may be able to get as high as 300,000. By equalling these numbers to the number r^n, we are able to determine the relation between process dimensionality n and grid coarseness r. The result is shown in Table 11-1. We realize that, barring any unforeseen breakthrough in core-memory development, even dynamic programming runs into the dimensionality barrier.

The last two observations serve to put the complexity of high-dimensional ($n > 5$) optimum processes in proper perspective. Maybe we should conclude that their solution is beyond reach.

observation 4 Inequality constraints imposed considerable mathematical difficulties on our attempts to solve optimum problems by means of variational calculus. How do they affect dynamic programming? We find to our pleasant surprise that they now work to our advantage. This is readily understood if we realize that dynamic programming is basically a *search* process, and inequality constraints reduce the number of possible solutions that we need to search among. This is a very attractive feature of this method.

observation 5 When preparing a computer program, it is essential to make the computer remember the optimum paths as we come to the end of the computational process. The framed numbers are being erased from the core memory as

† The reader should be aware of the fact that digital computers have two types of memories:

1. Fast memories (electrical core memories, for example)
2. Slow memories (mechanical tape memories, for example)

The slow-memory capacity is limited only by *cost*. Access time (i.e., the time it takes to find a specific memorized word) may be of the order of seconds.

The fast-memory capacity is limited for *technological reasons*. We here are talking of access times of the order of microseconds (or shorter) for *any* memorized word in the entire memory ("random" access). The core-memory size is the critical "bottleneck" when we are interested in sequential computational operations where many numbers must be preserved from one stage to the next in the computational process. This is obviously true in the case of dynamic programming.

soon as they have been used to make room for new ones. It would be disappointing and embarrassing to know the optimum value of the cost index at the end of the process but to have no idea as to how we obtained it.

Example 11-3

We shall conclude this very brief exposé of dynamic programming by working in detail a simple control problem. We shall study the same process as the one we worked in the previous section by means of variational calculus, i.e., the single-integrator plant in Example 11-2. To add to the realism, we shall minimize the process on the basis of the *linear* cost function

$$I = \int_0^{t_f} (x + 2u)\, dt \tag{11-25}$$

for which we conclude that calculus of variation does not work.

We shall compute specifically the optimum-control policy for the numerical case

$$x_0 = 5$$

$$x_f = 3$$

$$t_f = 5 \text{ sec}$$

In addition, we shall impose the x and u constraints

$$x \geqslant 1$$

$$-2 \leqslant u \leqslant 2$$

We divide the control interval into five equal parts, corresponding to a five-stage decision process and a discrete time increment $\Delta t = 1$. The plant differential equation $\dot{x} = u$ also must be discretized, and the result is the difference equation

$$\frac{x_{v+1} - x_v}{\Delta t} = u_v$$

As $\Delta t = 1$, we can write it as

$$x_{v+1} = x_v + u_v \tag{11-26}$$

We note that, due to the u constraint, the rate of change of x is limited to the values

$$|\dot{x}| \leqslant 2$$

or, in the discretized version,

$$|x_v| - 2 \leqslant |x_{v+1}| \leqslant |x_v| + 2$$

As a result of the x and u constraints and in view of the stated end conditions,

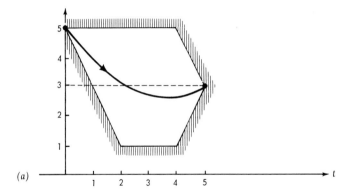

(a)

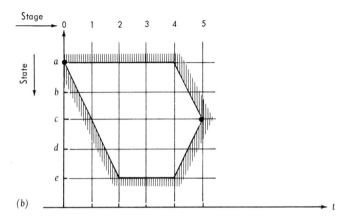

(b)

Fig. 11-9 Optimum trajectory: (*a*) continuous case, (*b*) discretized case.

we thus can block off the shaded regions in Fig. 11-9*a* as being beyond reach. We also have excluded the region $x > 5$ for the following reason:

As we are about to minimize a cost index the integrand of which equals $x + 2u$ and as we start in a *positive* state, it is reasonable,† particularly in view of the fact that $x_f < x_0$, to assume that u initially should take on *negative* values; i.e., we start in a *downward* direction, as indicated in Fig. 11-9*a*. The cost increment ΔI_v in this case will equal

$$\Delta I_v = x_v + 2u_v \tag{11-27}$$

and we have listed in Table 11-2 the cost increments corresponding to every conceivable step increment within the blocked-off range in Fig. 11-9.

---

† We cannot be *certain*, of course, that this will happen, but in practice we make assumptions of this type to get a computation process "rolling."

Table 11-2   The cost increments for process shown in Fig. 11-9

From state	*To state*	*Required u_v*	x_v *(average)*	$\Delta I_v = x_v + 2u_v$
a	a	0	5	5
a	b	−1	4.5	2.5
a	c	−2	4.0	0
b	a	+1	4.5	6.5
b	b	0	4.0	4.0
b	c	−1	3.5	1.5
b	d	−2	3.0	−1.0
c	a	+2	4.0	8.0
c	b	+1	3.5	5.5
c	c	0	3.0	3.0
c	d	−1	2.5	0.5
c	e	−2	2.0	−2.0
d	b	+2	3.0	7.0
d	c	+1	2.5	4.5
d	d	0	2.0	2.0
d	e	−1	1.5	−0.5
e	c	+2	2.0	6.0
e	d	+1	1.5	3.5
e	e	0	1.0	1.0

For example, assume that we compute the increment in transferring the state from level *b* to level *c* (see Fig. 11-9*b*). We need for this job a control force $u = -1$, resulting in

$$\Delta I_{b \to c} = 3.5 - 2 = 1.5$$

Note that we have chosen the average value, 3.5, for *x*, and note also that

$$\Delta I_{c \to b} \neq \Delta I_{b \to c}$$

We are now fully equipped to program this problem dynamically. The step-by-step results are shown in Fig. 11-10, which shows the final optimum trajectory in boldface. The optimum process corresponds to a minimum cost index of

$$I_{min} = 6.0$$

Caution: In this example, we chose to precompute and tabulate the cost increments because this is the simplest method to use in a book where the objective is ease of demonstration. This is *not* a recommended procedure when using a digital computer and when working a high-dimensional problem with very-fine-grid network. We would very rapidly fill up the core memory, which, as we earlier indicated, we should reserve for the step-by-step memorizing of the

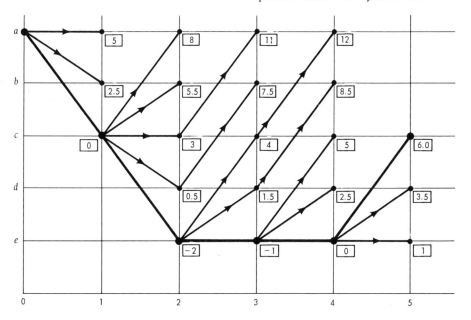

Fig. 11-10   Dynamic programming of system Fig. 11-9.

framed numbers.   A proper procedure is to let the digital computer use the formula (11-27) *actually to compute the cost increments whenever they are needed in the computational process.*

11-4   PONTRYAGIN'S MAXIMUM PRINCIPLE (PMP)

There exists a large class of variational-type problems which are of great engineering importance but which cannot for several reasons be handled by the Euler-Lagrange theory.   To be sure, they can be mastered by dynamic programming, but it must be remembered that this is basically a *numerical* technique, providing limited insight into the real nature of a specific problem.   We first shall give a few typical examples of the class of problems that we are referring to, and then we shall present an alternate method for their solution.

Example 11-4

Consider the simple, one-dimensional process shown in Fig. 11-11.   Liquid is pumped into a tank at the rate of u gal/sec.   If A is the sectional area of the tank, the process equation is clearly

$$\dot{x} = \frac{1}{A} u \tag{11-28}$$

We now can specify an optimum-control problem for this process in the following way:

In a given time t_f, we wish to increase the level x as much as possible!

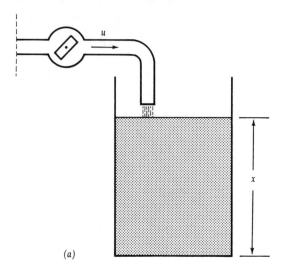

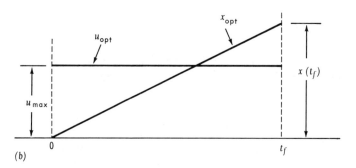

Fig. 11-11 Optimum control of one-dimensional process.

For simplicity we make the assumption that the tank is initially empty. Clearly, our performance index will be

$$I = x(t_f) \tag{11-29}$$

and the problem now is to find an optimum-control strategy u_{opt} that will do the job.

The solution is obvious and is depicted in the graph (Fig. 11-11b)—keep the pump working at maximum capacity u_{max} for the full period t_f. It is worth noting that this solution is obtained by *intuition*, and the reader may object that we waste time with trivial problems.

However, we can make a difficult problem out of this one just by adding one additional tank connected to the first one via a valve V (Fig. 11-12). For simplicity and to permit us to work with a linear model, we shall assume that the valve flow q is proportional to the head x_1,

$$q = \frac{1}{R} x_1 \tag{11-30}$$

(R is the valve resistance.)

With this assumption, we can construct the following two-dimensional dynamic model for this system:

$$\dot{x}_1 = -\frac{1}{A_1 R} x_1 + \frac{1}{A_1} u$$

$$\dot{x}_2 = \frac{1}{A_2 R} x_1 \tag{11-31}$$

A_1 and A_2 are the sectional areas of the two tanks. Again, we can specify an optimum process, but due to the higher dimensionality, we obviously have several possibilities.

case 1 Starting with empty tanks, find a control policy u_{opt} which, in *given* time t_f, maximizes

$$I = x_2(t_f) \tag{11-32}$$

$x_1(t_f)$ is *open;* i.e., it may take on whatever value is required to do the specified job.

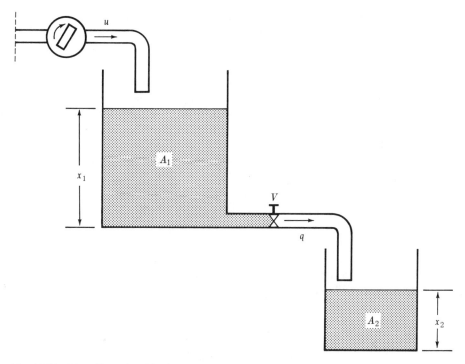

Fig. 11-12   Two-dimensional hydrodynamic process.

case 2 Same as above, but now we choose

$$I = x_1(t_f) \tag{11-33}$$

and $x_2(t_f)$ open.

case 3 Maximize

$$I = x_2(t_f) \tag{11-34}$$

but at the same time meet the constraint

$$x_1(t_f) = x_{1f}$$

case 4 Maximize

$$I = x_1(t_f) \tag{11-35}$$

and meet the constraint

$$x_2(t_f) = x_{2f}$$

case 5 Finally, we can conceive of a situation where it is desirable to maximize the weighted sum

$$I = \alpha_1 x_1(t_f) + \alpha_2 x_2(t_f) \tag{11-36}$$

Note that, in this case, we may not impose any constraints on either $x_1(t_f)$ or $x_2(t_f)$. Why?

The reader will agree that the problem is no longer trivial. We still can rely upon our intuition and find u_{opt} in cases 1, 2, and 5. As before, in all three cases we obviously should let the pump work at full capacity for the full period t_f.

This simple policy will not work in the other cases. Consider case 3, for example. We may again let the pump work at full capacity, but if we pass the specified level x_{1f}, we must stop the pump at some moment $t' < t_f$ so that the level will have a chance to drop back to x_{1f}. This "switching" instant t' could be chosen later, and we would obtain a better maximum if the pump permitted reversible action, i.e., if *negative u* were permitted.

In either case, we are left with the question of determining the *exact* moment t' at which to change the flow.

Note that if we have not reached the level x_{1f} before $t = t_f$, then the problem is nonsolvable, i.e., the specifications are inconsistent. (The student is referred to Example 11-6 for a further discussion of this system.)

Example 11-5

Consider as a second example the dynamics of the mass in Fig. 11-13. With position x_1 and velocity x_2 chosen as components of the state vector, this system will be described by the mathematical model

$$\dot{x}_1 = x_2$$

$$\dot{x}_2 = \frac{u}{m} \tag{11-37}$$

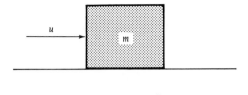

$\longrightarrow x_1$ Fig. 11-13   Inertia system.

We may wish to change the state of this system in specified time t_f so as to optimize either of the final states $x_1(t_f)$ or $x_2(t_f)$ or a combination of the two; i.e., we may wish to define criteria of the types

$$I = x_1(t_f)$$
$$I = x_2(t_f) \tag{11-38}$$
$$I = \alpha_1 x_1(t_f) + \alpha_2 x_2(t_f)$$

Again, it is important to make sure what types of constraints we should impose in each case. If, for instance, we optimize the position $x_1(t_f)$, then it is quite obvious that we must use different control strategies if in one case we permit the final velocity to be open and in another case require it to be zero.

In comparing the characteristic features of the above two examples, we make the following observations:

observation 1   The control time t_f is preset, and we optimize the process on the basis of a criterion function of the type

$$I = \alpha_1 x_1(t_f) + \cdots + \alpha_n x_n(t_f) \tag{11-39}$$

We may consider the α's to be components of an n-dimensional *objective* vector

$$\boldsymbol{\alpha} \overset{\Delta}{=} \begin{bmatrix} \alpha_1 \\ \cdot \\ \cdot \\ \cdot \\ \alpha_n \end{bmatrix}$$

and we thus can express the chosen criterion as a scalar vector product

$$I = \boldsymbol{\alpha}^T \mathbf{x}(t_f) \tag{11-40}$$

Without loss of generality, we may assume $\boldsymbol{\alpha}$ to be normalized, that is,

$$|\boldsymbol{\alpha}| = \sqrt{\alpha_1^2 + \cdots + \alpha_n^2} = 1$$

In accordance with formula (A-6) in Appendix A, the expression (11-40) geometrically means the projection of the vector $\mathbf{x}(t_f)$ on the vector $\boldsymbol{\alpha}$, *and the chosen criterion thus expresses the fact that we attempt to optimize the projection of* $\mathbf{x}(t_f)$ *along the objective vector.*

observation 2   Based at least on our intuitional findings, we can expect that the optimal strategies will utilize the *extreme* values of the control force $\mathbf{u}$ and also that *instantaneous* changes of the control-force components may be part of the optimum strategy ("inertia-less," "bang-bang" type of controls). *Indeed, an optimum of the type* (11-40) *actually does not exist unless the control force is assumed bounded.*

(It is fruitful to make a comparison with the type of optimal strategies that calculus of variations can provide—they are *always continuous*.)

observation 3 Although the control-force components will be *discontinuous*, the state-vector components must be *continuous*. Positions, velocities, waterheads, etc., cannot change instantaneously since we have assumed that the control forces are bounded.

observation 4 All the stated problems can be made into *time-optimal* problems by being viewed in an "inverted" sense. Instead of fixing the control time t_f, we leave it open and fix instead $\mathbf{x}(t_f)$, and we ask now for the control strategy that will transfer the state to the specified value $\mathbf{x}(t_f)$ in minimum time.

With a little mathematical trickery, we very conveniently can include the time-optimal control problem under the criterion function (11-40). We do this by *augmenting* the n-dimensional state vector with an $n + 1$ component, defined as

$$\dot{x}_{n+1} \triangleq 1 \qquad \text{with } x_{n+1}(0) \triangleq 0 \tag{11-41}$$

Therefore,

$$x_{n+1}(t_f) = \int_0^{t_f} 1 \, dt = t_f$$

Defined in this manner, $x_{n+1}(t)$ takes on the meaning of physical time t, and its final value $x_{n+1}(t_f)$ means the control time t_f.

As the criterion I can be written

$$I = t_f = x_{n+1}(t_f) = 0x_1(t_f) + \cdots + 0x_n(t_f) + 1x_{n+1}(t_f)$$

the time-optimal problem thus corresponds to the $(n + 1)$-dimensional objective vector

$$\alpha = \begin{bmatrix} 0 \\ 0 \\ \cdot \\ \cdot \\ \cdot \\ 1 \end{bmatrix}$$

We shall make use of this technique in later examples.

11-4.1 DERIVATION OF PONTRYAGIN'S MAXIMUM PRINCIPLE (PMP)

Processes of the above type (in particular, the time-optimal variety) had been studied extensively before 1956 by a number of researchers, but their various approaches lacked simplicity and, certainly, generality. In that year, the Russian mathematician Pontryagin published a paper, coauthored with two of his students, in which they presented their so-called *maximum principle.* The PMP closely resembles the "principle of least action" in analytical mechanics, and the reader who has had a background in the Hamilton-Jacobi theory will digest the present material with greater ease.

The Russian work in this field became generally known in the West through a series of exceptionally well-written articles by Rozonoer.[8] We shall give a brief proof of the maximum principle, and we start, appropriately, with a formulation of the problem.

Assume a system characterized by the vector differential equation

$$\dot{\mathbf{x}} = \mathbf{f}(\mathbf{x},\mathbf{u}) \tag{11-42}$$

(We shall find it necessary later to impose some restrictions on the function vector **f**, and in our examples, we shall concern ourselves mostly with linear and time-invariant systems.)

Find the optimum-control strategy $\mathbf{u}_{opt}$ that will transfer the state of the system from the specified initial value $\mathbf{x}(0) = \mathbf{x}_0$ to the final value $\mathbf{x}(t_f)$ in such a manner that the payoff function

$$I = \sum_{i=1}^{n} \alpha_i x_i(t_f) = \boldsymbol{\alpha}^T \mathbf{x}(t_f)$$

is optimized. The control vector **u** is amplitude-constrained, and as far as **x** is concerned, we shall differentiate between the "completely unconstrained," the "partly constrained," and the "time-optimal" cases.

$\mathbf{x}(t_f)$ Completely Unconstrained, t_f Fixed

In this case, the final state $\mathbf{x}(t_f)$ is completely open.

We shall assume that an optimum strategy $\mathbf{u}_{opt}$ has been found and that the corresponding optimal-state vector is $\mathbf{x}_{opt}$, and we shall set out to study the change dI that will occur in the payoff function if a variation $\delta\mathbf{u}(t)$ takes place from the optimum value. This is, as the reader will remember, the same approach as was chosen in deriving the Euler-Lagrange equation. There is, however, one basic difference.

In the E-L case, we assumed that the variations were *arbitrary* and *small* throughout the control interval (see Fig. 10-2). In the present case, the variations will be of a different nature. The situation is depicted in Fig. 11-14 for the case of a two-dimensional **x** vector and a one-dimensional control force u. As we can expect that the optimum strategy u_{opt} will be of the bang-bang variety, i.e., consisting of segments of the limit values of u and instantaneous switchovers (only one is shown), then it is natural to assume that the slightly off-optimum policy $u_{opt} + \delta u$ should differ from the optimum policy u_{opt} only in respect to the switching moment. The variation δu thus consists of one or several thin pulses.†

---

† It is important to realize, however, that E-L variations of the type depicted in Fig. 10-2 are *not excluded* in the following derivation of PMP, which therefore also can be used in solving typical "calculus of variation" problems. See Example 11-7.

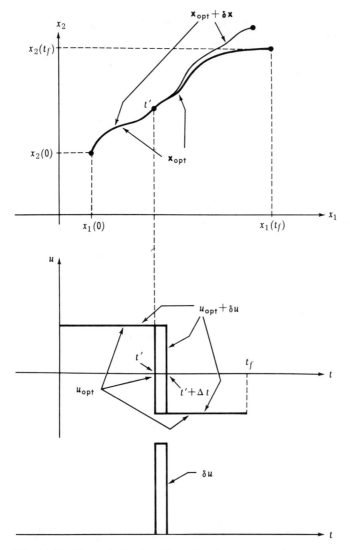

Fig. 11-14 The variation δu will consist of one or several pulses.

(We can express the situation in a different but more abstract fashion by the use of set theory.

The amplitude constraints on the m-dimensional **u** vector mean that

$$u(t) \in U$$

where U is the admissible set of control functions in m space. The E-L equation leads us to an optimum solution $\mathbf{u}_{opt}$ lying in the *interior* of U. The PMP is concerned with an optimum solution on the *boundary* of U.)

After this short excursion, let us resume our derivation of PMP. Of fundamental importance in the further development is the concept of *costate*, or *adjoint*, vector **p**.

The components p_i of this vector are *defined* as follows.†

$$\dot{p}_i \overset{\Delta}{=} -p_1 \frac{\partial f_1}{\partial x_i} - \cdots - p_n \frac{\partial f_n}{\partial x_i} = -\sum_{j=1}^{n} p_j \frac{\partial f_j}{\partial x_i} \tag{11-43}$$

with $p_i(t_f) = -\alpha_i$; $i = 1, 2, \ldots, n$.

Note: In the case of a linear system

$$\dot{\mathbf{x}} = \mathbf{A}\mathbf{x} + \mathbf{B}\mathbf{u}$$

the costate takes on the following very simple form:

$$\dot{\mathbf{p}} = -\mathbf{A}^T\mathbf{p} \tag{11-44}$$

The state **x** and the costate **p** together introduce a total of $2n$ variables. These variables must satisfy the $2n$ first-order differential equations (11-42) and (11-43) and, in addition, meet the $2n$ specified *split-boundary* end conditions

$$\mathbf{x}(0) = \mathbf{x}_0$$
$$\mathbf{p}(t_f) = -\boldsymbol{\alpha}$$

The introduction of the **p** vector therefore seems, at this juncture, to be an unnecessary complication. These fears will soon be dispelled.

We next consider the variation of the ith component of **x** as a result of the above-discussed variation $\delta \mathbf{u}$ of **u**. From (11-42), we have

$$\delta\dot{x}_i = f_i(\mathbf{x}_{\text{opt}} + \delta\mathbf{x}, \mathbf{u}_{\text{opt}} + \delta\mathbf{u}) - f_i(\mathbf{x}_{\text{opt}}, \mathbf{u}_{\text{opt}})$$

We first multiply both sides of this equation by p_i, and then we add all n components, and finally we integrate between $t = 0$ and $t = t_f$. These operations yield

$$\int_0^{t_f} \left(\sum_{i=1}^{n} p_i \, \delta\dot{x}_i \right) dt = \int_0^{t_f} \sum_{i=1}^{n} p_i [f_i(\mathbf{x}_{\text{opt}} + \delta\mathbf{x}, \mathbf{u}_{\text{opt}} + \delta\mathbf{u}) - f_i(\mathbf{x}_{\text{opt}}, \mathbf{u}_{\text{opt}})] \, dt \tag{11-45}$$

The left side of this expression can be integrated by parts:

$$\int_0^{t_f} \left(\sum_{i=1}^{n} p_i \, \delta\dot{x}_i \right) dt = \sum_{i=1}^{n} p_i \, \delta x_i \Bigg]_0^{t_f} - \int_0^{t_f} \left(\sum_{i=1}^{n} \dot{p}_i \, \delta x_i \right) dt \tag{11-46}$$

Consider for a moment the first term on the right side. As the initial variations $\delta x_i(0)$ must vanish and as $p_i(t_f) = -\alpha_i$ by definition, we obviously have

$$\sum_{i=1}^{n} p_i \, \delta x_i \Bigg]_0^{t_f} = -\sum_{i=1}^{n} \alpha_i \, \delta x_i(t_f)$$

† The reason for this will be clear as the derivation proceeds.

We recognize this last sum as the negative change $-dI$ *in the payoff function I,* and in view of that, we obtain from (11-43), (11-45), and (11-46) the quite formidable expression for dI:

$$dI = -\int_0^{t_f} \left\{ \sum_{i=1}^n p_i[f_i(\mathbf{x}_{\text{opt}} + \delta\mathbf{x}, \mathbf{u}_{\text{opt}} + \delta\mathbf{u}) - f_i(\mathbf{x}_{\text{opt}}, \mathbf{u}_{\text{opt}})] \right\} dt$$

$$+ \int_0^{t_f} \left(\sum_{i=1}^n \sum_{j=1}^n p_j \frac{\partial f_j}{\partial x_i} \delta x_i \right) dt \quad (11\text{-}47)$$

The factor within [·] in the first integrand is a small first-order difference, and we can expand it in a Taylor series as follows:

$$f_i(\mathbf{x}_{\text{opt}} + \delta\mathbf{x}, \mathbf{u}_{\text{opt}} + \delta\mathbf{u}) - f_i(\mathbf{x}_{\text{opt}}, \mathbf{u}_{\text{opt}}) = f_i(\mathbf{x}_{\text{opt}}, \mathbf{u}_{\text{opt}} + \delta\mathbf{u}) - f_i(\mathbf{x}_{\text{opt}}, \mathbf{u}_{\text{opt}})$$

$$+ \sum_{j=1}^n \frac{\partial f_i(\mathbf{x}_{\text{opt}}, \mathbf{u}_{\text{opt}} + \delta\mathbf{u})}{\partial x_j} \delta x_j + \text{higher-order terms}$$

Substitution into (11-47) yields

$$dI = -\int_0^{t_f} \left\{ \sum_{i=1}^n p_i[f_i(\mathbf{x}_{\text{opt}}, \mathbf{u}_{\text{opt}} + \delta\mathbf{u}) - f_i(\mathbf{x}_{\text{opt}}, \mathbf{u}_{\text{opt}})] \right\} dt$$

$$- \int_0^{t_f} \left\{ \sum_{i=1}^n \sum_{j=1}^n p_i \frac{\partial}{\partial x_j} [f_i(\mathbf{x}_{\text{opt}}, \mathbf{u}_{\text{opt}} + \delta\mathbf{u}) - f_i(\mathbf{x}_{\text{opt}}, \mathbf{u}_{\text{opt}})] \delta x_j \right\} dt \quad (11\text{-}48)$$

At this juncture, we shall find it necessary (as earlier hinted) to impose a restriction on the functions f_i that we shall consider. In fact, we shall only consider functions that are linear in $\mathbf{x}$ and that contain $\mathbf{u}$ in a separable fashion; i.e., the plant dynamics shall be of the form

$$\dot{\mathbf{x}} = \mathbf{A}\mathbf{x} + \boldsymbol{\varphi}(\mathbf{u}) \quad (11\text{-}49)$$

(**A** is not necessarily constant.)

For this class of functions, we obviously have

$$\frac{\partial}{\partial x_j} f_i(\mathbf{x}, \mathbf{u} + \delta\mathbf{u}) = \frac{\partial}{\partial x_j} f_i(\mathbf{x}, \mathbf{u})$$

and this fact causes the second integral in (11-48) to vanish; Eq. (11-48) then reduces to

$$dI = -\int_0^{t_f} [H(\mathbf{x}_{\text{opt}}, \mathbf{u}_{\text{opt}} + \delta\mathbf{u}) - H(\mathbf{x}_{\text{opt}}, \mathbf{u}_{\text{opt}})] dt \quad (11\text{-}50)$$

For brevity in notation, we have introduced the *hamiltonian H*, defined by

$$H \triangleq \sum_{i=1}^n p_i f_i = \mathbf{p}^T \mathbf{f} = \mathbf{p}^T \dot{\mathbf{x}} \quad (11\text{-}51)$$

Let us interpret this result: Clearly, if we can prove that for any arbitrary $\delta\mathbf{u}$, the integral (11-50) is positive (negative), this then would imply that dI would be negative (positive) for these arbitrary $\mathbf{u}$ deviations and the $\mathbf{u}_{\text{opt}}$ would indeed correspond to a maximum (minimum) in I.

The integral will certainly be positive (negative) if the integrand is positive (negative) in the *total* interval

$$0 < t < t_f$$

and a *sufficient* criterion for max (min) of I is therefore that

$$H(\mathbf{x}_{opt}, \mathbf{u}_{opt} + \boldsymbol{\delta u}) - H(\mathbf{x}_{opt}, \mathbf{u}_{opt}) \begin{cases} >0 \text{ for max} \\ <0 \text{ for min} \end{cases} \tag{11-52}$$

for all t in the control interval.

We have proved the *sufficiency* of (11-52). It is quite easy also to prove the *necessity* (see, for instance, Ref. 8), and Eq. (11-52) then constitutes the maximum principle. We formulate it in words:

A necessary and sufficient condition for a maximum (minimum) of the payoff function I is that the hamiltonian H be minimized (maximized) with respect to the control vector at all times.

We can obtain an interesting geometrical interpretation of the PMP by realizing that H equals the dot product of the $\mathbf{p}$ and $\dot{\mathbf{x}}$ vectors [see Eq. (11-51)]. The principle tells us that we should adjust $\mathbf{u}$ so that *at all times* this dot product is minimum or maximum, depending upon whether we seek a maximum or minimum I.

Example 11-6

We shall demonstrate the usage of PMP by working in detail the double-tank hydraulic system depicted in Fig. 11-12. We shall assume the following simple set of numerical values:

$$A_1 = A_2 = 10 \text{ sq ft}$$
$$R = 1 \text{ sec/ft}^2$$

The levels x_1 and x_2 are measured in feet. Our control objective will be to optimize the level in the second tank x_2, as measured after 10 sec, assuming that the pump flow is limited to the range

$$0 < u < 1 \text{ ft}^3/\text{sec}$$

and disregarding completely what happens to the level in the first tank.

We approach the problem in the following steps:

step 1 Construct the mathematical model of the system. From Eq. (11-31), we get directly

$$\begin{bmatrix} \dot{x}_1 \\ \dot{x}_2 \end{bmatrix} = \begin{bmatrix} -0.1 & 0 \\ 0.1 & 0 \end{bmatrix} \begin{bmatrix} x_1 \\ x_2 \end{bmatrix} + \begin{bmatrix} 0.1 \\ 0 \end{bmatrix} u \tag{11-53}$$

step 2 Settle on a proper initial-condition vector $\mathbf{x}_0$. We choose the simplest one possible:

$$\mathbf{x}_0 = \begin{bmatrix} 0 \\ 0 \end{bmatrix}$$

step 3 Determine the objective vector. As

$$I \triangleq 0x_1(10) + 1x_2(10)$$

we get directly

$$\alpha = \begin{bmatrix} 0 \\ 1 \end{bmatrix}$$

step 4   Write the costate equations.   As the system is linear, we get directly, by using Eq. (11-44),

$$\begin{bmatrix} \dot{p_1} \\ \dot{p_2} \end{bmatrix} = \begin{bmatrix} 0.1 & -0.1 \\ 0 & 0 \end{bmatrix} \begin{bmatrix} p_1 \\ p_2 \end{bmatrix} \tag{11-54}$$

or, written in component form,

$$\dot{p_1} = 0.1p_1 - 0.1p_2$$
$$\dot{p_2} = 0$$

with the end conditions

$$p_1(10) = 0$$
$$p_2(10) = -1$$

step 5   Solve the costate.   As $\dot{p_2} = 0$, we get

$$p_2(t) = \text{const} = -1$$

As a consequence,

$$\dot{p_1} = 0.1p_1 + 0.1 \qquad \text{with } p_1(10) = 0$$

We postpone for the time being the actual solution of p_1 until we see that there is a need.

step 6   Write the hamiltonian.   From (11-51), we get

$$H = p_1 f_1 + p_2 f_2 = p_1(-0.1x_1 + 0.1u) - 0.1x_1$$

step 7   Minimize H with respect to u.   The only term containing u in the expression for H is

$$H = \cdots + 0.1p_1 u + \cdots$$

If we wish to minimize H with respect to u, we must use the following control strategy:

If $p_1 > 0$, use *largest possible negative u*!
If $p_1 < 0$, use *largest possible positive u*!
If $p_1 = 0$, indeterminate!

Evidently, the behavior of $p_1(t)$ in the interval $0 < t < 10$ is of crucial importance, and we return therefore to step 5 to take a closer look at this costate variable.   We conclude two facts about $p_1(t)$:

1. Its value for $t = 10$ must equal zero.
2. Its homogeneous equation $\dot{p_1} = 0.1p_1$ gives the positive eigenvalue $\lambda = 0.1$, meaning, in effect, that $p_1(t)$ must be *increasing* with time.

If we combine these two facts, we can come to only one conclusion: $p_1(t)$ must be *negative for $t < 10$.*
This then settles the question of optimum strategy:
We must use the largest possible positive control force $(+1 \, ft^3/sec$ *in this case) throughout the entire control interval.*

Note that there was no need actually to solve for $p_1(t)$, and note also that the above result confirms our previous findings based on intuition.

Once we have settled for the control strategy $u_{opt}(t)$, we of course can easily solve the state equation (11-53). We leave this as an exercise for the reader.

$x(t_f)$ Partly Constrained, t_f Fixed

We now shall consider the case when some *but not all* of the n components of the final value $x(t_f)$ are constrained.† We shall assume the simplest type of constraints, namely, *fixed* values. Specifically, assume that we fix q ($q < n$) of the components at the following end values:

$$x_v(t_f) = x_{vf} \quad \text{for } v = 1, 2, \ldots, q \tag{11-55}$$

The remaining $n - q$ final values are open. In our expression for I,

$$I = \sum_{i=1}^{n} \alpha_i x_i(t_f)$$

it is clear that only those $n - q$ end values that are unconstrained can be made subject to variation. In effect, we have lost q degrees of freedom. Our expression for dI therefore will reduce to

$$dI = \sum_{i=q+1}^{n} \alpha_i \, \delta x_i(t_f) \tag{11-56}$$

where the summation is now extended over those remaining $n - q$ state variables which are unconstrained.

We now can go through a derivation identical to the one in the preceding subsection and end up with the same PMP as before [Eq. (11-52)]. *In the derivation, we must make one change, however; those q costate variables $p_v(t)$ which correspond to the constrained $x_v(t)$ variables will not as before end up in $-\alpha_v$ but must now be left open.* In effect, we have compensated for the q lost degrees of freedom by lifting exactly q specifications on the system.

Example 11-7

To demonstrate this case, we could have chosen the previous example for convenience and modified it to the extent that we fixed the end value of the water level in the first tank at some specified value. However, we shall choose a different problem, and in order to illustrate the versatility of the PMP, we shall apply it to a problem that we already solved by means of the E-L equations (Example 11-2).

We restate the problem: Minimize

$$I = \int_0^1 (x^2 + u^2) \, dt$$

---

† If *all* were constrained, we would not have a variational problem.

for a process characterized by the state equation

$$\dot{x} = u$$

(Note that, for simplicity, we have assigned numerical values to both t_f and the weighting factor α in the integrand.)

We shall impose no amplitude constraints on u but shall require that

$$x(0) = 0$$
$$x(1) = 1$$

The alert reader will probably be surprised at our attempt to use the PMP on a problem that, at first glance, does not at all fit our description of "typical" PMP problems. We have no u constraints; indeed, we know from earlier treatment that this problem has a "smooth" minimum corresponding to a *continuous* u_{opt}. And even the criterion does not fit the pattern.

The first objection we can dispose of immediately by pointing out that *nowhere in our derivation of PMP did we exclude the possibility that the variations δu and δx might be of the "calculus type."*

The second objection concerning the criterion function is not applicable either. By using the trick that we demonstrated earlier in this section [Eq. (11-41)], we can *make* the given system fit the PMP pattern.

We introduce for that purpose a new state variable x_2, defined as follows:

$$\dot{x}_2 \overset{\Delta}{=} x^2 + u^2 \quad \text{and} \quad x_2(0) \overset{\Delta}{=} 0$$

As we obviously have

$$x_2(1) = \int_0^1 (x^2 + u^2)\, dt = I$$

we in effect have reduced the given *one*-dimensional problem to the following *two*-dimensional problem: Optimize

$$I = x_2(1)$$

for a system characterized by the nonlinear state equations

$$\dot{x}_1 = u$$
$$\dot{x}_2 = x_1{}^2 + u^2 \qquad\qquad (11\text{-}57)$$

where

$$\mathbf{x}(0) = \begin{bmatrix} 0 \\ 0 \end{bmatrix}$$

and

$$\mathbf{x}(1) = \begin{bmatrix} 1 \\ \text{open} \end{bmatrix}$$

Clearly, this problem now has all the characteristics of a "PMP"-type problem. We proceed to solve it.

First, we note that the objective vector equals

$$\alpha = \begin{bmatrix} 0 \\ 1 \end{bmatrix}$$

and from Eq. (11-43), we get the adjoint equations

$$\dot{p}_1 = -2p_2 x_1$$
$$\dot{p}_2 = 0$$

(11-58)

with

$$\mathbf{p}(1) = \begin{bmatrix} \text{open} \\ -1 \end{bmatrix}$$

The hamiltonian takes on the form

$$H = p_1 u + (x_1^2 + u^2)p_2$$

From (11-58), we compute p_2:

$$p_2(t) = \text{const} = -1$$

Therefore,

$$H = p_1 u - (x_1^2 + u^2)$$

(11-59)

As I must be minimized, we must maximize H with respect to u; that is, we shall choose those u values that make the sum of the two terms $p_1 u - u^2$ as large as possible.   We can write

$$H = \cdots + p_1 u - u^2 = \cdots - \left(u - \frac{p_1}{2}\right)^2 + \cdots$$

and we realize therefore that we keep H at a maximum throughout the control interval if we make the expression within $(\cdot)$ equal to zero, i.e.:

$$u = u_{\text{opt}}(t) = \tfrac{1}{2}p_1(t)$$

(11-60)

$p_1(t)$ is not explicitly known, of course, so we must proceed to find it.   The first two equations of (11-57) and (11-58) yield

$$\dot{x}_{1\text{opt}} = \tfrac{1}{2}p_1$$
$$\dot{p}_1 = 2x_{1\text{opt}}$$

As $p_1(1)$ is open and $x_1(0)$ and $x_1(1)$ are both specified, these two equations have a unique solution which can be found most conveniently by eliminating p_1.

We obtain

$$\ddot{x}_{1\text{opt}} = x_{1\text{opt}}$$

which has the solution

$$x_{1\text{opt}} = A \cosh t + B \sinh t$$

By meeting the specified end conditions

$$x_1(0) = 0$$
$$x_1(1) = 1$$

we solve A and B and obtain the solution

$$x_{1\text{opt}} = \frac{\sinh t}{\sinh 1} \tag{11-61}$$

We finally compute the optimum control

$$u_{\text{opt}} = \tfrac{1}{2}p_1 = \dot{x}_{1\text{opt}} = \frac{\cosh t}{\sinh 1} \tag{11-62}$$

The reader can verify that these solutions agree with those we obtained in Sec. 11-2 by means of the E-L equation [Eqs. (11-20) and (11-21)]. We also conclude that the PMP compares very unfavorably with the E-L approach—this is definitely not an optimum problem matched to the capabilities of the PMP.

The Time-optimal Case

The previous cases were characterized by fixed control interval t_f. As we demonstrated earlier, we can "invert" the problem and turn it into a "time-optimal" one by specifying partly or completely the state vector **x** and then minimizing the control time t_f.

The problem basically is not different from the case in the previous sub-section. We introduce an $n + 1$ state variable [see Eq. (11-41)] having the property that its end value $x_{n+1}(t_f)$ actually is identical to t_f, and we then proceed as usual. We shall demonstrate with the following example.

Example 11-8

Consider the second-order mechanical system† depicted in Fig. 11-13 and characterized by the state equations (11-37).

We shall set out to find the time-optimum-control strategy required for transferring this system between the states

$$x_1(0) = 0 \qquad x_1(t_f) = 1$$
$$x_2(0) = 0 \qquad x_2(t_f) = 0$$

assuming that the control force is restricted to the amplitude range $1 < u < +1$.

We augment the given system with a third state variable, and our problem takes on the following mathematical character.

---

† This problem seems to have been with us since the beginning of control. It is difficult to trace the origin—everybody intent on making a contribution to the science seems to have been concerned with this "double-integrator" system at one time or another. We shall not be any different. Actually it is hard to find a simpler system that so perfectly brings out a point.

The augmented system is

$$\dot{x}_1 = x_2$$
$$\dot{x}_2 = u \tag{11-63}$$
$$\dot{x}_3 = 1$$

(For simplicity, we have put $m = 1$.)

Specified end conditions are

$$\mathbf{x}(0) = \begin{bmatrix} 0 \\ 0 \\ 0 \end{bmatrix} \qquad \mathbf{x}(t_f) = \begin{bmatrix} 1 \\ 0 \\ t_f = \text{open} \end{bmatrix}$$

Criterion function is

$$I = 0x_1(t_f) + 0x_2(t_f) + 1x_3(t_f)$$

Therefore,

$$\boldsymbol{\alpha} = \begin{bmatrix} 0 \\ 0 \\ 1 \end{bmatrix}$$

As usual, we start our solution by deriving the costate. We obtain

$$\dot{p}_1 = 0$$
$$\dot{p}_2 = -p_1 \tag{11-64}$$
$$\dot{p}_3 = 0$$

with

$$\mathbf{p}(t_f) = \begin{bmatrix} p_{1f} = \text{open} \\ p_{2f} = \text{open} \\ -1 \end{bmatrix}$$

Equations (11-64) are solved readily and yield the results

$$p_1(t) = p_{1f}$$
$$p_2(t) = p_{1f}t - p_{1f}t_f + p_{2f} \tag{11-65}$$
$$p_3(t) = -1$$

Note that the solutions are expressed in terms of the "open" final values p_{1f} and p_{2f}.

The hamiltonian H equals

$$H = p_1(t)x_2 + p_2(t)u + p_3(t)1$$

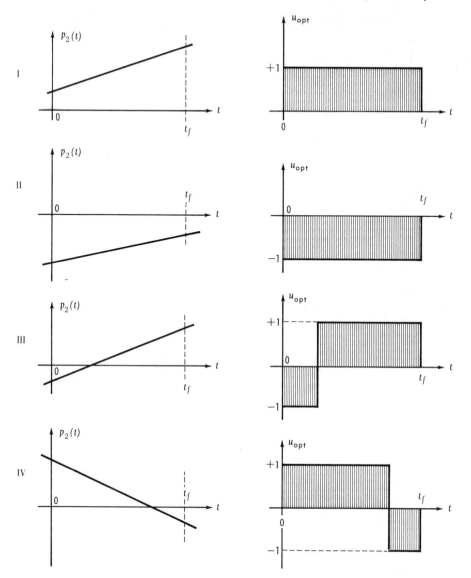

Fig. 11-15   All these control strategies satisfy PMP.

and for minimum I, we must therefore maximize

$$H = \cdots + p_2(t)u + \cdots$$

with respect to u.   The optimum-control strategy thus depends upon the sign of $p_2(t)$ in the control interval in accordance with the rules:

If $p_2(t) > 0$, use $u(t) = +u_{\max} = 1$.

If $p_2(t) < 0$, use $u(t) = -u_{\max} = -1$.

We note from (11-65) that $p_2(t)$ varies *linearly* with t, and depending upon the value of the "open" parameters p_{1f} and p_{2f}, we thus may conceive of the four possibilities shown in Fig. 11-15. *We must now choose the one alternative that will make it possible for us to meet the specified end conditions for the state vector* **x**.

We immediately can dispose of alternatives I and II, as they result in constantly increasing velocity $|x_2|$. A control force of type III accelerates the mass in negative x_1 direction and thus does not apply. Alternative IV remains, and it is easy to see that by applying this control policy and executing the switch-over in the middle of the control interval, we indeed can meet the specification on **x**. Note that this conclusion could have been reached very conveniently by constructing the phase plane for the first two state components of (11-63). We have

$$\frac{\dot{x}_2}{\dot{x}_1} = \frac{dx_2}{dx_1} = \frac{u}{x_2}$$

and as the PMP has told us that u can assume only the two values $u = \pm 1$, we readily can determine (see also Fig. 8-4) that the phase trajectories will be the two sets of parabolas depicted in Fig. 11-16. The boldface trajectory corresponds to the optimum strategy. This policy demands maximum acceleration half the way, followed by maximum deceleration to a full stop. (Any "hot rod" could have told us that in the first place.)

Once the optimum strategy has been found, we can compute the cost function $I = t_f$, which we set out to optimize in the first place. From Eq. (11-63),

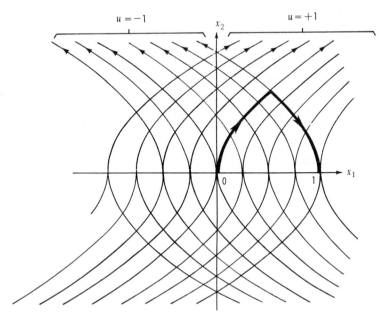

Fig. 11-16   Optimum-control strategy for the inertia system in Fig. 11-13.

we get

$$\ddot{x}_1 = u_{opt}$$

By integrating this equation, we get

$$t_f = 2 \text{ sec}$$

We conclude this brief exposé of the maximum principle by some general observations:

observation 1   On first reading the statement of the Pontryagin maximum principle, one is tempted to exclaim: "So what?"   What is so great about substituting a minimization of one thing with a maximization of another?

On second thought, one realizes the basic feature: the payoff "function" *I* is really not a function at all but a *functional* the value of which depends upon the control input *u(t) at all times* in the interval $0 < t < t_f$.

The hamiltonian *H*, on the other hand, is simply a *function*, depending, at each instant, only upon the *instantaneous* control input.

observation 2   We can draw some very important conclusions concerning the optimum-control strategy simply by *inspection* of the hamiltonian.   Note the difference in this respect from dynamic programming, where the *whole* problem must be solved before we know *anything* about the strategy.

observation 3   In certain classes of problems, the hamiltonian is independent of **u** under certain circumstances, and the PMP therefore tells us nothing. Such "singular" control situations require modified approaches.[9]

observation 4   The PMP tells us only about the *general* nature of the control strategy (for instance, that it must be of the bang-bang type).   The *exact* strategy (i.e., when to switch) must be obtained by other means, e.g., phase-plane techniques.

observation 5   The most difficult aspect of the PMP is the need for solving differential equations that must meet specified boundary conditions at *both* ends. Perhaps this difficulty has not been exposed too obviously in our simple examples, but in general this is indeed the biggest obstacle.   However, this is a difficulty inherent in the problem which no method ever to be designed will be able to eliminate.

observation 6   The information obtained by means of PMP is entirely of the "open-loop" variety.

The controller, be he man or machine, is given a set of instructions to follow in proper sequence.   In the last example, he is told to accelerate for 1 sec (exactly) at maximum rate and then decelerate for 1 sec, whereupon he should find himself at the desired destination.

If he does not, the reason may be any one of the following:

1. He has been given the wrong instructions.
2. His system does not function in accordance with the model used.
3. His physical system has encountered unpredicted disturbances, forcing him off course.

Switching Curves

Although, as we have observed, the information obtained by the analysis methods presented in this chapter is of open-loop character, it is still possible under certain conditions to utilize this information in the design of closed-loop structures. Let us demonstrate this by reference to the Example 11-8 discussed earlier. In this example, we found the control strategy u_{opt} required to transfer in time-optimal fashion the state between two specified *constant* values $\mathbf{x}_0$ and $\mathbf{x}_f$. It is logical now to ask the following questions:

1. Is it possible to develop a control strategy that will execute the state transfer time-optimally between arbitrary and *not necessarily constant* states?
2. Can it be done closed-loop?

We realize immediately that the problem thus stated is tantamount to asking whether it is possible to design a servo (Fig. 11-17) that is capable of following in time-optimal fashion any arbitrary reference input $\mathbf{r}(t)$.

Before we attempt to give an answer to these questions, it is necessary to point out that it is *not possible* to specify arbitrary reference settings $\mathbf{r}(t)$ in the first place because of physical constraints. We can exemplify this by reference to Example 11-8. In this example, we studied the requirements for transferring the state

$$\begin{bmatrix} 0 \\ 0 \end{bmatrix} \Rightarrow \begin{bmatrix} 1 \\ 0 \end{bmatrix}$$

This, then, translated to our servo in Fig. 11-17, corresponds to a reference vector

$$\mathbf{r}(t) = \begin{bmatrix} \sqcap \\ 0 \end{bmatrix}$$

This requirement obviously does not violate the physics of the problem.

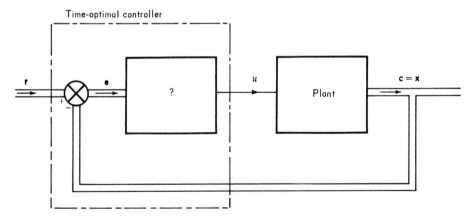

Fig. 11-17 Closed-loop time-optimal system.

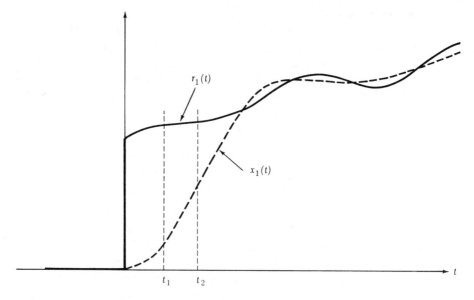

Fig. 11-18   Random reference input.

Assume now, in contrast, that we would have stipulated

$$\mathbf{r}(t) = \begin{bmatrix} \sqcap \\ \sqcap \end{bmatrix}$$

that is, we command both x_1 and x_2 to attain new *constant* values. This requirement is inconsistent with the physics as it violates directly the state equation's
(11-37).   (It is clearly impossible to keep the mass at a constant position and
constant velocity simultaneously.†)

    Therefore, we shall tacitly assume in our following discussion that those
reference trajectories that we specify are physically consistent with the problem.
In our simple mass problem, for instance, we are permitted to specify an arbitrary
reference trajectory $r_1(t)$ for the state variable $x_1(t)$ *if we leave $r_2(t)$ open.*

    We encounter, however, additional conceptual difficulties.   Assume, for
example, still with reference to Example 11-8, that our reference setting $r_1(t)$
looks as indicated in Fig. 11-18.   Specifically, we shall assume that it is *random*
in character.‡   Random processes are beyond our scope, but we shall point out
that the basic feature of such processes is their unpredictability.   It is physically
impossible to know at time t_1 what value the reference $r_1(t)$ will assume at the
later time t_2.   As a consequence, the controller is ignorant as to what target to

---

† Although it is obviously impossible to specify that the state of a given system should follow an
arbitrary reference trajectory $\mathbf{r}(t)$, *it is not inconsistent with physics to specify the end points of this
trajectory.*   This is indeed what we do in determining the controllability of a system.
‡ This situation is encountered when the servo tries to zero in on an evasive target.

aim for, and the output $x_1(t)$ will at best meander around $r_1(t)$ in the manner depicted. Clearly, under the circumstances, it is impossible to define "time optimality." It simply does not have any meaning.

Even in the case of a *deterministic* reference input, we run into difficulties. In the most general case, a deterministic signal can be written

$$r(t) = \alpha_0 + \alpha_1 t + \alpha_2 t^2 + \cdots + \alpha_m t^m$$

$$= \sum_{i=0}^{m} \alpha_i t^i \qquad (11\text{-}66)$$

where the α coefficients *are assumed known*. Quite clearly, if we know the value of this signal at $t = t_1$, we also, in principle, can find it at $t = t_2$; that is, we are able to *predict*.

The parabolic test signals used in Chap. 6 to evaluate servo performance are but special cases of this more general test signal. We remember that the coefficient m determined the severity of the signal. If the control force is *unbounded*, we can in principle design a servo that follows faithfully *any* reference input of type (11-66). However, as we are concerned with *physical* systems, this case is only of academic interest. We must consider realistically amplitude-constrained control forces. In so doing, we find that a particular system can only follow a reference signal characterized by some maximum value m.

In our specific mass system, we are unable to specify any reference signal $r_1(t)$ of order higher than $m = 1$ ($=$ ramp) if we wish to obtain a perfect follow-up (i.e., zero static error). If $r_1(t)$ is left open and we specify $r_2(t)$, then we can only ask for $m = 0$ ($=$ step).

In summarizing, we conclude that we must be very careful in specifying reference inputs to the servo in Fig. 11-17. Assuming that our specifications are consistent with the physics, we now shall demonstrate how it is possible to design an optimal closed-loop controller. Obviously, we must make use of the results given to us by the PMP, and we remember that we were told to apply the control force in bang-bang fashion if we wanted to achieve time optimality. Clearly, our system will therefore have to have the structure depicted in Fig. 11-19. (We have assumed, for simplicity, that the position variable x_1 is our only concern, so in effect, therefore, we are discussing a SISO-position servo.)

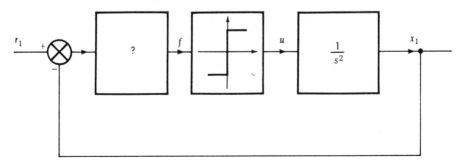

Fig. 11-19 An optimum switching strategy is sought.

The problem that remains to be solved is to develop a controller that supplies the correct *switching strategy*. In this case, we easily can conclude what this strategy should be by making use of the phase trajectories in Fig. 11-16. These trajectories have been redrawn in Fig. 11-20 with one change—we prefer to use $r_1 - x_1$ and $r_2 - x_2$ rather than x_1 and x_2 as our state variables, and we obtain thus an $e\dot{e}$ phase plane. A perfect control strategy should always lead us to origin in this plane in minimum time. It is easy to see that wherever we start in the phase plane, we always can reach origin with one switching only (three different situations are exemplified in the figure). This switching must take place along the boldface line *SS*, consisting of two parabolic segments. We refer to this curve as the *switching curve*

$$f(e,\dot{e}) = 0 \qquad (11\text{-}67)$$

The optimum-switching strategy therefore should be:

When $f(e,\dot{e}) > 0$, apply $u = +u_{max}$.
When $f(e,\dot{e}) < 0$, apply $u = -u_{max}$.

On the basis of this strategy, we are now in a position to design the closed-loop time-optimum-control system shown in Fig. 11-21. We can make the following observations in regard to this solution:

observation 1 As the switching curve is a function of both e and $\dot{e}$, it is necessary

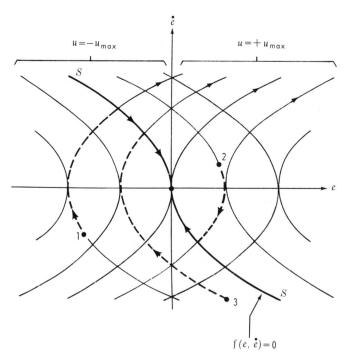

Fig. 11-20 Switching curve.

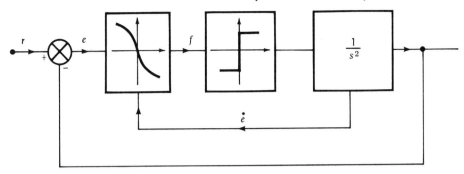

Fig. 11-21 This system is time-optimal for step and ramp inputs only.

to either sense $\dot{e}$ ($=$ velocity) directly or differentiate e (with all attendant difficulties).

observation 2 Though the plant is linear, the switching curve is highly nonlinear.

observation 3 The optimum controller may be instrumented easily utilizing simple logic and approximation of the parabolic curve by use of diode-resistor networks.[10]

observation 4 The system as designed performs time-optimally only for reference inputs consisting of steps and/or ramps.

observation 5 The concept of switching curves can be extended to higher-order systems in the form of *switching planes*. It becomes increasingly difficult to visualize and instrument the solutions. Generally, for an *n*-dimensional system, the switching surface is $(n - 1)$-dimensional and furthermore will always pass through origin.

observation 6 Upon reaching origin, a system like the one in Fig. 11-21 will proceed to switch back and forth; i.e., it will "chatter." This chattering (with resulting fuel consumption) can be avoided by disabling the controller when we are sufficiently close to origin and switching over to a low-magnitude on-off controller ("dual control").

11-5 CONCLUSIONS

We may summarize some of the important features of optimum control as we have discovered them in the last two chapters:

1. Optimum control of 1966 is more theory than practice—by far.

2. The greatest value of the optimum-control theory is that it shows us the ultimate capabilities of a specific system subject to specific constraints, which, for instance, "trial-and-error" design never can do.

3. It gives us information about how this ultimate achievement can be reached. It is then up to us to decide whether or not we should try for it. *Suboptimal* control may be an acceptable compromise and perhaps represents a more attractive solution from an engineering viewpoint.

4. Implementation of optimum-control theory into hardware heavily taxes our computational equipment, and the overall cost will determine in the end how far it is worthwhile to go.

Exercises

11-1 The E-L equations sometimes appear in a different form than that of Eq. (11-7). Assume, for instance, that we had set out to optimize

$$I = \int_0^{t_f} F(x,\dot{x}) \, dt$$

subject to the constraints

$$x(0) = x_0$$
$$x(t_f) = x_f$$

Note that we may now by the substitution

$$\dot{x} = u$$

put the integral under the form (11-1), with an associated constraint of the type (11-2).

a Prove that the E-L equation now reduces to

$$\frac{\partial F}{\partial x} - \frac{d}{dt}\left(\frac{\partial F}{\partial \dot{x}}\right) = 0$$

b Use this form to work Example 11-1 in Sec. 11-2 in a simpler fashion than we did in the text.

c Use this form to work the classic "brachistochrone" problem (this problem actually initiated "calculus of variation"). The problem is stated as follows:

Find the trajectory a particle should fall along between two points (not located along the same vertical) if minimum travel time is sought. Make the following assumptions:

1. Zero initial velocity
2. No other forces than gravity forces

Note that the performance index no longer will be quadratic; therefore, the E-L equation will not be linear and its solution will by no means be simple.

11-2 Use the method of dynamic programming to evaluate the minimum-time trajectory between *A* and *B* in Fig. 11-22. The particle cannot fall below the 4-ft level. Use a 1- by 1-ft grid network and disregard all forces but gravity.

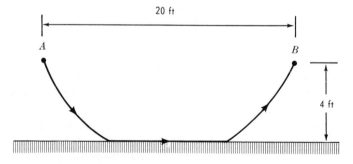

Fig. 11-22   Constrained brachistochrone.

11-3 The electrically heated oven shown in Fig. 3-4 is characterized by plant dynamics [Eq. (3-29)] of the form

$$\dot{\mathbf{x}} = \mathbf{Ax} + \mathbf{b}u$$

where (in some chosen unit system) the **A** and **b** matrices have the values

$$\mathbf{A} = \begin{bmatrix} -0.2 & 0.1 \\ 0.1 & -0.1 \end{bmatrix} \quad \mathbf{b} = \begin{bmatrix} 0.1 \\ 0 \end{bmatrix}$$

We wish to heat this oven in *minimum time* from the initial temperature state

$$\mathbf{x}(0) = \begin{bmatrix} 0 \\ 0 \end{bmatrix}$$

to the final state

$$\mathbf{x}(t_f) = \begin{bmatrix} 0.5 \\ 0.5 \end{bmatrix}$$

    a Determine proper heating strategy if the heater coil is characterized by $0 < u < 1$.
    b What is the minimum time?
    c Is it possible to keep the system in the new state in a steady manner?
11-4 Consider the hydraulic system depicted in Fig. 11-12.
    The system now (for a particular set of numerical values) will be characterized by the equations

$$\begin{bmatrix} \dot{x}_1 \\ \dot{x}_2 \end{bmatrix} = \begin{bmatrix} -0.1 & 0 \\ 0.1 & 0 \end{bmatrix} \begin{bmatrix} x_1 \\ x_2 \end{bmatrix} + \begin{bmatrix} 1 \\ 0 \end{bmatrix} u$$

The pump supplying the inflow u is reversible, so u can vary throughout the range

$$-1 < u < +1$$

    a Compute the maximum level x_2 that we can reach in 10 sec if we require that the level x_1 be 5 at the same time. The vessels are empty at $t = 0$.
    b Add another input to the lower vessel. We assume this input u_2 to have the same characteristics as the first one (which we now define as u_1). Compute $x_2(10)_{\max}$ under the same conditions as in problem *a*.
11-5 Consider the electrical circuit shown in Fig. 11-23a. The two voltage sources u_1 and u_2 are instantaneously and independently adjustable within the range 0 to 10 volts.
    a What control strategy would you use if you were to charge both capacitors to 5 volts each in *minimum time*? Initially the capacitors are discharged.
    b Is the problem as stated in *a* identical with the problem we would obtain by replacing each voltage source by a d-c battery of 10 volts emf plus a switch as shown in Fig. 11-23b? In this new problem we would ask how to "maneuver" the switches in order to charge the capacitors as requested.
11-6 In solving Example 11-8 in the text, there was no need to find an explicit solution for the costate $\mathbf{p}(t)$ [except for the third component $p_3(t)$]. If you actually try to find a solution for $p_1(t)$ and $p_2(t)$, you run into some trouble. Show this and also try to explain where the difficulties emanate from. Can you find a cure?
11-7 Work Example 11-8 in the text by using the method of dynamic programming.

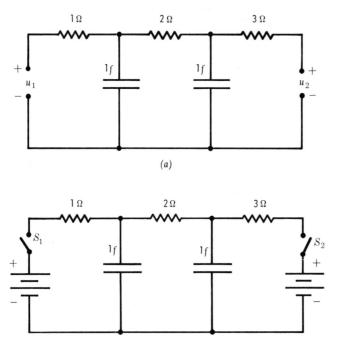

Fig. 11-23　A time-optimal capacitor-switching problem.

References

1. L. E. Elsgolc, "Calculus of Variations," Addison-Wesley Publishing Company, Inc., Reading, Mass., 1962.

2. John V. Breakwell and Arthur E. Bryson, Neighboring-optimum Terminal Control for Multivariable Nonlinear Systems, presented at Symposium on Multivariable System Theory, SIAM Meeting, MIT, Cambridge, Mass., Nov. 1–3, 1962.

3. Arthur E. Bryson and Walter F. Denham, A Steepest-ascent Method for Solving Optimum Programming Problems, *J. Appl. Mech.*, **29**(2) (June, 1962).

4. Walter F. Denham and Arthur E. Bryson, Steepest-ascent Solution of Optimal Programming Problems with Inequality Constraints, presented at IAS Winter General Meeting, New York, January, 1963.　Published as *Rept.* BR-2121 by Raytheon Co., Missile and Space Division, Bedford, Mass.

5. Felix Aasma, Design and Analysis of Optimal Multivariable Control Processes, *Rept.* 63-26-D, Institutt for Reguleringsteknikk, N.T.H., Trondheim, Norway (1963).

6. R. Bellman, "Adaptive Control Processes—A Guided Tour," Princeton University Press, Princeton, N.J., 1961.

7. *Proc. Dynamic Programming Workshop, JACC Conf.*, Boulder, Colo. (1961).

8. L. Rozonoer, Pontryagin's Maximum Principle in Its Application to the Theory of Optimum Systems, *Automation Remote Control*, **20** (1959—October, November, and December issues).

9. J. E. Gibson and C. D. Johnson, Singular Solutions in Problems of Optimal Control, *Rept.* TR-EE 63-3, Purdue University, Lafayette, Ind.

10. Olle I. Elgerd and L. B. Scheiber, A Study of Optimum Switching of On-Off Type Control Systems through Logic, *Proc. NEC*, **18** (1962).

chapter 12

THE ROLE OF THE COMPUTER IN DESIGN AND OPERATION OF CONTROL SYSTEMS

12-1 INTRODUCTORY REMARKS

In the past eleven chapters, we have given a brief introduction to those topics of deterministic control which in our opinion best serve to identify and characterize the field as it appears in the middle sixties. The reader has probably been left with the impression that the field is vast and maybe somewhat overwhelming. We have not even attempted to cover those new and important areas which are only now just beginning to be explored. We refer here to the fields of biological control and learning and adaptive systems.

A characteristic feature of control is its close relation and tie-in with a vast number of other branches of science and engineering, e.g., classical mechanics, electronics, and information and communication theory. We have tried to avoid straying off course into these fields even when temptations have been strong. We feel, however, that we would be guilty of gross neglect if we did not, at least summarily, introduce the reader to the tremendously important role played by the modern computer in design, development, and also operation of control systems. Our story by necessity must be sketchy and superficial, as the field of computers has become if possible even more vast and departmentalized than that of control itself. It also will be assumed that the reader has, at least, a rudimentary knowledge of the basic principles of computers. It seems that computer courses are slowly but surely penetrating down to the undergraduate level.

Historically, it has been customary to divide computers into *analog* and *digital*. As a result of the computer developments that have taken place in the last few years, it is necessary to add another important member to the computer family—the *hybrid* computer. This particular variety of computer has found extensive use in control—indeed, the specific computational needs of various control problems (particularly, optimal control) have had a strong influence on the development of this computer type—in very much the same way as the needs of control accelerated the development of the analog computer a quarter of a century ago. The use of computers ranges from pure computational assistance in the design stage by means of *general-purpose* computers to live, or *real-time*, operation of *special-purpose* computers incorporated as part of the control loop. When a computer is part of a control loop, we refer to the arrangement as *computer control*. In such an arrangement, the computer takes over the role of the controller. It is, however, very difficult to draw a dividing line. For example, a proportional-plus-integral type of controller performs the same mathematical operation as certain computational elements do in an analog computer.

A computer—any type—is a robot which can perform to various degrees of speed and perfection the following basic chores:

1. Computation
2. Memorization
3. Logic decision making

Being a robot, it requires human supervision and control.

We shall summarize first the basic features of the analog and digital computers, discuss the reasons for hybridization, and demonstrate with examples how these devices are being utilized in design and operation of control systems.

12-2 THE ANALOG COMPUTER

The analog machine computes, memorizes, and performs logic in terms of variables which always appear in *continuous* form. In the vast majority of cases, these variables, *machine variables*, are electrical voltages in the range -100 to $+100$ volts. The accuracy with which the above operations are performed depends entirely upon the quality of the components used and, under the best of conditions, may be as high as 0.01 percent of full scale. 0.1 per cent is a much more realistic figure for the majority of the analog computers used for research and industrial purposes.

12-2.1 COMPUTING ELEMENTS

The basic computing elements in the analog computer are shown in Table 12-1. Most of them are based on the high-gain d-c amplifier, which is the most critical component in any analog machine. Most computer manufacturers today market solid-state amplifiers which offer substantial advantages over the old tube-type amplifiers in respect to size, power dissipation, and reliability. These basic elements can be *interconnected* to perform any conceivable computation required.

12-2.2 MANUAL-MODE CONTROL—SLOW OPERATION

If one of the computing elements is supplied with an input voltage, it responds immediately with an output. For instance, if a constant voltage is applied to an integrator, the output increases linearly with time until the integrator saturates. We need to *control* its operation. In particular, we wish to start and stop the computations and be able to provide the integrators with the proper *initial-condition* (IC) values. This can be accomplished by means of the *integrator-mode control*

Table 12-1 Basic analog computing elements

Circuit	Symbol	Basic operation
v_i, N, aN, v_o	a	$v_o = av_i$ $0 < a < 1$ N = winding turns
v_i R_1 R_f v_o	v_i a v_o	$v_o = -av_i$ $a \triangleq \dfrac{R_f}{R_1}$
v_{i1} R_1 R_2 R_f, v_{i2}, v_{in} R_n v_o	v_{i1} a_1, a_n, v_{in} v_o	$v_o = -\displaystyle\sum_{\nu=1}^{n} a_\nu v_{i\nu}$ $a_\nu \triangleq \dfrac{R_f}{R_\nu}$
v_i R C v_o	IC v_i a v_o	$v_o(t) = v_o(0) - a\displaystyle\int_0^t v_i\, dt$ $a \triangleq \dfrac{1}{RC}$
v_{i1} Multiplier v_o, v_{i2}	v_{i1} a v_o, v_{i2}	$v_o = a v_{i1} v_{i2}$
v_{i1} Function generator v_o, v_{in}	v_{i1} $F(...)$ v_o, v_{in}	$v_o = F(v_{i1}, ..., v_{in})$ (n very seldom larger than one)

switches S_1 and S_2 depicted in Fig. 12-1. The three most important modes are RESET, COMPUTE, and HOLD.

In the RESET mode, the IC input is energized and the capacitor is charged with the (negative) voltage value appearing at this input. *Note*: The integrator is not instantaneously "reset"; the capacitor voltage changes exponentially with a time constant rC. With $r = 100$ kilohms and $C = 1$ μf, this means that the recharging process takes about 1 sec. (Compare Fig. 12-5.)

In the COMPUTE mode, the element integrates, with the output voltage starting out from whatever voltage value appears on the capacitor as a result of the previous RESET operation.

In the HOLD mode, we trap the momentary charge on the capacitor, and the output is "frozen." When we go back to COMPUTE, the integration process continues "as if nothing had happened."

This mode control is performed by *mechanical* switches upon *manual* command and represents the "classical" *slow* use of analog machines. Normal parameter values for an integrator are $R = 1$ megohm and $C = 1$ μf, corresponding

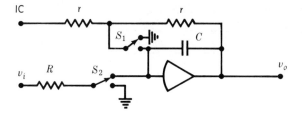

Integrator mode	Switch position	Resulting circuit
COMPUTE	S_1 S_2	
HOLD	S_1 S_2	
RESET	S_1 S_2	

Fig. 12-1 Basic integrator circuit.

to an integration constant $a = 1$ (see Table 12-1). For recording the solutions, we use mechanical *xy* plotters and stripchart recorders.

12-2.3 ELECTRONIC-MODE CONTROL—FAST OPERATION

The usefulness of the analog computer has been increased enormously in recent years by an idea which is as ingenious in its simplicity as it was late in arrival. It was first introduced in the late fifties by Computer Systems, Inc., on their Dystac computer. All major computer companies now provide their analogs with this innovation.

We are referring to the idea of *electronic-mode control* combined with *fast integrators*. "Fast" integration is obtained simply by decreasing the size of the capacitor C of the integrator. Assume, for instance, that we choose $C = 0.01$ μf. Then the integration constant a will increase to 100, meaning in effect that the rate of integration has been increased 100-fold. When simulating a certain process, the change to fast integration means, in effect, that we speed up the process by a factor of 100.

Electronic-mode control will be discussed in more detail in Sec. 12-4. In effect, we now leave the control of the integrators to *any device* that outputs actuating signals that match the electronic-mode control switches. This opens up tremendous possibilities. For instance, we may let a *digital computer* control the analog. In the simplest application, we can change the mode of a fast integrator *repetitively* between RESET and COMPUTE, and this permits us to obtain a *periodic* solution, which we can display on a cathode-ray oscilloscope (CRO). The beauty of the repetitive operation (REPOP) is that the effects of parameter changes can be viewed *instantaneously* on the scope.

12-2.4 THE CONCEPT OF SIMULATION—THE ANALOG AS A SYNTHESIS TOOL

Electronic-mode control makes it possible to use the analog computer for a whole score of sophisticated computing schemes, some of which we shall explore later. However, the "classical" use of the computer as a synthesis tool still predominates and will probably do so for the foreseeable future. In discussing the "trial-and-error" type of synthesis in Chap. 7, we indicated that the most time-consuming part of the whole design procedure was to check that a particular design met the specifications. Checking out the transient response of a system of order in excess of 4 may take days if slide rule and tables are employed.

By means of an analog computer, the transient response can be obtained in seconds *independent of the system order and also independent of whether or not the system is linear.* If REPOP is available, we actually can obtain instantaneous response pictures on the scope. This permits us to make as many trial runs as we see fit in a particular case and enhances to a great degree our chances for a good design. But more important—the analog computer eliminates the need for simplification of the mathematical model we have arrived at. This then means that all effects that we know of will be taken into account. It is probably safe to say that the analog computer used as a *simulator* constitutes our most valuable synthesis tool. It is important to point out, however, that the computer cannot "think" for us. We, the operators, must come up with the ideas—all the computer can do for us is to save us the drudgery of routine computations, giving us time for more productive chores.

Simulation on the Basis of State Models

When used as a *simulator*, the analog computer is called upon to perform the job it best knows—to integrate. The idea is to interconnect (to *program*) the basic computing elements in such a fashion that the machine variables obey the same set of differential equations as the actual physical system. The interconnection takes place externally to the computer on the *programming board* (or patch board).

We may use either the state differential equations or the transfer-function description as a starting point in the programming procedure. We consider the former first and assume that we have available the set of closed-loop equations [compare Eqs. (6-4) and (8-3)]

$$\dot{\mathbf{x}} = \mathbf{f}_c(\mathbf{x}, \mathbf{r}) \tag{12-1a}$$

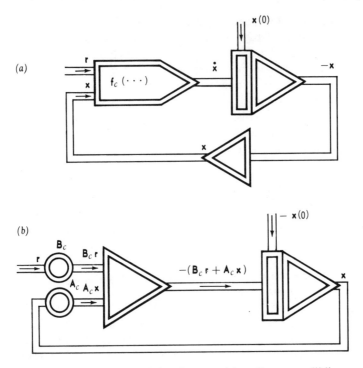

Fig. 12-2   Conceptual simulation diagrams: (*a*) nonlinear case, (*b*) linear case.

or, in the case of a linear system,

$$\dot{\mathbf{x}} = \mathbf{A}_c\mathbf{x} + \mathbf{B}_c\mathbf{r} \tag{12-1b}$$

In Fig. 12-2*a* and *b* are shown the *conceptual* programming diagrams in each of these cases.   Let us illustrate with a simple example.

Example 12-1

We shall consider the simple second-order system depicted in Fig. 12-3.   The plant consists of an "inertia load" which, as a simple root-locus plot will confirm, results in a marginally stable system.   It is suggested that we stabilize by means of rate feedback ($\dot{c}$ is assumed to be available) and that we control the speed of response by the amplifier gain K_1. K_1 and K_2 are therefore our two design parameters, and we would wish to study their effect on the system response.

We first establish the dynamic model and obtain directly from Fig. 12-3

$$u = \ddot{c} \quad \text{(plant)}$$

$$u = K_1 e \quad \text{(amplifier)} \tag{12-2}$$

$$e = r - (c + K_2\dot{c}) \quad \text{(comparator + feedback loop)}$$

We define then a state vector

$$\mathbf{x} = \begin{bmatrix} x_1 \\ x_2 \end{bmatrix} \triangleq \begin{bmatrix} c \\ \dot{c} \end{bmatrix}$$

In terms of these state variables, the dynamic model takes on the form

$$\dot{x}_1 = x_2$$
$$\dot{x}_2 = -K_1 x_1 - K_1 K_2 x_2 + K_1 r \tag{12-3}$$

These two differential equations can be simulated by means of two integrators, one inverter, and three pots, as shown in Fig. 12-4. We make the following observations concerning this computer diagram:

1. The original system structure cannot be discerned from the diagram.
2. To study the effects of changes in K_1, we need to adjust *all three* pots.
3. K_1 and K_2 are both "mixed up" in the setting of pot 3.

Although the scheme works, this is definitely not a *practical* procedure.

In general, simulation based upon the state differential equations should be avoided.† We gain several advantages by instead basing the programming on the block diagram or transfer-function description of the physical system, as will be

---

† In fairness to the state-variable programming method, we would like to emphasize that it has on occasion some distinct advantages. For example, we can always eliminate so-called "redundant integrators" by putting the differential equations in normal form. Also, it minimizes the need for amplifiers. A good discussion is given in Ref. 3.

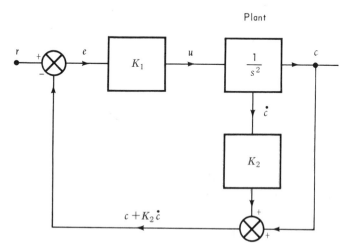

Fig. 12-3 A simple second-order servo with rate damping.

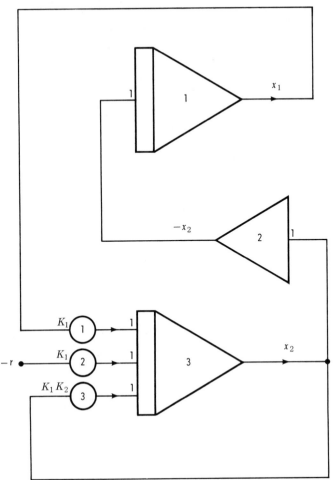

Fig. 12-4   Simulation of the servo in Fig. 12-3 on basis of state model.

demonstrated shortly.   Before we proceed with this, we wish to comment briefly on the *very important* topic of *scaling*.   In the example just treated, we let the state variables be identical with the machine variables.   We did this for reasons of simplicity and convenience.   In general, we must scale each state variable; i.e., we must make the corresponding machine variable proportional to, not identical with, the state variable.

The reason for this is that the numerical values for the state variables may not be at all in a range that fits the computer.   Like any instrument, the analog computer will give us best accuracy if we utilize full scale (-100 to $+100$ volts).

Let ξ_i be the machine variable (unit = volts) which corresponds to the state variable x_i.   We now introduce the *scale factor* s_{ii} and define the following relationships between the *physical* variables x_i and the *simulated* variables ξ_i:

$$\xi_1 = s_{11}x_1$$
$$\xi_2 = s_{22}x_2$$
$$\cdots\cdots$$
$$\xi_i = s_{ii}x_i \tag{12-4}$$
$$\cdots\cdots$$
$$\xi_n = s_{nn}x_n$$

or, in more compact form,

$$\boldsymbol{\xi} = \mathbf{Sx} \tag{12-5}$$

where $\mathbf{S}$ is the *diagonal scale-factor matrix*. The scale factors should be chosen so that the corresponding machine variables will vary throughout an appropriate range, i.e., as close as possible to ± 100 volts so as to utilize maximum accuracy. As we do not know these ranges in advance, we must proceed on a trial-and-error basis—make a first choice of $\mathbf{S}$ on the basis of a reasonable estimate and make a trial run. If some amplifiers are outputting too low voltages or if some are saturating, make proper adjustments.

It is important to realize that in the process of scaling, we may actually *change* the differential equations which we are about to study. For example, consider the nonlinear simple first-order equation

$$\dot{x} = -x^2 \tag{12-6}$$

By introducing the machine variable ξ, related to the state variable x through the equation

$$\xi = sx$$

we obtain the new *machine* equation

$$\dot{\xi} = -\frac{1}{s}\xi^2 \tag{12-7}$$

which guides the variation of the voltage, ξ, on the computer. Clearly, if $s \neq 1$, which usually is the case, the machine equation and the state equation *are different*, indicating that the time variation of ξ will be different from that of x. The machine equation can be written

$$\frac{d\xi}{d(t/s)} = -\xi^2 \tag{12-8}$$

which actually proves that we have changed the *time scale* by our amplitude scaling. For example, if $s = 10$, we have actually *slowed down* the process in ratio $1:10$.

It can be argued that our simulation is "improper." *For nonlinear processes, we always must be very careful to interpret our computer recordings, as the scaling in general will affect the differential equations. Only for linear differential equations will the simulation always be "proper" independent of the* **S** *matrix (except when it is singular).* (The student has an opportunity to prove this statement by working Exercise 12-1 at the end of this chapter.)

Simulation on the Basis of Transfer Functions

By utilizing so-called *operational amplifiers* (OA), we can simulate practically any transfer function $T(s)$ we desire. Figure 12-5 shows an example. Any standard text[1,2] contains tables of proper RC network configurations that will give the desired transfer characteristics. The simulation procedure is as follows:

Each block in the actual control system is simulated by means of a separate OA, whereupon the blocks are interconnected to form a simulation setup of the entire system.

Example 12-2

We demonstrate by simulating the earlier-chosen servo in Fig. 12-3. The resulting computer program is given in Fig. 12-6. The diagram motivates the following comments:

1. The actual system structure is preserved in the computer diagram.
2. The gains K_1 and K_2 can be tested by *separate* pots.

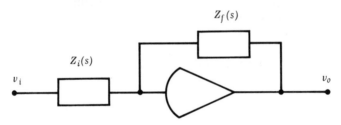

$$T(s) = \frac{V_o(s)}{V_i(s)} = -\frac{Z_f(s)}{Z_i(s)}$$

Example
  The RESET circuit in Fig 12-1

$$Z_f(s) = \frac{r 1/sC}{r + 1/sC} = \frac{r}{1 + sCr}$$

$$Z_i(s) = r$$

Thus $\quad T(s) = -\dfrac{1}{1+sCr} = -\dfrac{1}{Cr}\,\dfrac{1}{s+1/rC}$

Fig. 12-5 Operational amplifier.

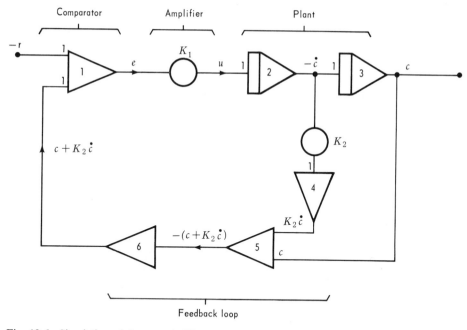

Fig. 12-6 Simulation of the servo in Fig. 12-3 on basis of transfer-function model.

3. As we can confirm by comparison with Fig. 12-4, this type of simulation requires more amplifiers than were needed in the previous method.

4. We can eliminate, as a rule, several of the amplifiers used in a diagram of the above type, *but in the process we shall destroy the structural equivalence.*

12-2.5 SUMMARY OF ANALOG FEATURES

We summarize the essential characteristics of the analog computer used in the "classical" sense.

advantages:

1. Combined with the classical "trial-and-error" techniques, it makes up our most powerful synthesis "team."

2. It works on continuous variables and in parallel; i.e., all computational elements operate simultaneously. This means that the *order* of the simulated system in no way delays the computation.

3. It operates equally fast for linear or nonlinear systems. The speed of operation basically is limited only by the bandwidth of the amplifiers. (This statement does not apply, of course, if mechanical servo-driven multipliers are incorporated in the simulation setup.)

4. It is extremely simple to program, so simple indeed that we are currently trying to use analog-type programming techniques for digital computers.

(See Sec. 12-3.3.) It is also important to point out that the analog programming language is almost universal, which serves to improve communications between users.

5. As it is particularly well suited to integrating, it is a "natural" for use on dynamic systems, e.g., control systems.
6. As parameter changes may be effected by simply turning a pot, it is extremely convenient in synthesis work.
7. It can work in conjunction with simple output equipment, and the output data appear in immediately useful form.
8. The two last points combine to establish an almost perfect communication link between the operator and the machine.
9. Actual hardware can be connected directly to the analog computer and operated with it in real time.
10. An error in programming will not, as a rule, result in complete failure of the computation (which sometimes is a disadvantage if the error is not detected).
11. Small analog computers are available at a very reasonable price, making this kind of computer almost universally available.

disadvantages:

1. Scaling is necessary and can be quite problematic in case of nonlinear systems.
2. Accuracy is limited to 0.01 per cent in slow operation and maybe only 1 percent in REPOP. In most engineering applications, however, this is sufficient, since our models are not that accurate in the first place. Also errors within the computer tend, as a rule, to cancel each other due to the parallel operation. (In a digital computer, the errors, although very small, will accumulate.)
3. Poor memory capability. Variables can be memorized only for the period of time that we can retain the capacitor voltages on the integrators. Due to inevitable leakage, this means that accuracy can be obtained only for a matter of seconds or possibly minutes. (More will be said about analog memory in connection with hybrid computation.)

12-3   THE DIGITAL COMPUTER

The digital machine computes, memorizes, and performs logic in terms of variables which always appear in discrete form as data sequences. All continuous-type mathematical operations (integration, for instance) must thus be discretized in order to be accepted by the computer. The data sequences are converted into a binary number system and processed sequentially by the central arithmetic unit, which is designed to perform the following elementary operations:

1. Add (or subtract) two binary numbers
2. Compare two binary numbers
3. Dispatch a binary number to or remove one from a memory cell

These elementary operations, executed in a proper sequential order, are sufficient to handle *any* mathematical problem, however complex—assuming, of course, that we have enough memory and time available. For example, let us see how the digital computer computes sin x. As no memory would be sufficiently large to *tabulate* sin x for every conceivable argument x, the digital computer will *generate* sin x whenever it is needed. For instance, it could use the series

$$\sin x = x - \frac{x^3}{3!} + \frac{x^5}{5!} - + \cdots + (-1)^{n-1}\frac{x^{2n-1}}{(2n-1)!} + \underset{\substack{\text{Remainder}\\\text{term}}}{R(x,n)}$$

and compute and add term by term (note that multiplications and divisions can be performed by repeated additions) in the series. It would stop only when it found that the remainder term $R(x,n)$ was less by comparison than some prescribed number.† The power of the digital computer lies in the fact that it can perform these elementary operations:

1. Tremendously fast
2. With perfect accuracy
3. Sequentially, without human intervention

12-3.1 PROGRAMMING

The operator communicates with the analog computer via the patch board and the mode-control switches. The computer responds instantly (or almost instantly, at least) via the stripchart recorder, xy plotter, or CRO screen. The "program," i.e., the patchup and pot settings, can be changed at any time, *even during the COMPUTE mode.* The man-machine relationship is almost perfect (except when the electronics acts up).

The situation is indeed different in the case of the digital computer. The program consists here of a set of instructions presented to the computer in the form of, for instance, a deck of cards or a magnetic or paper tape. These instructions tell the computer in a coded binary language which elementary operations to perform and in what chronological sequence to perform them. The program must, of course, also advise the computer where in the memory it can find those numbers that will be involved in the computation. Prior to 1957, such a program had to be a detailed tabulation of *every* elementary operation. In computer lingo—we were forced to write the program on the *machine-language level.* This was a nerve-racking business, and a programming breakthrough was necessary.

---

† It should be noted that the remainder term $R(x,n)$ is expressible only as an infinite series. A *bound* $R_b(x,n)$ is found which can be expressed as a *closed* expression and which has the property $R_b(x,n) > R(x,n)$.

The computer keeps track of $R_b(x,n)$ and terminates the computations when this bound is below the prescribed value.

For example, in the cited series we can say with certainty that, because of the alternating sign,

$$|R(x,n)| < \frac{|x^{2n+1}|}{(2n+1)!} \triangleq R_b(x,n)$$

We had to be able to communicate with the computer in an easier language.   The breakthrough came—unfortunately for the digital-computer user, in a completely disorganized and nonstandardized way.   The digital industry has developed into a "Tower of Babel," with, as of this writing, over 1,000 programming languages and an uncounted number of dialects in use.   Some of these *source languages*, like FORTRAN and ALGOL, have been widely accepted by both users and manufacturers.   The common feature of all these languages is so-called *subroutines*, which contain in a packaged form all those machine-language instructions that are necessary in order to perform a specific computation.   For instance, if we wish the computer to compute sin x, we can command it to do so simply by the FORTRAN statement SINF X.   The computer interprets this as a sequence of machine-language instructions which result in a computation of sin x along lines earlier outlined.

Specifically, the communication procedure between the programmer and the machine is as follows:

1. A flow diagram of the computation process is prepared (see Example 12-3).
2. The programmer *translates* the computational operations into the source language, e.g., FORTRAN.   This "translation" consists of first writing in proper sequence the FORTRAN statements and then having them punched on cards.   *It obviously is necessary for the programmer to know the source language.*   The card punching is performed on typewriterlike keyboards producing cards with appropriately punched holes.   We are now in possession of a deck of cards containing in coded form the source language.
3. This deck of cards is now *fed in proper sequence* into the machine for translation into the *machine language*.   This process results in a new (and thicker) deck of cards called the *object program*.   This is now the program that actually is used in running the problem.
4. The program is run, and the answer will be printed out in a *format* that the programmer has earlier selected and included as part of the source language.

It is important to realize that a language like FORTRAN is a *specialized* language, in this case intended for scientific use.

An instruction repertoire of the kind offered via a source language will consume a large part of the core memory,† but the availability of FORTRAN and similar compilers has in large part been responsible for the fantastic growth of computer installations within the last seven or eight years.   It should be noted that no knowledge of the machine language is necessary when working with FORTRAN. It *is* necessary, however, to completely understand the problem at hand so that a logical buildup of the computer program can be performed.   As the digital computer performs the computations *sequentially, it is very important that the flow of instructions follow in proper sequence.*   It is very helpful, whatever computer program one employs, to make a *flow diagram* of the problem.   We shall demonstrate with an example.

† Memory types were discussed on p. 463.

Example 12-3

Let us discuss the digital programming of the servo problem (Fig. 12-3) which we earlier programmed for the analog computer. This will provide a good comparison between the two methods.

We derived the state differential equations (12-3). Our first step in preparing these equations for the digital computer is to write them as difference equations. Using the method sketched in Chap. 8 [Eq. (8-9)], we get

$$\frac{x_{1_{v+1}} - x_{1_v}}{\Delta t} \approx x_{2_v}$$

$$\frac{x_{2_{v+1}} - x_{2_v}}{\Delta t} \approx -K_1 x_{1_v} - K_1 K_2 x_{2_v} + K_1 r_v$$

We can write these equations as

$$x_{1_{v+1}} \approx x_{1_v} + \varphi_v$$
$$x_{2_{v+1}} \approx x_{2_v} + \psi_v \tag{12-9}$$

where, for the sake of brevity, we defined

$$\varphi_v \overset{\Delta}{=} \Delta t\, x_{2_v}$$
$$\psi_v \overset{\Delta}{=} \Delta t\, (-K_1 x_{1_v} - K_1 K_2 x_{2_v} + K_1 r_v)$$

We must understand that these difference equations provide an *approximate* solution for the given differential equations. In fact, our chosen set of difference equations is the most approximate but, at the same time, the simplest one that we can write.

Solution of differential equations by digital methods is always based upon some sort of *prediction scheme*. We start out with the initial data points for $v = 0$, corresponding to the initial conditions. Based upon available data, we then predict what the state must be Δt sec later in the data point corresponding to $v = 1$. The basic tool for such a prediction is the *forward-interpolation* formula

$$x(t_0 + \Delta t) = x(t_0) + \Delta t\, \dot{x}(t_0) + \frac{\Delta t}{2!}\, \ddot{x}(t_0) + \cdots$$

which simply tells us that if we know the state and *all* its derivatives at $t = t_0$, we can predict the *exact* state at $t = t_0 + \Delta t$. How many terms to use is a matter of compromise. The formula we have proposed to use (12-9) is obtained by terminating the series after the second term and thus only making use of the first derivative. This is called *linear interpolation*. There exist considerably more accurate numerical integration methods based upon higher-order derivatives (Kutta-Runge, Gill, Mod Gurk, and others), but for the sake of simplicity, we shall settle for this one.

We next decide upon parameter ranges for K_1 and K_2, type of reference input r, possible initial values for x_1 and x_2, and proper size of the discrete integration step Δt.

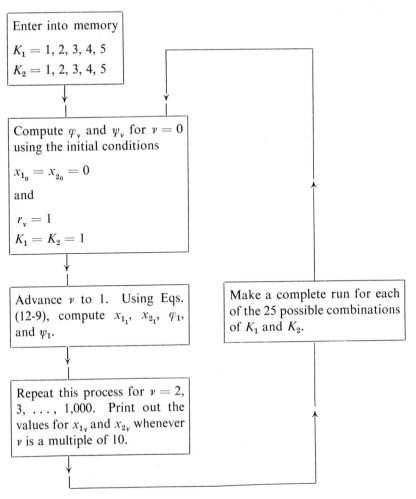

Fig. 12-7　Flow diagram for preparation of digital-computer program.

reference input　Let us assume that we wish to study the system response for a unit-step input; i.e., we shall use $r_v = 1$ in our computations.

initial conditions　The system will be assumed initially at rest; that is,

$$x_{1_0} = x_{2_0} = 0$$

parameter ranges　We shall assume that root-locus plots have indicated that the response specs should be met by K_1 and K_2 values in the ranges

$$1 < K_1 < 5$$
$$1 < K_2 < 5$$

In our computations, we shall let both K_1 and K_2 assume the integer values in these ranges.

integration step This is a very critical choice. In general, the finer the discretizing we use, the better the results we shall get. However, if we choose too small steps, we reach a point of diminishing return. This is due to the fact that for a given control interval, the finer discretizing results in a larger number of *smaller* terms to handle. As the *relative* accuracy of any computation operation (digital or analog) diminishes with the size of the number, we realize that eventually we "drown in the noise."

Error analysis and estimation are difficult subjects in numerical analysis, and we shall not linger upon them. A good rule of thumb established by Connelly[4] and others is that one should compute each variable at least 10 to 20 times per cycle of its highest frequency. Not knowing a priori the magnitude of this frequency, we again must resort to estimates. Such estimates are not too hard to make in our case as we know from root-locus sketches the *approximate* locations for the closed-loop eigenvalues and therefore also the frequency of the response terms. By choosing $\Delta t = 0.01$, we believe that we have a sufficient margin. It is also necessary to decide on the *length* of each run. We decide that 10 sec should show the essential features of the response picture.

We are now in a position to draw the flow diagram shown in Fig. 12-7. From a diagram of this type, it is relatively simple to write a FORTRAN program (assuming one knows this language).

After the program is prepared, cards must be punched and the deck presented to the computer center, which usually is run on a "closed-shop" basis. If we are lucky, we may receive the answer sheet the same day; usually, we receive instead a diagnostic statement telling us that we forgot a decimal point somewhere in the program. Whenever we do receive the computation results, they come in the form of a tabulation, and we must plot them to judge their relative value.

The communication between man and machine is extremely poor, and it is no surprise that the control engineer, whenever possible, turns to the analog computer for assistance.†

12-3.2 SUMMARY OF DIGITAL FEATURES

We summarize the characteristics of the digital computer.

advantages:
1. There is no practical limit to the accuracy we can obtain if we are willing to trade computing time.
2. The digital computer handles any type of mathematical operation with equal ease.
3. No scaling is required.

---

† It is only fair to report that the man-machine rapport is constantly being improved. The computer industry is, of course, well aware of the fact that this is a serious bottleneck. Time-shared systems, where a large number of operators can work in parallel with almost uninterrupted input and output, are being designed, and we shall certainly see considerable progress in this field.

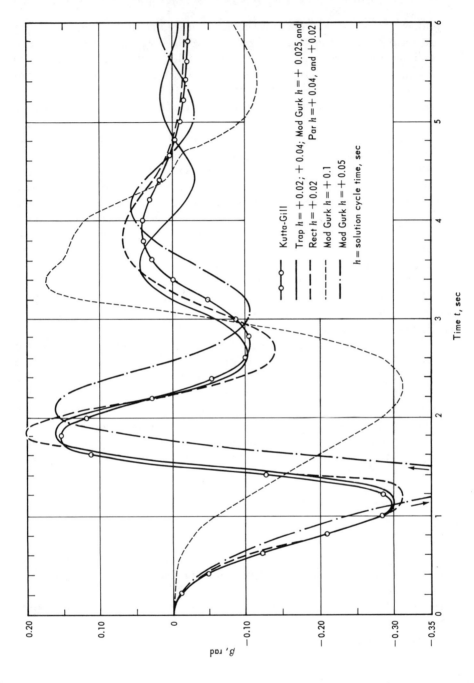

Fig. 12-8 Effect of length of integration step (Δt) and integration formula on simulated aircraft transient. (*The curves from Ref. 4 by permission of author.*)

The following legend appears within the figure:

Kutta-Gill

Trap $h = +0.02; +0.04;$ Mod Gurk $h = +0.025,$ and
Rect $h = +0.02$ Par $h = +0.04,$ and $+0.02$
Mod Gurk $h = +0.1$
Mod Gurk $h = +0.05$

$h =$ solution cycle time, sec

4. High reliability.
5. Unlimited memory capacity. Stored information can be kept indefinitely. (There is a practical limit, however, to the size of *fast* random-access core memory.)

disadvantages:

1. Extremely poor man-machine communication combined with a language barrier.
2. Cost and size of the computer unit as a rule prohibits open-shop operation.
3. The sequential type of operation results in a computation time which grows in proportion to the size of the problem.
4. Inability to perform true integration. This fact, combined with point 3, results in a natural "inability" to handle large sets of differential equations. Of course one can trade off computing time by increasing the size of the integration steps. However, this can lead to dire consequences, as demonstrated by the curves in Fig. 12-8, depicting the effect of "marginal step size." The different curves relate to different integration formulas.

12-3.3 DIGITAL SIMULATION

Due to the very basic differences between the analog and digital computers, two different schools of computer programming have developed throughout the years. Once a computer user feels that he has become proficient in one, he usually is apt to turn all his affection to that particular computing device. Very often, he does not even know about the existence of the other, much less its potentialities. There has been in the very last years an awakening to the fact that we really do not fully utilize our computer resources if we do not *combine* the analog and digital and take advantage of their total capabilities. This has lead to the vigorous activities in the *hybrid-computer* area, to be discussed later.

In this section and as part of our digital-computer story, we wish to introduce the reader briefly to a digital-computer programming technique which is of particular importance to the control engineer. It is referred to as *digital simulation* and is basically an attempt to incorporate some of the operational and programming features of the analog computer into the digital computer. It is a very *special technique* inasmuch as it is intended only for study of dynamic systems and is therefore centered around differential-equation solving.

Two compelling reasons for using the digital computer to solve a dynamic problem are:

1. The absence of scaling problems
2. The added confidence of having the digital-computer solution serve as a check on the analog solution

Often, in very extensive simulation setups, the scaling problem can be a real nuisance, and the operator, having nothing to compare with, does not have full confidence in his results. It would be very helpful to have at least *one* run performed on the digital computer in order to get:

1. A comparison solution
2. An idea about the magnitudes of the variable excursions so that good scaling can be done on the analog from the outset.

The analog operator, having little experience in translating his problem into digital-computer language, shies away from even trying. The digital programmer, on the other hand, if presented with the set of differential equations pertaining to the particular problem probably, *if given time*, can make a translation into FORTRAN and eventually come up with a solution. The time delays involved are often unacceptable and usually preclude this kind of cooperation.

Here is where *digital simulation* (DS) enters the picture. *DS gives the analog operator a means of communicating with the digital computer in a language which he, the operator, understands.* Several such languages have been designed in the last three years, of which the more prominent are MIDAS, DYSAC, and MADBLOC.[5-7]

All these languages take the same approach: They permit the analog programmer to use the block-diagram method of programming the digital computer. We can view all these programs as compilers that are still more specialized than ALGOL and FORTRAN. The "vocabulary" of, say, MIDAS is made up of operational building blocks, e.g., "integrators," "summers," and "multipliers," and the programming procedure consists simply of an interconnection of these blocks into a structure that represents the physical system. The procedure is therefore almost identical to the one that an analog programmer uses, which we discussed in Sec. 12-2.

All the above-mentioned block-oriented languages are just that—languages. Except for easing the programming pains, they do nothing to achieve a better man-machine intimacy.

A couple of digital-computer manufacturers have gone one step further in DS.[8,9] One example is Scientific Data Systems' DES-1. Here, a block language (no acronym given) has been incorporated with a specific digital computer (SDS 9300) *and a console*. The latter feature permits the programmer actually to control the digital computer in the analog modes: RESET, OPERATE, and HOLD. The output is provided, via conversion equipment, by stripchart recorders, CRO, and *xy* plotters. The input data are fed via tape, card, or typewriter.

It seems reasonable to expect that the next and final step in the evolution of DS will be to provide a digital computer with an analog console complete with patch board and everything.

12-3.4 COMPUTER CONTROL

We have discussed briefly the essential features of analog and digital computers and have given a couple of examples of their use as design tools. It is appropriate to take a look at the role played by the computer incorporated as part of the control system. *Computer control* is a vast topic, and it would be hard to do it full justice even in one full chapter. Instead of setting for ourselves an unreachable goal, we shall limit our coverage to a survey-type discussion. It is difficult to be specific in a discussion of computer control for the simple reason that the control tasks which are usually assigned to a process-control computer far transcend those that we have discussed in this book. The information and data-processing abilities of a modern general-purpose computer (and we refer here to a digital one) are very impressive, and it is customary to assign a variety of duties to it—duties that may have nothing to do with the plant being controlled. There are process-control computers which simultaneously do all the computational tasks needed in an industrial concern, ranging from the payroll to optimum control of a particular process. Indeed, we optimize the use of a computer only when its computational ability is being taxed to the limit. The computer-control area abounds with examples where this simple economic fact has been neglected. Indeed, the name "computer control" has a bad connotation in certain circles where the installation of a complex control computer turned out to be a costly mistake.

In theory, control computers can handle optimization problems of both the static and the dynamic variety; in the latter case, we must require, however, that the dynamics of the process does not "outrun" the computer.

In practice, computer control of static processes is dominating the field. Although digital computers are in the majority, there are many analog computers represented as well. A control computer can be used directly in the control loop, in which case we talk about *on-line* computer control, or it may be used *off-line*, in which case it serves as a "consultant" to the operator. The two schemes are shown in Fig. 12-9 and 12-10. These are the two extreme cases; we have a whole spectrum of variations in between.

The "off-line" computer is a suitable arrangement when the process changes take place very slowly, as in many chemical processes. On the basis of process instrument readings, laboratory analyses, and other process information gathered by the operator, the computer is asked to make regular computations of whatever criteria we are operating on. On the basis of these computations, the operator makes the proper adjustments of those inputs which affect the process. The regular check computations may tax only a small fraction of the computational ability of the computer, and it may be used for a number of other chores on a time-sharing basis.

The "on-line" variety of computer control is employed when the process supervision must be performed on a more or less continuous basis. A good example is the operation of a power-utility company, as described in Chap. 10. Here the computer takes over the role of the NOC's in Fig. 10-8. This is, by the way, a good example of an application area where an *analog* computer can be used to great advantage (see, for example, Ref. 5 in Chap. 10). The "on-line" computer is, as a rule, less available for time-sharing for other tasks. For this reason, they very often are designed as "special-purpose computers," which will do one job only—that of controlling the process.

The control computer has invaded the aerospace field in a big way. Space vehicles must be guided along trajectories which are *precomputed* on the basis of various criteria, such as minimum fuel consumption, minimum bending moment on a launch vehicle, and certain desired orbit configurations. These are examples of *dynamic* optimum control. Consider, for example, the problem of launching an earth satellite. After the vertical takeoff, the launch vehicle will be commanded to execute a so-called "gravity turn," which, after a total pitch-angle change of 90°, will result in orbit injection. The change of pitch angle versus time is programmed in a digital computer, which, as the launch progresses, commands the vehicle via telemetry to execute this program. A specific gravity turn depends upon the vehicle velocity, which in its turn depends upon the engine thrust. Should this thrust now deviate from the nominal value, then it becomes necessary to change the pitch

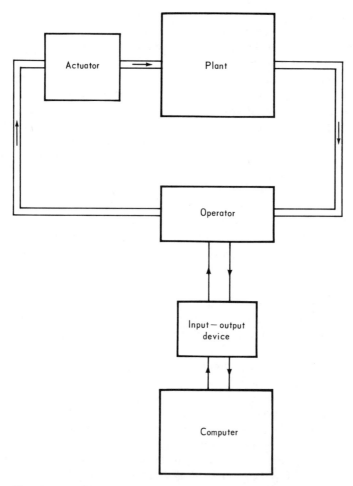

Fig. 12-9 "Off-line" computer control.

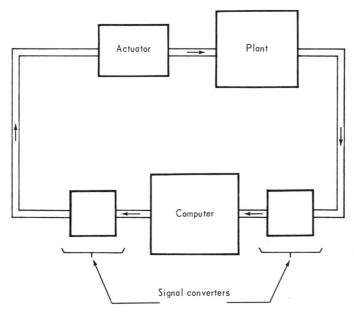

Fig. 12-10   "On-line" computer control.

strategy *quickly*.   A human controller could hardly be expected to make the fast decisions necessary, but a computer can.

There are other examples of dynamic optimization where the changes occur so fast that even a digital computer cannot handle the situation.   A very good example is offered by so-called *predictor systems*.   In a variety of vehicle control systems, exemplified by lunar landing, orbital rendezvous and docking, diving maneuvers in submarines, and all-weather aircraft landing systems, the basic problem is this: How should we execute the maneuver to get "from here to there" if it is necessary to arrive with certain strict limitations on one or several state variables?   This is a very difficult control problem, in particular if we are required to perform the maneuver under simultaneous observance of certain optimum criteria.   (Compare the LEM problem discussed in Chap. 10.)   There is much hope that many of these problems can be solved by adding computer control systems that serve as *pilot support*.   The hybrid computer seems to fit this particular job well, and we shall discuss some control schemes in the next section.

12-4   HYBRID COMPUTERS

As of this writing the term "hybrid computation" is not properly defined, nor does any uniform symbol standard exist for all the special computing elements of the "hybrid machine."   It is hoped that this matter will be attended to very soon to avoid a repetition of the confusing situation existing at present in the digital-computer-language area.

As things now stand, the prefix "hybrid" refers to any computing facility that employs the analog or digital computer in a "nonclassical" sense. The first hybrid computer that was marketed under this new name was the Dystac machine, marketed in the late 1950s by Computer Systems, Inc., which incorporated the REPOP feature and electronic (solid-state) mode control. The trend caught on rapidly, and it is probably safe to predict that all analog computers (with the possible exception of small, inexpensive units) marketed after 1966 will have both REPOP and patchable logic installed as standard equipment. They will all then be "hybrid" computers, and the analog will be a museum piece in the Smithsonian.

There are those that believe, for the above reason, that the term "hybrid" should be reserved for a facility that incorporates a *general-purpose* analog (with REPOP and electronic-mode control) and a *general-purpose* digital. This is a matter of semantics and is really of no practical significance. What *is* important, however, is the need for a standardized programming language. If full utilization of these new breeds of computers is to be achieved, it is obvious that we must penetrate the programming barrier. The majority of today's engineers are either analog- or digital-oriented, and we are now asking them to be good at both. This is no small task.

12-4.1   REASONS FOR HYBRIDIZATION

Even if we cannot agree on terminology, there is no disagreement concerning the need for these new advanced computer concepts. By the marriage of analog and digital devices, we have bred a new generation of computers that are characterized by those features which are truly associated with the digital computer alone, i.e.,

Accuracy and speed
Arithmetical ability
Memory capacity
Logic decision capability

and those which we only find with the analog device, i.e.,

Excellent *true* integration ability both in real time and in fast mode
Insensitivity to system order
Excellent man-machine communication features

If we limit attention only to the field of control, we can mention the following specific application possibilities for hybrid computation:

1. Simulation of those control systems which, in a sense, are themselves hybrid, e.g., sampled-data systems.
2. Predictor systems. (Here, the hybrid computer actually will constitute part of the system.)
3. Mechanization of time-optimal control systems.
4. Simulation of biological systems.

5. Simulation studies of adaptive and learning systems.
6. The general field of optimization.
7. Guidance and control of aerospace vehicles. Here, the accuracy of the digital portion is employed for the relatively slow guidance part; the analog handles the fast, high-order dynamics of the vehicle.

These are only a few examples chosen from the field of control engineering. If we include all areas of engineering and science, there are countless computational problems that are either extremely difficult or downright impossible to master with analog or digital computers alone but which can be solved with relative ease by means of a hybrid facility. The hybrid computer is particularly well suited to performing iterative-type computations.

12-4.2 HYBRID COMPUTING ELEMENTS

Hybrid-computer installations come in all sizes and varieties. The largest units are used for studies of special aerospace systems (Apollo, for instance) and therefore, in a sense, could be referred to as special-purpose computers. There is a tendency among universities and research institutes to acquire what we could call a "general-purpose" hybrid facility. Representative of such facilities is the Beckman-SDS integrated computer facility, containing as its main components Beckman 2200 analog computer and the Scientific Data Systems SDS 920 digital computer plus linkage system. The latter provides the link between the computers. As the two computers work with different signals, the main feature of the linkage system is a number of $D \rightarrow A$ and $A \rightarrow D$ channels over which data information can be exchanged between the two computers. The analog computer is the more inaccurate of the two and determines therefore the degree of conversion accuracy. The highest accuracy is nominally 1 part in 10,000 (0.01 percent), and there is therefore no sense in using higher conversion accuracy than 14 bits ($2^{13} = 8,192 + 1$ bit for sign). These are the *numerical data links*. In addition, we have *control links*. Signals from the digital computer will be able to control the mode of the integrators in the analog computer ("sense lines"), and signals from the analog computer will be able to stop the computations in the digital computer ("interrupt lines"). The pots in the analog will be adjustable on command from the digital computer without human intervention, and for this purpose, the analog has a set of servo-operated pots. In addition, the analog is equipped with a patchable control module containing basic logic elements like AND and OR gates, flip-flops, "single shots," and comparators. The analog also contains a clock providing pulses for control of iterative computations. The control of the overall unit is vested in the digital machine, but it is worth noting that because all mode control is available on the analog-computer panel, we can operate each computer separately if we wish.

A facility like the one just described has a fantastic versatility. We have a choice of delegating the various computations in an overall problem to either the digital or the analog, wherever they fit best. The servo pots permit us to perform parameter adjustments automatically, and the electronic-mode control of the integrators makes it possible to operate the analog completely "hands off."

Two basic difficulties stand in the way of a full utilization of the capabilities of a hybrid facility:

1. The problem of reliability
2. A general lack of understanding of how to operate and program the facility

As of this writing, the first point seems not to be a serious one. The first hybrid facilities built turned out to be inoperative because of frequent component failures. The linkage system was a particularly weak area. Better circuitry and 100 per cent utilization of solid-state components have about eliminated reliability as a problem.

Table 12-2   A selection of hybrid components with their symbols

No	Symbol	Description
1		This integrator is placed in RESET when the control signal $U=1$. When $U=0$ it is placed in COMPUTE.
2		This integrator is placed in REPOP by changing U repetitively between 0 and 1, in accordance to the rules in 1. (The capacitor may be 0.1, 0.01, or 0.001 depending upon speed desired)
3		TRACK–HOLD or direct memory unit. Tracks in RESET (for $U=1$) Holds in COMPUTE (for $U=0$)
4		HOLD–TRACK or complementary unit Tracks for $U=0$ (i.e., $\bar{U}=1$) Holds for $U=1$ (i.e., $\bar{U}=0$)
5		Comparator If $x>y$ $U=1$ ($\bar{U}=0$) If $x<y$ $U=0$ ($\bar{U}=1$)
6		AND gate $U=1$ only if V and W both are 1, otherwise $U=0$
7		OR gate $U=1$ only if V or W are 1, otherwise $U=0$
8		Switch (obtained by replacing capacitor with resistor) when $\begin{cases} U=1 \; e_o=-e_1 \\ U=0 \; e_o=-e_2 \end{cases}$

The second point is more serious. Education is, of course, the most effective solution for elimination of this one. A standardized language would be extremely valuable. It should be added that, in addition to providing the *hardware*, most manufacturers are also providing *software*, consisting of subroutine libraries (often in FORTRAN form) especially adapted to their equipment.

After this general discussion, we shall take a more detailed look at some of the possibilities for advanced computations available through the use of hybrid techniques. We shall limit our attention to analog computers with electronic-mode control, logic components, and clock-controlled REPOP. Let us first look at some of the characteristics of the components listed in Table 12-2. In Sec. 12-2.3, we mentioned that by replacing the mechanical-mode control switches with solid-state switches, we can achieve fast nonmanual-mode control. These switches change (in a matter of a microsecond) between the states OPEN and CLOSE upon command of a control voltage (indicated dotted in our diagrams). This control voltage can take on only two values, which we shall refer to with the *symbolic binary* symbols 1 and 0. (Typically, these voltages range between 0 and -3 to -12 volts.) Whenever there is a need for a letter symbol for these control voltages, we shall use the symbols U, V, ... We wish to make the following remarks concerning the items in Table 12-2.

1. The actual electronic circuitry, including that of the switches, varies, of course, between the various equipment manufacturers. Typical circuits can be found in Ref. 1.

2. An important difference should be noted between manual- and electronic-mode control. In manual RESET, the charging process took, as we remember, about 1 sec for completion. The electronic RESET is *instantaneous*, made possible through the use of special "forced-charging" circuits. This has a very important consequence; whenever the integrator is placed in RESET, the output *immediately* takes on the (negative) value of the IC input. *Should this input now change, then the output will faithfully follow; i.e., the integrator TRACKS.*

3. If we provide no regular input to the integrator, then the output will remain *constant* during the COMPUTE mode. A unit used in this fashion will successively TRACK and HOLD the IC input. We refer to it as a TRACK-HOLD unit, or *direct memory* (item 3 in the table). By reversing the effects of the control voltage on the electronic switches, we can obtain a so-called *complementary memory* (item 4).

4. A very useful element unit is obtained by cascading two of the just-described memory units. "Analog memory," "point storage," and "memory pair" are some of the names used for this unit. This unit can be used to memorize variable values from one iteration cycle to the next. We shall demonstrate in examples to follow.

5. If the integrator capacitor is replaced by a resistor, the TRACK-HOLD element changes to a *switch* (item 8 in table).

12-4.3 **EXAMPLES OF HYBRID COMPUTATION**

Three examples will be discussed, each illustrating some aspects of computation using hybrid techniques. We start out with a relatively simple problem demonstrating how to integrate a differential equation of the split-boundary type.

Example 12-4

In Chap. 11, we concluded that many dynamic optimum-control problems were of the "split-boundary" type, i.e., we had to meet specified state conditions at both ends of the control interval. To be specific, consider the differential equation for an undamped, undriven pendulum

$$\ddot{x} + x = 0 \tag{12-10}$$

If we were to specify the "initial values" for this system, we would have to assign values to both the initial position $x(0)$ and the initial velocity $\dot{x}(0)$. Assume now that we specify instead the positions at two different values of time, as follows:

$$
\begin{aligned}
x(0) &= 1 \\
x(1) &= 1
\end{aligned}
\tag{12-11}
$$

[Note, by the way, that because the system is undriven (=uncontrolled), we can specify only two independent conditions. If we were to specify, for instance, both position and velocity at both $t = 0$ and $t = 1$, then we could only meet the requirements by adding a control force u.]

How would we use an analog computer to solve Eq. (12-10) subject to the boundary conditions (12-11)? In Fig. 12-11, we show a simulation diagram for the system. We know the IC only for integrator 2; that is, we can only set pot 2. The IC for integrator 1, that is, the initial velocity, is a priori *unknown*. However, we can, proceed as follows: Guess a value for $\dot{x}(0)$, set pot 1 accordingly, and make a computer run, marked 1 in the figure. Evidently this setting did not meet the required value for $t = 1$, so we try another setting, make a new run, etc. After several trial runs, we converge on the required end condition at $t = 1$.

The iterative procedure just outlined is neither particularly difficult nor time-consuming, particularly if we are equipped with REPOP so that we can see the response directly on the CRO screen. Evidently, the procedure is nothing but a closed-loop control process, where the "error" (see Fig. 12-11) is sensed by the operator's eyes, who then takes corrective action to eliminate it. Let us now see how we can solve this problem *automatically* by means of hybrid computation. The *automatic* feature may be extremely important if a problem of this nature has to be solved in real time on board a spaceship where the astronauts have their hands full with other duties.

A possible scheme is shown in Fig. 12-12.† We have drawn the figure in a way that stresses the closed-loop nature of the iterative computation process. The "plant," i.e., our second-order system, is placed in REPOP, and we assume that we

---

† This approach was suggested by Computer Systems, Inc.

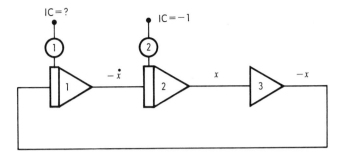

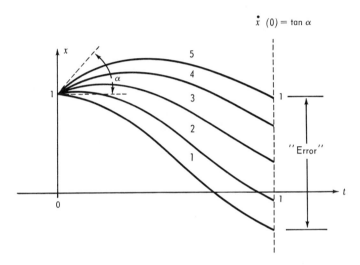

Fig. 12-11   Simulation of split-boundary problem.

have adjusted the length of the COMPUTE interval so that it corresponds *exactly* to 1 sec. (If we use a REPOP speedup ratio of 100:1, then the COMPUTE interval must be exactly 10 msec. It should be added that both the COMPUTE and the RESET intervals are continuously and independently adjustable on most computers.) Our "sensor" consists of a memory pair being controlled from the *same control voltage that controls the "plant" integrators.* The output voltages of each memory unit are shown in the figure for two consecutive computation cycles. The important thing to realize is that the $\bar{M}$ memory tracks during the COMPUTE portion of the REPOP cycle and the M memory during the remaining RESET portion. It should also be pointed out that the points marked by arrows in the z graph are somewhat critical. These are the instants when the M memory takes over the HOLD job from the $\bar{M}$ memory. It is important that the M memory "grabs hold" of the y voltage an instant *before* the $\bar{M}$ memory goes into TRACK mode. This is accomplished by means of a slight overlap built into the electronic

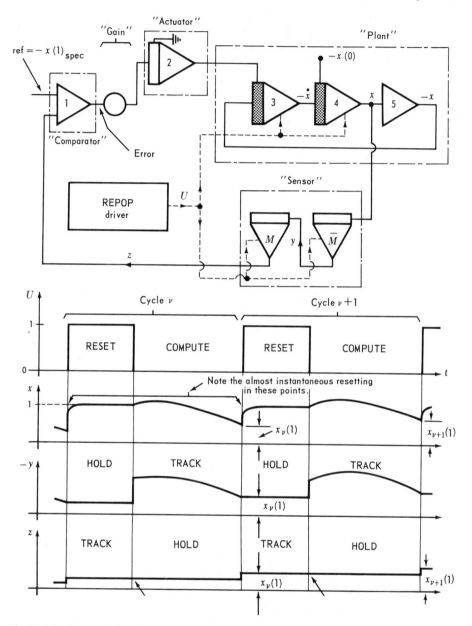

Fig. 12-12 Automatic hybrid solution of split-boundary problem.

switching circuit.   We realize from this discussion that the output voltage from the memory pair is constant during the entire cycle and is equal to the voltage $x(1)$ as it appeared at the end of the COMPUTE interval of the previous cycle.   *The memory pair thus memorizes a variable value from one cycle to the following one.* (If we had triggered the two memory units at some other moment than the end of the COMPUTE cycle, we could have memorized some other voltage.)

The memorized voltage $x(1)$ is compared in summer 1 with the specified value $x(1)_{\text{spec}}$ ($=1$, in our case), and the resulting error is fed via a gain pot into a *slow* integrator (2) which feeds directly into the IC terminal of "plant" integrator 3. As long as there is an "error," the output of the former integrator will increase, thus changing the IC setting of the velocity integrator.   When the iterative process has converged on the required end value, the error will be zero, the integrator 2 will have a constant output, and the REPOP runs will all be equal.   The pot setting determines the speed of convergence.

The procedure becomes more involved, but can still be handled, if the system is of higher order and if more than one state component is specified at the end of the control interval.   The closed-loop iterative procedure now takes on the nature of a MIMO system.   The problem has been studied at the University of Florida.[10]

Example 12-5

Our next example will concern the use of hybrid techniques to solve a minimum-time problem.   We shall choose the oven-heating problem outlined in Exercise 11-3 and shall assume that the reader already has tackled the problem using the analytical techniques discussed in that chapter.   The maximum principle informs us that, in order to reach the end state

$$\mathbf{x}(t_f) = \begin{bmatrix} 0.5 \\ 0.5 \end{bmatrix}$$

in minimum time, we should use the heating strategy depicted in Fig. 12-13*b*. If we chose the switching moment t_s properly, the temperatures x_1 and x_2 will vary as shown in Fig. 12-13*a*, both passing through the required value, 0.5, at the same time t_f, which then will represent the minimum time.   If we switch too late or too early, the state variables will vary as shown in Fig. 12-13*c*; in both cases, we shall miss the target.

The laborious part of this problem is to determine the proper switching time. We shall suggest an iterative process which automatically converges on the right value.   The dynamical equations for the system read

$$\dot{x}_1 = -0.2x_1 + 0.1x_2 + 0.1u$$
$$\dot{x}_2 = 0.1x_1 - 0.1x_2 \tag{12-12}$$

and they have been simulated in REPOP in the part labeled "plant" in Fig. 12-14.†

---

† It is assumed that all REPOP integrators (1, 2, and 7) are controlled from a REPOP driver, as indicated in Fig. 12-12.   In order not to clutter up the figure, we have omitted the control-signal lines.

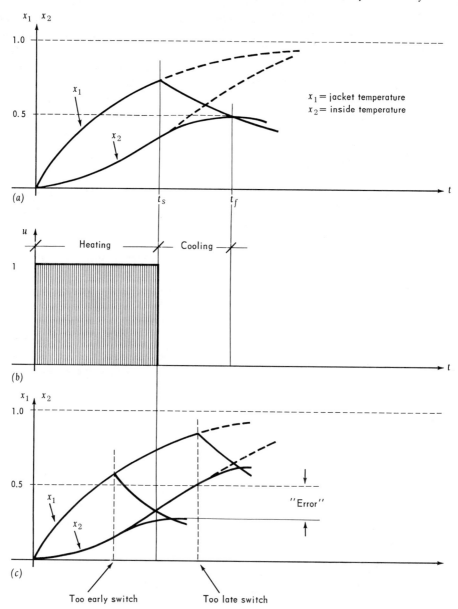

Fig. 12-13 Optimum oven-heating strategy.

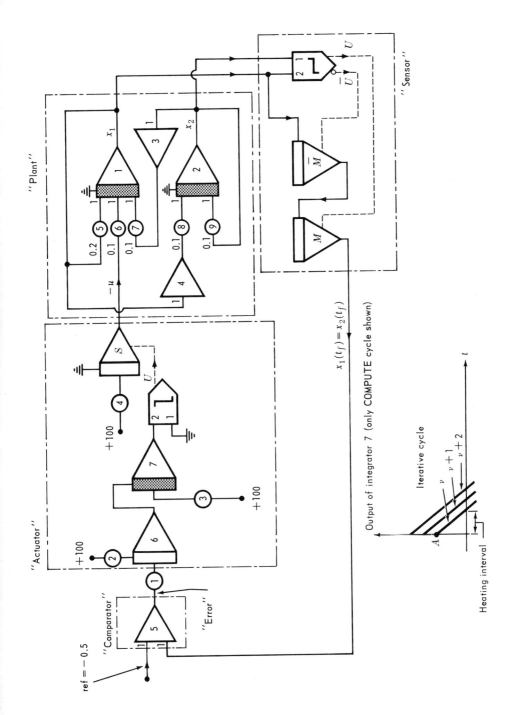

Fig. 12-14   Hybrid scheme for automatic solution of oven-heating problem.

We shall now propose an automatic computer setup which senses the error indicated in Fig. 12-13c and takes steps to eliminate it by adjusting the length of the heating interval t_s. The system is shown in Fig. 12-14. We shall discuss each individual subsystem, and we start out with the "sensor" part. The sensor is made up of a comparator and a memory pair. The comparator compares x_1 and x_2, continuously and in view of the relative magnitudes of these variables (see Fig. 12-13a), we can conclude that the comparator switches twice per REPOP cycle and that its output U will alternate between 1 and 0 in accordance with the rule

Between 0 and t_f, $U = 0$

Rest of the cycle, $U = 1$

(*Note*: As both x_1 and x_2 are driven to zero in the RESET part of the REPOP cycle, there is a chance that the comparator will be "unstable" in that part of the cycle. Should this prove to be the case, we can cure it with a very minute IC setting on one of the "plant" integrators.)

As the comparator output is controlling the memory pair, it is simple to see that the output from this pair must be equal to the value of the state variable (either one) as it appears at time t_f. We conclude therefore that our sensor provides us with the proper output.

The sensor output is next compared (in adder 5) with the specified output (0.5, in this case), and an error voltage is produced. This error voltage will control the length t_s of the heating interval in the following manner:

If the error is *positive*, this is an indication that the heating interval is *too short*. The circuitry labeled "actuator" will actually provide an iterative increase in the heating interval until the error disappears. It works as follows: The positive error from amplifier 5 is fed via pot 1 into a *slow* integrator (6). The output from this integrator thus will increase *slowly*, in a negative sense, with a rate that can be controlled on pot 1. This voltage is used as the IC voltage for the REPOP integrator 7. As this latter integrator has a constant *positive* input, it will output a negative ramp, which will begin at a point A that *slowly* moves upward. As a result, the output of 7 will be positive for increasing periods of the COMPUTE cycle. The comparator plus the switch provide the input $-u$ to plant integrator 1, and this input is applied as long as the output of 7 is positive. The heating interval will thus increase in length from cycle to cycle in the iterative process. This will result in a decreasing error, and when this error eventually is zeroed, the output of integrator 6 will be constant and the iteration process will get stationary. The whole process can be viewed by displaying both x_1 and x_2 on a cathode-ray oscilloscope. It makes for an excellent and impressive display, and if the student has a hybrid computer available, he is encouraged to perform the experiment.

The example just discussed demonstrated one possible approach to the solution of time-optimum problems. The methods can be varied *ad infinitum* depending upon the computer equipment available. See Ref. 11, for example.

Example 12-6

Our last example of the use of hybrid computing equipment concerns so-called *predictor control systems.* These are control systems where the specifications are very keen on one point—the absolute necessity to control a system in such a way that some future state is reached with given accuracy. The control problem is complicated by the fact that the control forces are bounded. Consider, as an example, an astronaut performing a docking maneuver in space. He is approaching the target, and at a certain point he applies the retro rockets. If the timing is not perfect, he will close in on the target with nonzero velocity, and as he has no means of increasing the thrust, a collision is inevitable. The problem is further complicated by the lack of air damping, which causes considerable conceptual difficulties. As this type of control situation has become of particular importance in the field of aerospace, it has attracted considerable interest lately.

A number of solutions have been suggested; the most promising one seems to be the technique based on "fast-model control." This method seems to have been first suggested by Ziebolz and Paynter as early as 1954.[12] Later, the method was refined and extended by a number of researchers.[13-17] The ideas of fast-model control are very simple, but the difficulties enter into the picture when we try to transform theory into hardware. This is so often the case in modern control.

Consider the block diagram of Fig. 12-15, illustrating a control situation where man constitutes an essential part of the loop. The controller is realistically of a multilevel on-off type (coarse, medium, and fine thrust adjustments).

Not possessing the normal "feel" which the pilot of an aircraft usually has, the pilot of this system is supported by a subsystem consisting of a fast model plus

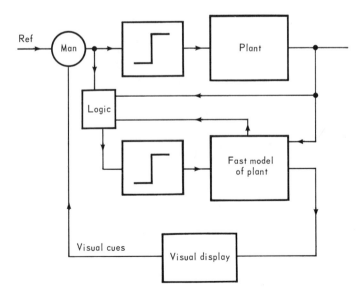

Fig. 12-15 Fast-model predictive system.

visual-display units. The fast model, the heart of the subsystem, is a dynamic replica of the actual system speeded up by a factor of, say, 100:1. Whenever the pilot applies a certain control force to the actual system, he simultaneously applies the same force to the fast model. The model responds in exactly the same way as the real system *but 100 times faster.* If now the model response is properly displayed (and this is a very essential feature of all these systems), the pilot can obtain an *immediate visual* cue of what is going to happen to his actual system if he continues his present control action. For instance, he may find out that he will miss the target, and he therefore immediately proceeds to seek out a better control strategy.

Hybrid-computer components play a very important role in instrumenting a system of this type. The fast model itself would be built as a special-purpose REPOP analog computer. The control logic would involve both purely digital logic plus analog-type logic components like the ones we have discussed in this section. We do not intend to go into a detailed description of the actual instrumentation. The reader may find a detailed diagram for a particular system in Ref. 13. It may be added that, as of this writing, systems of this type are being perfected for use in this country's ambitious future space missions.

12-5 SUMMARY

We have tried in this chapter to give a fairly representative view of the role played by the modern computer in the design and operation of control systems. The elementary skills of the computer are very simple indeed; it becomes a potential design aid or an indispensable part of a system only when controlled and operated by human ingenuity. It is also clear that the computer will never replace the need for analytical tools, but used in proper ways, it will enhance them. It is important that control engineers avail themselves of the services of all types of computers. As long as analog and digital computers both have serious shortcomings in certain areas, there will be a need for hybridized equipment. Future breakthroughs in computer technology may very well eliminate such a need.

Exercises

(Several of the examples necessitate the use of a computer.)

12-1 Consider a linear system described by the differential equations

$$\dot{x} = Ax$$

and subject to the initial conditions

$$x(0) = x_0$$

We wish to simulate this system on an analog computer, and for that purpose we represent each state component x_i by a machine variable ξ_i in accordance with the relations

$$\xi_1 = s_{11}x_1$$
$$\xi_2 = s_{22}x_2$$
$$\cdots\cdots\cdots$$
$$\xi_n = s_{nn}x_n$$

or, more briefly,

$$\xi = Sx$$

where S is a *diagonal* scale-factor matrix

$$S = \begin{bmatrix} s_{11} & & & 0 \\ & \cdot & & \\ & & \cdot & \\ & & & \cdot \\ 0 & & & s_{nn} \end{bmatrix}$$

The physical system has the solution

$$x(t) = e^{At}x_0$$

and for *proper simulation*, we therefore must require that the ξ solution be of the form

$$\xi(t) = Se^{At}x_0$$

> *a* Motivate the last statement!
> *b* Using matrix algebra, prove that we indeed obtain "proper simulation."
> *c* Confirm also that the results in problem *b* hold for *arbitrary* scale factors s_{ii}, except *zero*.
> *Note*: The conclusion of your findings will be that a *linear* system can be scaled *arbitrarily* on a computer, and the computer solution will be a true replica of the physical system. The simple example mentioned in the text shows that this is *not* true for *nonlinear* systems.

12-2 Make a simulation of the MIMO regulator depicted in Fig. 7-45 and determine from computer recordings that all those requirements have indeed been met that form the basis on which the system was designed. (This simple double-input–double-output servo makes an excellent demonstration example on an analog computer. You may study how the noninteraction condition depends upon exact tuning of the compensation network. By displaying both control forces u_1 and u_2, you can show the physical reason why noninteraction is achieved. By simulating external forces on the platforms, you can study the compliance conditions, etc.)

12-3 Simulate the servo depicted in Fig. 7-39 using the transfer-function-simulation approach. Then confirm the response graphs shown in Fig. 7-37.

12-4 Consider the differential equation

$$\ddot{z} + \dot{z} + z = 0$$

with

$$z(0) = 1$$
$$\dot{z}(0) = 0$$

> You can easily find an exact solution for this equation.
> Using a digital computer, perform a numerical integration of the equation throughout the interval

$$0 < t < 10 \text{ sec}$$

using the relatively coarse integration step of $\Delta t = 1$ sec. Use two different integration formulas obtained from the series

$$z(t + \Delta t) = z(t) + \Delta t\, \dot{z}(t) + \frac{(\Delta t)^2}{2!}\, \ddot{z}(t) + \cdots$$

by using in one case two terms, in the second case three terms in the series.
> Compare the numerical solutions with the exact one.

12-5 Write the differential equation in the previous example in normal form

$$\dot{\mathbf{x}} = \mathbf{A}\mathbf{x}$$

Then write a FORTRAN program for

$$e^{\mathbf{A}t} = \mathbf{I} + \mathbf{A}t + \frac{\mathbf{A}^2}{2!}t^2 + \cdots$$

and obtain a digital-computer solution for

$$\mathbf{x} = e^{\mathbf{A}t}\mathbf{x}_0$$

in the same t range as in the previous example.
Compare the solution with the ones in Exercise 12-4.

▲ *12-6* Develop a hydrid-computer scheme that will solve Exercise 11-5 automatically! (This is a tough one.)

References

1. G. A. Korn and T. M. Korn, "Electronic Analog and Hybrid Computers," McGraw-Hill Book Company, New York, 1964.

2. L. Levine, "Methods for Solving Engineering Problems Using Analog Computers," McGraw-Hill Book Company, New York, 1964.

3. J. L. Hammond, Application of State Variable Techniques in Analog Computer Programming, *Simulation*, **4**(5) (May, 1965).

4. M. E. Connelly, Analog-Digital Computers for Real-time Simulation, *Rept.* ESL-FR-110, MIT, Electronic Systems Lab. (June, 1961).

5. R. T. Harnett, F. J. Sansom, and L. M. Warshawsky, MIDAS—An Analog Approach to Digital Programming, *Simulation*, **3**(3) (September, 1964).

6. V. C. Rideout and L. Tavernini, MADBLOC—A Program for Digital Simulation of a Hybrid Computer, *ibid.*, **3**(1) (January, 1965).

7. R. Linebarger and R. Brennan, A Survey of Digital Simulation, *ibid.*, **3**(6) (December, 1964).

8. L. Levine, The DES-1, a New Digital Computer for Solving Differential Equations, *ibid.*, **4**(4) (April, 1965).

9. R. Brennan, PACTOLUS—A Simulator Language That Makes a Digital Computer Feel like an Analog Computer (Sorta Kinda), *ibid.*, **3**(2) (August, 1964).

10. D. S. Amberntson, Hybrid Solution Methods of Split Boundary-value Problems, M.S. thesis, Department of Electrical Engineering, University of Florida.

11. E. G. Gilbert, Hybrid Computer Solution of Time-optimal Control Problems, paper presented at the Spring Joint Computer Conference, 1963.

12. H. Ziebolz and H. M. Paynter, Possibilities of a Two-time Scale Computing System for Control and Simulation of Dynamic Systems, *Proc. NEC*, **9** (1954).

13. Olle I. Elgerd, Hybrid Computation—A Means to Study Predictive Control System Behavior, *Proc. IEEE Spring Conf.*, New York (March, 1964).

14. H. Chestnut, W. E. Sollecito, and P. H. Troutman, Predictive Control System Applications, *Trans. AIEE, Appl. Ind.*, **55** (July, 1961).

15. C. R. Kelley, Predictor Instruments Look into the Future, *Control Eng.* (March, 1962).

16. L. C. Fargel and E. A. Ulbrich, Predictor Displays Extend Manual Operation, *ibid.* (August, 1963).

17. A. L. Adey, L. F. Coales, and L. A. Stiles, The Control of Two-variable On-Off Systems, *Proc. IFAC Conf.*, 2d, Basle (1963).

appendix A
ELEMENTS OF
VECTOR AND
MATRIX ALGEBRA

A-I VECTORS

We define a vector **x** as an ordered set of numbers, the *components* $x_1, x_2, \ldots, x_n$,

$$\mathbf{x} \triangleq \begin{bmatrix} x_1 \\ x_2 \\ \cdot \\ \cdot \\ \cdot \\ x_n \end{bmatrix} \tag{A-1}$$

In most of our applications, the x_i's will be real, but this is not a necessary restriction.

n defines the *dimensionality* of the vector.

Although the above column arrangement will be used most commonly, it proves convenient sometimes to use the row, or *transposed*, representation

$$\mathbf{x}^T \triangleq [x_1 \quad x_2 \quad \ldots \quad x_n] \tag{A-2}$$

A-I.I SPECIAL VECTORS

The *null vector* **0** and the *sum vector* **1** are defined as follows:

$$\mathbf{0} \triangleq \begin{bmatrix} 0 \\ 0 \\ \cdot \\ \cdot \\ \cdot \\ 0 \end{bmatrix} \quad \mathbf{1} \triangleq \begin{bmatrix} 1 \\ 1 \\ \cdot \\ \cdot \\ \cdot \\ 1 \end{bmatrix}$$

The *unit vector* $\mathbf{e}_i$ is defined as the vector

$$
\mathbf{e}_i \triangleq \begin{bmatrix} 0 \\ 0 \\ 1 \\ \cdot \\ \cdot \\ \cdot \\ 0 \end{bmatrix} \leftarrow i \text{ component}
$$

A-I.2   ELEMENTARY VECTOR OPERATIONS

Two vectors $\mathbf{x}$ and $\mathbf{y}$ are said to be equal if and only if $x_i = y_i$ for $i = 1, 2, \ldots, n$. In such a case, we write

$$\mathbf{x} = \mathbf{y}$$

By the product of a vector $\mathbf{x}$ with the scalar λ, we define a new vector $\lambda\mathbf{x}$ having each component amplified by the same scalar, that is,

$$
\lambda\mathbf{x} \triangleq \mathbf{x}\lambda \triangleq \begin{bmatrix} \lambda x_1 \\ \lambda x_2 \\ \cdot \\ \cdot \\ \cdot \\ \lambda x_n \end{bmatrix} \tag{A-3}
$$

Addition and *subtraction* of two vectors $\mathbf{x}$ and $\mathbf{y}$ result in new vectors

$$
\mathbf{x} \pm \mathbf{y} \triangleq \begin{bmatrix} x_1 \pm y_1 \\ x_2 \pm y_2 \\ \cdot \\ \cdot \\ \cdot \\ x_n \pm y_n \end{bmatrix} \tag{A-4}
$$

Clearly, these two last operations make sense only with vectors of the *same* dimensionality.

The following properties apply to the defined operations:

$$\mathbf{x} + \mathbf{y} = \mathbf{y} + \mathbf{x}$$
$$\mathbf{x} + (\mathbf{y} + \mathbf{z}) = (\mathbf{x} + \mathbf{y}) + \mathbf{z}$$
$$\lambda_1(\lambda_2\mathbf{x}) = (\lambda_1\lambda_2)\mathbf{x}$$
$$(\lambda_1 + \lambda_2)\mathbf{x} = \lambda_1\mathbf{x} + \lambda_2\mathbf{x}$$
$$\lambda(\mathbf{x} + \mathbf{y}) = \lambda\mathbf{x} + \lambda\mathbf{y}$$
$$0\mathbf{x} = \mathbf{0}$$

A-I.3　THE INNER VECTOR PRODUCT

The so-called *inner* or *scalar* multiplication of two vectors **x** and **y** *of equal dimension* results in a very useful product. This multiplication is defined by

$$\mathbf{x}^T\mathbf{y} \stackrel{\Delta}{=} \sum_{i=1}^{n} x_i y_i \tag{A-5}$$

Our chosen symbol $\mathbf{x}^T\mathbf{y}$ will be explained later in connection with matrix multiplication. In addition to this symbol, one often finds one of the following:

x · y

(x,y)

$\langle \mathbf{x},\mathbf{y} \rangle$

(It should be noted that other *useful* vector products exist—for instance, the so-called *cross product* in three-dimensional space. However, for our present objectives, the inner product will suffice.)

Consider the two vectors **x** and **y** in ordinary 2-space, defined by

$$\mathbf{x} = \begin{bmatrix} x_1 \\ x_2 \end{bmatrix} \stackrel{\Delta}{=} \begin{bmatrix} |\mathbf{x}| \cos \alpha \\ |\mathbf{x}| \sin \alpha \end{bmatrix}$$

$$\mathbf{y} = \begin{bmatrix} y_1 \\ y_2 \end{bmatrix} \stackrel{\Delta}{=} \begin{bmatrix} |\mathbf{y}| \cos \beta \\ |\mathbf{y}| \sin \beta \end{bmatrix}$$

and shown in Fig. A-1. $|\mathbf{x}|$ and $|\mathbf{y}|$ represent here the geometric lengths of each vector.

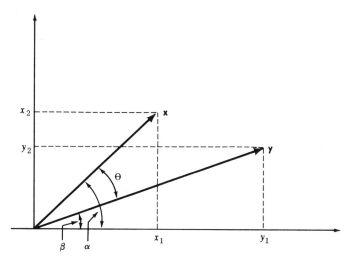

Fig. A-1　Two-dimensional vectors.

From the definition of inner product, we have

$$\mathbf{x}^T\mathbf{y} \overset{\Delta}{=} x_1y_1 + x_2y_2 = |\mathbf{x}|\,|\mathbf{y}|\,(\cos\alpha\cos\beta + \sin\alpha\sin\beta)$$

$$= |\mathbf{x}|\,|\mathbf{y}|\cos(\alpha - \beta) = |\mathbf{x}|\,|\mathbf{y}|\cos\theta$$

We also note that

$$\mathbf{x}^T\mathbf{x} = x_1x_1 + x_2x_2 = |\mathbf{x}|^2$$

and

$$\mathbf{y}^T\mathbf{y} = |\mathbf{y}|^2$$

We conclude, therefore, that the inner product between **x** and **y** indicates the *degree of parallelism* between the two vectors, and the inner product of **x** by itself gives information about the length of the vector.

By extending the concepts of *length* $|\mathbf{x}|$ and *angle* θ between vectors to n-dimensional space, we now get

$$|\mathbf{x}|^2 \overset{\Delta}{=} \mathbf{x}^T\mathbf{x}$$

$$\cos\theta \overset{\Delta}{=} \frac{\mathbf{x}^T\mathbf{y}}{|\mathbf{x}|\,|\mathbf{y}|} \tag{A-6}$$

It is not possible to visualize these concepts beyond $n = 3$.

Note that if **x** is *normalized* (i.e., the length $|\mathbf{x}|$ equals unity), then we have

$$|\mathbf{y}|\cos\theta = \mathbf{x}^T\mathbf{y}$$

In words: The inner product gives us the *projection of* **y** *on* **x**.

Two *nonzero* vectors are said to be *orthogonal* if

$$\mathbf{x}^T\mathbf{y} = 0 \tag{A-7}$$

(The scalar product of the "sum vector" and **x** equals

$$\mathbf{1}^T\mathbf{x} = \sum_{i=1}^{n} x_i$$

and this explains the name.)

The following rules for scalar products are easily verified:

$$\mathbf{x}^T(\mathbf{y} + \mathbf{z}) = \mathbf{x}^T\mathbf{y} + \mathbf{x}^T\mathbf{z}$$

$$(\mathbf{x} + \mathbf{y})^T\mathbf{z} = \mathbf{x}^T\mathbf{z} + \mathbf{y}^T\mathbf{z}$$

$$\mathbf{x}^T(\lambda\mathbf{y}) = \lambda\mathbf{x}^T\mathbf{y} \tag{A-8}$$

$$(\lambda\mathbf{x}^T)\mathbf{y} = \lambda(\mathbf{x}^T\mathbf{y})$$

A-2   MATRICES

A $m \times n$ matrix **A** is defined as a rectangular array of mn numbers

$$
\mathbf{A} \triangleq \begin{bmatrix} a_{11} & a_{12} & \cdots & a_{1n} \\ a_{21} & a_{22} & \cdots & a_{2n} \\ \cdots & \cdots & \cdots & \cdots \\ a_{m1} & a_{m2} & \cdots & a_{mn} \end{bmatrix} \triangleq [a_{ij}]
\tag{A-9}
$$

The mn numbers a_{ij} are referred to as the *matrix elements*.

The integers m and n associated with an $m \times n$ matrix refer to the numbers of rows and columns, respectively.

An $n \times n$ matrix is called a *square matrix*.

An $m \times 1$ matrix is a *column vector* obeying all the rules of the preceding section.

A $1 \times n$ matrix is a *row vector*.

A-2.1   ELEMENTARY MATRIX OPERATIONS

Two matrices **A** and **B** are said to be equal if and only if

$$
a_{ij} = b_{ij} \qquad \text{for } i = 1, 2, \ldots, m; j = 1, 2, \ldots, n
$$

In such a case, we write

$$
\mathbf{A} = \mathbf{B}
$$

A matrix is multiplied by a scalar λ if all mn elements are multiplied by λ, that is,

$$
\lambda \mathbf{A} \triangleq \begin{bmatrix} \lambda a_{11} & \cdots & \lambda a_{1n} \\ \cdots & \cdots & \cdots \\ \lambda a_{m1} & \cdots & \lambda a_{mn} \end{bmatrix}
\tag{A-10}
$$

Addition and *subtraction* of two matrices result in new matrices in accordance with

$$
\mathbf{A} \pm \mathbf{B} \triangleq \begin{bmatrix} a_{11} \pm b_{11} & \cdots & a_{1n} \pm b_{1n} \\ \cdots & \cdots & \cdots \\ a_{m1} \pm b_{m1} & \cdots & a_{mn} \pm b_{mn} \end{bmatrix}
\tag{A-11}
$$

Clearly, these operations apply only to matrices with the same number of rows and columns.

    Matrix multiplication is defined to facilitate the operations necessary in connection with *linear transformations*. Consider the linear transformation

$$y_1 = a_{11}x_1 + a_{12}x_2 + \cdots + a_{1n}x_n$$
$$y_2 = a_{21}x_1 + a_{22}x_2 + \cdots + a_{2n}x_n$$
$$\cdots\cdots\cdots\cdots\cdots\cdots\cdots\cdots\cdots\cdots\cdots$$
$$y_m = a_{m1}x_1 + a_{m2}x_2 + \cdots + a_{mn}x_n$$

                                                                          (A-12)

or

$$y_i = \sum_{j=1}^{n} a_{ij}x_j \qquad \text{for } i = 1, 2, \ldots, m \tag{A-13}$$

We now can consider *formally* the a_{ij}'s as elements in an $m \times n$ matrix $\mathbf{A}$ and write the above equations in *compact* form

$$\mathbf{y} = \mathbf{Ax} \tag{A-14}$$

This symbolism will have no meaning, of course, *until we prescribe that the product* $\mathbf{Ax}$ *will mean an m vector whose ith component will be defined by* (A-13).

    This fully defines the *matrix-vector product*. In itself, this new concept would be useful only as a shorthand notation. The full power of the concept of matrix multiplication will be evident only upon definition of a *matrix-matrix product*. Consider for that purpose a new linear transformation

$$x_1 = b_{11}z_1 + b_{12}z_2 + \cdots + b_{1p}z_p$$
$$x_2 = b_{21}z_1 + b_{22}z_2 + \cdots + b_{2p}z_p$$
$$\cdots\cdots\cdots\cdots\cdots\cdots\cdots\cdots\cdots\cdots\cdots$$
$$x_n = b_{n1}z_1 + b_{n2}z_2 + \cdots + b_{np}z_p$$

                                                                          (A-15)

or

$$x_k = \sum_{r=1}^{p} b_{kr}z_r \qquad \text{for } k = 1, 2, \ldots, n \tag{A-16}$$

    Using the accepted shorthand notation, we can also write the last equations

$$\mathbf{x} = \mathbf{Bz} \tag{A-17}$$

where $\mathbf{B}$ is an $n \times p$ matrix and $\mathbf{z}$ a p vector.

    By substituting (A-16) into (A-13), we can eliminate the x components, and we end up with the following m relations between $\mathbf{y}$ and $\mathbf{z}$:

$$y_i = \sum_{j=1}^{n} a_{ij} \sum_{r=1}^{p} b_{jr}z_r \qquad \text{for } i = 1, 2, \ldots, m \tag{A-18}$$

    We rearrange the summation signs in this last expression:

$$y_i = \sum_{r=1}^{p} \left(\sum_{j=1}^{n} a_{ij}b_{jr} \right) z_r \qquad \text{for } i = 1, 2, \ldots, m \tag{A-19}$$

and by introduction of the *mp* new *c* coefficients, defined by

$$c_{ir} \triangleq \sum_{j=1}^{n} a_{ij}b_{jr} \qquad \text{for } i = 1, 2, \ldots, m; r = 1, 2, \ldots, p \tag{A-20}$$

we can write the *m* equations (A-19) as

$$y_i = \sum_{r=1}^{p} c_{ir}z_r \qquad \text{for } i = 1, 2, \ldots, m \tag{A-21}$$

Suppose that, instead, we *formally* had eliminated the **x** vector in (A-14) by using the vector expression (A-17), that is,

$$\mathbf{y} = \mathbf{ABz} \tag{A-22}$$

As we can consider Eq. (A-21) as a vector equation

$$\mathbf{y} = \mathbf{Cz} \tag{A-23}$$

where the $m \times p$ matrix **C** is defined by (A-20), it is at this point quite obvious *that we have indeed defined a matrix product*

$$\mathbf{C} \triangleq \mathbf{AB} \tag{A-24}$$

where the mp equations (A-20) *constitute the rule for multiplication of* **A** *and* **B**.
We note immediately that this product matrix is defined only if the number of columns in **A** equals the number of rows in **B**.
We note also from the definition that, in general,

$$\mathbf{AB} \neq \mathbf{BA}$$

(Indeed, unless *p* equals *m*, the product **BA** is not even defined.)
If **AB** and **BA** are both defined and if

$$\mathbf{AB} = \mathbf{BA}$$

then the matrices are said to *commute*.
The associative and distributive laws hold for matrix multiplication (when the appropriate operations are defined), that is,

$$\begin{aligned}(\mathbf{AB})\mathbf{C} &= \mathbf{A}(\mathbf{BC}) = \mathbf{ABC} \\ \mathbf{A}(\mathbf{B} + \mathbf{C}) &= \mathbf{AB} + \mathbf{AC}\end{aligned} \tag{A-25}$$

A-2.2 SPECIAL MATRICES

The *null matrix* **0** is defined by

$$\mathbf{0} \triangleq \begin{bmatrix} 0 & \cdots & 0 \\ \ldots\ldots\ldots \\ 0 & \cdots & 0 \end{bmatrix} \tag{A-26}$$

For a null matrix, we have

$$\mathbf{A} + \mathbf{0} = \mathbf{A}$$
$$\mathbf{A0} = \mathbf{0A} = \mathbf{0} \qquad\qquad\qquad\qquad (A\text{-}27)$$
$$\mathbf{A} - \mathbf{A} = \mathbf{0}$$

Note: In the *scalar* case, we know that the equation $ab = 0$ implies that either a or b or both are zero.

The matrix equation $\mathbf{AB} = \mathbf{0}$ does *not* imply the same thing, as is exemplified by the product

$$\begin{bmatrix} 1 & 4 \\ 0 & 0 \end{bmatrix} \begin{bmatrix} 4 & 0 \\ -1 & 0 \end{bmatrix} = \begin{bmatrix} 0 & 0 \\ 0 & 0 \end{bmatrix}$$

A matrix is referred to as *diagonal* if it is square ($m = n$) and if $a_{ij} = 0$ for $i \neq j$.

A diagonal matrix of special importance is the *identity matrix* $\mathbf{I}$:

$$\mathbf{I} \triangleq \begin{bmatrix} 1 & & & & 0 \\ & 1 & & & \\ & & \cdot & & \\ & & & \cdot & \\ 0 & & & & 1 \end{bmatrix} \qquad\qquad (A\text{-}28)$$

For the $\mathbf{I}$ matrix, we have

$$\mathbf{IA} = \mathbf{AI} = \mathbf{A}$$
$$\underbrace{\mathbf{II}\cdots\mathbf{I}}_{n \text{ times}} \triangleq \mathbf{I}^n = \mathbf{I} \qquad\qquad\qquad\qquad (A\text{-}29)$$

The *transpose* $\mathbf{A}^T$ of a matrix $\mathbf{A}$ is formed by interchanging rows and columns. Transposition follows the easily confirmed rules:

$$(\mathbf{A} + \mathbf{B})^T = \mathbf{A}^T + \mathbf{B}^T$$
$$(\mathbf{AB})^T = \mathbf{B}^T\mathbf{A}^T \qquad\qquad\qquad\qquad (A\text{-}30)$$
$$(\mathbf{A}^T)^T = \mathbf{A}$$

We now can explain better why we earlier denoted the inner vector product of $\mathbf{x}$ and $\mathbf{y}$ by the symbol $\mathbf{x}^T\mathbf{y}$.

The reason is simply that the two vectors $\mathbf{x}^T$ and $\mathbf{y}$, viewed as $1 \times n$ and $n \times 1$ matrices, respectively, can be multiplied and result in the 1×1 matrix ($=$ scalar) defined by Eq. (A-5).

A matrix is *symmetric* if it satisfies the equation

$$\mathbf{A} = \mathbf{A}^T \qquad\qquad\qquad\qquad (A\text{-}31)$$

A-2.3   DETERMINANTS AND ADJUGATE MATRICES

Consider the $n \times n$ matrix **A**. Now select an element from each row and column of this matrix and form the following product of n elements:

$$a_{1i}a_{2j}a_{3k} \cdots a_{nr}$$

The set of second subscripts $(i, j, k, \ldots, r)$ is a *permutation* of the set of integers $(1, 2, \ldots, n)$. We can form $n!$ different products of the above type. For example, in the case of a 3×3 matrix, the six products are

$$a_{11}a_{22}a_{33}$$
$$a_{12}a_{23}a_{31}$$
$$a_{13}a_{21}a_{32}$$
$$a_{11}a_{23}a_{32}$$
$$a_{12}a_{21}a_{33}$$
$$a_{13}a_{22}a_{31}$$

We define now the determinant $|\mathbf{A}|$:

$$|\mathbf{A}| \triangleq \sum (\pm)\, a_{1i}a_{2j}a_{3k} \cdots a_{nr} \tag{A-32}$$

The sum has to be extended over the $n!$ different permutations of the second subscripts. Each term will be assigned a sign ($+$ or $-$) in accordance with the following rule: If the permutation is *even*, use the $+$ sign; if *odd*, use the $-$ sign. [A permutation is even or odd depending upon the number of integer interchanges in the set $i, j, k, \ldots, r$. For example, the sequence 132 has one interchange (3-2) and is, therefore, odd, whereas the sequence 231 has two (2-1 and 3-1) and is thus even.]

For example, returning to the example of the 3×3 matrix, we find the determinant in that case

$$|\mathbf{A}| = a_{11}a_{22}a_{33} + a_{12}a_{23}a_{31} + a_{13}a_{21}a_{32} - a_{11}a_{23}a_{32} - a_{12}a_{21}a_{33} - a_{13}a_{22}a_{31}$$

The following properties of determinants can be deduced directly from the definition

$$|\mathbf{A}| = |\mathbf{A}^T|$$
$$|\lambda\mathbf{A}| = \lambda^n |\mathbf{A}| \tag{A-33}$$
$$|\mathbf{AB}| = |\mathbf{A}|\,|\mathbf{B}|$$

Another very useful property is that an interchange of two columns or rows changes the sign of $|\mathbf{A}|$. We see that this follows directly from the definition when we realize that such an interchange changes all odd permutations to even, and vice versa. As a corollary, it follows that $|\mathbf{A}|$ must equal zero if the matrix has two equal rows or columns.

Any element a_{ij} of **A** will appear as a factor in $(n - 1)!$ of the $n!$ terms of $|\mathbf{A}|$. Furthermore *all* the n elements of *any* particular row or column of **A** are represented as factors in *all* the *n*! terms of $|\mathbf{A}|$. It is therefore possible to rearrange (A-32) into either of the following two alternate forms:

$$|\mathbf{A}| = \sum_{j=1}^{n} a_{ij}A_{ij} \quad \text{or} \quad \sum_{i=1}^{n} a_{ij}A_{ij} \tag{A-34}$$

where *i* can be *any* row and *j any* column. The A_{ij}'s, the so-called *cofactors*, will each contain a sum of $(n-1)!$ terms involving those $(n-1)^2$ elements not to be found in row *i* and column *j*. By a very simple reasoning, we find that the rule for computing A_{ij} is:

$A_{ij} = (-1)^{i+j}$ times the determinant of the submatrix formed by deleting row *i* and column *j*.

From Eq. (A-34), we can derive an extremely useful relationship.

Consider the *n* cofactors A_{i1}, A_{i2}, ..., A_{in}. They are evidently *completely independent* of the elements of row *i*. If, therefore, we replace these elements with those in row $k(k \neq i)$, we have, in effect, a matrix with two equal rows and therefore zero determinant. From (A-34), we thus obtain the relationship

$$\sum_{j=1}^{n} a_{kj}A_{ij} = 0 \qquad \text{for } k \neq i \tag{A-35}$$

By applying the same discussion to a column, we similarly get

$$\sum_{i=1}^{n} a_{ik}A_{ij} = 0 \qquad \text{for } k \neq j \tag{A-36}$$

At this time, we define an $n \times n$ matrix $\mathbf{A}^{+}$, having as elements the A_{ji}'s (note, *not* the A_{ij}'s) and referred to as the *adjugate* of matrix $\mathbf{A}$, that is,

$$\mathbf{A}^{+} \triangleq \begin{bmatrix} A_{11} & A_{21} & \cdots & A_{n1} \\ A_{12} & & & \\ & & \cdot & \\ \cdot & & \cdot & \\ \cdot & & \cdot & \\ \cdot & & \cdot & \\ A_{1n} & & \cdots & A_{nn} \end{bmatrix} \tag{A-37}$$

(A-34), (A-35), and (A-36) represent a total of $2n^2$ scalar equations. By recalling the definition of a matrix product (A-20) we can summarize them all in the compact matrix formulas:

$$\mathbf{A}\mathbf{A}^{+} = \mathbf{A}^{+}\mathbf{A} = |\mathbf{A}|\ \mathbf{I} \tag{A-38}$$

A-2.4 THE MATRIX INVERSE

Consider the linear transformation

$$\mathbf{y} = \mathbf{A}\mathbf{x} \tag{A-39}$$

where $\mathbf{A}$ is a square matrix of dimension *n* having a *nonzero* determinant.

Assume we desire to solve the x_i's from the n equations (A-39). Intuitively, we feel that the solution should read

$$\mathbf{x} = \mathbf{By} \tag{A-40}$$

where **B** is one as yet unknown matrix.

If this solution is substituted back into (A-39), we obtain

$$\mathbf{y} = \mathbf{ABy}$$

On the other hand, if the original **y** vector is substituted into the solution (A-40), we have

$$\mathbf{x} = \mathbf{BAx} \tag{A-41}$$

In either case, if the solution is correct, we evidently must require that the **B** matrix satisfy

$$\mathbf{AB} = \mathbf{BA} = \mathbf{I} \tag{A-42}$$

A matrix **B** possessing this property is called the *inverse of* **A** and is designated with the very special symbol $\mathbf{B} \triangleq \mathbf{A}^{-1}$.

By comparing Eqs. (A-42) with Eqs. (A-38), we find a matrix that satisfies our requirements, that is,

$$\mathbf{A}^{-1} = \frac{1}{|\mathbf{A}|} \mathbf{A}^{+} \tag{A-43}$$

It is very simple to prove that the inverse is *unique* so that indeed this $\mathbf{A}^{-1}$ is *the* one.

We can deduce the following properties characterizing the inverse:

$$\begin{aligned} (\mathbf{AB})^{-1} &= \mathbf{B}^{-1}\mathbf{A}^{-1} \\ (\mathbf{A}^{-1})^{T} &= (\mathbf{A}^{T})^{-1} \\ (\mathbf{A}^{-1})^{-1} &= \mathbf{A} \end{aligned} \tag{A-44}$$

References

1. G. Hadley, "Linear Algebra," Addison-Wesley Publishing Company, Inc., Reading, Mass., 1961.
2. R. Bellman, "Introduction to Matrix Analysis," McGraw-Hill Book Company, New York, 1960.

FOURIER AND LAPLACE TRANSFORMS — A SUMMARY

This appendix contains a compilation of the most useful results of the Fourier and Laplace transform theories. As the proofs of the formulas can be found in a number of undergraduate texts, they have not been included.

B-I FOURIER SERIES AND TRANSFORMS— THE PERIODIC CASE

A *periodic* function $f(t)$ as depicted in Fig. B-1 can be expressed as a *Fourier series:*

$$f(t) = A_0 + \sum_{v=1}^{\infty} (A_v \cos v\omega t + B_v \sin v\omega t) \tag{B-1}$$

or

$$f(t) = A_0 + \sum_{v=1}^{\infty} C_v \sin (v\omega t + \varphi_v) \tag{B-2}$$

where

$$A_0 = \frac{1}{T} \int_{-T/2}^{+T/2} f(\tau)\, d\tau$$

$$A_v = \frac{2}{T} \int_{-T/2}^{+T/2} f(\tau) \cos v\omega\tau\, d\tau \tag{B-3}$$

$$B_v = \frac{2}{T} \int_{-T/2}^{+T/2} f(\tau) \sin v\omega\tau\, d\tau$$

and

$$C_v = \sqrt{A_v{}^2 + B_v{}^2}$$

$$\varphi_v = \tan^{-1}\frac{A_v}{B_v} \tag{B-4}$$

The fundamental radian frequency ω is computed from

$$\omega = \frac{2\pi}{T} \tag{B-5}$$

τ is a dummy integration variable.

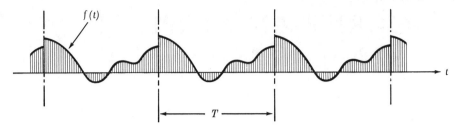

Fig. B-1   Periodic time function.

The C_ν's are the amplitudes of the *spectral components*, or *harmonics*, of the periodic function.   The *spectrum* is obviously *discrete*.

By using the identities

$$\cos \alpha = \frac{e^{j\alpha} + e^{-j\alpha}}{2}$$

$$\sin \alpha = \frac{e^{j\alpha} - e^{-j\alpha}}{2j}$$

we can write the set of Eqs. (B-1) and (B-3) in the following very compact form, referred to as a *Fourier transform pair:*

$$f(t) = \sum_{\nu=-\infty}^{+\infty} F(j\omega_\nu)e^{j\omega_\nu t}$$

$$F(j\omega_\nu) \overset{\Delta}{=} \frac{1}{T} \int_{-T/2}^{+T/2} f(\tau)e^{-j\omega_\nu \tau} \, d\tau \tag{B-6}$$

where

$$\omega_\nu \overset{\Delta}{=} \nu\omega \qquad \nu = 0, \pm 1, \pm 2, \ldots$$

In symbolic form, those equations are usually written

$$f(t) \overset{\Delta}{=} \mathscr{F}^{-1}[F(j\omega_\nu)]$$

$$F(j\omega_\nu) \overset{\Delta}{=} \mathscr{F}[f(t)] \tag{B-7}$$

$\mathscr{F}$ is the *direct* and $\mathscr{F}^{-1}$ the *inverse Fourier transform*.

The amplitudes $F(j\omega_\nu)$ are complex numbers and can be written

$$F(j\omega_\nu) = |F(j\omega_\nu)| \, e^{j\underline{/F(j\omega_\nu)}}$$

$|F(j\omega_\nu)|$ gives the amplitude distribution in the frequency domain and is referred to as the *spectral intensity*.   As the *energy* in a signal is directly related to the amplitudes of the spectral lines, the spectral intensity gives us information about the frequency distribution of signal energy.

As $f(t)$ must be *real*, we have

$$|F(j\omega_\nu)| = |F(-j\omega_\nu)|$$

$$\underline{/F(j\omega_\nu)} = -\underline{/F(-j\omega_\nu)} \tag{B-8}$$

As a consequence, the first of Eqs. (B-6) can be written†

$$f(t) = F(0) + \sum_{v=1}^{\infty} 2 |F(j\omega_v)| \cos [\omega_v t + \underline{/F(j\omega_v)}]$$

(B-9)

Example B-1

Consider the pulse train in Fig. B-2.

Direct Fourier transformation yields

$$F(j\omega_v) = \frac{1}{T} \int_{-\alpha T/2}^{+\alpha T/2} A e^{-j\omega_v \tau} d\tau$$

and upon integration, we have

$$F(j\omega_v) = \frac{A}{\pi v} \sin v\alpha\pi$$

(B-10)

† If Eqs. (B-8) did not apply it would not be possible to write the first of Eqs. (B-6) in this *real* form.

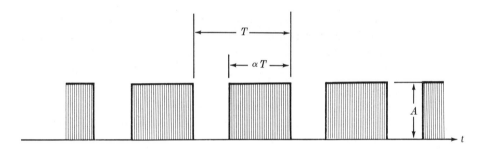

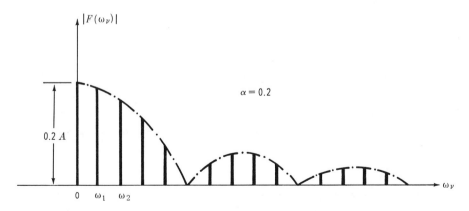

Fig. B-2 Periodic pulse train and its spectrum. The spectral lines are shown for positive frequencies only. Because of Eqs. (B-8) the spectrum for negative frequencies looks identical.

the spectral intensity therefore equals

$$|F(j\omega_v)| = \frac{A}{\pi v} |\sin v\alpha\pi|$$

and is depicted in Fig. B-2 for the numerical case $\alpha = 0.2$.

B-2 FOURIER TRANSFORMS— THE APERIODIC CASE

An aperiodic function is a function that does not show any periodicity in a finite time interval. This case may be studied as a limit case of the periodic case with $T \to \infty$. In this limit process, the following asymptotic changes take place:

1. The *finite* frequency difference $\Delta\omega_v = 2\pi/T$, that is, the frequency distance between spectral components, approaches zero. It thus takes on the form of a *differential*, and we rename it accordingly

$$\lim_{T \to \infty} \Delta\omega_v = d\omega$$

2. As the distance between the spectral components approaches zero, the spectrum ceases to be discrete and takes on a *continuous* character. As a consequence, the discrete frequency variable $\omega_v = v(2\pi/T)$ turns into the *continuous* variable ω, that is,

$$\lim_{T \to \infty} \omega_v = \omega$$

3. The sum in (B-6) turns into an integral. This follows directly from the definition of an integral.

By incorporating all these changes, it is easy to show that the discrete transform pair (B-6) changes to a *continuous* transform pair

$$f(t) \overset{\Delta}{=} \mathscr{F}^{-1}[F(j\omega)] = \frac{1}{2\pi} \int_{-\infty}^{+\infty} F(j\omega)e^{j\omega t} \, d\omega$$

$$F(j\omega) \overset{\Delta}{=} \mathscr{F}[f(t)] = \int_{-\infty}^{+\infty} f(\tau)e^{-j\omega\tau} \, d\tau \tag{B-11}$$

Example B-2

Consider the single pulse in Fig. B-3. Direct Fourier transformation yields

$$F(j\omega) = \int_{-T_0}^{+T_0} Ae^{-j\omega\tau} \, d\tau$$

and upon integration, we have

$$F(j\omega) = \frac{2A}{\omega} \sin \omega T_0 \tag{B-12}$$

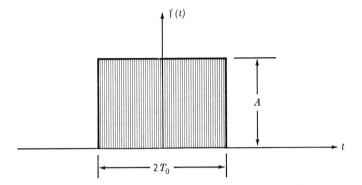

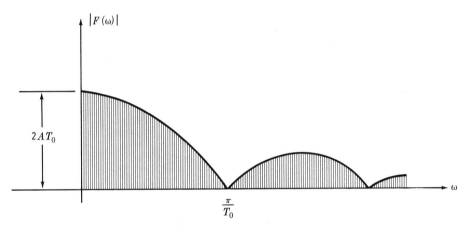

Fig. B-3 Single pulse and its spectrum.   The spectral lines are shown for positive frequencies only.   Because of Eqs. 13 the spectrum for negative frequencies looks identical.

The spectral intensity equals

$$|F(j\omega)| = \frac{2A}{\omega} |\sin \omega T_0|$$

and is depicted in Fig. B-3.

In analogy with (B-8) and (B-9), we find

$$|F(j\omega)| = |F(-j\omega)|$$
$$\underline{/F(j\omega)} = -\underline{/F(-j\omega)}$$

(B-13)

and

$$f(t) = \frac{1}{\pi} \int_0^{\infty} |F(j\omega)| \cos [\omega t + \underline{/F(j\omega)}] \, d\omega$$

(B-14)

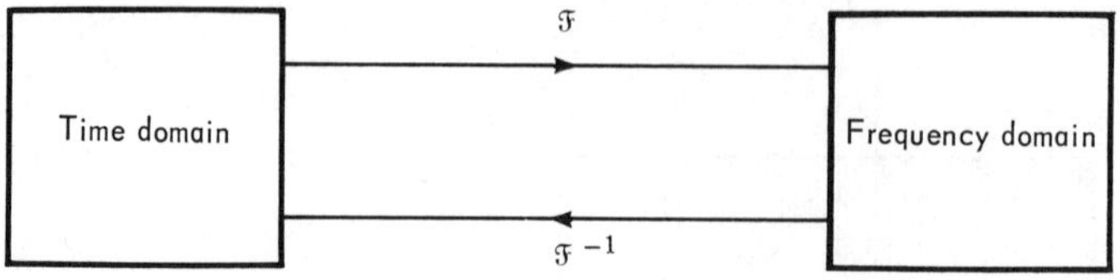

Fig. B-4   A dynamic process may be viewed as either a time-domain or a frequency-domain phenomenon.

The Fourier transform pair permits us to view a dynamic process from either a *time-domain* or a *frequency* point of view. This conceptual duality symbolically displayed in Fig. B-4 is of extraordinary importance in the applications.

B-3 LAPLACE TRANSFORMS

An interesting result is obtained if we take the Fourier transform of the function $f(t)e^{-\sigma t}$, where σ is a *real constant*.   From (B-11), we get

$$f(t)e^{-\sigma t} = \frac{1}{2\pi} \int_{-\infty}^{+\infty} F(j\omega)e^{j\omega t}\, d\omega$$

$$F(j\omega) = \int_{-\infty}^{+\infty} f(\tau)e^{-\sigma\tau}e^{-j\omega\tau}\, d\tau$$

Therefore,

$$f(t) = \frac{1}{2\pi} \int_{-\infty}^{+\infty} F(j\omega)e^{(\sigma+j\omega)t}\, d\omega \triangleq \frac{1}{2\pi} \int_{-\infty}^{+\infty} F(j\omega)e^{st}\, d\omega$$

and

$$F(j\omega) = \int_{-\infty}^{+\infty} f(\tau)e^{-(\sigma+j\omega)\tau}\, d\tau \triangleq \int_{-\infty}^{+\infty} f(\tau)e^{-s\tau}\, d\tau$$

We here have introduced the *complex frequency*

$$s \triangleq \sigma + j\omega$$

As

$$ds = j\, d\omega$$

and as the last integral is a function of s rather than $j\omega$ and thus motivates the name change

$$F(j\omega) \rightarrow F(s)$$

we can write the two integrals as the following *Laplace-transform pair:*

$$f(t) = \frac{1}{2\pi j} \int^{\uparrow} F(s)e^{st} \, ds$$

$$F(s) = \int_{-\infty}^{+\infty} f(\tau)e^{-s\tau} \, d\tau$$

(B-15)

or, symbolically,

$$f(t) \stackrel{\Delta}{=} \mathscr{L}^{-1}[F(s)]$$

$$F(s) \stackrel{\Delta}{=} \mathscr{L}[f(t)]$$

(B-16)

The symbol $\int^{\uparrow}$ indicates integration in the s plane along the line $s = \sigma + j\omega$ from $\omega = -\infty$ to $\omega = +\infty$.

If the function $f(\tau)$ is zero for $\tau < 0$, the last integral, the *direct* Laplace transform, takes on the simpler form

$$F(s) = \int_0^\infty f(\tau)e^{-s\tau} \, d\tau$$

(B-17)

The usefulness of the Laplace transform ties in with the following set of theorems:

1. *Linearity*

$$\mathscr{L}[f_1(t) + f_2(t)] = \mathscr{L}[f_1(t)] + \mathscr{L}[f_2(t)]$$

(B-18)

2. *Constant multiplication*

$$\mathscr{L}[af(t)] = a\mathscr{L}[f(t)]$$

(B-19)

3. *Real differentiation*

$$\mathscr{L}[\dot{f}(t)] = s\mathscr{L}[f(t)] - f(0)$$

(B-20)

4. *Real translation*

$$\mathscr{L}[f(t - t_0)] = e^{-t_0 s}\mathscr{L}[f(t)]$$

$$f(t - t_0) = 0 \quad \text{for } t < t_0$$

(B-21)

5. *Complex translation*

$$\mathscr{L}[e^{-at}f(t)] = F(s + a)$$

(B-22)

6. *Scale change*

$$\mathscr{L}\left[f\left(\frac{t}{a}\right)\right] = aF(as) \quad a = \text{real, positive const}$$

(B-23)

7. *Heaviside expansion formula.* Assume that $F(s)$ can be written as a proper rational algebraic fraction

$$F(s) = \frac{A(s)}{B(s)}$$

Then we have

$$f(t) = \mathscr{L}^{-1}[F(s)] = \sum_{v=1}^{n} \frac{A(s_v)}{B'(s_v)} e^{s_v t} \tag{B-24}$$

The n s_v's are the n distinct roots of the characteristic equation

$$B(s) = 0 \tag{B-25}$$

and B' indicates differentiation with respect to s.

8. *Initial- and final-value theorems*

$$f(0) = \lim_{s \to \infty} [sF(s)] \tag{B-26}$$

and

$$f(\infty) = \lim_{s \to 0} [sF(s)] \tag{B-27}$$

B-4 ROUTH CRITERION

If at least one of the roots s_v of the characteristic equation (B-25) has a positive real part, then the function $f(t)$ (B-24) will be unbounded for $t \to \infty$. We say that the corresponding system is *unstable*.

By means of *Routh's array*, we can determine the number of such *unstable roots* by direct manipulation of the coefficients of $B(s)$.

Assume $B(s)$ to be an nth-order polynomial of the form

$$B(s) = b_n s^n + b_{n-1} s^{n-1} + \cdots + b_1 s + b_0 \tag{B-28}$$

It is assumed that all n b coefficients are real, positive, and nonzero. (If any coefficient is zero or negative, there are either unstable or purely imaginary roots present and the Routh test is unnecessary.)

Construct now the array

s^n	b_n	b_{n-2}	b_{n-4}	$\cdots$
s^{n-1}	b_{n-1}	b_{n-3}	b_{n-5}	$\cdots$
s^{n-2}	c_1	c_2	c_3	$\cdots$
s^{n-3}	d_1	d_2	$\cdots$	
$\cdots$	$\cdots\cdots\cdots\cdots$			
s^1	f_1			
s^0	g_1			

The entries in the first two rows are obtained directly from (B-28). The entries in the third row are computed from the entries in the two previous ones, as follows:

$$c_1 = \frac{b_{n-1}b_{n-2} - b_n b_{n-3}}{b_{n-1}}$$

$$c_2 = \frac{b_{n-1}b_{n-4} - b_n b_{n-5}}{b_{n-1}}$$

(B-29)

. . . .

The entries in the fourth row are computed similarly from the entries in the second and third rows, as follows:

$$d_1 = \frac{c_1 b_{n-3} - b_{n-1}c_2}{c_1}$$

$$d_2 = \frac{c_1 b_{n-5} - b_{n-1}c_3}{c_1}$$

(B-30)

. . . .

The pattern is now set, and after computing all the $n + 1$ rows, we end up with a triangular array. *Routh criterion then states:*

The number of unstable roots equals the number of sign changes in the first column of the array.

Example B-3

Consider the equation

$$s^3 + 0.5s^2 + 3s + 3.5 = 0$$

We construct the array

s^3	1	3	0
s^2	0.5	3.5	0
s^1	−4	0	
s^0	3.5		

We have *two* sign changes in the first column, from 0.5 to −4 and from −4 to 3.5. Thus the given equation must have *two* unstable roots.

Reference

M. F. Gardner and J. L. Barnes, "Transients in Linear Systems," John Wiley & Sons, Inc., New York, 1942.

INDEX